Teaching Arithmetic to Children

Teaching Arithmetic to Children

ESTHER J. SWENSON
College of Education, University of Alabama

THE MACMILLAN COMPANY, NEW YORK
COLLIER - MACMILLAN LIMITED, LONDON

First Printing

Library of Congress catalog card number: 64-12528

THE MACMILLAN COMPANY, NEW YORK

COLLIER-MACMILLAN CANADA, LTD., TORONTO, ONTARIO

Printed in the United States of America

DESIGNED BY ANDREW P. ZUTIS

Preface

SURELY ENOUGH BOOKS have been written—even published—on arithmetic and the teaching of arithmetic! The writer of this book has complained at times of the repetition and duplication of content in existing books on this and other subjects; she has even gone so far as to wish for a moratorium on professional writing to allow time for critical appraisal and use of those books already in print. Why, then, does she write this book?

To answer this question, it is necessary to point out that the author has taught courses in the teaching and learning of arithmetic for many years. She has often experienced difficulty in finding a single textbook, or even a combination of texts and other references, that offers the particular combination of content, organization, and format that she finds most useful to the teacher and most valuable for the students. Further, her students, both undergraduate and graduate, have varied widely in their understanding of arithmetic. In each class have been some students who needed a better understanding of arithmetic itself before they could derive much benefit from discussion or demonstration of how to teach arithmetic. This book, therefore, is designed to meet the needs of those prospective teachers, teachers-in-service, and *parents,* who wish to improve their guidance of children's arithmetic learning but have little background for doing so.

As its name indicates, this book is intended for use in courses usually designated as "methods" courses. It is, however, a blend of basic ideas concerning arithmetic itself and methods for presenting those ideas to children in meaningful ways. Some readers will think it is "heavy on arithmetic"; others will think it is "heavy on method." The writer hopes only that it will prove helpful to many teachers and prospective teachers and, through them, help many children to learn and enjoy arithmetic.

The omission of any systematic treatment of algebra and geometry should not be interpreted as expressing disapproval of modern programs of elementary school mathematics that include them. Algebraic and geometric ideas have been used when they fitted naturally into the presentation, but it is impossible to include extended treatment of them without going beyond the limits of this book. Also, any reader who is well-informed on current developments in the teaching of arithmetic may be surprised at the lack of emphasis on some of the favorite ideas being promoted through the efforts of various experimental programs and projects. This does not indicate a negative attitude toward such programs.

Much of the content of this text is presented in terms of familiar forms and procedures. The intention of the writer has been to help readers see new and more fundamental meanings in the familiar processes and procedures of arithmetic. As much of the "new" has been included as these readers can reasonably be expected to assimilate during the difficult period of readjustment to ideas that have a somewhat different orientation from those traditionally presented in arithmetic courses. The arithmetic program of the elementary school should retain what is defensible in the past curriculum while changes are being made in the direction of a modernized program. However, time and preparation are needed in establishing a new program; forcing a "new way" of teaching arithmetic could result in effects as artificial and mechanical as the mechanical and rigid "old ways." Further, such a book as this will better serve its purpose if it is not tied to any one program or set of materials.

A real effort has been made to make this book mathematically sound; but the writer lays no claim to being a mathematician. During the current upheaval in the teaching of mathematics in general, many controversies concerning mathematical interpretations have arisen. These the mathematicians must solve. This book represents one teacher's effort to make arithmetic more meaningful to other teachers and to encourage teachers and children to enter an area of the elementary school curriculum that can and should be an open field for discovery, exploration, and mastery of elementary—but nonetheless exciting—mathematical ideas.

The writing of this book has been a "one-man job" in terms of actual writing and responsibility for its content and form. In another sense, it could not have reached its present form without the assistance of many: college students and elementary school children with whom the ideas have been tried; teachers who have shared their experiences in teaching arithmetic; colleagues, friends, and relatives who have given assorted varieties of encouragement and support during the long and often interrupted course of the writing. Some of them share my relief in completing the task; all deserve and have my appreciation.

ESTHER J. SWENSON
University, Alabama

Table of Contents

ix

Teaching Arithmetic to Children

CHAPTER 1

Improvement of Arithmetic

THE TITLE "Improvement of Arithmetic" seems to imply that something about arithmetic is wrong and needs to be bettered. This is most certainly true. What human endeavor is not in need of improvement?

What is particularly in need of improvement in children's school experiences with arithmetic? The answer is twofold. The content of arithmetic as a school subject needs to be improved, and the teaching of that content needs to be improved.

Unfortunately, large numbers of adults and children associate arithmetic with difficulties of one kind or another. One of every ten titles in a recent research bibliography on the subject refers to difficulties, errors, disabilities, or misconceptions.[1] Perhaps this suggests a negative approach to teaching and research in arithmetic. How can we move from contemplation of difficulties to an accentuation of the positive? One way is to focus attention on ways of helping children understand arithmetic.

A subject tends to seem easy to the person who has mastered it. The person who feels that he has control of the

[1] G. T. Buswell, "Arithmetic," in *Encyclopedia of Educational Research*, New York: Macmillan, 1960, pp. 63-77.

situation as he plays golf or drives his car or solves a puzzle says confidently, "That's easy!" Children in our elementary schools should learn arithmetic so well that they see sense in its operations and can apply them skillfully in everyday situations. Arithmetic should not be made easy for the sake of being easy; it should and can be taught so that most children can truthfully say, "I can do it. It makes sense. I know how to use it."

Making Arithmetic Easy

Perhaps it is just modern "soft pedagogy" that dwells on making arithmetic easy. Hardly!

OLD TEXTBOOKS' EMPHASIS ON "EASE"

Robert Recorde has been credited with writing the most important sixteenth-century arithmetic textbook in England, *The Ground of Artes*, first printed about 1542 and later running through nearly thirty editions. A 1654 edition of this work, "augmented by Mr. John Dee," shows on its title page some concern for making arithmetic easy, claiming to teach "The perfect work and practise of Arithmetick, both in whole

Numbers and Fractions, after a more easie and exact form then in former time hath been set forth."[2]

John Ward wrote an arithmetic book (1707) that was popular both in England and in New England, being used as a textbook at Harvard University. He too wanted people to understand that his book was easy. On its title page appeared this title: *"The Young Mathematician's Guide.* Being a Plain and Easie Introduction to the Mathematicks."[3]

The "Five and Twentieth Edition" (1719) of one popular arithmetic worked up to the superlative in ease by announcing on the title page *"Hodder's Arithmetick: Or, That Necessary Art Made Most Easy.* Being explained in a way familiar to the Capacity of any that desire to learn it in a little Time." On the same page we learn that this edition was "Revised, Augmented, and above a Thousand Faults Amended, by Henry Mose, late Servant and Successor to the Author."[4] And, if we are to believe the title page of a book printed by Benjamin Franklin and D. Hall in Philadelphia in 1748, this was a still easier book. This was a reprint of an English work by George Fisher. Its title page calls it *"The American Instructor: or, Young Man's Best Companion,* containing Spelling, Reading, Writing, and Arithmetick, in an easier Way than any yet published."[5]

As a matter of fact, when compared with the typical adult of American Colonial days, the typical 10-year-old Johnny in our country today has a far, far greater chance of saying truthfully

and confidently that the solution of an arithmetic problem is "easy" for him to accomplish. In the early 1800's arithmetic was a regular college subject. While Harvard University raised its admission standards in 1802 to include a minimum of arithmetic, it was not until 1816 that "the whole of arithmetic was required for admission."[6]

CONTINUING NEED
FOR IMPROVEMENT

To say that the present generation is more competent in arithmetic than a past generation is not to say that the present generation is as competent as it could or should be. In fact, one does not need to go far to find many adults as well as children who confess to inadequacy in arithmetic skill and understanding. Oddly enough, many of them are not only willing to confess inadequacy in mathematics; they provide the information without being asked. A woman who would never dream of saying, "I just never could learn to read," will exaggerate her difficulties with arithmetic in some such fashion as this: "I can't add 2 and 2. I just never *was* any good in mathematics." The implication is that she never will be "any good" and is not going to struggle to improve — in mathematics, that is.

On the other hand, some people who feel inadequate are embarrassed about it. A woman of demonstrated intelligence in other areas of activity and understanding was helping out in her husband's store. She sold a customer an item that cost $2.98 and had difficulty adding the 12-cent tax without using pencil and paper. Assisted by the customer in performing this calculation,

[2] See facsimile of title page as given in: Louis Charles Karpinski, *The History of Arithmetic,* Chicago: Rand McNally, 1925, p. 67.

[3] Facsimile and discussion, Karpinski, *ibid.,* p. 74.

[4] Facsimile, Karpinski, *ibid.,* p. 82.

[5] Karpinski, *ibid.,* p. 86 (facsimile of title page on p. 87).

[6] F. Cajori, *The Teaching and History of Mathematics in the United States,* Washington: Bureau of Education, Circular no. 3, 1890, p. 60.

she had trouble making change from a $5 bill. She apologized profusely and said: "I had trouble in arithmetic when I was in the third grade and it has been hard for me ever since. I'm ashamed of myself, but I just get *so* mixed up!"

Is arithmetic so difficult that a person needs to have some special mathematical ability to use it satisfactorily? Is it so hard to understand that only a certain chosen minority with a "flair for figures" can grasp its fundamentals? To answer these questions with a firm "Yes" might lend comfort to the arithmetically inadequate. It might give them a respectable excuse for failure, but it is more accurate to answer the question with a "No."

Human beings vary in their ability to learn arithmetic as in their ability to learn other school subjects, but all normal children can develop reasonable competence in arithmetic just as all normal children can learn to read. If this is true, why do some of them find arithmetic to be anything but easy?

PREVENTION OF DIFFICULTY
WITH ARITHMETIC

The most obvious answer, and perhaps the most correct one, is that something went wrong in the process of learning. Maybe the teacher had an inadequate understanding of arithmetic herself; maybe there were too many children for one teacher to teach satisfactorily; maybe the child had been told that arithmetic was very hard and believed this so firmly that it became true; maybe the pupil was confused by too rapid presentation of number facts and relationships; maybe lack of success led to fear of failure, which in turn became a guarantee of failure.

Prevention of these and other possible causes of difficulty in learning arithmetic is crucial. A child does not need to be

a mental giant or possess a special aptitude for mathematics to experience a reasonable degree of success with elementary-school arithmetic. What is more, he can *enjoy* it as he enjoys doing any other endeavor in which he is competent. This book is directed toward helping teachers help children to learn more arithmetic and learn it more effectively.

Today's elementary-school teacher[7] has a very real responsibility for her pupils' learning of arithmetic, but it is not correct to assume that she is always or totally to blame when something goes wrong with their learning. Many factors beyond her control enter into the success of her pupils—factors such as the pupils' previous learning experiences, good or bad, at home and in school; the availability of instructional materials, including books and manipulative aids; the curriculum pattern of the school; the organization of the school; time schedules; and pupil-teacher ratio.

There are also certain phases of a teacher's own competence for which she is not entirely responsible. Perhaps she herself received inadequate arithmetic instruction as a child. Perhaps her education for teaching did not prepare her properly for her responsibilities in this area. Sometimes a teacher may even be doing a very conscientious and thorough job of teaching as she was taught and still not be teaching arithmetic as well as her pupils should be taught. Sometimes she needs help in lifting her horizons to see possibilities not now within her professional vision.

---

[7] Feminine pronouns are used throughout this book in referring to the elementary-school teacher. Though this is contrary to general usage, it is done to make the distinction easy between the teacher (feminine) and the pupil (masculine). Further, the majority of elementary-school teachers are women, though the proportion of men in such positions is fortunately increasing.

The purpose of this book is, therefore, to give teachers help on two fronts: arithmetic content and arithmetic teaching. A teacher can teach well only that which she herself knows and understands well. For that reason, this book presents the actual arithmetic subject matter an elementary school teacher needs to know in order to teach children that which they should learn. As Palmer[8] said in his description of the ideal teacher, the teacher needs to know more than what he teaches to his students. If he teaches up to the edge of his knowledge, he does not teach as well as if he is released by his own knowledge to move about freely within the area of study.

Knowing arithmetic is not enough to make a person a skillful teacher of arithmetic. One must also know how to teach. There are better ways and poorer ways of presenting the same content. Therefore, this book provides frequent suggestions for better ways of teaching the subject matter of arithmetic. These are offered not as a strait jacket of set procedures but rather as a framework of constructive suggestions for the teacher to adapt to the children, the content, and the situation in which she teaches.

How easy or how difficult should arithmetic be for the person who is learning it? The answer is simple to state but more difficult to achieve. Arithmetic should be made easy enough so that the learner can understand it clearly; it should be difficult enough to present a challenge to the learner.

If the teacher is to guide learners at their proper levels of ease or difficulty, she must first acquire as much understanding as possible in three major areas: (1) understanding of arithmetic

as a subject, (2) understanding of the purposes for which arithmetic is taught to children, and (3) understanding of the learner and the learning process.[9]

What Is Arithmetic?

Arithmetic is what arithmetic does. Arithmetic is what we do with it. A formal definition of arithmetic at this point is of no more use to the prospective teacher than is any formal definition at the beginning of the study of any subject. Definitions mean most when they serve to summarize experience and understanding already achieved. They come more appropriately at the end rather than the beginning of a study.

What is a ball? A formal definition tells us that it is "a spherical or approximately spherical body" or a "round or roundish body, of different materials and sizes, hollow or solid, for use in various games, as baseball, football, tennis, or golf."[10] Such definitions have their greatest utility for persons who already have a good deal of experience with "spherical bodies," "hollow or solid" objects, and "tennis" or "golf." To someone who is a beginner in experience with balls, "ball" is best defined in terms of *what is does* and *what he can do with it.* A child says that a ball rolls or bounces; he says that it "is to play with" or "is to throw" or "is to catch."

One can best tell what the elementary-school subject of arithmetic is by discussing what arithmetic does and what the child or adult user does with arithmetic.

[8] George Herbert Palmer, *The Ideal Teacher,* New York: Houghton, 1910, p. 17.

[9] The remainder of this chapter deals with the first of these understandings. The next chapter deals with the second and third.

[10] Definitions from the *American College Dictionary,* New York: Random, 1948.

ARITHMETIC IN USE

When a child counts three buttons on his coat or when his father takes inventory of the stock in his store, each of them is using arithmetic. When two boys compare their marbles to see who has more or when the owner of an old car compares its trade-in value with the cost of a new car, they are using arithmetic. When Susie helps her mother measure out 2 cups of milk needed in a recipe or when the building contractor measures materials needed in building a house, they are using arithmetic. Counting, comparing quantities, measuring — these are arithmetic.

He who thinks he uses arithmetic infrequently should check up on his own speech for a day. Even the young child makes frequent reference to size and quantity. He wants the *big* piece of cake and objects if Big Brother gets a *bigger* one, just as his father prides himself on a *high* record of sales and strives to reach a *higher* record next month. Billy says he ate "a million cookies," meaning that he ate *many*. The daily newspaper speaks of billions of dollars for governmental expenditures, which also to many adult readers means not an exact sum but a vague but impressive *many* dollars. Sometimes Junior and Daddy are more exact. Junior has five pennies and knows they are worth the same as one nickel. Daddy checks on the cost of an airplane ticket and learns that it is $34.62. We count items; we report expenditures or sales or enrollments or vacant chairs. We refer to quantity and size repeatedly every day. We use quantitative terms to describe our world and what is going on in it.

Arithmetic has much to do with the way we organize our living. We plan our day's work in hours and minutes and find ourselves often the slaves of time schedules and clocks. Plans for future activities usually must include arrangements of time and place involving number, e.g., Monday, June 12, at 2:00 P.M. in Room 115. Even the subjects and verbs of our sentences, to be correct, must agree in number; the verbs must be accurate as to time. We order our lives, and we express that order in and through arithmetic.

Children add their dolls, toy cars, and sticks and stones; adults add their possessions, their assets and their liabilities. They seek to multiply their gains and divide their expenses. Computing is arithmetic, but not all of arithmetic is computing as some people seem to think.

When a problem is to be solved and number is involved in the problem, we must think in terms of number to solve the problem. Thinking about and with numbers is arithmetic.

Children use arithmetic. Adults use arithmetic. It is inescapable in our civilized world. We need to use it well if it is to serve us well.

THE FORM AND
THE SUBSTANCE

Human history is full of instances in which man has invented a device or a procedure for accomplishing a given purpose, only later to become a slave to the device or procedure when it no longer served its original purpose. Look at the buttons on men's coat sleeves, originally devised to serve a purpose but now serving only as sources of irritation when they get caught on something and must be disentangled. Look at forms of government or worship or social behavior, some of which have long since lost their reason for existence but which often linger on as empty practices devoid of meaning and even at times obstructing the proper conduct of government or worship or social behavior.

Yes, and look at arithmetic. Far too often it is largely *form* devoid of *substance*. To many learners—worse, to many teachers—arithmetic is just a set of forms and procedures. Learning arithmetic becomes a matter of acquiring skill in routine manipulations of symbols for numbers and processes. Oh, yes, the forms were devised to aid and abet clear thinking in number situations. They can still serve the purposes for which they were invented. If that is to happen, they must be taught as what they are: *forms* and *procedures* for aiding and recording real thinking about and with number. The ways we write long-division examples, for instance, are useful forms to aid us in doing the long-division process. But the form must not be taught as if it were the process! What does it profit a child or a man to know how to set down the numbers if he knows not when to do so or why he should be dividing in the first place?

Arithmetic is a set of human inventions for dealing with number as man has faced problems involving the quantitative aspects of his world. Man invented symbols for number, symbols to indicate processes he performed with numbers, and forms for keeping records of those processes. We take our arithmetic forms too much for granted, as if they had always existed and always would. We deal with them sometimes as if they *were* arithmetic itself. The algorisms (that is, the forms) for writing long-division or multiplication of fractions or even simple column addition are useful to guide our procedures with numbers. But the written forms are not the arithmetic. They should rather be thought of as the *records* of the thinking about number,

which is the real arithmetic. Some of these algorisms are very efficient, some not so efficient. If we will only appraise them in terms of the purposes they should serve, we can decide which to keep, which to modify, and which to discard completely.

ARITHMETIC AS MAN'S INVENTION

We might look at man's invention of a highly efficient number system in another light. Are we masters, really, of this set of arithmetical inventions dreamed up by other human beings?

Let us digress for a moment to consider some more recent inventions of the human mind. Take our automobiles or our refrigerators or our television sets. They are a part of our everyday lives. Legal limitations restrict the operation of automobiles to persons of supposedly appropriate age, mental and physical competence, and driving skill, but the advertisement writers are quick to tell us that "any child can operate" our amazing refrigerators, radios, television sets, and dozens of appliances and gadgets. Being a good "operator" or "driver" of a given modern mechanical invention means knowing enough about the controls and being skillful enough in doing what one knows how to do so that the machine operates efficiently and safely.

Many of us—perhaps most of us—have that much knowledge and that much skill. We can "run" an amazing number of mechanical inventions without knowing what makes them run and without having the slightest idea why pulling or pushing a certain control has the effects it obviously does have.

This situation provides a fairly good analogy for the way a majority of us moderns "operate" or "run" or "work" that not-so-recent bundle of human inventions known as *arithmetic*. Oh, yes, there are some people who never learn to drive an automobile really well, driver's license notwithstanding, and there are some people who never learn to do arithmetical operations well either, years of schooling notwithstanding. Let us discuss, however, those who do run automobiles and arithmetic fairly well. By "well" we mean that they have no serious setbacks or accidents in moving from a given starting point to a given destination (solution). Such people say of driving a car: "Oh, it's almost second nature. I'm so used to doing it that I do it almost automatically." They might well say of the way they do arithmetic: "It never causes me any trouble. I just do what I was taught and I usually get the right answer. When I get the wrong one, it's just carelessness."

The automobile driver pulls the right levers, pushes the right buttons, and steps on the right pedals—all at the appropriate times. He is considered by many, and usually by himself, as being "good at driving." The arithmetic operator copies the right numbers in the right places, mechanically goes through the right "steps," and writes the correct figures—all at the appropriate times and places. He is considered by many and usually by himself as being "good in arithmetic." Many teachers of arithmetic fit into this category rather well.

Perhaps the average user of arithmetic processes is not quite as lacking in understanding of how and why it works as is the average driver of an automobile; perhaps he is. Or he may be even more ignorant of the interrelatedness of the parts than is the average driver of an automobile. What does it matter in either case?

When we have smooth going, it matters little. We may go for days and weeks and months and even years with little trouble with either the car or the arithmetic. We do not need to understand what makes automobiles or arithmetic run when all goes well with the way we operate them and the results obtained. It is when things do not go so smoothly that it is a great asset to have more understanding.

The naïve driver of a car with poor brakes has no idea of any other way to "brake" the speed of the car. A more sophisticated motorist knows enough about the mechanism to adjust to a changed situation by utilizing his understanding of how else the car may be slowed down. This bit of extra knowledge may be a lifesaver.

So also with arithmetic. The person who knows only the routine forms and processes, the one who has learned to work arithmetic in all the usual types of situations, gets along all right until he finds himself in a less usual situation— one he never learned about in the arithmetic class. Now he must analyze a new situation, one for which he has no memorized prescription for steps to follow. Now he must judge for himself what operations and what parts of the arithmetic machine to call into play. The seriousness of his inability to cope with the situation depends on how crucial the problem's solution is.

Have we neglected something in our little analogy? There is always the repair man. Just get the car to the nearest garage; have it towed in if necessary. Get help from someone who *does* understand the mechanism better than you do. Yes, if disaster has not already taken over the situation, you can always get someone else to do the thinking for you. You pay, of course, in time and money, because he can solve problems you cannot. (Sometimes you even pay the "expert" who knows just enough more than you do so that he can deceive you as to how little he knows. That can be *very* expensive.)

Who are the arithmetic repair men? Who straightens us out when our lack of understanding of the number machine has us baffled and in trouble? Well, there's Father. He was reputedly always good at mathematics. The bank statement will straighten out our checkbook errors. The accountant will complete our income tax returns. Our lack of understanding may still cause delays, embarrassment, time, and money. And in the case of arithmetic we could so easily have known just that little bit more, understood a little bit better. It does not take longer to learn arithmetic with enough understanding to give one this extra power to meet arithmetical problems; in fact, it probably takes less time to learn arithmetic with understanding because in that case there is less blind trial and error in the learning process, less fumbling, less waste effort.

Really knowing a subject gives a person competence. Competence gives him confidence. Confidence in his ability to use the subject gives him freedom of operation. Teachers should know arithmetic well enough that they have this competence, this confidence, this freedom in using arithmetic. How else can they help children attain a similar competence, confidence, and freedom?

Lest some reader protest that the theory of numbers and their relationships, the ultimate "why's" of arithmetic, are beyond the grasp of the average citizen, we should perhaps say that the preceding references to understanding did not go that far. The person who knows enough about motors to use them very effectively, to repair them when need be, or to adapt them to serve new uses does not need to know as much as

did the inventor or the designer. The person who knows enough about arithmetic to use it effectively, to find errors in thinking when they appear, or to adapt arithmetic facts and relationships to new uses as they appear does not need to know as much as did the people who made arithmetic's great inventions of system and operation. He does not need to know as much as do the men who play with the theory of numbers and go on to new mathematical inventions.

This is not a case of "shooting for the moon." To ask for all average children and adults a modicum of understanding of how arithmetic works is not unreasonable. The people who first used zero, place value, and the algorisms of division had to understand in order to invent these things; the irony of it all is that the inventions were so very efficient that we who inherit them can run them without understanding — and often do.

LOGICAL ORDER
IN ARITHMETIC

The order in which children may best learn the content of arithmetic, which is the order in which it should be taught, is to some degree inherent in arithmetic itself as a logical organization of ideas and relationships. In teaching elementary-school science the particular topics (or should we say units?) of study may be interchanged as to order of teaching much more freely than the topics in arithmetic. The topic of the weather and the topic of bird life may either one precede the other, with appropriate adjustments in the light of material already taught. Even history, with its built-in time sequence, may be taught from the past to the present or from the present backwards.

Arithmetic cannot be so easily rearranged except for details. It seems to work out better to teach multiplication *after* addition, and division *after* subtraction. Children must know something about counting before adding, subtracting, multiplying, and dividing can make much sense to them.

A child might be absent from school because of a lengthy illness and miss out on the study of the westward movement preceding the Civil War. Coming back for a study of the Civil War, he might not do quite as well as otherwise, but he still has a fair chance of learning a great deal about that period of our national history. Not so with arithmetic. If a child misses out on the introductory work on the meanings of fractions and comes back when his group is studying subtraction of fractions with unlike denominators, his chances of success with the latter topic are very low indeed unless he makes up what he missed.

The consideration of the question of double promotions in the elementary school is too complex for full discussion here, but a careful check on "double-promoted" pupils a few years later would probably point up the fact that many of them who "skipped" any grade above the second found that the content loss for the omitted grade was a more serious handicap in arithmetic than in most other subject areas.

The logical order of basic arithmetic topics is not an argument for fixed placement of arithmetic topics at certain grade levels. Children learn at widely varying rates, and the right time for one child to begin a given topic is by no means the right time for all others to begin it. A more sensible application of topical sequence in arithmetic is to take care that each child, so far as possible, has an opportunity to gain understanding and skill with a given topic before he is pushed on to other topics that are built of necessity on those that precede.

COMPUTATION AND PROBLEM SOLVING CONTRASTED

For purposes of emphasis, arithmetic as computation and arithmetic as problem solving are sometimes contrasted. Common practice in standardized tests of the past has separated arithmetic into these two phases. A child gets a score in problem solving and a score in computation. If his scores are very different in the two, his teacher may conclude that he is a good computer but a poor problem solver, or the other way around. Perhaps a group of children exhibits such a contrast. In either case, a campaign may be instituted in the classroom to "bring up" pupil competence in the weaker phase of arithmetic performance. (This is not a statement of what should be done; it is rather a statement of what is frequently done.)

Professional books on the teaching of arithmetic often have a separate chapter or special treatment of some kind for problem solving. Presumably, problem solving is considered to greater or lesser degree as a separate entity in arithmetic as a school subject. Should this be true? The answer depends on what we mean by problem solving in arithmetic.

Problem solving as working word problems. All modern textbook series in arithmetic include "word problems." The authors cannot go with their textbooks into the classroom to utilize social situations in which problems need to be solved or to devise problem situations suited to the content to be taught. Therefore, they describe probable problem situations in as few words as possible because of space limitations. Some teachers lean so heavily on these "word problems" that these substitutions for reality become the only basis for arithmetic problem solving, a very limited basis indeed.

Problem solving as resolution of real problems. Contrasted with hypothetical word problems, we have the type of problem that actually occurs in children's daily affairs, in or out of school. A boy has a problem to solve in order to determine how much profit he is making on his paper route. The class group has a problem to solve working out quantities of food needed for the class picnic. Actually, the reality of these problems may vary from child to child, but they are at any rate the type we refer to as *real* contrasted with *word* problems. They arise in social situations, in the practical affairs of life involving number. They have a definite advantage over verbal problems in that the child has a better chance to see and understand the situation and what the *problem* really is. They also dramatize the usefulness of arithmetic in daily living.

In the typical classroom more practice is needed in solving arithmetic problems than is provided by these problems which actually occur. The teacher needs to use word problems from texts and problems of her own devising to provide additional practice.

Problem solving as number thinking. In both types of problem solving activity suggested above, the emphasis is on the social setting of the problem to be solved, on the practical application of arithmetic. In fact, sometimes problem solving in arithmetic is thought of almost exclusively in terms of its particular applications. If so, that emphasis is likely to interfere with another important way of looking at problem solving.

Whenever a person needs to think about quantitative aspects of a situation, whenever he needs to think through quantitative relations, whenever he works out the answer to a felt difficulty by using arithmetical facts or principles, he is doing arithmetic problem solving.

When Jim sees that a certain combination of blocks will not fit into a certain box and substitutes other blocks until he finds a combination that does fit the available space, he is doing problem solving concerning size or quantity. Maybe he never puts the problem into words, maybe he does, but he sees a difficulty and he works out a solution. Maybe Susie hears a friend say that 2000 tickets have been sold for a school entertainment, but she knows the school auditorium seats only 800 people and concludes that the friend is misinformed. She is doing thinking about numbers.

We recognize thinking with and about quantitative relationships as problem solving in the best sense so long as there is a problem to be solved or a question to be answered about those relationships and so long as the person in question actually reasons out the solution. This is not to exclude the practical applications discussed above; it includes them, but it also goes beyond them. Mathematics deals with the abstract. Even elementary school children can do problem solving on the abstract level, divorced from objects and practical applications. When a child reasons that $25 + 25$ are 50 and that $24 + 24$ ought to be $50 - 2$, or 48, he is dealing with abstractions, but his thinking is still *real* reasoning even though it does not deal with *real* objects.

Computation and problem solving related. When we decide not to limit our concept of arithmetic problem solving or reasoning[11] to the first two ideas discussed above but decide rather to include those as part of the third, we no longer have much use for a contrast

---

[11] Actually, *reasoning* would be a better term than *problem solving* in the preceding discussion. The latter term is used because it is the one typically used in discussions of arithmetic teaching.

between problem solving and computation except to talk about them as one or the other is emphasized. Thinking with and about quantity and quantitative situations should be present in all arithmetic teaching and arithmetic learning. Computation should be a rational process; it should be understood; the human computer should see sense in what he is doing. Problem solving should obviously be a process involving understanding of relationships, a process of making better and better sense out of the available data.

True, computation may be understood very well and still become a mere routine one carries out in order to get a desired answer to a question. The same might also be said of much so-called "problem solving," particularly of word problems from books. This routine manipulation of numerals is all right provided that (1) computation was first learned in terms of meaning and (2) the person using the routine procedure knows when and how to use it in the solution of problems.

The reader may feel that this point is belabored. Not so! It is the crux of much poor teaching in arithmetic. In

and out of classrooms, arithmetic computation has little place except in problem solving about quantity; it had better be taught in relation to problems to be solved, not all by itself as a series of routine forms and meaningless operations. And arithmetic problem solving, though it does not *always* involve what we call computation, *usually* does; accordingly, here too they need to come together. Computation and problem solving in arithmetic must be taught and must be learned as interrelated phases of the arithmetic whole if each is to have its proper place. The divorce of computation and problem solving in classroom practice is a divorce that should have been prevented; the sooner they are remarried the better!

This is not a complete description of arithmetic. The details are yet to be supplied. Arithmetic as described above must be taught differently from the ways it has often been taught. If this description of arithmetic is true, much current teaching of the subject needs rapid and extensive revision so that arithmetic can become for the learner what it really should be—a vital and integral part of daily lives and thinking.

STUDY QUESTIONS

1. What is your own conclusion about how easy arithmetic should be made for children? What is the basis for your conclusion?

2. In your own experience, did you have any difficulty in learning arithmetic? What was it that caused your difficulty? Do you think it could have been prevented? How?

3. Give an example of "form" being made more important than "substance" in arithmetic. Give a contrasted example of "substance" being made more important than "form."

4. Discuss what should be the proper balance between problem solving and computation in elementary school arithmetic.

5. Try to secure copies of old arithmetic books. Compare them with modern arithmetic materials. (Perhaps your pupils will know of someone who has an old arithmetic and can get permission to bring it to show to the class. Perhaps a public or college library in your community has a collection of old books, and you can take your class to visit it and examine the books on arithmetic. Be sure to impress on the children that these old books may be very valuable and must be handled with special care.)

6. Compare a modern series of elementary school arithmetic texts with those you remember from your own elementary school days. List similarities and differences.

CHAPTER 2

Teaching and Learning Arithmetic

WHY TEACH ARITHMETIC in the elementary school? Many books have been written on the teaching of arithmetic, and each has its own classification of aims and purposes. This book is no exception. Its classification of purposes, which comes later in this chapter, stresses relatedness among the various listed purposes. To clear the air of differences before stressing relatedness, let us first appraise some commonly expressed contrasts.

COMMON CONTRASTS OF PURPOSES
FOR TEACHING ARITHMETIC

Contrasts are often useful in pointing up and clarifying differences in ideas or points of view. Sometimes we contrast phases of an over-all topic so as to make sure that each phase is considered, as in contrasts between practical and theoretical uses of arithmetic. Sometimes the educational pendulum swings too far in one direction, and the contrasting view must be emphasized to bring practice into balance again, as in the case of overemphasis on drill. Occasionally, someone gets too enthusiastic about what he wants to emphasize and revels too long and too loudly in contrasts between what others do and what he thinks should be done. A useful purpose

may be served by pointing out some common contrasts and appraising each.

Teaching children vs. teaching arithmetic. The discussions of whether we should teach children or whether we should teach arithmetic (or any given subject matter) should have ended by this time through sheer weariness on the part of the arguers, but the echoes linger on. This contrast is not only useless; it is based on a most naïve conception of the learning process. True, some teachers do overemphasize subject matter; they do act as if the arithmetic in and of itself were more important than the people who are to learn arithmetic. The critics of this attitude, however, are just as naïve when they declare that we should teach children *instead of* arithmetic. Both these points of view lead us nowhere; they advocate purposes impossible of achievement.

In any learning situation we *must* have one or more *learners;* we *must* have *something to be learned,* whether it be a fact, a skill, or a broad ability. The learner and the material to be learned are both essentials; neither can be omitted; neither can be substituted for the other. No teacher can teach children without teaching them something, e.g., arithmetic. No teacher can teach anything, e.g., arithmetic, without teaching it to someone. The teacher teaches *arithmetic* to *children* (or adults, for that matter.)

Now that this needless controversy has been recognized as such, it will be ignored. The large place assigned to arithmetic content in this book recognizes the importance of knowledge of subject matter for a successful teacher. The latter part of this chapter will deal specifically with the learner and the necessity for planning the arithmetic program in terms of his needs and characteristics; all following chapters assume that teaching method must be devised in relation to the potential learners and the content they are to learn.

Preparing children for present or future use of arithmetic. Should we teach children arithmetic only to make them competent to deal with their present needs for arithmetic, or should we seek rather to prepare them for future demands? No choice is necessary; we should help them to meet both present and future situations in which they will need arithmetic insofar as we can do so without sacrificing other important learnings.

A word of caution is in order. The logical organization of arithmetic, referred to earlier, sometimes makes it impractical if not impossible to take up with children some process for which they may have a present use. Let us say that a third-grade group wants to find the cost of 28 books that cost $2.75 each, but that this particular group of children does not know enough about multiplication facts and multiplication by a one-place number to deal with a two-place multiplier or to devise any other original multiplication scheme. They may recognize that this is a multiplication situation, and the teacher may do the actual computation for them. They may add if time permits. This is meeting present

need better than a hurried introduction of a confusing explanation of two-place multiplication would do.

Caution is also appropriate regarding meeting of adult needs while the learners are yet children. A very large part of the elementary school curriculum in arithmetic, perhaps all of it, is useful in adult life, assuming that it is well taught. Present-day curricula, however, make no claim to include every possible adult use of arithmetic. Certain topics of adult usage such as installment buying and insurance usually belong more appropriately in the junior or senior high school.

In summary, though the elementary school should not attempt to teach every child every bit of arithmetical knowledge or competence he needs, now and later, it should seek to teach arithmetic to him in such a way that it does meet a large majority of both his present and his future needs for arithmetic understanding and skill.

Contrast between mathematical and social phases of arithmetic. The contrast that is often drawn between the mathematical and social phases of arithmetic serves a useful purpose in the discussion of the subject. The terms may vary; we have the *theoretical* contrasted with the *practical,* the *speculative* contrasted with the *applied,* or *mathematical meaning* contrasted with *social significance* of number.

The phase of arithmetic labeled "mathematical" or "theoretical" or "speculative" or "mathematically meaningful" is that which makes arithmetic a logical and unified system of related concepts, facts, operations, relationships, and generalizations. It presents the number system as it has been developed through the centuries and as it is still developing. Much of theoretical arithmetic, e.g., the theory of numbers, is beyond the realm of elementary school arithmetic, but even young children can be led to see structure and pattern in quantitative relationships. They can make sense of such ideas as base and place value. Recent stress on "meaning" in arithmetic instruction has encouraged teachers to devote more time and energy to helping children see how our number system works as well as seeing how they can mechanically work it.

The phase of arithmetic labeled *social* or *practical* or *applied* or *socially significant* is that which we bring into everyday use in our affairs. Sanford says: "Today, applied mathematics is the mainspring of our civilization, for we are becoming increasingly conscious that 'to measure is to know.'"[1] Such arithmetic includes activities like measuring the dimensions of a room and computing the area in order to know how much surface is to be covered with paint, then using the table of estimated paint coverage on the can to see how much paint is needed. This phase of arithmetic is sometimes forgotten by the teacher who is more interested in "covering the book" than in making arithmetic function in the affairs of every day.

In order that the practical and the theoretical phases of arithmetic be adequately represented, each needs to be emphasized in its appropriate place. This does not mean that they are to be set one against the other. The child needs both. Usually, the better he sees the relationships within the number system (on his level of understanding), the more competent he becomes in using number in practical ways. Conversely, the more opportunities he has to use arithmetic in practical situations of his own experience, the better are

[1] Vera Sanford, *A Short History of Mathematics,* Boston: Houghton, 1930, p. 1.

his chances of understanding abstract number relationships. The practical and the theoretical phases of arithmetic are both "useful," each in its own way. Therefore, we should teach arithmetic so as to help each child attain both so far as he can benefit from them.

Enough of reconciling contrasts! How are we going to classify our purposes for teaching arithmetic?

AIMS OF ARITHMETIC TEACHING IN ELEMENTARY SCHOOLS

In reconciling to some extent the preceding contrasted views of arithmetic objectives, we have indicated the importance of relating rather than separating our objectives. In actual classroom practice, this is not only desirable; good teaching can hardly do otherwise. Accordingly, the aims stated below must also be interwoven in practice.

An effective program of arithmetic teaching should aim at helping the learners achieve these objectives:

1. Each child should learn to use arithmetic in recognizing and describing the quantitative features of his world.

2. Each child should learn to use number relations and processes in solving problems involving number.

3. Each child should gain a systematic and logical overview of our number system as a structure of abstract relationships.

4. Each child should develop an appreciation and enjoyment of number and number relationships, both practical and theoretical.

All this sounds very ambitious. Many teachers will say such a set of aims is unrealistic. Obviously, it cannot be accomplished for all children to the same degree. For all normal children it can be accomplished to some degree, the level of aspiration for each being suited to his equipment and opportunities for learning.

Recognition and description of the quantitative features of his world. Preschool children acquire an amazing amount of knowledge before they ever go to school. Because they already possess this knowledge, many adults (fond relatives perhaps excluded) take it for granted and do not appreciate how much the young child is learning. A few are even impatient with him because he does not already know what they themselves may not have known either when they were his age.

Much of what children have to learn in order to get along satisfactorily in their everyday world is quantitative. As with other learning expressed in language, the child has to learn to recognize meanings and also the words that express the meanings. The child has a big ball and a little ball; he recognizes the difference in size but does not have a way to describe the difference. Let us say he prefers the large ball. He can reach for it. If he can crawl or walk, he can go and get it for himself. If he can talk and knows how to describe the "big" one by that single word, he can ask for it. The ability to describe quantitative features of the environment is a notable achievement. In some ways, this is a very confusing process for him. He knows *more* and *less, bigger* and *smaller, fatter* and *thinner.* Then someone plays a trick on him, asking him to choose between a dime and a nickel. He chooses the *big* coin and is ridiculed by more sophisticated older children. They say it is *bigger,* but it will buy *less* candy! He has more learning to do about quantity, for now he is introduced to intangible *value* of a tangible object. He will struggle with that idea for the rest of his life!

The young child also has to learn by progressive refinements of his thinking about the difference between *few* and *many,* finally giving an exact number to express the difference. He has to learn to count objects to help him in recognizing quantities exactly and in describing those quantities to other people exactly. This too continues for many years, extending to larger numbers, to fractional numbers, to a wide variety of measures and other complexities. The more he learns, the better he understands and the better he can get along in his quantitative world. He does not know about Thorndike's famous statement that everything that exists exists in some amount and can be measured, but he works on that "measuring" just the same as he recognizes quantity and tries to describe it.

Many other examples could be given. The arithmetic program in the elementary school has a heavy responsibility to take note of each child's competence in this process of recognizing and describing the quantitative aspects of his environment, then to assist him in the development of that competence. Meanings like *four, ten, hundred, twenty-fifth of May, half a yard, two and six-tenths miles,* and *half-past twelve* must be developed before and while we teach him how to compute using those meanings. In their enthusiasm for teaching computation many teachers neglect instruction in recognition, understanding, and description of size and quantity as children meet it in a quantitative world. This is a crucial objective, and it must not be neglected in considering why we teach arithmetic.

Use of number relations and processes in solving problems involving quantity. This objective for teaching arithmetic is well recognized because it includes computational skill, highly regarded as a tool in the world of private and public business affairs. He who can compute quickly and accurately has a recognized asset on hand for instant use.

Though the first-mentioned objective does give a person some control over his environment as well as helping him adjust to it, this second objective with the first offers even greater control over situations. The child—or the house-wife—on a shopping expedition has much greater control of his private treasury if he can do the necessary addi-tions and subtractions "in his head" quickly and accurately. This ability will have much to do with how much he has left to spend another day.

So far as the number processes are concerned, children must be taught not only *how* to add, subtract, multiply, and divide but also *when* to add, subtract, multiply, and divide. The practical value of skill in computation lies in its applica-tion. An essential of proper application is knowledge of *when to use* each process. Further, if the processes of arithmetic are to be well taught, children should learn (as much as possible for each) the meaning of the particular forms (algo-risms) that they learn to handle. For example, it is not enough to teach chil-dren to write partial products in multi-plication "in the right places"; they should also be helped to see how the meanings of the numerals depend on the places in which they are written. This objective of developing understanding of the mathematical operations leads us to the next reason for teaching arithmetic.

A systematic and logical overview of our number system as a structure of abstract relationships. An abstraction is an idea considered apart from mate-rial objects or situations. "Ten pennies" or "four people" represent concrete ideas involving quantity, but "ten" and "four" are abstractions that are not dependent for their meanings on associ-ation with any particular kind of beings or things.[2]

In his classic discussion in 1935 of "Psychological Considerations in the Learning and Teaching of Arithmetic," Brownell emphasized the merits of the "meaning" theory of arithmetic teaching and its dependence on a conception of "arithmetic as a closely knit system of understandable ideas, principles, and processes." He said that the true test of learning arithmetic "is an intelligent grasp upon number relations and the ability to deal with arithmetical situa-tions with proper comprehension of their mathematical as well as their practical significance."[3] Note that he says "as well as," not "instead of," their practical significance.

In the score and more years since Brownell's statement, the "meaning" theory has gained support from a major-ity of experts in the teaching of arith-metic. To claim that it is being practiced in a majority of elementary school class-rooms in our country would be fool-hardy indeed. Besides the usual lag between what is recommended by ex-perts and what is done by practitioners, there is here a particular drag on the wheel of progress. In this case, teachers need not only to change their ways of teaching, but they must change their conception of arithmetic itself. Before they can *teach* it as such, they them-selves must *see* arithmetic not as an

[2] How abstractions are built up through con-crete experience will be discussed in the latter part of this chapter.

[3] William A. Brownell, "Psychological Con-siderations in the Learning and Teaching of Arithmetic," *The Teaching of Arithmetic,* Tenth Yearbook of the National Council of Teachers of Mathematics, New York: Bureau of Publica-tions, Teachers College, Columbia University, 1935, p. 19.

assortment of unrelated facts and procedures and rules to be memorized but rather as a system of such closely related ideas and processes that each derives much of its meaning from its relationships to the other ideas and processes. This is not easy. In fact, it is probably easier for children to learn arithmetic systematically in the first place than it is for adults to have to "unlearn" erroneous notions before they can relearn arithmetic relationships more correctly and more adequately.

We speak of number *system*.[4] Wheat has said that "number as a science is systematic and consistent; on the other hand, number as a practical art is often a series of rule-of-thumb procedures."[5]

What happens to the teaching of arithmetic when this idea of arithmetic is set up as an objective? In achieving such a purpose, teachers help children to see such relationships as these:

a. Every number bears a definite relationship to other numbers. (The number 4 is 1 more than 3, 2 less than 6, twice as much as 2, half of 8.)

b. Our numeration system has place value. (In the numeral 33,333, every 3 represents a different value because it takes on, in addition to its 3-value, the *value* of the *place* it occupies.)

c. Though other bases may be used, our number system is a decimal system. (We use a base of ten; the numeral 15 means 1 ten and 5 ones.)

d. The same meanings may be presented in different ways. (Common fractions and decimal fractions are just different ways of showing the same meanings.)

e. The number processes are related. (Addition and multiplication are "putting-together" processes; subtraction and division, "taking-apart" processes.)

f. The processes proceed according to certain fundamental laws or principles, such as the principles of commutation and association for addition, the principles of commutation and association for multiplication, and the principle of distribution in multiplication with respect to addition. Much of this book is devoted to developing relatedness.

Appreciation and enjoyment of number and number relationships. Enjoy arithmetic? Appreciate arithmetic? Many people do not, but they could! One of our objectives in teaching arithmetic should be to help children do just that—appreciate and enjoy arithmetic.

To appreciate anything—a symphony, a painting, friendship, or our number system—we need to realize its worth. Appreciation involves awareness of and insight into that which is being appreciated. The more one knows and understands about the symphony, the painting, friendship, or our number system, the more one can appreciate its true worth or importance. We say: "I can appreciate what you have gone through. The same thing happened to me once." We are saying: "I understand your experience because I have lived through a similar one. I know, I understand; therefore, I can appreciate." Each person has that degree of appreciation that is consistent with his knowledge and understanding. The more one learns about the number system, the more one learns about the significance of number applications, the more relationships one sees among arithmetical processes, the more one appreciates arithmetic. One

---

[4] While other number systems are also in use, elementary school arithmetic is based on our prevalent decimal-place-value system. Superior learners may well be introduced to other systems, but the objective under discussion here relates to the typical system of everyday arithmetic.

[5] Harry G. Wheat, *The Psychology and Teaching of Arithmetic,* Boston: D. C. Heath, 1937, p. 150.

does not expect of children the degree of appreciation of the number system that is possible for the master of mathematical theory, he who uses it to predict unseen and heretofore unknown events. One can reasonably expect of children much more appreciation of arithmetic as the wonderful creation it is if we will teach them in such a way that its orderliness, its inherent relatedness — yes, and its beauty — are apparent to them on their level. Appreciation of arithmetic, like appreciation of other things, is usually a by-product of knowledge.

Appreciation and enjoyment are next of kin; at times appreciation is the parent, enjoyment the offspring. Provided our experience with the matter in question has been pleasant, increased appreciation gives birth to increased enjoyment. The more we appreciate arithmetic as a science of number and an art of calculation, the better are our chances of enjoying arithmetic. Children are no different from adults on this point; they tend to enjoy doing that which they do well, be it playing marbles or doing arithmetic.

A skeptical reader may say: "But I have known children who *enjoyed* just plain drill in arithmetic. They didn't concern themselves with all that about the number system, but they did enjoy computing." That may well be. A teacher gave a homework assignment that consisted of looking up and copying all the telephone numbers of doctors in the local directory, then adding them. One parent was amazed to hear his child react to this peculiar assignment by saying: "That was fun. I guess I'll do the lawyers!"

The point still holds that the child tends to enjoy doing that which he does well. Perhaps he is good at computing; he enjoys doing it. This does not by any means prove that he could not experience even greater enjoyment of his arithmetic experiences if he understood the processes better. The chances are very good that he would do just that. It is indeed a worthy objective for teachers of arithmetic to seek to help children appreciate what arithmetic really is and really does in order that they may enjoy it more fully.

The role of pupil discovery and the development of creativity in the arithmetic program are very closely associated with building appreciation and enjoyment. They will be discussed as integral parts of learning and teaching method.

How Is Arithmetic Learned?

Arithmetic has been learned in as many ways as there are people who have learned it. Different learners, different materials, different teaching methods, even different arithmetic content have produced an endless variety of results. Some critics of the educational program take delight in pointing out that many of these results fall far short of what might be desired. Conscientious professional workers in the field of elementary education are well aware of the inadequacies of past and present arithmetic teaching. Only the biased or foolhardy or poorly informed, however, would recommend any one method as providing the perfect answer to all instructional problems in arithmetic. There is no simple solution, but enough is known about how children learn and about arithmetic as a school subject to provide us a basis for working out many improvements in arithmetic teaching. The present chapter provides one person's way of fusing these elements into a framework for arithmetic teaching within which the individual teacher can work out instructional procedures with a particular group of children.

ATTACK ON IGNORANCE

All teaching is, in a sense, an attack on ignorance. What is ignorance, and why should it be attacked? Ignorance is *not* synonymous with stupidity. Children —or adults for that matter—are ignorant when they are uninformed or lacking in knowledge. To say that a child is ignorant of arithmetic is to say merely that he has not learned arithmetic. The young child's ignorance of arithmetic is likely to be the "blank-page" type of ignorance due to lack of experience. To teach arithmetic well to such a child is easier than to teach it to the older child or adult who is inadequate in his performance of arithmetic tasks and who also possesses a confused assortment of right and wrong ideas about arithmetic. These latter persons have much to "unlearn" before they can acquire clear, well-organized knowledge of number and its relationships.

The teacher must also recognize various levels of ignorance. To be accurate in our appraisals of ignorance, we must be specific. A particular child is ignorant concerning multiplication; he is not ignorant concerning addition. To be even more specific, a child may be ignorant so far as some addition facts are concerned even though he knows others. To be really fair, we should call no one ignorant without specifying what it is of which he is ignorant.

INSTRUMENT OF ATTACK

What shall be our instrument of attack on ignorance in arithmetic? If we were to give it likeness to a physical form, we might call it a two-pronged fork; one prong represents knowledge of arithmetic; the other prong represents knowledge of how children learn. Since precision is a characteristic of mathematics, a precision instrument seems appropriate for our attack on ignorance in arithmetic. Both prongs should be sharp; they should "have point." The points should have direction. Since the prongs of this figurative instrument are parallel, they take their direction from the handle.

Just as strands of textile fiber or wire or steel are twisted into ropes in which the strength of each strand is augmented by the presence of the others, knowledge of arithmetic and knowledge of how children learn can be tapered toward each other and intertwined and strengthened in the "handle" of our instrument. This handle that gives a common direction to the two prongs of our instrument represents *development*. The teacher seeks to develop arithmetic and to help children develop into more competent and well-rounded human beings simultaneously.

To complete the analogy, the instrument of attack on ignorance that is recommended here might be named "developmental learning of arithmetic." Development of arithmetical ideas and processes and development of learners through the learning process are not the same thing. Neither are they in opposition one to the other. They are entirely compatible. When the teacher aims consistently to develop both, each is strengthened by the other.

MATCHING THE LOGICAL
AND THE PSYCHOLOGICAL

Arithmetic has a logical structure, which makes sense to the person who sees that structure. Arithmetic, or any other subject matter, serves its purpose only when it becomes a part of the learner. The important question becomes: how can we reconcile the logic of the subject and the psychology of the child and his learning? It must be done. It will be done only if we respect each without doing violence to the other.

The expanding experiential environment. Every man, woman, and child lives in his own world. In his explorations of living he roams farther and farther afield, pushing the boundaries of his world ever outward until they encompass not only his own home, his own school, his own town, but as much of the world outside as he can reach either directly or indirectly through the marvelous channels of modern communication.

The progression from the here and now to the more remote is not a rigid sequence, allowing for no deviations. Rather, it is a rough framework that helps teachers help children to begin with the familiar and proceed by manageable stages to an understanding of an expanding environment. As each new bit of information or understanding is added, it should be fitted in with what is already known. Thereby both old and new information and understandings become integrated into an expanding and ever richer picture of the world in which the learner finds himself.

The "here and now" of the typical modern child is by no means the same "here and now" of his teacher's childhood. For example, it includes contacts with the geographically or spacially "distant" that were not possible when his teacher was a child. The real "here and now" is that which is psychologically close in any particular child's experience.

Interaction with the arithmetic environment. What does all this have to do with learning arithmetic? In learning arithmetic, as in learning social studies or science, the child is the center of the learning process; he learns in an environment. The school provides a curriculum, including arithmetic, that is part of his school environment just as much as the tables and the chairs and the people around him. As he learns arithmetic, it becomes part of him; he is a changed person with changed behavior. He is "a part of all that he has met," and it is a part of him. He assimilates first that which is near to him in experience and works out from there to wider experiences, wider knowledge.

A few people believe that a child can learn arithmetic incidentally. They think that if a teacher is alert to the quantitative features and problems of the school day, these provide an adequate arithmetic curriculum. That view places too much reliance on the accidental events of school life, and it ignores the logical structure of arithmetic as a school subject. Certainly, the skillful teacher does *use* opportunities for arithmetic experiences and arithmetic instruction and application as these occur, but the teacher must also *introduce* planned experiences with number if the children are to achieve a well-balanced knowledge of the subject.

The arithmetic teacher[6] must introduce arithmetic to the pupils. Olga Adams has described in delightful fashion how she did just that with kindergarten children.[7] In teaching social studies the primary-grade teacher virtually says, "Children, this is your school!" Similarly, she points out the quantitative and numerical features of their immediate environment and says,

[6] The use of the term "arithmetic teacher" is not meant to indicate support for the practice of having a special teacher for arithmetic in elementary schools.

[7] Olga Adams, "Arithmetic Readiness in the Primary Grades," *Arithmetic 1947*, Chicago: U. of Chicago Supplementary Educational Monographs no. 63, October 1947, pp. 10-16.

"Children, this is arithmetic!" How surprised some of them will be to find that they know something about arithmetic! Big brothers and sisters have sometimes made them think of arithmetic as some remote and foreign area of experience within whose boundaries the younger ones should not dare venture for years and years. But here it is. They counted the number of boys, the number of girls, then the number of boys and girls. The teacher said it was arithmetic, and it was!

The teacher helps the boys and girls learn about their community. She is saying in effect, "Children, this is the community in which you live." The same teacher introduces the same boys and girls to new arithmetic ideas and their uses and lets them know: "This is arithmetic, too. We counted to find how many in all. Now we add to find how many in all. This too is arithmetic." The children move thus into a wider and wider number environment.

The teacher already knows—or should know—arithmetic as a total elementary school area of study. Each teacher has to know what arithmetic topics, skills, and meanings may naturally precede or follow those which her particular pupils are learning. Only thus can the best use be made of what the children already know; only thus can the best foundation be laid for what is to follow.

The teacher sees—or should see—the logical structure of arithmetic as an elementary school subject. This broad overview of the number meanings and processes as seen by the teacher is a logical, organized pattern of relationships built up through years of experience with numbers. It is the end product of much learning of arithmetic.

The individual learner's logical view. The logical overview of arithmetic that we want children to have is not the adult's comprehensive pattern. We cannot take a large body of organized subject matter as viewed by the experienced adult and say to children: "Here it is, all of it. This is arithmetic. Learn it." Even to suggest such a procedure is ridiculous. What we want and can expect from children is a logical mental organization of that body of arithmetic knowledge that they possess at any given time. Johnny cannot count above 100, he has not learned about place value or a base of ten; these ideas cannot be included in *his* overview of number relations. But Johnny *can* count by rote to 100, he can count objects accurately past 20, and he has noticed that "the next bigger number" when he counts is always "1 more" than the preceding one. Four is one more than 3; 5 is one more than 4; and so on. Johnny has *some* logically organized knowledge of number relations which make sense to *him*. His teacher's business is to help him expand what he does know about number and to help him to integrate new learnings with what he already knows. Thus at any point along the line Johnny can have in his possession a logically organized body of arithmetic knowledge.

An expanding logical structure. Now what should be the plan by which Johnny is led from his logically organized but limited knowledge of arithmetic to what an average adult would consider a well-rounded, logical, integrated knowledge of arithmetic? At least four considerations are essential:

1. The teacher should have a well-organized knowledge of arithmetic.

2. The content of arithmetic should be introduced to the learners in such a sequence as will make it easy for the learner to see how each idea fits into the pattern of what he already knows.

There must be no "gaps," omissions of content essential for seeing subsequent relations.

3. The teacher should know the learners and their present status in arithmetic learning well enough to know what is a reasonable expectation as a next step.

4. Teaching methods should encourage children to think about relationships. Relationships are a large part of the subject; arithmetic cannot be well taught without emphasis on them.

The reader may try to classify these four essentials as emphasizing the logic of arithmetic or as emphasizing the psychology of learning, but in the teaching of arithmetic each is best served when the other is given its proper emphasis. Let us avoid any tendency to think of logical *versus* psychological order in teaching arithmetic; what we want is logical *and* psychological order.

Logic, after all, is a *process* of reasoning from given data or ideas to a conclusion consistent with the given data or ideas. Mathematics depends on logic. The reasoning process is a psychological phenomenon; able teachers applying a sound psychology of learning aid and abet the reasoning process. A logical organization of what a person knows is the result of this process. This is true for children as well as adults. Each individual learner can have his own logical structure of what he knows about arithmetic; every time he learns something new, he can fit it into the pattern. Sometimes new learnings serve to enrich and fill out the pattern; sometimes they involve rearrangement and reorganization of the old.

Too many children and too many adults possess a heterogeneous collection of arithmetic information and skills. Each of the pieces would mean so much

more if they were related, fitted into a logical structure. Adults who have to do all this at once, or perhaps tear apart a hodgepodge and partly erroneous structure before they can build a better one, have a difficult adjustment to make. This discussion is a plea for more attention to organization of learning all along the line—logical organization, if you please, accomplished through the application of sound psychological principles of learning.[8]

RECONCILING THE CONCRETE AND THE ABSTRACT

"Abstract" is not a "bad word." It is a word used mostly by adults, and some adults use it only in a negative sense. College students say, "Oh, that's so abstract, I can't understand it." Teachers say of in-service programs, "I wish they would give us something concrete, something we can use in our teaching, instead of a lot of abstract theory." Yes, many adults talk as if anything that is abstract is also vague, useless, the opposite of that which is practical. While a given abstraction *may* be difficult or vague or lacking in usefulness to a given individual, it is by no means true that abstractions in general *must* be vague or hard to understand and use. Far from it!

The same people who grumble about not being able to use that which is abstract are using abstractions easily even as they speak. The words they use in speaking are all of them abstract symbols, yet meaningful to the speaker and to the listener. How did they become meaningful? Through experience!

[8] See T. R. McConnell, "Recent Trends in Learning Theory: Their Application to the Psychology of Arithmetic," *Arithmetic in General Education,* Sixteenth Yearbook of the National Council of Teachers of Mathematics, New York: Bureau of Publications, Teachers College, Columbia U., 1941, pp. 268-89.

Nick, a second-grade boy, was visiting his grandmother. She told him they would take a week-end trip to an island off the coast from her home. He asked how they would get there and was told that they would take a "ferry." Nick's only previous experiences with that sound having been associated with "fairies," he was mystified. He could not understand how a fairy could take them to the island; he had been led to believe that fairies were delightful figments of the imagination; now he was told that a "fairy" would carry a car and all its passengers from the mainland to an island. Persistent questioning finally made his grandmother see what the trouble was and she described a "kind of boat" called a "ferry." That helped, but Nick was still greatly confused until he actually saw the ferry and rode up on it and off again. The next day he had the air of the real sophisticate as he told his playmates about riding on the *ferry.* The word "ferry" was an abstraction, but a meaningful one. Nick had had some experience with a ferry; he had seen it, been on it, felt its motion, and had observed the cars driving on and off its deck. He was later to learn more about the meaning of "ferry" from other ferries, large and small and of varying shapes and modes of propulsion. Then the word, still an abstraction, would be still richer in meaning.

Arithmetic is full of abstractions. One cannot learn arithmetic without dealing in abstractions. That does not mean that arithmetic must remain a bundle of confusing obscurities "signifying nothing." It does mean that learners need adequate experiences with concrete, quantitative situations so that abstractions like "14" and "+" and "$\frac{2}{3}$" can be meaningful abstractions from experience.

The artist uses lines, shapes, and colors to represent real objects—tables, houses, trees. In abstract art he also uses lines, shapes, and colors, but he does not intend them to represent natural objects; rather, they convey ideas or feelings that the artist has associated with those lines, shapes, and colors.

Abstractions in arithmetic. The abstractions of arithmetic are like that. The numeral "4" might be used in connection with 4 wheels on a wagon, 4 buttons on a coat, 4 corners of a handkerchief; that is, it might represent a quantitative description of real things. The number for which "4" is a symbol can also be used apart from any of these real things to stand for an abstract quality of "fourness" that is present in a wide variety of concrete situations: 4 wheels, 4 buttons, 4 corners, 4 houses, 4 walls, 4 table legs. We cannot draw a picture of the idea "4." We can draw pictures of 4 dots, 4 lines, 4 dogs, or 4 something else, but we cannot draw a picture of the "4" quality all by itself. This does not mean that it is impossible for us to have a clear idea of "4" as an abstract idea. Every person who reads these words has some sort of abstract idea of what "4" means and can recognize the "4" quality whenever, wherever, and however he meets it—4 flowers, 4 knocks on the door, 4 flaps of a bird's wing, 4 spoonfuls of vanilla. These "4's" vary in concreteness, but all are associated with something perceived by the senses. The *real* though *intangible* idea that helps one recognize the "4" quality in these situations is not present to the senses but is the result of all the past experiences one has had in seeing, touching, and hearing "4's" of one kind or another. If children are to gain *clear* abstract ideas in arithmetic, they must have ample experience with those ideas within tangible, concrete settings.

In a sense an adequate abstraction is a summary. We *abstract* a book or a report by summarizing the key ideas in the complete version. When we buy a piece of real estate, we get an *abstract* that reviews the significant facts about the history of ownership or title to the piece of property. One's title to property is said to be "clear" when there is no doubt of the owner's possession. When we arrive at a clear title to an abstract idea in arithmetic, such as the idea of subtraction, we have a summary idea of subtraction that has been built up through meaningful experiences with the subtraction process in a variety of situations: having a certain quantity of money and giving some of it away; selling an object and making change for the buyer; comparing heights of two boys; checking supplies on hand against supplies needed; and so on and on.

An abstraction in the best sense represents the very essence of the meaning of a variety of experiences. Far from being cold and narrow and disagreeable, an abstract idea can and should be warm and rich with meaning as well as broad in its application and usefulness.

Concrete aids to learning. Concrete aids for the learning and teaching of arithmetic have gained much attention in recent years, and rightly so, but their value derives from the assistance they give to learners in acquiring correct and varied abstract ideas of quantity and size, of number and number relationships. The concrete and the semiconcrete are not to be used for their own sake; they are to be used in the ways and to the extent that they contribute to children's learning of arithmetic ideas. There is danger in emphasis on concrete aids to learning when they are treated as ends in themselves.

The ultimate objective is to make the learner independent of concrete aids.

As long as the child has to count on his fingers or with blocks, he is dependent on them. When he can count abstractly (and with meaning), he has far greater independence. He must acquire that independence through the abstracting of the idea of counting and number sequence in many concrete situations (the number of situations varying with the individual's needs). When he no longer needs the concrete aids, it is to his advantage to dispense with them. They will then have served their purpose.

Definitions and "rules to be memorized" are verbal abstractions. They have little value for the learner who has not had the experiences or acquired the meanings on which those abstractions rest. The child who memorizes such statements has memorized words and sentences; he has not necessarily acquired the abstract ideas expressed by someone else in those words. That is why chapter summaries in a textbook mean relatively little to the student until he has first read and studied the preceding material. That is why there may be readers of this chapter who will get more from rereading it after thinking through the content of later chapters than they are getting from reading it in advance of that more detailed presentation of arithmetic content and teaching method.

LEARNING AS DISCOVERY

The professional literature on the teaching of arithmetic for the past three decades has included many references to the role of discovery in pupils' learning of arithmetic. Much emphasis has been placed on inductive teaching. It is probably safe to say that any teacher who does a good job of helping children to understand arithmetic must give an important place to these ideas. It is fitting and proper for elementary-school children to discover generalizations about number and number relations through a process of inductive reasoning. Many of the recommendations in this book will emphasize this point. It would, however, be misleading to give the impression that all of the child's learning of arithmetic must be through a process of discovery on his part or to insist that all teaching of arithmetic should be inductive.

The meaning of pupil discovery. Although the terms "discover" and "invent" are often used interchangeably, a discussion of the role of pupil discovery in learning will be clarified if a distinction is made between them. To discover something means to find that which was there all the time; to invent means to make something new. Columbus *discovered* America; Eli Whitney *invented* the cotton gin. The continent we now call America was there before Columbus found it, but he did find it and bring it to the knowledge of the world. Eli Whitney made a new machine that had never existed before. To dis-cover means to un-cover. We can surely expect children in the elementary school to do much more discovery of arithmetic than inventing.

Arithmetic as we know it is a man-made body of knowledge. Number system and the processes of arithmetic as we know them are the end result of a long series of human inventions. No single human being could invent all of them in a lifetime, but a normal child who is well taught can discover a large portion of arithmetic.

Though invention is on a higher plane of creativity than is discovery, the person who discovers something for himself can experience a thrill in his personal achievement. A child may, for example, discover that adding 2 to any

other number is "just like counting by 2." Though the teacher may have skillfully led the child to this discovery, his wide-eyed look of delight bears witness to the joy experienced in making the discovery. He revels in feeling that he did it himself. It gives him a feeling of accomplishment, of independence.

Other advantages of learning through discovery are the authenticity and the relative permanence of such learning. The child who discovers a relationship and can state it in his own original way is proving his understanding in a way that cannot be matched by the child who must repeat the exact words of the book or the teacher. One never knows in the latter case whether the child is revealing his knowledge or concealing his ignorance. Furthermore, that which the child discovers for himself (the assistance of the teacher often being assumed by us though not recognized by the child) is much more likely to be remembered by him; even if it is not always remembered, the child can rediscover it more easily the second time.[9]

Inductive and deductive methods. Inductive reasoning considers available facts and draws from them a general conclusion. Inductive learning or teaching method, similarly, works from several specific facts or examples toward the development of a generalization that covers all of them.

Inductive method might well be used in the development of a generalization about the addition doubles. The child discovers through his experience with concrete objects that two plus two equals four, three plus three equals six, four plus four equals eight, five plus five

---

[9] For more detailed discussion of discovery in the learning of arithmetic, see: Esther J. Swenson "How and Why of Discovery in Elementary School Arithmetic," *The Arithmetic Teacher*, **1**:15-19, April 1954.

equals ten, and so on. The teacher who wishes to assist him in developing a generalization about the relationships among sums of doubles has him show with blocks, e.g., three plus three; then she has him change "three objects plus three objects" to "four objects plus four objects." That completed, she asks him to change the "four plus four" demonstration to "five plus five." By skillful questioning as to what he did, she gets him to notice that it took two extra blocks to change "three plus three" to "four plus four" or to change "four plus four" to "five plus five." She may also have him write addition doubles as shown here:

1	2	3	4	5	6	7	8	9
+1	+2	+3	+4	+5	+6	+7	+8	+9
2	4	6	8	10	12	14	16	18

The teacher is setting the stage to help the child discover that the sum of any double is two more than the sum of the next smaller double. But this is adult terminology. She works with him until he sees it for himself and states it in his own words. He may say, "You add one to each part and the answer is two more," or "The next bigger double is always two more." This is an example of inductive method in the development of a generalization.

Deductive reasoning starts with the generalization and proceeds to specific applications. It is sometimes described as "if-then" reasoning; *if* this statement is true, *then* such and such should follow. Deductive method in learning and teaching, similarly, begins with the generalization or the rule, proceeding therefrom to specific applications.

After the elementary school child understands place value in our number system, for example, he may draw therefrom deductions as to where he should write certain figures in the quo-

tient of a division example. Or let us return to the example of the young child who has learned the generalization about the relation between adjacent addition doubles. After he has once learned this generalization and understands it, he uses it deductively. He knows that 25 plus 25 equals 50. He does not know the sum of 26 plus 26, but he reasons (deductively) that 26 plus 26 should have a sum that is 2 greater than the sum of 25 plus 25. He gets the sum of 26 plus 26 by thinking "50 plus 2 equals 52."

This is just another case in which no exclusive choice needs to be made between two items. Inductive and deductive learning and development of ideas are both useful in helping children learn and use arithmetic. Mathematics is a deductive system with "if-then" relationships. Even the elementary school child can be led to seek and to use these relationships. This fact does not in any way conflict with the use of inductive procedures in helping children discover relationships in arithmetic.

The "villian of the piece" is neither inductive method nor deductive method but rather a stultifying lack of either. Too much classroom time has been taken up with *telling* by the teacher and *repeating* by the pupils. When this is the general pattern of classroom activity, there is little or no encouragement of pupil thinking. Exploration is not encouraged, reasoning not needed, understanding ignored.

In the teaching of arithmetic, we have had too much emphasis on telling children how to work arithmetic. We need much more emphasis on helping children to discover how arithmetic works. Leading children to discover relationships in the number system and among the number processes takes time and patience and faith in children's ability to figure things out for themselves. Giving adequate experiences from which children can draw correct generalizations takes time. Waiting for them to formulate the relation they discover takes time. But it is time well spent.

The preceding discussion should not be interpreted as suggesting that all of a child's learning of arithmetic takes place through reasoning on his part. When an American child is taught to read English, he is not expected to reason out the direction in which he should follow the words printed on the page. The teacher takes pains to teach him that our printed language is read from left to right on the page and from one line to the next lower line. This order of placing the words on the page is an arbitrary one, but it is an important feature of the culture in which the child lives. Therefore, it is very important that he should learn "the way we do it."

There are similar arbitrary items that children need to learn in arithmetic. No amount of reasoning on his part would change them or even give him a logical reason for their use. In this category come the particular names that are given to numbers. Zero would not have to be called by that name; the idea represented by that name might well have had a different name assigned to it. The place value system does not have to have a base of ten, but our system does have such a base. Children need to learn that we have a decimal number system; they should not be expected to defend this choice although they may be interested in the probable history, advantages, and disadvantages of that choice. A decimal number system is a part of our culture just as reading from left to right is a part of our culture.

Relatively few number relationships will be stumbled on accidentally even by the brighter children. The teacher usually has to set up or at least use situations in which discovery is made possible, or even probable. Perhaps the largest single factor in such learning situations is the presence of a goal to be achieved. There must be a question to be answered, a problem to be solved, a perplexity to be clarified, and a classroom environment that furthers constructive learning.

Goal-directed learning. All learning is purposive. All learning is motivated. Teachers speak of motivation, interests, attitudes, needs, incentives, purposes. They must not only speak of these but deal with them. Differentiation among these terms is not important at this point. What is important is that we recognize our responsibility in helping learners achieve the goals that are important to them.

Teacher goals and pupil goals may or may not be the same. They will never be identical for the simple reason that any goal is an integral part of the person who holds it and is therefore unique. Teacher goals and pupil goals can, however, be in agreement one with the other. This agreement, when it does not already exist, can be brought about by modification of teacher goals, modification of pupil goals, or both.

Although it is not the main point here, we may prevent some confusion by recognizing that closely similar goals may be held for very different reasons. A boy may snow real evidence of wanting to master the multiplication tables. He may have set himself this learning goal because Jimmy Jones knows them, and he wants to show Jimmy that "I'm just as good as he is." He may understand the multiplication process rather well and may be able to figure out answers to multiplication facts but sees that he can speed up the solution of multiplication problems if he learns the multiplication facts to a level of automatic performance. He may want to master the multiplication tables because he fears the consequences at home or at school if he does not. He may—and this is not far-fetched—want to master the multiplication tables through sheer enjoyment of their structure. Why a boy wants to learn the tables is a separate consideration from the fact that he does want to learn them.

If a teacher has a good understanding of arithmetic herself and of the probable uses to which it will be put, if the teacher also possesses a good understanding of the learning process and how it takes place, and if the teacher knows how to relate all this to the pupils' capacities and needs, chances are excellent that her teaching goals will need little modification in the direction of pupil goals. This is true because with such a teacher the pupil needs have already been taken care of.

Unfortunately, this description fits the ideal teacher better than the typical teacher, who often needs to revise her teaching goals considerably. For example, some teachers of arithmetic tend to have no goal for pupils other than "right answers." Certainly in arithmetic it is important for children to achieve right answers, but if those answers are to have appropriate meaning and significance for them, the learners must do more asking of questions and more setting of problems. The pupil may well have a "so what?" attitude toward answers that he did not seek except to satisfy someone else. The wise teacher knows that if the learners see a problem to be solved, if they have questions they want to have answered, the opportunity for learning is greatly increased. Not only is the *process* of learning changed, but the *results* of learning as well. If a

learner's goal is merely to obtain an answer that checks with the answer key, the result of his learning activity is as shallow as the process itself. If, on the other hand, he had something to do with setting up the question, if he really needs to know the answer, the manipulation of numbers and number processes must give way to real problem solving. The process of reaching a solution makes sense to the learner and the answer he achieves also makes sense, because he knows how he got it and why he followed that particular procedure.

The teacher needs frequently to ask herself the question posed earlier in this chapter, "Why teach arithmetic?" The conscientious reply to that question will often involve a shift in teacher goals for pupil learning.

Children also need to modify their goals in learning arithmetic. Not only do they need to change erroneous notions that they may hold as to the purposes for learning arithmetic, but they also need to be guided, into seeing and accepting as their own certain goals of which they have not been aware. Since goal and interest are closely related, they are subject to similar misinterpretations. When we say that we should recognize and use children's interests and goals, we are not saying that our teaching or their learning should be limited to present interests or goals. One of the largest responsibilities of teachers is to teach children new interests, to help them establish new goals. No elementary school child should be expected to establish all his own goals for his learning of arithmetic unassisted. Someone who already knows this area of study and the uses to which it can be put must help him to see where he should go and why.

The question is not whether children

shall engage in goal-directed learning; there *is* no other kind. The question is rather one of helping them to achieve reasonable goals they set for themselves and to open up to them new goals to be achieved.

The role of the teacher. The role of the teacher is set forth in this quotation from Rasey:[10]

There you have the crux of the matter. Teaching is concerned with the *want* to. To help those learn who want to is a relatively simple matter . . . But teaching . . . also deals with focusing desires now diffused, and stabilizing focused purpose until it ignites that upon which it falls, as does the light through a burning glass. This, too, is teacher business, but in this the teacher is not the giver as we imagine. He is scene shifter and stage manager—manipulating circumstances about the learner, turning full spotlight on some items, shrouding others in intriguing shadows. Teachers sometimes get mixed up as did Rostand's Chanticleer. Roosters don't crow up the sun, whatever they think. They just announce it. Teachers do not educate. They are by-standers. It is experience that educates. We facilitate the learner's experiencing so that he becomes more skilled in living and learning.

So often teachers complain, "I could teach these children if they only wanted to learn." Of course! But it so happens that making people want to learn is a teacher responsibility. Sometimes, as we have said, the learner already wants to learn. Sometimes he does not. In the former case the teacher uses directly or indirectly the pupil's desire to learn. In the latter case, she sets up a situation in which the desire to learn particular material can be aroused.

Tom and Harry got into an argument as to which boy traveled farther from home on his vacation. Tom went to Chicago, and Harry went to Cleveland. Noting that the argument seemed to be

[10] Marie I. Rasey, *This is Teaching,* New York: Harper, 1950, p. 5.

settling down to a "'tis-'taint" stalemate, Miss Jones suggested that they get out a road map and settle the argument. Tom indicated on the map the route he and his family followed in going to and from Chicago. Harry did the same for his trip to Cleveland. Both recorded the appropriate set of mileages for each trip. The distance from Hometown to Chicago was 312 miles; the distance from Hometown to Cleveland was 342 miles.

What indication do we have in this illustration that Miss Jones was playing the teacher's role well? Tom and Harry were motivated; there is no question on that point. They were not motivated toward arithmetic learning, but each one was highly desirous of proving that he was right. Miss Jones might have ended the argument (temporarily, at least) by telling the boys to be quiet or by changing the subject. She recognized, however, that they were highly motivated. She recognized the opportunity to use this motivation while solving the problem that concerned the boys and, at the same time, giving practice in addition and practice in a more mature procedure for settling differences. The teacher's goals and the boys' goals were quite different, but the teacher handled the situation in such a way that teacher and pupil goals were entirely compatible. The boys' goals of the moment and the teacher's goal of developing skill in problem solving and meaningful addition were handled so that each supported the other.

Miss Smith taught first-grade children. She felt they needed better understanding of one-to-one correspondence. She told the children a little story about four children who had four little kittens who needed four feeding bowls and four ribbons around their necks. Each child had one kitten; each kitten had one feeding bowl; each kitten had one ribbon. The children delighted in dramatizing various situations that from a teacher's point of view are called one-to-one correspondence. The youngsters enjoyed it so much that they wanted to change the story. They wanted to have five of each item, and it was not long before they wanted to change the items themselves. Miss Smith wanted the children to learn about one-to-one correspondence. The children could not possibly share her concern for that particular goal. Nevertheless, she provided a situation in which their interest in the story and the accompanying dramatization went right along with her teaching aims in such a way that the children did learn something about one-to-one correspondence.

Sometimes the approach is much more direct. The teacher presents an arithmetic problem that she herself might solve by division. The children have not studied division. She asks how many three-cent stamps she can buy for fifteen cents. The children, without using division, can devise various ways to solve the problem, giving an excellent basis for proceeding to a "quicker way" of solving the problem through a new process (division). The teacher asks a direct question about arithmetic. Because of their past experiences with numbers, these children are not only willing but eager to see what they can do to answer the question. They accept the solution of the problem as their own goal.

The teacher is an organizer. She knows what she wants the children to achieve. She takes them where they are—in goals as well as in abilities—using, modifying, and building goals to beckon children toward new achievements in arithmetic.

Individual differences in learning. We might say of anyone, as Carl Phillips

said of Napoleon, that he is "wrapped in the solitude of his own originality." The infinite diversity of personality in any elementary school classroom poses a very difficult problem for the teacher.

Variety may at times be the spice of life, but many a teacher has wished for more homogeneity. In truth, a great deal of wishful thinking takes place with regard to this problem. Experienced teachers all know that pupils are different. Most accept this fact and try to do something about it. A few prefer to complain and do nothing.

Those who complain most about differences in the children's learning capacities and present levels of knowledge and skills are often quick to place the blame on the children's earlier teachers. They like to think that if teaching of arithmetic in earlier grades had been more effective, the children would be more homogeneous in their knowledge of arithmetic. This is a completely wrong assumption. The more effective teaching is, the greater will be the range of individual differences in pupil's knowledge and performance. Under ideal learning conditions, the rapid learners get farther and farther ahead of average and slow learners even though these are achieving up to maximum capacity. Whether we like it or not, this is the situation. So long as we have group instruction, the problem of dealing with individual differences in school learning cannot be wished away. Though no one may solve it completely, facing the problem will be the first step in the direction of solution.

When this fact has been faced, rigid boundaries separating the subject matter content for adjacent elementary school grades must be dissolved. What any child should be learning at any given time and the way he should be learning it will depend on what he already knows, his attitude toward what he knows about arithmetic, what is available in the way of new learning content, and the teacher's skill in leading him from what he already knows to new learnings. Completely individualized instruction is not essential. Children learn much from one another and from group experiences.

Arithmetic practice. Practice is a necessary part of any well-planned arithmetic program. It would be incorrect to say that we learn *through* practice —we learn *during* practice. The amount of practice needed by individual learners varies widely. The same individual may need very little practice on one phase of arithmetic learning and need a great deal on another. The amount of practice should be determined on the basis of how much is needed by the particular learner in the particular situation. Practice for its own sake has no place at all.

Much has been said about practice following understanding. This emphasis has been necessary to outweigh the notion held in some quarters that children should practice first and understand later. Surely there is little point in practicing in advance of understanding, but understanding and practice may proceed simultaneously. This is partic-

ularly true when practice takes place in meaningful situations. Practice should always be viewed as a means to an end, not as an end in itself.

As increasing emphasis is placed on providing children with simple meaningful experiences in arithmetic, there is less and less need for separate practice of the drill type, since meaningful experiences with number are in themselves arithmetic practice. And as more time is spent helping children develop number ideas and relationships and as these ideas are better and better understood, the amount of subsequent practice will be noticeably reduced. Actually, the more meaningful the practice, the less need there is to speak of it as a separate phase of the instructional program. Its only real contribution is the help it gives the child as he develops into a competent user of arithmetic. Thus it becomes an integral part of the learner's arithmetic development.[11]

[11] The writer's viewpoint on certain matters in the field of learning that from time to time have been the occasion of controversy have been discussed here as a frame of reference for the reading of later chapters. Whether or not the reader agrees with the positions taken in this chapter, he will at least know the assumptions on which suggestions for teaching method are based.

This chapter is by no means intended to represent a complete summary of teaching objectives or of basic principles of how people learn. Many important considerations have been omitted and others merely mentioned in passing.

STUDY QUESTIONS

1. This chapter discusses four broad aims for teaching arithmetic. Criticize this list of aims. Can you think of other aims that are not listed? If so, why do you suppose they were omitted? Do any of the listed aims seem to you to be less important than others? Which ones? Why are certain aims more or less important, as you see the situation?

2. Think of an example of a specific learning situation in school that might be handled from a *logical* point of view. Discuss this same situation as it is handled from a *psychological* point of view? What is the difference in the two points of view? What is the relationship between the two points of view?

3. Read today's newspaper. List as many social applications of arithmetic as you can find on one page or more of that newspaper. Compare your findings, if you do this, for one page each from different sections of the newspaper (sports, society, financial, general news).

If you are a teacher, have your pupils do this too. Someone may wish to keep a record for a week of uses of arithmetic in comic strips.

4. Read William A. Brownell's "Psychological Considerations in the Learning and Teaching of Arithmetic," in *The Teaching of Arithmetic,* Tenth Yearbook of the National Council of Teachers of Mathematics, New York: Bureau of Publications, Teachers College, Columbia U., 1935, pp. 1-31. How "modern" is Brownell's discussion as compared with present-day statements concerning learning?

5. Answer the same question (4 above) for T. R. McConnell's "Recent Trends in Learning Theory: Their Application to the Psychology of Arithmetic," in *Arithmetic in General Education,* Sixteenth Yearbook of the National Council of Teachers of Mathematics, New York: Bureau of Publications, Teachers College, Columbia U., 1941, pp. 268-89.

6. Why does the learning of arithmetic by children have to involve the learning of abstractions? How does use of concrete situations and materials help build abstractions?

7. What is meant by "goal-directed learning"?

3

Number, Numeration, and Notation

In SEPTEMBER, 1963, the American Bible Society reported that some part of the Bible had been published in 1202 different languages and dialects.[1] Nida has estimated that no part of the Bible exists in about 1000 additional languages and dialects now spoken.[2]

What diversity! More than 1200 languages, and still not reaching all of the world's people! Anyone who has tried to "get along" in a foreign country whose language he does not speak can testify to the discouraging reality of language barriers. How can one ask questions or get answers when the questioner and the respondent do not speak the same language? Even when sign language proves fairly effective, the situation is not wholly satisfactory. The United Nations headquarters are equipped to handle translation from one language to another, or to several simultaneously, but even so the men who participate in discussion there could certainly communicate more effectively if they had one language in common. This will still be true when modern translation machines are more generally distributed.

[1] "The Bible in 1202 Languages," *Bible Society Record*, **108**:101, September 1963.

[2] Eugene A. Nida, *God's Word in Man's Language*, New York: Harper, 1952, p. 14.

A Universal Language

Of all written languages, only one can lay claim to approaching universality. This is the language of number. In a science fiction movie this fact was used as the key to communication between an American scientist and a visitor from outer space. It is actually used every day by earth dwellers as they carry on their interchange of ideas and goods. Let us suppose you wish to order an article you saw in a Paris shop but did not buy at the time. You get a friend who writes French to compose the letter for you. When a written reply comes, you open it even though you do not expect to "read" it, i.e., get any meaning from the words on the page. You are right about the words; assuming you do not know French, you do not get meaning from the words. But look at the numbers! You can read the date the letter was written *because it is in numbers*.[3] You can read the price you will have to pay for the article *because it is written in numbers*. French numbers? English numbers? No, Hindu-Arabic numbers! For our universal—or nearly so—number system uses numerals of Hindu-Arabic origin.

[3] Strictly speaking, the numbers are expressed in *numerals*. See pp. 34-35.

"The Hindu-Arabic system of notation is a universal language. Silks and tea from the Orient, rugs and figs from the Levant, copra and jute from the South Seas—all these, though called by a hundred names in as many tongues, are labeled and invoiced in the same number system that you and I use every day. The *names of the numbers* differ with different people, but the manner of writing the numbers in figures is known everywhere. Men have dreamed of one language for all people. Here it is, a number language."[4]

He who "is born with a silver spoon in his mouth" is not necessarily lacking in appreciation of the material blessings that are his. Most of us who cannot claim that type of inheritance are inclined, however, to suspect that he is less grateful for his worldly goods than is the person who has to earn them by his own labor or who never receives them at all. Human beings are inclined to take for granted that which comes easily; they tend to appreciate fully many of the good things of life only when those things are absent. This human tendency may be at least partly responsible for the common lack of appreciation of the numeration system that is so much a part of our everyday world that it is assumed to have always been available to all men everywhere.

Every man, woman, and child who learns arithmetic today *was* "born with a silver spoon in his mouth" mathematically speaking. He has at his disposal a numeration system that is a comparatively recent invention (or series of inventions) in the annals of history. This system, which is taken so much for granted, has been available for anything approaching general use for only about 400 years. The average modern boy has

at his disposal a notation system for number that was unknown to great minds of the past—Plato, Aristotle, Julius Caesar, Cicero. These men knew nothing of it for a very simple reason; they were born too soon, or the invention came too late. Leonardo da Vinci, one of the early users of the + and − signs to indicate addition and subtraction, probably appreciated them much more than we usually do.

Much of modern scientific progress depends so much on number that such progress would never have been made without it. Then why is it not more fully appreciated? Perhaps because it is not well enough understood and because too many people just do not know how it came into being. Teachers of arithmetic need very much to know more than they usually do about the origin and significance of the particular type of numeration system that we take for granted. No matter how well a person can manipulate this system, he is not ideally prepared to teach it unless he knows something of its origin and its essential characteristics.

Number Quality of Groups[5]

To be exact, the word "number" really applies to the *value* expressed by a number name like "six" or a written numeral like "6." The numerals we write (also called "figures," or "digits") are written symbols that stand for the number quality of "sixness." In everyday usage, however, as in the immediately preceding paragraphs, the word "number" is also sometimes loosely applied to the forms in which the number meanings are expressed. In the

---

[4] B. R. Buckingham, *Elementary Arithmetic: Its Meaning and Practice,* Boston: Ginn, 1947, p. 15.

[5] The discussion in this chapter is confined almost entirely to whole numbers, which include the natural (or counting) numbers and zero. Fractions will be discussed in chap. 14 and later chapters.

discussion that follows we shall consider *numeration* and *notation*. The former applies to use of numbers in the form of words, as in oral counting or "enumeration." The latter applies to use of written number symbols to record our number thinking. In numeration, each man uses his own spoken language. In notation, men of different languages easily use the same written symbols.

PRIMITIVE NUMBER WORDS

Some primitive languages—of long ago and in primitive tribes today—do not have any number words. Most, however, do have a few number words, which, students of the matter tell us, may represent centuries of progress. Even if a tribe knows only the words "one" and "two," they have recognized plurality. If all things came "one of a kind" with no common characteristics, people could go along nicely without number words representing "more than one" or even "one," since everything would then be one. As soon as men began to sense the plurality of things and beings in their world, they were on the way toward number concepts. An early stage of this sensing of number is shown in words for twins or for pairs (two of a kind) and in words for indeterminate larger groups such as flocks of sheep or schools of fish, designated as "many." This recognition of a pair of eyes or a pair of animals or a pair of human beings did not necessarily indicate possession of the abstract meaning of "twoness" applied to any group of two. This distinction is evident in the variety of different words for the same number in some primitive languages—one word applying to people, one to animals, and perhaps another to inanimate objects. "The Thimshian language of a tribe in British Columbia illustrates this very point but nevertheless indicates progress toward complete abstraction. There are seven different words for 'two,' seven others for 'three,' etc., as far as they count. One set is for animals and flat objects, one for time and round objects, one for human beings, one for trees and long objects, one for canoes, one for measures, and one for miscellaneous objects not in the other six categories. The last of these, of course, may eventually become the general number word if the tribe progresses to a better number comprehension."[6]

Because they have already achieved the abstraction of "twoness," "threeness," "fourness," and so on for other numbers, it is difficult for teachers to understand that some of the immature children in their classrooms may not have achieved these meanings. A young child may know "five fingers" on one hand or "five dots" in a domino pattern but not know "five in general" as applied to any and every group of five when the members of the group of five may be fingers or men or leaves or days or clouds in the sky. So it was, and still is, with primitive peoples. Modern languages of peoples who have long ago mastered number concepts have vestiges of the days when number meanings had not been abstracted to apply to things in general. In English we still have a "couple" of dancers, a "brace" of pistols or partridges, a "pair" of trousers, a "yoke" of oxen, a "span" of horses—all different words but all meaning "two of a kind."

THE CONCEPT OF A GROUP

Perhaps we should clarify the meaning of "group" as used in arithmetic. A group is more than an accumulation; the items in a group are separate but share in having a common characteristic that serves as a basis for our considera-

[6] Edna E. Kramer, *The Main Stream of Mathematics*, New York: Oxford U. P., 1951, p. 9.

tion of them together. Groups are most easily recognized as such when the separate items appear close together, are arranged in a pattern, or are clearly similar in appearance. Essentials of a group are (1) plurality, more-than-one-ness, (2) commonality, having something in common, and (3) togetherness, in space, in time, or otherwise.[7] Primitive man (and immature young moderns) recognize only those groups in which the something-in-common and the togetherness are obvious, as with a "school of fish," all looking alike, acting alike, and appearing close together physically. A more mature person, quantitatively speaking, also recognizes groups such as "all American children" — widely scattered, quite diverse in physical characteristics, most of them never having been seen as individuals though known to exist, but all of them belonging to the given group because they are alike in being American children, an intangible but significant reality.

Many groups occur in nature and were observed by primitive man as his number sense developed — wings and eyes and ears and hands in groups of two, paws in groups of four, fingers in groups of five. He came to use these groups as models for the given numbers. In recognizing the use of such model groups to express quantity, one should not necessarily presuppose counting, i.e., arranging the number names or the quantities in order of size. The "group quality" for each number was recognized, but the groups were not at first arranged in serial order as we think of them.

[7] The reader may feel that essentials 2 and 3 are identical. They are certainly closely related and do overlap to some extent. They are mentioned separately because objects or beings do often have something in common, e.g., color, but are not in a given situation *being considered together* and do not constitute a group.

THE CONCEPT OF A SET

The idea of "group" as presented here might have been called "set" instead. Some current experimental programs and some recently published arithmetic materials rely heavily on the concept of the set. The word "set" is used at times in this book interchangeably with the word "group." The position taken by the writer is that natural, correct use of these words is better at the elementary school level than insistence on set terminology.

The use of the word "set" along with other synonyms is shown by the list below:

flock of sheep	*group* of boys
gang of adolescents	*team* of players
herd of cattle	*family* of people
set of books	*club* of members
swarm of bees	*cluster* of leaves
bunch of grapes	*company* of soldiers
litter of puppies	*set* of dishes
bundle of sticks	

Informal conversations with children seem to indicate that they tend to think of "sets" as having a fixed number of members, a set of checkers or chess pieces or croquet balls and mallets or dishes or silverware as "supposed to have" certain numbers of items per set. This may come from the common references in everyday speech to "complete sets" or to "broken sets," with the implication that a set that does not have the standard number of items in it is somehow "incomplete." If a teacher senses this interpretation, she should seek to extend the idea of "set" to include other groups than those with certain specified numbers of members.

On the other hand, one important advantage of using the word "group" for the collection idea in elementary school arithmetic is that its verb forms may also be used to express arithmetic processes. Items are *group*ed and re-*group*ed as well as being members of *groups*. Both as noun and as verb, *group* is used extensively in this text—not as the one right choice but as the choice preferred by many elementary school teachers and successfully used by their pupils.

ONE-TO-ONE CORRESPONDENCE

Not only natural groups but also other groups of man's own devising were used as models in answering the question: How many? How many birds did a man kill? As many as the fingers of one hand. How many animal skins were needed to enlarge the tent? As many as the paws of an animal. How many days' journey? As many as the notches cut in a stick. How many sheep in the flock? As many as the pebbles in the shepherd's pouch. In each case a given group was used to tell how many of something else. This is *one-to-one correspondence.*

The importance of the idea of one-to-one correspondence is not adequately appreciated by a majority of its users. It is a fundamental mathematical idea basic to counting, as we shall see, and basic also to much of higher mathematics.

Telling *how many* by one-to-one correspondence in its early form did not yield a number name as the answer to the question. The hunter cut a notch for each animal trapped or each day's journey. If someone asked him how many animals or how many days, his answer was "as many as there are notches in this stick." A shepherd put a pebble in his pouch for each sheep as it passed before him. When asked how many sheep there were in the flock, he did not answer that there were forty-five or sixty-two. He said there were as many

sheep as pebbles in the pouch. He could *show* how many or *tell by reference* to the other group, but he was *not* counting by using number names in order.

How primitive! Yes, in a way. But, since it sometimes seems easier than counting, we sometimes do the very same thing ourselves. A child or an adult is asked to pass out songbooks to everyone in a group. He passes out books—one book for each person—until all the people have books or until he runs out of books. A parent who has volunteered to serve ice cream at the school picnic gives one scoop of ice cream to each child—one-to-one correspondence—without counting either children or scoops of ice cream. In either case the person in charge could probably not tell (without counting) exactly how many songbooks or how many children.

Sometimes nowadays we use one-to-one correspondence in keeping a record of quantity and then count afterward. We count tallies in a classroom election *after* writing a tally mark for each vote. A score is kept with markers that are counted at the end of the game.

Eventually men came to rely more and more on standard models of number groups. The most convenient standard model group should be something readily available to anyone at any time. What could be more convenient and readily available than man's fingers? There they were, a ready-made standard group of five or ten depending on whether one or two hands were used.

Man Learns to Count

FINGER COUNTING

Adults who severely criticize children for reverting to the use of their fingers in counting had better start observing their own actions. The public speaker emphasizes his point 1, point 2, and point 3 by holding up his fingers—one, two, three. The hostess in a crowded restaurant signals to a waitress with three upraised fingers; she needs a table for three. It is perfectly respectable.

The use of the fingers as "counters" is so natural and so universal that it seems to be a reasonable assumption that it played a large part in man's early counting. Many number words in different languages refer also to fingers and hands. Take, for example, the word "digit," referring to number symbols and also to fingers and toes, or the similarity of the Russian words for "five" (*piat*) and for "hand" (*piast*). Five was a "hand"; six, a "hand and one more"; and so on.

It is difficult to find evidence as to exact sequence in the development of number concepts, but certainly the one-to-one matching of objects with a model group preceded counting.

NUMBER NAMES

Counting involves calling the number values by name. The names for the number concepts are symbols for abstractions derived from experiences with concrete things. Prehistoric man's concept of "five" was probably developed out of experiences with five arrows, five birds, five leaves on a branch, five fish, five fingers on each hand. Having found how many arrows or birds or leaves or fish by matching them with his five fingers, what would be more natural than that he should give his developing concept of "fiveness" the name borne by the model "hand" of five fingers? And so also other number values were given names.

But even with names for the abstract

meanings "three" and "five" and "four," there is no counting until the names are arranged in order of their number values. One cannot *count* until he knows which number value and number name come first, which second, and so on. Here again the fingers are helpful as guides to number sequence. Eventually, single words were used for six, seven, eight, nine, and ten, but the sequence of number values was probably established first with a "handful" of "five" as a base.[8]

CARDINAL AND ORDINAL NUMBER MEANINGS

Various writers on the subject seem to disagree as to the order in which *cardinal* and *ordinal* number ideas were developed. Since this matter has a bearing on sequence of number experiences for children, it represents more than a scholastic quibble. *Cardinal* numbers, simply defined, are those which answer the question "How many?" *Ordinal* numbers answer the question "Which one?" The disagreement seems to hinge on a distinction between telling "how many" by use of model groups and telling "how many" by assigning a number name. Before the number values were arranged in serial order (ordinal number), a man might have recognized the "twoness" quality of twins or the "three-ness" quality of three leaves closely grouped (as in clover). Or he may have used one-to-one correspondence to tally the number of logs cut down by tying knots on a string. In both of these cases he did tell how many (cardinal number), but he did it by recognizing a familiar group's number quality or by comparing with a model group. In neither case did he necessarily know

---

[8] The meaning of "base" will be more fully explained in the next section.

a sequence of number names. He told "how many" by recognizing a group in itself or by showing that there were "as many as" some other group.[9] The situation is somewhat analogous to the well-demonstrated fact that children can and do recognize individual letters and can use this recognition in reading and spelling activities without knowing the order of those letters in the alphabet.

But the time came when men did perceive that the number values could be placed in such an order that each successive value would be one more than the immediately preceding one. This was an *ordinal* idea. Having given the number values their individual names, he could say the names in order. When he did that, he began to *count*. And having worked out the sequence of the number names, he could then use that sequence in helping him find "how many." He no longer needed to match the birds killed with notches in a stick, or the logs cut with knots on a string, or the sheep in the flock with pebbles in a pouch. Now he could match birds and logs and sheep with number names, and the last name he matched would be the "how many" or cardinal number name for the whole group.

Summarizing the above argument, one might say that cardinal number (how many) ideas may well have preceded the use of the ordinal number idea in counting, but that the ordinal idea had to be involved in counting-to-find-how-many. That is, a modern child may recognize a five-pattern ($\because$) and not use five correctly in counting, but if he is to find by counting that there are five dots, he must first have acquired the ordinal idea so that he knows in what

order to use the number names as he counts.

Another matter of sequence is also most interesting. This is the probable precedence in time of naming before counting. The shepherd could tell when all his sheep were in the fold if he knew every one by name and could remember all the names at a given time. The modern Christmas shopper names his relatives and friends to see that no one is omitted on his gift list. This works very well if the list of names is not so long that one or more are inadvertently omitted. But saying the names is not counting. The names of the relatives and friends are not number names. Number names have to come in one particular order; that is the only way they will "work." "One for you and one for me and one for Sister Annie" may help a person distribute ice cream cones in adequate quantity, but it is not counting.

A woman has a large number of nieces and nephews. Every now and then she receives an announcement of another one. She has difficulty keeping track of just *how many* nieces and nephews she has. When she had one or two or three or even ten, it was easy to remember, but when the number went past thirty, she started getting confused. When someone asks her how many nieces and nephews she has, she says, "Well, let me see." Her gaze becomes fixed in the distance as she names them all mentally—John and Alice and Susan in Brother Joe's family; Billy and Ned and Helen in Sister Betty's family; and so on and on. As she names them mentally, she may tally them on her fingers (a college graduate too, no less!), or she may count, using number names as she names each subgroup or each individual child. She can *name* the nieces and nephews *in any order,* but she must *count*

---

[9] The cardinal number of a group or set is a property of the set. All groups or sets that match each other in one-to-one relation have the same cardinal number.

in *one and only one order!* Number names used in counting have a *fixed* order.

The preceding account of the beginnings of numeration (oral language of arithmetic) is based partly on facts from the study of primitive peoples, partly on deductions from those facts, and partly on a synthesizing of fact and conjecture into a story that seems to be a reasonable one. This is the best we can do in the light of present knowledge since the beginnings of numeration go back before recorded history. As Brooks commented back in 1880: "Numeration treats of the method of naming numbers; Notation treats of the method of writing numbers. As oral language always precedes written language, it is seen that Numeration precedes Notation. . . ."[10]

Establishing a Number Base

The beginnings of the idea of a number *base* are implied above in the idea of "five" as "a hand," "six" as "a hand and one more," or "ten" as "two hands."

MEANING OF "BASE"

It may be fruitful at this point to leave arithmetic for a short while to review the meaning of the word "base" in other contexts. A "base" is a foundation or "that portion of an object on which the remainder rests." In baseball a base is a stopping-off point on the round trip made by the runner, a place from which to start, a place to stop and again to start. The military services have put the term to extensive use in the sense of a "base of operations"; businesses use it

the same way. There too it means a focal point for activities of one sort or another — a place that is first established itself and then used as a starting point for various military or commercial activities that extend from it.

These other uses of the word are helpful in setting forth just what a base is in a number system. Objects are counted by reference to the fingers of one hand; then "one hand," or "five," becomes a base from which to count further. With only five number names one can count many more than five objects. First there is the one five; then five and one, five and two, five and three, five and four, and finally two whole fives. So it goes, building up fives until there are five fives. There a new collection may be started, a collection of collections as it were, a collection of five fives. This can go on and on, as number needs and concepts develop.

The number five was a commonly used base among various peoples, probably because of the five-model of the hand in finger counting. Bases of two, three, four, six, eight, ten, twelve, twenty, and sixty have been used at various times and places.

Ten is of course the base used by most peoples, the advantages of eight or twelve notwithstanding. Finger counting no doubt suggested the choice of ten as a number base, a stopping and starting point in counting. A man counted as far as ten, using the fingers of both hands. All his fingers had been used; now what did he do? He could start over with the fingers of another person, as is indicated by a number name in one language for our twenty that meant "two men." Or he could indicate one whole set of ten by a tally of some sort and start over on his own hands.

[10] Edward Brooks, *The Philosophy of Arithmetic*, Lancaster, Pa.: Normal Publishing Company, 1880, p. 93.

BENEFITS FROM USE OF A NUMBER BASE

Think how the use of a base reduces the number of words needed in counting! If he had to have a new word for every number, man would not only have become discouraged in the number-naming process, but the learning of the names after they were assigned would have become too burdensome before he reached really large numbers. Except for the use of a number base, we would need one hundred different number words to count to one hundred, a different word for each number value. With our base of ten, we use the first nine number words over and over. The "stopover points," multiples of ten, all originated in combinations of the first ten number words: twen*ty* (two tens), thir*ty* (three tens), for*ty* (four tens), fif*ty* (five tens), six*ty* (six tens), seven*ty* (seven tens), eigh*ty* (eight tens), and nine*ty* (nine tens), with the syllable *-ty* replacing "tens." The numbers in the second decade, also, use variations of simple combinations of the first ten number names: eleven (one and ten), twelve (two and ten),[11] thirteen (three and ten), fourteen (four and ten), fifteen (five and ten), sixteen (six and ten), seventeen (seven and ten), eighteen (eight and ten), and nineteen (nine and ten). In its original form, our number name system from one to one hundred uses no entirely new word from "ten" all the way to "hundred"—eleven word names for one hundred number values. Even if we considered the words from "eleven" through "nineteen" and the words for multiples of ten ("twenty" through "ninety") as new words, we would have only 28 different words used in counting to one hundred. From there on to one thousand, we use *no new word* until we get to "thousand." From "thousand," we need *no new word* until we come to "million." What a saving! What a simplification in language learning and use! Having a number base for our counting system make this saving possible.

Another inestimable advantage of using a number base lies in the fact that the collections represented by the base values can be handled the same way we handle individual items. They can be added, subtracted, multiplied, divided just as units are added, subtracted, multiplied, and divided. This point will be fully explored later.

The number base makes larger numbers manageable, both for counting and for computing. This statement of course applies to bases other than ten as well as to ten. The smaller bases, e.g., two, are awkward for writing because they require so many places to express a given number, but the base of two is very useful in high-speed computers. A larger base such as twenty would require fewer place values, but more number symbols would be required. Twelve has been a popular nomination for a standard number base because it is evenly divisible by 2, 3, 4, and 6, whereas ten is evenly divisible only by 2 and 5.

[11] Our word "eleven" is a modern form of the Teutonic *ein-lifon*, "one left," or "one over." Compare the Latin *un-decim,* or "one-ten," meaning one more than ten. Our word "twelve" is a modern form of the Teutonic *twe-lif*, "two left," or "two over". Compare the Latin *duo-decim,* or "two-ten," meaning two more than ten.

Written Symbols for Number

Being able to count (orally) gave a certain freedom from the clumsy use of objects in one-to-one correspondence with the items to be counted. The next step toward freedom of use was a scheme for *writing* number symbols corresponding to the number names being used orally. This is *notation.* When keeping records of numbers of sheep or fish or trees or soldiers, men needed written number symbols.

WRITING MATERIALS AND METHODS

Writing was not as simple a matter in the days when number symbols were first written as it is today. Moderns assume the availability of pencil and paper, not to mention all the more elaborate media for writing by hand or by machine. The earliest notations of number that have been preserved to date were written with more difficulty on more permanent materials. A clay tablet from Nippur (c. 2400 B.C.) has numbers recorded in cuneiform (wedge-shaped) characters made by pressing the point of a stick or stylus into soft clay, which was later baked. The oldest known book on mathematics, now in the British Museum, was copied by an Egyptian scribe named Ahmes (c. 1650 B.C.) from an earlier work (c. 2200 B.C.). It is written on papyrus made of crossed layers of "bulrushes" or papu reeds — pressed, dried, and polished. The earliest Hindu precursors of our present numerals were carved on stone pillars by King Asoka some two hundred years before Christ and variants on them were also cut a hundred years later in the walls of a cave, also in India. Not to exclude the relatively permanent in animal form, we may note the Chinese magic square,[12] said to have been found by the Emperor Yu (c. 2200 B.C.) on the back of a tortoise. Easier methods of

writing were certainly used, e.g., scratching in sand, but such records were easily destroyed.

WRITTEN NUMBER SYMBOLS

As with the number names, men invented written symbols to represent *collections* (tens, hundreds, etc.). If this had not been done, they would have needed a different symbol for each number value they used. It was well enough to start out with a simple tally mark to represent the meaning of *one,* two tally marks for *two,* three tallies for *three,* and four tallies for *four;* but at that point a new symbol was often invented to represent *five.* If the change to a new symbol did not come at five, it usually came at *ten.* Though other bases were used, alone or in combination with the decimal (ten) base, the recurrence of the decimal base indicates that it was a natural one to use as men went on

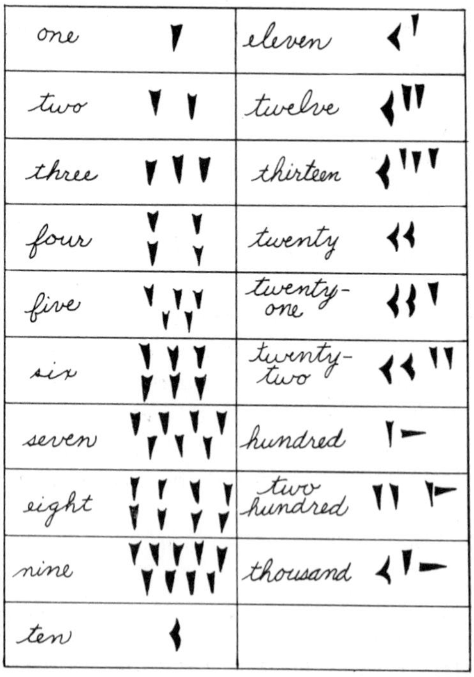

one	▼	eleven	◀▼
two	▼▼	twelve	◀▼▼
three	▼▼▼	thirteen	◀▼▼▼
four	▼▼ ▼▼	twenty	◀◀
five	▼ ▼▼ ▼▼	twenty-one	◀◀▼
six	▼▼▼ ▼▼▼	twenty-two	◀◀ ▼▼
seven	▼▼▼▼ ▼▼▼	hundred	▼▬
eight	▼▼▼▼ ▼▼▼▼	two hundred	▼▼ ▬
nine	▼▼▼▼▼ ▼▼▼▼	thousand	◀▼▬
ten	◀		

Figure 1. Child's Drawing of Babylonian Number Symbols.

[12] Magic squares are arrangements of numbers in squares so that the sums of rows, columns, and diagonals are equal.

from finger counting to written number notations.

Babylonian forms. In the cuneiform writing of the Babylonians we see the symbol for "one" repeated the requisite number of times for "two" through "nine." See figure 1. For "ten" they had a new symbol, which could then be combined with the "one" symbol to show "eleven," "twelve," through "eighteen."[13] "Twenty" and the other "even tens" numbers were written by repetition of the "ten" symbol. For "hundred" a new symbol appears, and "two hundred" is shown by the symbol for "two" followed by the symbol for "hundred." Again at "thousand," a "new" symbol is really a combination of symbols for "ten" and "hundred." Actually, as shown in figure 1, the only independent symbols are those for "one," "ten," and "hundred." Those symbols are repeated, added, and multiplied to show intervening number values and also to represent numbers beyond a thousand.

EGYPTIAN NUMBER SYMBOLS

The Egyptians used hieroglyphic or picture writing in showing *one* as a vertical staff or stick or finger; *ten* as a heelbone, handle, or arch; *hundred* as a coiled rope or scroll; *thousand* as a lotus flower or sheaf of wheat; *ten thousand* as a pointing finger; *hundred thousand* as a pollywog or burbot (fish); and *million* as a man with arms raised in astonishment at such a quantity.[14] See figure 2. By repetition and addition of these symbols, the Egyptians recorded

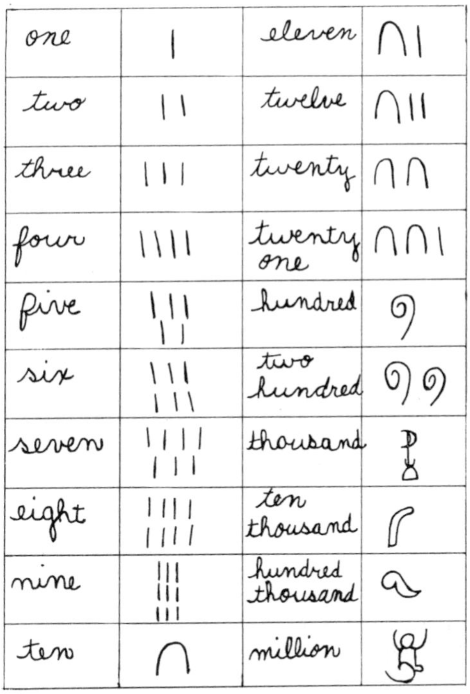

---

[13] The Babylonians used the principle of subtraction to show *nineteen* as one less than two tens rather than as ten and nine ones. This is an exceptional case. (Harriet E. Glazier, *Arithmetic for Teachers,* New York: McGraw, 1932, p. 28.)

[14] The alternatives indicated represent varying interpretations that have been made of what the pictures represented.

one	│	eleven	∩│
two	│ │	twelve	∩│ │
three	│ │ │	twenty	∩ ∩
four	│ │ │ │	twenty one	∩ ∩ │
five	│ │ │ │ │ │	hundred	୨
six	│ │ │ │ │ │	two hundred	୨ ୨
seven	│ │ │ │ │ │ │	thousand	⚱
eight	│ │ │ │ │ │ │ │	ten thousand	∫
nine	│ │ │ │ │ │ │ │ │	hundred thousand	૨
ten	∩	million	ૹ

Figure 2. Child's Drawing of Egyptian Number Symbols.

various intervening quantities, using the base of ten. Large numbers were rather cumbersome as, for instance, our number 27,529. In Egyptian numerals, it required 25 symbols.

Letters as number symbols. The letters of their individual alphabets were used by some peoples as number symbols, the Phoenicians probably being the first to do so. The Greek and Roman systems are examples of this practice.

The Greek notation was particularly awkward.[15] See figure 3. Although it used a base of ten, the lettering system did not capitalize on obvious relationships within a ten system. Three obsolete characters added to the Greek alphabet made a total of seven symbols, with independent values assigned to the

---

[15] The Greek and Roman symbols shown in figs. 3 and 4 and discussed here are representative examples at certain periods in the history of the people who used them. Several variations are known.

1	A	10	I	100	P
2	B	20	K	200	Σ
3	Γ	30	Λ	300	T
4	Δ	40	M	400	Y
5	E	50	N	500	Φ
6	F	60	≡	600	X
7	Z	70	O	700	Ψ
8	H	80	Π	800	Ω
9	Θ	90	ϟ	900	↗

Figure 3. Child's Writing of Ancient Greek Number Symbols.

repetition, addition, multiplication,[16] and subtraction, the latter occurring only in the case of *four* and *nine* and their multiples.

Mayan numerals. The Mayan numerals are shown in figure 5 as a deviation from the common tendency to use a base of ten. This native American system used symbols for *one* (a dot), *five* (a horizontal line), and *zero* (variously interpreted as a half-closed eye or mollusk shell). Since the Mayan system is chiefly interesting because of the use of place value and zero, it will be discussed more fully in the next section. Notice that *ten* is represented as two fives, not by a separate symbol of its own. The base of the Mayan system is twenty, relating to the concept of finger-and-toe counting, which suggested a base that represented "one

numbers *one* through *nine*, to even decades *ten* through *ninety*, and to even hundreds *one hundred* through *nine hundred*. *Thousand* was indicated by an accent mark with the number of thousands. To avoid confusion of numerals and words, a line was drawn above each numeral. These symbols were combined by addition to show various number values; multiplication was used in numbers greater than *ten thousand*.

Roman notation is more familiar to modern eyes. See figure 4. The letter symbols *I, V,* and *X* are said to have represented, respectively, a finger, a hand, and crossed hands. *C* and *M* were probably chosen because they are initial letters of the number names *centum* (hundred) and *mille* (thousand). The Roman system is a decimal one, but it also emphasizes *fives*, with special symbols for *five* (V), *fifty* (L), and *five hundred* (D), thus harking back to the one-hand –two-hands finger-counting bases. Roman numerals use the principles of

one	I	eleven	XI
two	II	twelve	XII
three	III	thirteen	XIII
four	IIII or IV	twenty	XX
five	V	twenty-one	XXI
six	VI	fifty	L
seven	VII	hundred	C
eight	VIII	two hundred	CC
nine	VIIII or IX	five hundred	D
ten	X	thousand	M

Figure 4. Child's Writing of Roman Number Symbols.

[16] Multiplication was used only for the larger numbers and is seldom met nowadays.

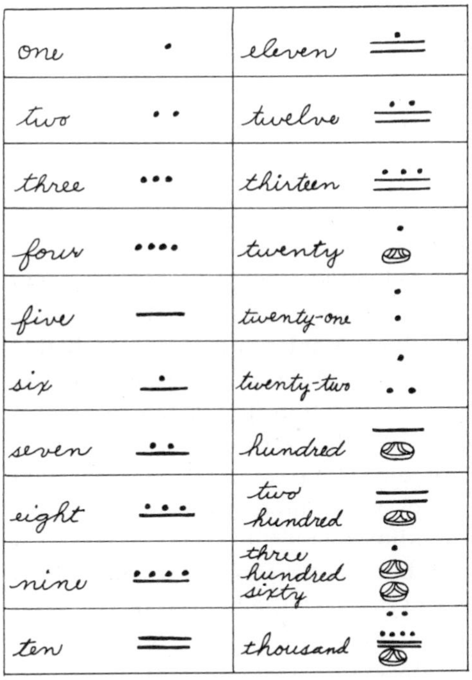

one	•	*eleven*	
two	• •	*twelve*	
three	• • •	*thirteen*	
four	• • • •	*twenty*	
five	—	*twenty-one*	
six	— •	*twenty-two*	
seven	— • •	*hundred*	
eight	— • • •	*two hundred*	
nine	— • • • •	*three hundred sixty*	
ten	=	*thousand*	

Figure 5. Child's Writing of Mayan Number Symbols.

whole man" by the number of his fingers and toes combined.

NUMERALS FOR
KEEPING RECORDS

The old number notation systems of the Babylonians, Egyptians, Greeks, Romans, and Mayans should be viewed as systems of *recording* numbers, not as *computational* systems. They served their purpose in providing a scheme for making records of quantities; they were too cumbersome to be useful in computing. Therein lies the reason for the long delay in development of computational procedures among peoples far advanced in other areas of study, such as the Greeks.

One should remember also that all these notational systems were handwritten and therefore subject to frequent changes that came about through individuality in handwriting. This fact is responsible for some of the difficulty in tracing the evolution of notational symbols. Not until the invention of printing from movable type in the fifteenth century did our own number symbols become stabilized.

Numbers, then, came to be expressed by a few symbols, usually with a base of ten, so that any number could be written by repetition, addition, multiplication, or subtraction of those few symbols. The Babylonians, Egyptians, Greeks, Romans, Chinese, Hebrews, and others came that far, but none of their decimal systems of notation used the invaluable principle of position, or *place value*.

Place Value

Place value is the value of any number symbol that it derives from its place or position with respect to other number symbols. In our modern notation, each of the 2's in 2,222 has a different value, depending on its position among the other digits. The *place* of the left-hand 2 gives it a *value* that is a thousand times that of the right-hand 2. This idea of place value was used in two other ways before it was used as shown in the above example from modern number notation. Those two uses were (1) in written records such as those of the Babylonians and Mayans and (2) in mechanical computing devices like the abacus.

BABYLONIAN POSITIONAL
NOTATION

A decimal base was used in number symbols of the Babylonian cuneiform notation. The Babylonians also used a base of *Sixty* in connection with their scale of weights and measures, this scale surviving today in our table of time (60 seconds = 1 minute, 60 minutes = 1 hour). On a tablet probably dating back to 1600 or 2300 B.C. there appears a table of squared numbers up to 60^2. This table includes notations such as 1.4 8^2 and 1.21 9^2 (using our numerals). Using the scale of sixty, these notations would mean that 1 sixty and 4 ones (our 64) = 8^2 and that 1 sixty and 21 ones (our 81) = 9^2. A similar use of position value is shown on a tablet concerning the moon's phases. According to Cajori:

> In Babylonia some use was thus made of the principles of position, perhaps 2000 years before the Hindus developed it. This was at a time when Romulus and Remus, yea even Achilles, Menelaus, and Helen, were still unknown to history and song. But the full development of the principle of position calls for a symbol to represent the *absence* of quantity, or zero. Did the Babylonians have that? Ancient tablets thus far deciphered give us no answer; they contain no number in which there was occasion to use a zero. Indications so far seem to be that this notation was a possession of the few and was used but little. While the sexagesimal division of units of time and of circular measure was transmitted to other nations, the brilliant device of local value in numerical notation appears to have been neglected and forgotten.[17]

Later Babylonian records (c. 200 B.C.) used a symbol that signified the omission of a figure. It resembled two hastily written angular dots ⦃. Neither of the above-mentioned indications of place value was accompanied by any evidence of its use in computation.

USE OF POSITION

BY THE MAYANS

When Francisco de Cordoba, in 1715, landed on the coast of Yucatan, he found the remains of the highly developed Mayan civilization, which is

thought to date back beyond 3000 B.C. These people had developed a remarkable numeration system with a base of *twenty,* which they used to tell the time between dates. The scheme was as follows: 20 *kins* (days) = 1 *uinal* (20 days), 18 *uinals* = 1 *tun* (360 days), 20 *tuns* = 1 *katun* (7200 days), 20 *katuns* = 1 *cycle* (144,000 days), and so on. The most important part of their system was their symbol for *zero,* which they used in a place-value system. (See the Mayan notation for *twenty* in fig. 5, p. 45.) The zero resembled a half-closed eye, one variant being ⬯ . The places were indicated vertically rather than horizontally as in our system. The number *twenty* was represented by a zero symbol in the bottom place, with a single dot representing one *uinal,* or *twenty,* above it. The number *360* was shown by two zero symbols, one above the other, and a single dot above them in third place (one *tun*).

The last five entries in figure 5 show an attempt to apply the system described above. *Twenty-two* is shown as one *uinal* above two *kins. Hundred* is shown as five *uinals* above zero *kins,* the straight line being a symbol for five. *Two hundred* is shown as ten *uinals* above zero *kins.* Three hundred sixty uses three places. *Thousand* is shown as two *tuns* in the top row, fourteen *uinals* in the next row, and zero *kins* in the bottom row (or 2[360] + 14[20] + 0 = 720 + 280 + 0 = 1000).[18]

The Mayan place-value system, with its zero symbol, was not used in computation, so far as available evidence indicates; and with the demise of its originators, this remarkable American invention was lost until the proof of its

---

[17] Florian Cajori, *A History of Elementary Mathematics,* New York: Macmillan, 1897, p. 10.

[18] If the teacher finds this explanation tedious or difficult to follow, she may well ponder the difficulties of the child being introduced for the first time to the mysteries and intricacies of *our* decimal place-value notation.

earlier existence was rediscovered by a civilization that had by then inherited the concepts of place value and zero from a different source, the Hindus.

Smith has suggested that the use of the pebble and rod (dot and dash) by the Mayas in their notational system in-

number, the abacus—in one form or another—appeared in almost all parts of the ancient civilized world. Adding and subtracting on the abacus were relatively simple; multiplication and division were possible, though ·more tedious and difficult. Later chapters will

Figure 6. Dust Abacus Showing 4352.

dicates their probable early use of the abacus,[19] which leads us to a consideration of that useful computational device employing place value.

THE ABACUS

The *abacus* is a simple tool or instrument to facilitate computation. Even with the invention of symbols such as those reviewed earlier (Egyptian, Babylonian, Greek, Roman, and others), the writing of large numbers was difficult and inefficient both as to time taken for writing and amount of space required. Since civilization had reached a point that demanded some method of computation to solve everyday problems of

[19] David Eugene Smith, *The History of Mathematics,* New York: Dover, 1958, Vol. II, p. 45. (The Dover edition is an unaltered republication of the 1953 edition of Ginn and Company.)

develop more fully the uses of the abacus in computing; here we are chiefly concerned with the fact that it used place value.

The dust abacus. The earliest type of abacus was the *dust abacus,* or *sandboard.* Dust or sand was strewn over a smooth, flat surface such as a large board or tabletop. Parallel lines were drawn with the finger (or a stick) in the dust, just as children now sometimes draw pictures or write their names in the dust on the family automobile. On the lines or in the spaces between lines the computer laid objects used as counters. Pebbles were frequently used. Figure 6 shows a modern imitation of a dust abacus, in which the number 4,352 is shown. The first line on the right has 2 pebbles on it, representing 2 ones. The next line to the left has 5 pebbles on it, representing 5 tens. The other lines have 3 and 4 pebbles, showing 3 hundreds and 4 thousands, respectively. Sanitary considerations laid aside, the dust abacus was an improvement over the cumbersome notations then available for recording large numbers, to say nothing of computing with any numerals.

Suppose you were to add 1,236 to the 4,352 shown on the dust abacus. You merely place 6 more pebbles on the *ones* line, 3 more on the *tens* line, 2 more on the *hundreds* line, and 1 more on the *thousands* line. There on the board is your answer: 5,588. If the person doing the computing wanted to make a record of his answer, he could copy it down in whatever notational system he knew. How much simpler this was, all because of the use of place value! The *place* a pebble occupied assigned it a *value*. The

principle used in calculating on the abacus was that one could add or subtract[20] collections (tens, hundreds, thousands, and so on) as simply as one could add or subtract ones, *provided* they were all kept in their *proper places*. One could forget about lotus blossoms and polliwogs; one need not think of various letters representing various quantities; one could simply add and subtract pebbles, which represented either ones or collections, keeping each size collection in its home place.

The line abacus. The dust abacus gave way to other types, one of which was a board on which the lines were permanently drawn or scratched and on which uniformly shaped objects were used as counters. This is usually referred to as the *line abacus*, or *counter abacus*. It was sometimes called a "counting table" or simply "counter." Com-

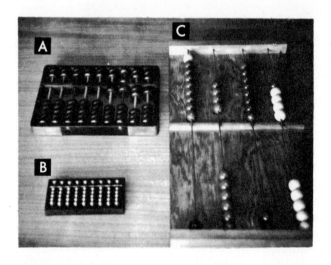

Figure 7. Three Types of Abacus:
A, Chinese Suan Pan;
B, Japanese Soroban;
C, School Abacus.

number of pebbles in each place told *how many* of that place value were being used. The same pebbles could be used over and over. Any pebble might at different times represent a single unit, a collection of ten, a collection of one hundred, of a thousand, or any higher power of the base ten. The fundamental

puting on the line abacus was called "reckoning on the lines." A person who handled this abacus well was said to "know the lines." Computation was done as with the dust abacus. The line abacus with horizontal rather than

[20] Multiplication was done by successive additions; division, by successive subtractions.

vertical lines was used so that the bottom line represented ones; the next line, tens; and so on through the higher place values.

The rod-and-bead abacus. A third type of abacus continues in use in the twentieth century, though its use was common in the days of the Roman Empire. This is the rod-and-bead abacus. This abacus has beads that move on rods, though the Romans used beads that moved along a groove. Modern forms of the rod-and-bead abacus have different numbers of beads on each rod, as seen in figure 7, but all are based on the decimal system in assigning values to the places. The Chinese *suan pan* and the Japanese *soroban* both have the rods divided into a lower part with 5 beads worth 1 each and an upper part that has beads worth 5 each (2 on the *suan pan* and 1 on the *soroban*). The Russian abacus has a simple arrangement of ten beads on each wire, with no separation, similar to the school abacus.

Hindu-Arabic Notation

IMPORTANCE OF ZERO

Zero (0) is our symbol for the absence of quantity. It means *none*, or *not any*. In the numeral 2,306 the zero tells that there is *no quantity* in the tens place, that there are *no tens*. No quantity might be assumed to have little or no consequence, but that is a hasty and incorrect assumption, as anyone who worries about *no* money or *no* time or *no* books or *no* resources of other kinds can attest.

Mathematicians sometimes were most eloquent in discussing the significance of zero. Dantzig says that the discovery of zero "was destined to become the turning-point in a development without which the progress of modern science, industry, or commerce is in-

conceivable. . . . In the history of culture the discovery of zero will always stand out as one of the greatest single achievements of the human race."[21]

The importance of a *number base* and of *place value* has been reviewed earlier in this chapter. The base, be it two or ten or twelve or twenty, gives man a stopping place in his counting, a place to "wrap up" a collection of units and start over. The base is essential because without it one would have an endless number of different number names and symbols. Place value makes it possible for us to handle collections (tens, hundreds, etc.) just as we handle units. When we have place value (as on the abacus), we can add and subtract these collections as we add and subtract ones. Long centuries before the advent of zero in computation, men invented number names, arranged them in order so they could use them in counting, used various bases but usually a base of ten, and calculated using place value on mechanical devices such as the abacus; but they did not know how to use written number symbols in computing. They could add and subtract on the abacus, but they could not add or subtract on paper—or on papyrus or wax tablets or stone, for that matter. They wrote the numerals *after* they had counted or derived them by calculations on the abacus, but the writing of numerals was only to make records, not to aid in computing. All the long delay was due to lack of a written symbol for zero, for nothingness.

Any average eight-year-old schoolboy, with a minimum of instruction in the use of the abacus, can add on that device, then transfer his sum to written form on his paper, but he can also add on paper without the abacus. Only a thousand years ago the latter process was unknown to all but a very small group of the privileged few. Such a simple step from abacus to computation with written symbols! Why did not the wise men of ancient times take that simple step? Simply because they had not conceived of using a symbol for absence of number as they used the empty wire on the abacus. The numeral 104, for example, when transferred to paper becomes 14 if we have no symbol to indicate the absence of tens. The empty wire on the abacus served that function.

CREDIT TO THE HINDUS

To the Hindus goes the credit for the invention of zero. The Hindus had devised a notation for numbers, using a base of ten. Numerous variations of this set of sumbols are known; some of these are shown in figure 8 and indicate the resemblance of our number symbols to the Hindu characters. This type of Hindu numerals in the first line of figure 8 appeared in the second or third century B.C. (without the zero). The

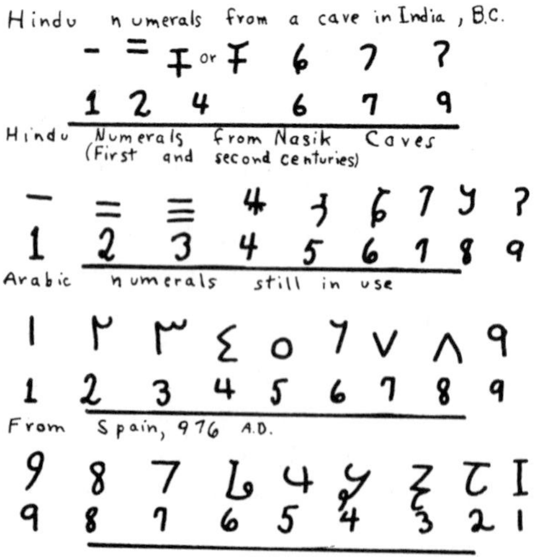

symbols in and of themselves were no better than others that had been devised elsewhere. They did have the advantage —as did some others—of having only one symbol to represent each number from one through nine. This is an essential for a symbolism that is to be combined with the idea of place value. If the symbol for three, for example, had three tally marks, it would occupy three places. The Hindu symbols needed only *one space each.*

No one knows who invented zero or exactly when he did it. We know that symbols for "the vacant place" were used by early Babylonians and Mayas, but more as punctuation marks. Probably about A.D. 300[22] zero was first used in combination with the other nine Hindu number symbols in a place-value system. Sanford says: "Thus, although the man who first devised the numerals and the man who first devised a symbol for zero did great service to mathematics, they were less great than was the thinker who saw that the two might be combined in a place-value system which would require only as many different characters as there are units in the base."[23]

The inventor of zero provided the "missing link" to complete the positional number system we use today. With its ten symbols and the idea of place value, not only can we *record* numbers more quickly and efficiently, but we can *compute* more quickly and efficiently, as will be shown in succeeding chapters. One wonders if the inventor realized the consequences of his own inventive genius. Perhaps not. Certainly his contemporaries and those who succeeded him were in no hurry to adopt his scheme.

Figure 8. Child's Copy of Hindu-Arabic Number Symbols.

[22] Aryabhata (A.D. 475-550) (Kramer, *op. cit.,* p. 6).

[23] Sanford, *op. cit.,* p. 14.

The first definite mention of the Hindu numerals and place value outside of India occurred in a work by Severus Sebokht in western Syria (A.D. 662). Sebokht spoke of the Hindus, "their valuable methods of calculation; and their computing that surpasses description." The Arabic mathematician al-Khowarismi wrote an arithmetic book (c. A.D. 825) explaining the use of this system; this book was preserved through a Latin translation of the twelfth century.

We call our numerals "Hindu-Arabic," not because the Arabs had anything to do with their invention but because they probably transmitted them to the Western world through merchants and through scholars who studied in Arab centers of learning.

THE *LIBER ABACI*

Leonardo of Pisa published a book called the *Liber abaci* in 1202. In that work he summed up the Hindu number system and pointed out that with the nine figures of the Hindus (1 through 9) and with the 0, which in Arabic is *sifr,* any number could be written.[24] Therein lies the beauty of the system. *We can write any number with only ten symbols!* The symbols 1 through 9 tell how many ones, or tens, or hundreds, and so on. When there are *no* ones, or tens, or hundreds, the 0 is put in the proper place to indicate that fact. The digits 1 through 9 represent the number of beads in use on any wire of the abacus. The 0 represents an empty wire. No other symbols are needed.

Take any number — for instance, 14,362 or 12,354. Each symbol 4 has a "face value" that represents "fourness" whether it is written in the "14,362" or

[24] The *Liber abaci* also included numerous problem solutions using these numerals.

"12,354"; in one case it shows 4 thousands and in the other case 4 ones, but it shows "4 of something." The symbol 4 also has a value in each case that comes not from itself but from the *place* it occupies. Therefore, the "4" in "14,362" and the "4" in "12,354" are very different in value, the "4" in the former being worth a thousand times as much as the "4" in the latter number. These two ideas in combination (the *individual values* represented by the symbols and *place value*) make it possible for us to represent any number in our decimal system with ten symbols because when the *place* has no value symbol from 1 through 9, the 0 holds the place. If the place were left vacant, all the values to the left of it would be misplaced; therefore, a zero symbol is *essential* if the other symbols are to show their proper place value.

ZERO AS A NUMBER

Arithmeticians have argued about whether or not zero is a number. Some say it is a place holder, not a number. It is more accurate to say that it is both. Like the symbols for 1 through 9, "0" does hold a place; this use has been emphasized above. If one left out the "2" in "129" or the "0" in "109," in either case one would have "19." Both the "2" and the "0" *hold* the tens *place.* Zero is not only a place holder, however, any more than "2" is only a place holder. Zero has a position in the number series as other numbers have. Each successive cardinal number is one more than the preceding number in value, or one less than the succeeding number, e.g., 5 is one more than 4 and one less than 6. The number 0 holds a similar position on the number scale; it is one more than −1 and one less than +1. In a scale of positive numbers, 0 always precedes 1 as being 1 less than 1. Zero comes between negative and positive numbers. The distance from −1 to 0 or from 0 to +1 is one step, just as is the distance from 2 to 3 or from 6 to 7. See the number line in figure 9. Zero does exhibit exceptional behavior when used in computation (e.g., impossibility of dividing by 0), but it is a number, and the positive-negative number scale would be incomplete without it, regardless of its use in a positional (place-value) number system. Can you conceive of a thermometer without a 0 to indicate a certain temperature as well as a reference point for all other temperature readings?

ABACISTS VS. ALGORISTS

Leonardo of Pisa, the author of the *Liber abaci,* had studied in Constantinople and Syria, and recommended the adoption of the Hindu-Arabic notation. Recognition of its value was slow, particularly in learned circles and in those countries where reckoning on the abacus was popular. The Italian merchants accepted it more readily than did the German merchants, where counter reckoning was popular. As late as the reign of Queen Elizabeth I the change from Roman to Hindu-Arabic numerals was not complete in England. Roman numerals were used in govern-

The advocates of computation on the abacus were called "abacists"; those who preferred computation with the Hindu numerals were called "algorists," from al-Khowarizmi. Dantzig summarizes the rivalry between the two groups very neatly:

Today, when positional numeration has become a part of our daily life, it seems that the superiority of this method, the compactness of its notation, the ease and elegance it introduced in calculations, should have assured the rapid and sweeping acceptance of it. In reality the transition, far from being immediate, extended over long centuries. The struggle between the *Abacists,* who defended the old traditions, and the *Algorists,* who advocated the reform, lasted from the eleventh to the fifteenth century and went through all the usual stages of obscurantism and reaction. In some places, Arabic numerals were banned from official documents; in others, the art was prohibited altogether. And, as usual, *prohibition* did not succeed in abolishing, but merely served to spread *bootlegging,* ample evidence of which is found in the thirteenth century archives of Italy, where, it appears, merchants were using the Arabic numerals as a sort of secret code. As to the final victory of the Algorists, no definite date can be set. We do know that at the beginning of the sixteenth century the supremacy of the new numeration was incontestable. Since then progress was unhampered, so that in the course of the next hundred years all the rules of operations, both on integers and on common and decimal fractions, reached practically the same scope and form in which they are taught today in our schools.[26]

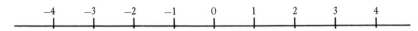

Figure 9. Zero on the Number Line.

ment accounts as late as 1734.[25] One objection was that the numerals were not as plain as Roman numerals; the invention of printing served to stabilize forms and removed that objection. Some of the objection was of a superstitious nature.

Extensions of the Numeration System

In our system we need only ten number symbols to express any number, but so far as number names go, we do occasionally have to employ a new one. We have distinct words for *one* through

[25] Sanford, *op. cit.,* p. 96.

[26] Dantzig, *op. cit.,* pp. 33-34.

ten, for *hundred, thousand, million, billion,* and so on up through the names of successive new place-value names. Actually, we rarely use number names above *billion,* or certainly not beyond *trillion. Million, billion,* and *trillion* appeared in the fifteenth century, but did not come into general use until World War I.[27]

The history of the development of our system of numeration thus far has dealt with whole numbers only. First came the "natural" numbers (that is, the counting numbers), followed by the introduction of zero. The natural numbers and zero together comprise the whole numbers. Much of this book is devoted to whole-number meanings, whole-number relationships, and processes in which whole numbers are used.

Rational numbers include both whole numbers and fractions, which are common and very important in elementary school arithmetic. Their development and their meanings are discussed in chapter 14 and following chapters.

The extension of our number system to include positive and negative numbers (integers) has few applications in elementary school arithmetic. Elementary school uses for negative numbers, such as negative (below-zero) temperatures, can be handled very well without introduction of computation with positive and negative numbers.

Other kinds of numbers (e.g., irrational numbers) are not usually treated in elementary school arithmetic.[28]

---

[27] Karpinski, *op. cit.,* p. 149. For large place values, American usage is not the same as that of some other countries, e.g., England. In England a "billion" = a million millions, not a thousand millions. That is not, however, a matter of concern to elementary school children.

[28] Such irrationals as "pi" and "$\sqrt{2}$" are usually developed in the junior high school.

Our Numeration and Notation System Reviewed

While much of the story of man's use of number is lost in a past that reaches beyond written records, the general pattern of development is fairly clear. The development of forms for our particular system of number is comparatively recent, as is shown by figure 10, a time line—incidentally, also a number line—that places important events in the history of the system alongside other better-known historical events. Careful study of this time line will not only provide a review of the development of our number system but should also impress on the reader the fact that what we are prone to call "simple arithmetic" was not known to many of the outstanding figures of history. This fact has great significance for those who would explore its implications.

Notice how much history had been lived before our written number system reached its present form. The Seven Wonders of the Ancient World were already ancient before this apparently simple structure for arranging numbers had been built. Moses led the Jews out of Egypt; Rome was established on its seven hills; the Greeks established a democracy; and Alexander the Great conquered the world of his day before the date of any clear record of the Hindu numerals "1" through "9."

The Roman Empire, with its accompanying procession of influential personalities—the Caesars, Mark Antony, Cleopatra, Constantine, Alaric, and more—rose and fell before an unknown genius combined the idea of a symbol for emptiness with the idea of place value and devised zero to complete the Hindu-Arabic notational system still in use. Mohammed, Charlemagne, the Crusaders, Genghis Khan, Joan of Arc,

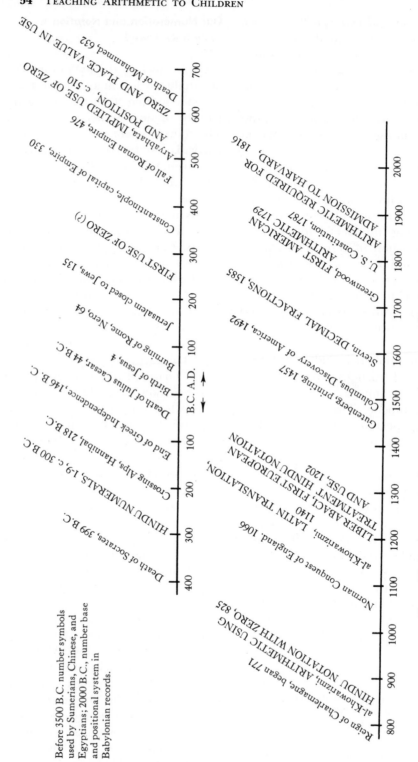

Figure 10. Number Line Showing History of Hindu-Arabic Notation in Relation to Other Events.

and Leonardo da Vinci came and went before that system was accepted at its true worth as a key to rapid and efficient calculations for everyday use. Columbus discovered America, and many other explorers of the Western world came and went before the publication of the first book in which decimal fractions were presented. In fact that book was published just over twenty years before the founding of the Jamestown Colony in Virginia. The general use of these fractions came much later.

While for some persons our numeration and notation system — one of man's greatest inventions — may not seem like the "music of the spheres," the chances are that the more they learn about it, the closer they will approach that appraisal.

STUDY QUESTIONS

1. What is the difference between a *number* and a *numeral?*

2. What is the difference between a *cardinal* number and an *ordinal* number? Give several examples of the use of the numeral "12" with cardinal number meanings. Give just as many examples of the use of the numeral "12" with an ordinal number meaning. Which of the following numerals may be used *only* for ordinal meanings? For either ordinal or cardinal meanings? 3, 4th, 25, 32nd, 67, 100.

3. Which of the numeration systems reviewed in this chapter deal with a base of ten? Which do not have a base of ten? Do all the decimal systems have place-value notation? Which do or do not?

4. Why is zero so important?

5. Discuss the relative merits of different abacus styles. Which of those you know are most useful with children? Why do you think so?

6. Make a simple abacus, using such simple materials as coat hanger wire or dowel rods, corks, kindergarten beads or beads from old necklaces. Practice using it.

7. Look up the discussion of sets in one of these books or some other modern treatment of the topic. (Use the index.) How can set concepts be applied in arithmetic?

Swain, Robert L. *Understanding Arithmetic.* New York: Rinehart, 1957.

Bell, C.; Hammond, C. D.; and Herrera, R. B. *Fundamentals of Arithmetic for Teachers.* New York: Wiley, 1962.

CHAPTER 4

Learning about Numbers and
Numerals

Do you remember this conversation between Alice in Wonderland and the Cheshire Cat?

> "Would you tell me, please, which way I ought to walk from here?"
> "That depends a good deal on where you want to get to," said the Cat.
> "I don't much care where —," said Alice.
> "Then it doesn't matter which way you walk," said the Cat.
> "— so long as I get *somewhere,*" Alice added as an explanation.
> "Oh, you're sure to do that," said the Cat, "if you only walk long enough."

Where do you want to get when you teach arithmetic? Where do you want your pupils to get by learning arithmetic? To a vague *somewhere?* Or to some definite destination? In the former case, you and your pupils are sure, like Alice, to arrive *somewhere,* but what consolation is that? Too many learners of "arithmetic" have arrived only at a state of confusion and frustration.

The teacher must care where she leads and must know fairly well the destination to be reached. Only under such conditions can anyone help her find the way to go, the methods to use in her teaching. In teaching arithmetic, as in traveling, the choice of the goal should come first; after that, one can usually find alternate ways to reach the goal. Sometimes one way is as good as another; sometimes certain ways are much better than others.

Helping Children Understand Numbers and Numerals

If one may judge by the minor role to which study of our numeration and notation system has sometimes been relegated in many classrooms, one might assume that teachers have not considered it very important. Fortunately for today's children, more and more teachers are realizing the importance of this phase of arithmetic instruction and are doing something about it.

The merit of the Hindu-Arabic notation system lies chiefly in its simplicity for expressing numbers and for computing with them. That system, however, is simple only to those who learn how to use it and know what it means. To some people nothing about the system seems simple; others vary in their perception of its simplicity — from those who see only the simplicity of the manipulations of the symbols to those who see the total framework in its over-all simplicity and order.

Take three people as examples: one who sees no sense at all in arithmetic, one who says it is simple but is just talking about knowing procedures that give right answers, and one who thinks it is simple because he has insight into the over-all pattern of relationships. These three users of arithmetic are analogous to persons who handle and operate machines: one who gets confused and can see no rhyme or reason to the controls and gadgets to be manipulated, another who feels quite confident and really enjoys operating the controls but who has no notion of why those operations lead to the given results, and still another who knows what happens when each knob or button or lever is manipulated and therefore sees sense in the operations as well as having confidence in the results of the operations.

No child needs to be taught arithmetic on the level of "no rhyme or reason." Most children can develop the confidence that comes with successful performance of the operations on numbers in elementary school arithmetic. How many can also see clearly "what happens" through use of the fundamental processes with numbers and can "see sense in the operations" of arithmetic depends largely on how they are taught. It is a mistake to hurry children into addition, subtraction, multiplication, and division of numbers without allowing adequate time for them to understand the numbers themselves and the number system within which they operate.

LEARNING AS AN ACTIVE PROCESS

Learning about our number system is a complex process. If the child is to acquire clear and usable ideas of number and number relationships, he must play a very active role, which may involve observing, manipulating, exploring, experimenting, discussing,

reasoning, reading, and putting into application. All these processes are pertinent at one time or another to the child's experiences with number and number relations in the everyday course of his living in a "world of number."

Wise teachers of arithmetic do not conceive of the subject as so much ready-made content to be "imparted" to children, with the teacher playing the more active role and the learner the more passive role. The learner, if he is to learn the most and learn it more effectively, must be an active participant. The more the child can be led to discover for himself, the better is the teaching. Most of the teacher's activity should be directed toward creating a situation in which children are challenged to discover meanings for themselves and in which they have opportunities to apply what they have discovered.

DIVERSITY OF CHILD READINESS

When children start school (at either the kindergarten or first-grade level), they bring with them widely diverse backgrounds of experience with number. The wise teacher recognizes this and immediately begins to provide opportunities for them to show what they can already *do* so far as number is concerned. She asks a child to bring her *three* books from the reading table; she directs another to find his missing crayons on the *fourth* shelf of the cupboard; she suggests that another *count* how many children are present today. Through such requests she learns what they can already do and what they need to learn. If a child does not already know how to do these things, he is not rebuked or embarrassed for his inability; the teacher lays plans instead to give him the experiences he needs to develop the abilities he lacks.

One child can count accurately only as far as ten; another does well until he reaches nineteen. The teacher makes mental note of such facts and adjusts her requests of individual children accordingly, asking each to do what *he can* do and helping him to do just a little more. If he can count only to ten, it would be ridiculous and entirely out of place for her to ask him to count the 36 children in the room, but it would be reasonable to help him in counting 12 or 13 or even 14 children—letting him practice what he already can do and also assisting him to next steps. He must have opportunities to do if he is to learn. He learns to count by counting; therefore, his teacher uses and makes opportunities for him to practice counting.

So it is with all the child's doing in arithmetic learning; we have him *do* not only for the activity itself but also for the sake of learning to do more.

NUMBER IDEAS
ON EACH CHILD'S LEVEL

Teachers sometimes feel that understanding of our number system is too high-flown an objective for elementary school children, that many children cannot understand anything so abstract, and that it is not worthwhile trying to teach it. True, children will vary widely in their understanding, but that does not mean the attempt should be abandoned. All children will not reach the same level or the same quality of appreciation and understanding of literature; still we try to develop in each that appreciation and understanding of which he is capable. All people do not achieve the same level of understanding of our political and governmental agencies; we try to build some understanding of them in all our citizens. All children will not attain the same degree or quality of understanding of arithmetic; this need not mean that teaching for understanding is either futile or useless. It means, rather, that the teacher must adjust the choice of ideas to be presented and standards of expected achievement in the light of individual differences in ability to achieve understanding of one or another phase of our number system.

Assuming the positions taken here, what does a teacher do to teach children our numeration and notation system? First, she seeks conscientiously to understand it herself. For some teachers, that means a good deal of unlearning, relearning, and new learning of arithmetic content such as that presented in chapter 3. Second, she tries to help children to get "a better break" than she had in the fortunes of living and learning by building these meanings correctly from the beginning.

LACK OF GRADE DESIGNATIONS

Suggestions for teaching are not classified by grade levels or arranged in a strict sequence in which they will be used. The reasons for lack of emphasis on grade levels are: first, suitable content for learning should be determined in relation to individual and group readiness for learning that content, not by arbitrarily assigning identical content to all pupils who happen to be in the same school class or grade; second, no teacher should limit her knowledge of teaching procedures to a restricted level, since to be a good teacher she must know where the learners have been and what they have already done as well as knowing where they are going and what they are going to need to learn in later grades; and third, most teachers follow, at least in a general way, the sequence of arithmetic content set up by the particular textbooks they are using. The ideas presented in this chapter may be fitted in as the teacher sees them to be appropriate.

Experiences with Quantity

When does a child begin to learn arithmetic? Too many people think he begins arithmetic when he learns to add and subtract. Since these people may well be parents or even teachers of young children, many opportunities for other number learning may go unnoticed. Such waste of opportunity is unnecessary and tragic, before or after the child comes to school.

VOCABULARY OF SIZE AND
COMPARISON

The child begins to learn arithmetic when he begins to notice size and quantity. When he consistently reaches for the larger of two pieces of candy, he is on his way in his dealings with relative sizes. When he talks about "many cars," he is noticing relative quantity. His acquisition of the vocabulary of size and quantity is not only language learning but also arithmetic learning. Before he begins his school days, he usually acquires a long list of such vocabulary: "many," "much," "big," "little," "large," "small," "high," "low," "short," "tall," and the comparative and superlative forms of the same words. Peculiarly, he does not seem to learn "few" as soon as "many," perhaps because "not many" serves the purpose. The adults in his life can help him a great deal by just taking time to listen to him and to talk with him in ways that give him a chance

to develop correct ideas of these words and to practice using them.

The vocabulary of comparison is particularly valuable as preparation for dealing with exact quantity later. The ideas of "more" and "less" are basic to the recognition of relative sizes of numbers. Knowing that 4¢ is worth more than 2¢ depends on knowing what "more" means. If children are to count with understanding, they *must* know which number is "next bigger"; the child who gets to 7 and does not know whether 8 or 12 is "next bigger" is stuck in a bog of miscellaneous numbers whose names he knows but whose relative values are confusing.

A child needs to be able to recognize the *larger* of two boxes or the *largest* of three or four trees (assuming that differences in size do not demand too much discrimination) before he can be expected to recognize the *larger* of two groups of children or the *largest* of three or four groups of bananas. Vocabulary development rests on understanding of the ideas expressed in the vocabulary; number concepts rest on both.

When primary-grade teachers meet with parents of children before their school entrance, they will be doing both the parents and the children a favor by pointing out the importance of talking with the children in correct language relative to size and quantity.

EXPERIENCES WITH EACH NUMBER

Some children have very well-developed ideas of numbers under one hundred when they come to school; others do not really know the meanings of the number names they know how to say. The kindergarten or first-grade teacher must begin where each child is. The concept of "four" is not taught by having a child laboriously copy figure "4's" or by counting by rote to four. The concept of "four" is taught by providing opportunities for the child to experience the quality of "fourness" in many forms and situations and by taking the time to discuss with him the number quality of all these situations. Risden's book[1] gives excellent suggestions for parents and teachers along this line.

Of course, the "four group" is only one of many to be developed. How many different size groups are needed before a child can generalize about "groups" will vary from child to child. Adults should realize, however, that it is unnatural to follow a pattern of teaching the meanings of cardinal numbers in rigid order of size. For instance, a child may learn the meaning of "four" before he is sure of the meaning of "three" or of "eight" before "seven." Anyone who doubts this might try playing dominoes with a young child who does not yet know all the number patterns on the dominoes.

Certainly, the meaning of "one" is much more difficult than the meaning of "two" or "three," not only for the younger child but also for those who are mystified and confused by the meaning of "four times one" or "six divided by one" at the intermediate-grade level.

Primary-grade children can derive much benefit from experiences with model groups of one size or another. They enjoy noticing all the things that come in "twos" or "pairs," including parts of their own bodies (eyes, ears, hands, feet, arms, legs, nostrils). They own pairs of mittens, shoes, glasses, and other articles that must come in pairs to be most useful. They can inspect plants to see whether the leaves grow in clusters of three (as in clover) or in some other number group. They can draw up long lists of things that come in fours, both in and out of the classroom, ranging from the more obvious sets of four legs on tables and chairs to the four corners of the room or the four sides of a window frame. Upper-grade children can also benefit from observing model groups that occur in nature, e.g., six legs on an insect, or everyday man-made standard groups, e.g., seven days in the week or eight musical tones in an octave.[2]

Teachers should be aware of the difference in difficulty of recognizing patterned and unpatterned sets of objects. Notice the markedly greater difficulty in recognizing immediately the number of items in the *A* sections of figure 11 as contrasted with the *B* sections. One should never assume that a child who knows a domino "four" will also surely know there are four cats in an unpatterned and probably mobile group of cats.

LEARNING THE MEANINGS

OF A GROUP

Every cardinal number represents a set or group. Each of the four fundamental processes is a grouping process. Children cannot really understand the meanings of numbers or number processes without knowing what groups are, in general and specifically. Not only preceding introduction of the processes of addition, subtraction, multiplication, and division but all along with the development of these processes, teachers have a responsibility to help children develop and expand their meanings of groups.

[1] Gladys Risden, *How Much? How Many?* Boston: Christopher, 1951.

[2] See discussion of this point and examples of common model groups for each of the smaller numbers in: Esther J. Swenson, "Making Primary Arithmetic Meaningful to Children," Washington, D. C.: N. E. A. Department of Kindergarten-Primary Education, 1961.

The teacher should have in mind the characteristics of a group as used in arithmetic: plurality, commonality, and togetherness (developed in chapter 3). In more childlike terminology, these characteristics of a group might be stated thus: (1) there must be more than

cept of "group" develop from experiences with many particular groups of various objects and living things. His idea of the meaning of "four in a group" depends on having seen, heard, felt, handled, or otherwise become aware of 4 legs on a table or a chair, 4 legs on

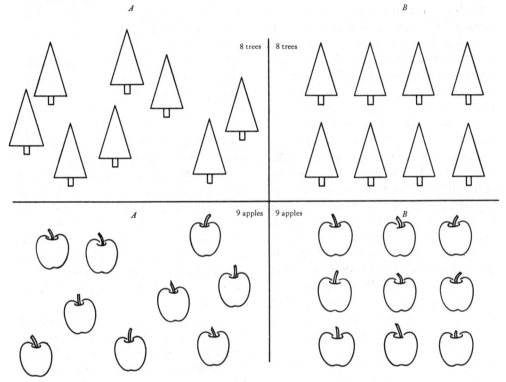

Figure 11. Patterned and Unpatterned Groups.

one thing in a group, (2) the things in the group must be alike in some way, and (3) the things in the group must be considered together. These are the meanings to be developed, but one does not start by having children learn these statements. Far from it!

A child's general concept of automobiles develops through experiences of seeing, touching, riding in, and hearing about many specific automobiles (of various makes, sizes, models, colors, body styles, speeds, sounds, and states of repair). Just so does his general con-

dogs and cats, 4 quart bottles of milk on the front step every morning, 4 people in his family, 4 plates used to set the table for the 4 people, 4 dots on the "4 domino," 4 strokes of the clock when Mother says, "It's 4 o'clock and time to put your toys away."

If there is only one apple, it is just "an apple." We need a number designation only when we have more than one apple. And of course here we have the meaning of plurality in a group—more than one. The teacher should use opportunities to refer to groups as such. She can talk about "this *group* of three children" or "that *group* of four books" about as easily as "these three children" or "those four books." Finally, she should discuss the word "group" and ask questions to see whether the boys and girls understand that it takes more than one to make a group.

With or without reference to the term "group," the day at school is actually crowded with opportunities for building and refining concepts of particular groups—arranging chairs in groups of four, distributing materials "two to each child," playing games requiring "so many on a side," getting three books from the bookcase. When the numbers are larger, the procedures are the same, based on development of concepts through actual experience with groups.

These grouping experiences can easily be expanded to include consideration of the fact that the members of a group should be alike in some way. This consideration should not be left to chance observation by children; the teacher should make a point of discussing it with them to see if they have noticed this characteristic of a group. There may be sorting activities such as arranging a group of *red* flowers and a group of *blue* flowers, a group of *girls* and a group of *boys,* or three groups of coins *(pennies, nickels, dimes).* Of course, these same items may be regrouped too so they are all alike in some other way—all the *flowers,* all the *children,* all the *coins.* But then we have a different group because we have a different basis for saying the things are alike. The teacher should always check to see that the boys and girls notice the common characteristic.

Situations are also sure to arise in which the children observe more than one of a kind but without a group quality because the items are not to-

gether: books scattered here and there, children working individually and without relation to other children in the room, or a pencil in each child's hand but not "together" in a single group of pencils. Strictly speaking, the items in a group do not need to be physically together to be considered together, but for young children learning about groups, physical proximity is the easiest kind of "togetherness" to understand. As for the other group characteristics, teacher and children need to consider, "Why is this a group?" or "Why is this not a group?" If they can do that successfully, they do not need a formal definition of the word "group"; but they might enjoy making their own.

The concept of "group" as a verb perhaps demands a higher level of understanding than the concept of "group" as a noun, but both ideas are very much a part of arithmetic. Both meanings are developed rather fully in later chapters on the four fundamental processes, which are basically grouping processes.

Teachers who prefer "set" terminology will want to develop the same basic concepts suggested for "groups." (1) While sets may include one item or no items, development of the set concept with young children should certainly stress plural sets. (2) Some writers stress the wide range of different items that may be included in the same set. Children will, however, grasp the set concept much better if the teacher starts with sets of obviously similar items. In any case, there is always a criterion for including the various items in a set, a criterion that applies to all members— hence, likeness. (3) The idea of being considered together is characteristic, whether the collection of items thus associated is called a "group" or a "set."

LEARNING ONE-TO-ONE
CORRESPONDENCE AND COUNTING

Through many concrete experiences the child learns what he needs to know in order to develop a *clear abstraction,* whether it be rational counting, one-to-one correspondence, or place value. The idea of one-to-one correspondence is basic; the child who is to understand simple counting needs to learn this idea as much as does the child who needs it to understand something on a more mature level, such as comparative subtraction. He does not need to learn the term "one-to-one correspondence"; what he needs is the idea: *one of this goes with one of that.*

Take the child who has learned to say the number names in order but cannot count accurately. He needs to learn that he must say one number name and only one number name for each object counted. Often such children need actually to touch each object being counted to get the idea. They may touch each book in turn, pick up or move each block, put a hand on each child's head, or at least point at each item to be enumerated. When this is not done, it is so easy to say more number names than there are objects or to skip an object here or there. How long should such activity be continued? It should be used as long as it is needed to give the child confidence and to check on his accuracy, no longer. We must not be too rigid in our judgments as to such matters. What adult has not, at one time of another, counted and recounted a set of plainly visible objects without getting a consistent total? And what does he do in such a case? Very often he resorts to touching or moving the objects to be counted. Shall be deny to children a similar aid?

Not only in counting do young children need to use one-to-one correspondence. They encounter all sorts of other matching situations. Each child needs a chair, a book, a locker, a pencil, a sheet of drawing paper, and a desk or table at which to work. In certain games each child in one group chooses one partner from another group; there must be as many partners as there are children in the first group. Sometimes there must be an opposing player for each child on one side or team; the two teams must match up in size. Sometimes the one-to-one correspondence is less obvious: one date on the calendar for every day of the month or one tally mark for every vote. Older children deal with one-to-one correspondence in such concepts as "a mile a minute" for rate of travel or "one article per second" for production rate in a factory.

One-to-one correspondence is basic to the understanding of certain subtraction situations. The success of subtraction instruction will depend in no small measure on previous learning about one-to-one correspondence.

Pupils' counting should be done for reasons that make sense to them — counting to find how many children are here today so the number can be reported to the principal's office, counting how many children will be eating in the cafeteria at noon, counting how many children do not have chairs, getting that many chairs for them. Of course, the teacher can do all these things herself; she can do them more quickly than the boys and girls can, but she has them do the counting so they will learn to do counting accurately and quickly. The teacher must not do as some mothers do when a bungling child wants to "help" her with the cooking — become impatient and do it all herself because the child is really no "help" to her. The point is that the child will not learn to cook (or to count) without a chance to *do* it. He does not become a full-fledged cook or counter or computer all in a single step, but by degrees; at each level of maturity he needs time to do for himself.

This doing for himself should not be a "sink-or-swim" procedure, but one in which constructive assistance is available when needed. Perhaps a child is asked to get enough sheets of paper for all the children in the class of 34. He may just take some paper, distribute it one sheet to one child as far as it goes, then return to the supply cabinet for more, distribute it one for one, and finally have to return a surplus to the cabinet. This is a good time to discuss more efficient ways of doing the job. Perhaps another child will suggest counting children and then counting the same number of sheets of paper. The acting out of this more mature procedure will show its superiority over the hit-or-miss way. Also, counting will be seen as matching number names to children and then matching number names to sheets. This leads at a mature level to the concept that all groups (sets) that match each other one-to-one have the same number property (in this case, 34).

In the illustrations above, the counting was done to find *how many* (the cardinal number idea); counting to find *which one* (the ordinal number idea) must also be practiced. Teachers sometimes neglect the latter. Every day's activities include many chances to use ordinal number—to find *which one* (in order). Listing a few may serve to remind the teacher of many others: bringing a book to Miss Jones in the fourth room down the hall; finding a story in the sixth book on the shelf; looking for gate no. 6 on the class visit to the airport or railroad station; telling the hour at which the small clock hand is pointing; "counting off" first and then taking correct places in line so the first child is first and the tenth is tenth. Remember always, telling the child is not the same as helping him to do for himself. Time spent here is time well spent, for it is time for learning.

What of the ever-recurring question, "Is it bad for children to count on their fingers?" One might counter by asking, "Is it bad for the minister in his Sunday sermon to hold up fingers as he makes his first, second, and third points?" Or, "Is it bad for the waitress in the restaurant to hold up four fingers to notify the hostess that she has places for four people?" A hand of five fingers is a natural model group. Children who use their fingers in counting are trying to "keep straight" by reference to concrete objects, and what should be more natural than to use the standard set (of fingers) that comes as part of our natural equipment?

Counting on the fingers is correct when it is the most convenient and efficient for the particular individual in the particular situation. For a child to continue to count on his fingers indefinitely is not good. He needs to be "weaned away" from finger counting as he is able to rely on other concrete objects and finally not need any such helps. If a child does count on his fingers, the teacher should first make sure he does it correctly and then consider whether he is ready to go on to a more mature procedure.

Learning to Read and Write Number Symbols

LEARNING THE WRITTEN SYMBOLS FOR NUMBER

"He can write his numbers to one hundred." How often a parent or a teacher has said those words! What do they mean? What sort of accomplishment is it for a child to be able to write the numerals from 1 through 100 in their appropriate counting order? Of course, the answers to these questions must vary for individual cases, but too frequently the mere writing of number symbols is less of an accomplishment than the speaker assumes.

A child (or an adult, for that matter) might learn to draw the ancient Egyptian number symbols shown in figure 2 or the Mayan symbols shown in figure 5. He might learn to reproduce these hieroglyphics and even their names so that he could "read" them aloud. This accomplishment might be a mechanical exercise in the matching of sounds and symbols with no meaning whatsoever for the performer. Saying the names of the numbers or writing the numerals is by no means a guarantee of knowing the values for which those names and numerals stand. Similarly, children sometimes learn the writing of our number symbols as a mechanical exercise without development of corresponding number meanings.

NUMERALS AS RECORDS

Number symbols came into use, historically speaking, when men had need to record number meanings. Tally marks served very well for small numbers, but the number of tallies required for larger numbers made them cumbersome and confusing. The great invention discussed in chapter 3, the idea of having a single symbol represent quantities from 1 through 9, is still a great invention that children can appreciate to a certain extent. If the child has used tally marks to represent the quantity of books to be "checked in" or of "pencils sold" in the classroom supply store by one-to-one correspondence, he can easily be led to see that it is a clear saving of time and energy to know and be able to write a single symbol that stands for each particular quantity from 1 through 9 and that these symbols plus 0 can be combined to show any quantity with which he will ever have to deal! If he has too little background or mental capacity to see this, he probably has no business writing the particular numerals anyway.

To teach mechanical writing (really "drawing") of number symbols prior to any need for using them is not only unnecessary; it is also unwise, for it may easily give the child the wrong idea of what the symbols are. He may think of them as entities in themselves rather than as symbols needed to record number meanings. As with the writing of our English language, too many parents and teachers hurry children into the reproduction of the written symbols before they have any real need for writing them. Not only is the writing task very difficult to teach to children who are not ready for it; more serious objections to such a practice are these: (1) the child is likely to get a wrong idea of what writing is and may think of it as a mechanical exercise rather than a new way of "saying something" that he already understands, (2) the difficulty and uselessness of the task as taught may cause him to develop a distaste for an activity that should be seen as useful and worthwhile from his point of view as well as that of some adult, and (3) he may get the idea that he "knows" numbers when he knows only how to say and write the symbols that represent them. The real number is not the word; neither is it the written symbol. The number is the quantitative meaning represented by the spoken name or written numeral. The number meaning of "four" or "4" is not "known" in the sense of being understood merely because the child can say "four" or because he can write "4."

THE TIME TO TEACH
NUMBER SYMBOLS

But when *should* a child be taught to write numerals (number symbols)? When he has need for them in that form. Just as he learns to write his name when he has need to mark his belongings as being his own or as he learns to write a caption for one of his drawings that he has named, so he should learn to write numerals when he has need to record number ideas. As with his early experiences in reading and writing words and sentences, he learns much by seeing other people use these skills. The parent or the teacher writes a numeral so as not to forget it or so that it can be sent to someone else for his information. The child's mother writes a numeral on a slip of paper to tell the milkman how many quarts of milk to leave. The teacher writes a numeral on the blackboard (so she will not forget it) and later on a slip of paper to tell the principal how many children are present today or to tell the lunchroom manager how many children will be buying lunch in the cafeteria. At first the children help by counting and reporting the right number to the teacher so she can write the numeral. Soon the children can one by one take over the writing of the numeral on the blackboard or on the report form to the principal or lunchroom manager. These number symbols mean something; they will tell how many children or how many lunches needed or how many bottles of milk for midmorning refreshment. It is important that they be written clearly so that whoever reads them will know what is meant and can respond accordingly.

OPPORTUNITIES FOR
WRITING NUMERALS

The everyday affairs of the classroom demand many such recordings of quantity. The teacher should see to it that such situations are used as learning opportunities: recording the room temperature, recording how many children have completed a task, recording how much money has been received for Christmas seals, or recording the dimensions of a box needed to house a piece of classroom equipment. Some children will be able to handle the actual recording of numbers sooner than others, but all can benefit from observing the use of number symbols for understood purposes. This is essential: the idea that number symbols represent real quantities, that people learn to write them so that they can record quantities when necessary. Of course, this idea is also basic later when children use written symbols in computation. Too many children have the idea that writing the number symbols *is* the computation instead of the idea that we write in order to keep a record of the number thinking we are doing.

When number symbols really mean something specific, the necessity for writing them legibly is obvious. If "7" and "9" stand for different amounts of ice cream, if 9 quarts cost too much and only 7 quarts are needed, it becomes important to be sure that "7" is not written so it might be confused with "9."

The forms of the numerals are arbitrary; there is no point in displaying originality in their formation. We are indeed fortunate that there are only ten of them to learn to write: 0, 1, 2, 3, 4, 5, 6, 7, 8, 9.

NUMERALS FOR CARDINAL

AND ORDINAL USE

The time and place for practice of number names in order is usually in oral rather than written usage. To understand this point thoroughly, the teacher must be conscious of the difference between cardinal and ordinal uses of numbers. In using cardinal numbers (to tell *how many*) children and adults have little or no use for writing the numerals in order from 1 to 100, 1 to 1,000, or in any other sequence. So far as cardinal number uses are concerned, writing is for recording, not for counting. The items are counted; then only the *last* cardinal number in the sequence is recorded with a written symbol. The children are counted orally or mentally; the total number is then written as a record of daily attendance. There is no need to write: 1, 2, 3, 4, 5 ....27. Only the total 27 needs to be written. Sometimes the counting is not necessary at all, as when the children read or are told that the price of a notebook is 25¢. Obviously, to write the number symbols from 1 to 25 in such a situation is entirely beside the point.

In using ordinal number meanings, one occasionally does need to write number symbols in order. The children are planning for a program they are preparing for their mothers. If the order in which the activities take place is important, they will number them from 1 on as far as the sequence needs to go. Perhaps they have made a list of all the things they can think of that are made of paper. The order is not important, but it is convenient to number the items so that "which one" can be desig-

nated by giving the number of the item instead of reading the name of the item. If a child did not hear a spelling word clearly, he may ask his teacher to repeat no. 5. These are ordinal uses of numbers and writing the number symbols in order is appropriate. Few indeed are the occasions on which such sequences or lists run as far as the traditional "1-to-100" written assignment would seem to indicate.

If practice comes in situations of actual use, the teacher will not need to worry about whether or not it is appropriate; the situation itself will dictate what number uses are appropriate. Incidentally, when ordinal numerals are written in sequence, they are usually written vertically, not horizontally, as is so frequently done in formal written exercises.

Another point of caution is in order concerning the writing of ordinal numbers. Too many teachers—and too many texts and other printed materials—give children the impression that ordinal numerals are always written in the form at the left below, when actually the form at the right is equally appropriate:

1st or first	1 or one
2nd or second	2 or two
3rd or third	3 or three
4th or fourth	4 or four

Children should be given practice in using both forms to designate ordinal (which one) ideas. The child is in the *second* grade or in grade *two*. The girl is seated at the *4th* table or at table no. *4*. The date is January *14th* or January *14*. Either form is correct. What matters is the meaning. One can never tell whether a number symbol like "6" or "12" is ordinal or cardinal just by the form alone. One must see how it is used to know whether it tells "how many" or "which one." If it tells how many legs on the table or how many eggs in the basket, it is a cardinal (how many) number. If it tells the number on a football jersey or which month of the year, it is an ordinal (which one) number. "Fourth" or "4th" always refers to ordinal number, but "four" or "4" may be either ordinal or cardinal, depending on its meaning in a particular situation. Teachers must have this straight if they are to help children distinguish properly. Certainly, they must not perpetuate the error indicated above. (For the children, the words "cardinal" and "ordinal" are not essential; the ideas they represent are essential.)

READING AND WRITING LARGER NUMERALS

All that has been said about the reading and writing of smaller numerals is equally true for reading and writing larger numerals. Practice should be in a setting of purposeful use of larger numbers. Since so much of the meaning of two-place and larger numerals involves place value, that concept must be developed preceding and concurrently with the reading and writing of larger numbers. In this book, most of the development of base and place meanings occurs as an integral part of the development of the fundamental processes (chaps. 5 through 13 and 17), but these meanings must not be neglected in relation to the reading and writing of larger numerals.

One aid to building such meanings is the Hundred Chart, shown in one of its most common forms. The concept of "100" as "ten tens" is obvious. Counting by tens to one hundred receives a visual assist when seen in relation to the

Hundred Chart. The relative values of numbers is emphasized as their symbols

Hundred Chart

1	2	3	4	5	6	7	8	9	10
11	12	13	14	15	16	17	18	19	20
21	22	23	24	25	26	27	28	29	30
31	32	33	34	35	36	37	38	39	40
41	42	43	44	45	46	47	48	49	50
51	52	53	54	55	56	57	58	59	60
61	62	63	64	65	66	67	68	69	70
71	72	73	74	75	76	77	78	79	80
81	82	83	84	85	86	87	88	89	90
91	92	93	94	95	96	97	98	99	100

are located on the chart. For example, "23" may be seen as "one more than 22," "one less than 24," "one row lower than 13," "worth ten more than 13," "two tens before 43," "1 ten and 2 ones more than 11." Counting by ones, by fives, by fours, by tens, or by other number groups is facilitated with the chart. The use of three separate number symbols for "100," whereas other numbers on the chart require only one or two numerals, brings up the need for seeing "what happens here." Why do we now need three numerals instead of two? Use of bundles of sticks or other aids to dramatize the meaning of "ten tens" as "one hundred" supports the numeration as seen on the chart.

The ideas of base and place value are used quite early to develop a concept of multiplace numbers as *sums*. The sum idea is expressed in progressively more mature ways as the years pass, the latest of the expressions below probably being postponed beyond elementary school for most children:

$$428 = 4 \text{ hundreds} + 2 \text{ tens} + 8 \text{ ones}$$
$$428 = 400 + 20 + 8$$
$$428 = 4(100) + 2(10) + 8(1)$$
$$428 = 4(10)^2 + 2(10)^1 + 8(10)^0$$

Children sometimes have use for numbers larger than those which have been developed meaningfully with them. For instance, in social studies or science materials population figures may be given in millions or even billions when most of the children reading the text may not as yet have worked with such large numbers. The teacher must then decide which is better—to take time out to develop carefully whatever extension of previous number meanings seems necessary or to give a brief treatment of major ideas essential for understanding the meaning of the printed text. In the former case, the social studies or science material may be made the opportunity for developing an arithmetical concept. In the latter case, enough help is given to remove obvious barriers to reading comprehension; if this is the case, the teacher should make an opportunity for further development as soon as feasible.

READING HOUSE AND TELEPHONE NUMBERS

Even very young children need to be able to tell their street addresses or telephone numbers. These are numbers that are read and even written differently from most other numbers. One does not say "one thousand, two hundred, six" if one's house number is 1206. One says, "one, two, oh, six." And a telephone number is read similarly; for example, 752-4321 is read "seven, five, two; four, three, two, one" with a longer pause between the two and four. These useful numbers should be taught as children need to use them without regard for the place-value concept, since they are strictly "which one" designations in which the number does not designate a value. The telephone number does not indicate any sequence as for a true ordinal number.

Learning about Base and Place

LEARNING PLACE VALUE WITH THE BASE TEN

Computing machines all take base and place value into account since they operate on the basis of a number system that includes place value. This is true no matter how simple or how complex the machine. Fortunately for us, we still have and can use to good advantage man's first calculating machine, the human fingers; his second, the abacus; and on through all sorts of modern electrical devices commonly known as "mechanical brains." At various levels of learner maturity these different calculating aids can assist children or adults in understanding our number system.

Dramatizing base and place value. Young children who have reached a point at which they need to develop an understanding of two-place numbers will be helped toward that understanding by simple dramatizations. Perhaps the teacher has told the children a story about how early people counted and how ten was called by a name meaning "man" and twenty by a name meaning "two men." In that case, the dramatization may be an acting out of the story. Or perhaps the children are counting how many days until Christmas and are trying to show how it can be done with fingers for counters. One child does the counting and uses other children as "machines" to help him. He checks off the days one by one on the calendar, counting as he does so. For each number name, the first child in the "counting machine" raises one finger (one-to-one correspondence). At "ten" the first child has used all his fingers. Now what shall be done? Let the children figure this out. "We need another child with another set of fingers? All right, let's use one." After all his fingers are "used up," we can have a third child help, and so on until we have perhaps used 4 children's whole sets of fingers and 3 fingers of a fifth child. There are 43 days until Christmas—four tens of days and 3 days more.

Now a variation may be proposed. Can we use only two children and their fingers to show a big number like 43? Let's go back and start over. When we get to ten, the first child has all his fingers raised. Could we start over counting the next ten with the same child's fingers? How will we remember how many tens we have already counted? The second child? How will he show the number of tens? Here we have a situation in which a little detail may sometimes make a big difference in the learning result. It takes so little special attention for the teacher to see that the child who represents *ones* on his fingers stands at the right and the child who represents *tens* stands at the left. Then the tens' place and ones' place as shown by the two children will correspond to the ways tens' and ones' places are written, with ones on the right.

This sort of dramatization of place value can be used also for showing three-place and four-place numbers or even larger ones. In such circumstances the counting would not need to be done from 1 through 4,357, for instance, but the right-hand child could hold up 7 fingers to show 7 ones; the next child to the left, 5 fingers to show 5 tens; the next child, 3 fingers to show 3 hundreds; and the left-hand child, 4 fingers to show 4 thousands. The human counting machine can also be likened to the inanimate variety. If we use children to show a six-digit number, we need 6 children just as we would need a six-column

calculating machine to record such a number.

In the second dramatization above—using only two children for any two-place number instead of another child for each new set of ten—we have a direct analogy to point out the efficiency of our numeration system, which needs a new "place value" only when, in the dramatization, we need a new child to help show the number. We can get along with one child until we get to ten; then we need a second child (or place). We need no more helpers until we get to hundred; then we need a third child (or place), and so on indefinitely. The teacher should not try to force such analogies on the children for them to memorize or parrot after her. She should use skillful questioning and encouragement of their own observations concerning what is happening to help them discover these relationships for themselves. If the discoveries are not forthcoming, she should remember there is likely to be another day and another opportunity and that haste toward a generalization is more than wasteful. Forcing the idea may confuse the children to the point that the making of the generalization on that "other day" may be hindered.

The abacus as a learning aid. The abacus is most useful in teaching the base of ten and place value in our numeration system. This is particularly true in computation involving place value and will be discussed in detail in chapters dealing with the fundamental processes of arithmetic. The abacus does, however, have some uses aside from computation. Young children can use it as an aid in counting. The fact that the child cannot count beyond ten on the first (right-hand) rod of the abacus forces him to pay attention to this point as a sort of counting milestone. He has to learn to "trade in" his ten beads on the ones rod for a single bead on the tens rod. He sees 11 as 1 bead on the tens rod and 1 bead on the ones rod; 12 as 1 bead on the tens rod and 2 beads on the ones rod; and so on until he has another ten and again trades in 10 one-beads for 1 ten-bead. In using the abacus as a counting aid, children should be encouraged to hold it so the rods are in vertical position. This will pay good dividends when the child learns to write numbers in terms of place value, for the written place value will then correspond to a familiar placing on the abacus.

Some practice on the abacus is worthwhile even after a child "has the idea" of the meanings of the different place-value rods. Later, when he adds and subtracts on the abacus, particularly when those processes include changing ("carrying" and "borrowing"), it is important that he already have enough skill acquired in manipulating the beads that he is not distracted from the processes of addition or subtraction by the routine procedures of handling the beads.

Children throughout the elementary school level can use the abacus as a recording instrument for showing larger numbers meaningfully. The actual presence of the beads in different quantities on each rod serves to emphasize an essential of our numeration system: that each digit in a numeral has two values, the value it represents "on its face" in and of itself and the value it represents by its place among the other digits. The digit "4" in "142" has a "face value" of *four* and a "place value" of *ten*. Many teachers and other adults will admit that they just never thought very much about this. They need to think of it and help children think about it if the children are to have an adequate understanding

of what the figures *mean*. Showing a written numeral like 14,582 on the abacus necessitates a kind of *doing* that goes somewhat beyond the mere writing of the number symbols. The doer *must* pay attention to both sources of value. He must actually move the number of beads represented by a digit like 4; he must bring down or up *4 beads*. He must also pay attention to the place value of 4 in order to bring down the 4 beads on the *right rod*, in this case the thousands rod. Practice in showing on the abacus either written or spoken large numbers and practice in reading and writing numbers shown on the abacus represent an excellent type of practice in value meanings of number symbols.

For the superior learners, learning to manipulate more than one type of abacus is a stimulating exercise in number meanings. The abacus referred to in the above discussion of its use with younger children is the simple modern abacus of the Russian variety. The Chinese and Japanese abaci are just enough different to confuse the less mature pupil but to serve as an interesting challenge to the more mature.[3]

Money and place values. Since more everyday computations are done with money numbers than in any other single type of situation, teachers in all elementary school grades will find many opportunities to develop the place-value idea in terms of money. Primary-grade children have numerous opportunities to write money numbers. Beginning with simple money numbers like 5¢, the use of the ¢ sign is usually introduced. It may also be called the "pennies sign." The number "5¢" may be read either "five

[3] Reference will be made in later chapters to the use of various types of abacus that have been specifically designed for use in arithmetic instruction. Some of these have more than ten beads in each place, a convenience, e.g., in transforming 15 ones to 1 ten and 5 ones.

cents" or "five pennies." When the number of cents exceeds nine, two places are needed, representing two coin values, e.g., 12¢ meaning 1 dime and 2 pennies. Children who do not already know that 12 pennies are equal in value to 1 dime and 2 pennies will need some experience in changing money. Play money – either the kind that is readily obtainable at school supply or variety stores or cardboard money made by the children – can be used to good effect in giving some experiences in the classroom. Of course any situation in which real money is used in school is even better.

Most children will already have had many out-of-school experiences in which they have learned that 12¢ may be shown as 1 dime and 2 pennies, as 2 nickels and 2 pennies, as 1 nickel and 7 pennies, or as 12 pennies. If so, they may still need some discussion accompanying manipulation of coins to help them notice the significance of the place value of each digit in a two-place number. They may know that 1 dime and 2 pennies are 12 cents but never have intellectualized the idea that the figure "1" in "12¢" means 1 dime and the figure "2" means 2 pennies. The time spent in doing this is well worthwhile. All two-place numbers may be handled similarly, through 99¢.

The question may arise as to when to introduce the form for writing money numbers less than a dollar with the use of the decimal point and the dollar sign instead of the cents sign. When should the teacher use with the children the form $.12 and $.99 instead of or in addition to 12¢ and 99¢? The answer is again: when he needs it. This is likely to be rather early because the child reads prices of items in stores or in newspaper ads that are usually written with the decimal point. The question arises as to whether the introduction of this form necessitates the introduction of the deci-

mal fraction concept. It does not. Children have so much use for this form of writing money numbers before they understand decimal fractions fully that it would be rather silly to avoid its use. Boys and girls are willing to accept the simple explanation that we have two ways to write money numbers less than one dollar. We may write either "25¢" or "$.25." Either one means 2 dimes and 5 pennies or 25 cents. It is not necessary at this early stage to go into the fact that the 25 cents are $\frac{25}{100}$ of 1 dollar, though children should learn that 1 dollar is equal in value to 100 pennies. This should cause no confusion, since the "pennies place" does always have the pennies value and since the "dimes place" does always have the dimes value. The decimal-fraction idea can be developed in due time. When that time comes, it will be learned more easily by children who have had ample experience with the concepts mentioned above and who have had practice in changing coins for equivalent values, e.g., exchanging 25 pennies for 2 dimes and 5 pennies, and vice versa.

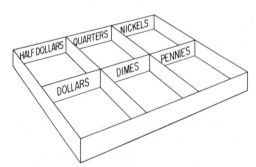

Figure 12. Place Values and Positions in a Cash Box.

In this connection, children can "play store" and have a "cash register" drawer with a *place* for each type of coin. Again, time for discussing the *places* will be valuable for children in terms of added understanding. In figure 12, for example, the places for pennies, for dimes, and for dollars have been arranged so as to have them match up with those place values as written. Places for nickels, quarters, and half-dollars can be placed in a different row so as not to interfere with the pattern of places that *does* fit the way we write money numbers.

Place value is used so continuously in the development of the fundamental processes that other aids to development of place-value ideas are developed in later chapters dealing with those processes. These aids include such items as pocket charts and sets of blocks to show place values.

LEARNING ABOUT OTHER BASES THAN TEN

Some elementary school faculties are currently having a good deal of discussion as to whether or not elementary school children should be taught to use bases other than our decimal (ten) base. Some teachers say, "It is not needed; why teach it?" Others say, "It is too difficult. Children will just get confused." Some say, "I have enough to do getting the children to understand our base of ten. Why drag in other bases?"

On the other hand, teachers who have taken the time and spent the mental effort needed to get a firm grasp of the idea of the number base are surprised to notice that they understood the base of ten better after they became familiar with bases other than ten. Children probably have less difficulty working with several different number bases than do adults who have grown up either ignoring the base concept entirely or thinking of it as synonymous with "ten."

Most of the "new mathematics" materials for use with elementary school children include suggestions for use of other bases than ten and exercises for children to do with such bases. Fre-

quently, the base five is used since it is an easier grouping for children to handle.

A teacher who is trying to develop the concept of the base will do well to begin with concrete materials of some kind — checkers, play pennies, buttons, blocks, or uniformly shaped items to be used on a magnet board. The first step requires the regrouping of the objects into groups of a given size, e.g., fives. A group of OOOOOOOOOOOO is regrouped into OOOOO OOOOO OO. Then the new grouping is described as "2 fives and 2 ones." Or xxxxxxxxxxxxxxxxxx is regrouped as xxxxxx xxxxxx xxxxxx x and described as "3 sixes and 1 one." In early experiences this sort of rearrangement and oral description is enough. Later the oral descriptions will be recorded in written form as:

2 fives 2 ones	OR	22_{five}
3 sixes 1 one	OR	31_{six}

An interesting variation as children are ready for it is to change the same objects from grouping in one base to grouping by another base, for example, changing a six grouping to a five grouping. Then OOOOOO OOOOOO OOOOOO OOO (3 sixes and 3 ones) becomes OOOOO OOOOO OOOOO OOOOO O. The written record of the change becomes: $33_{six} = 41_{five}$.

Changing various sizes of groups to the base ten should also be used. It occurs extensively in later chapters dealing with base and place ideas in development of basic addition and multiplication facts (chaps. 5 and 9).

When children have two-place numeration under control and are ready for three-place numerals, the concept of the base should be extended to include the idea of the "base times the base," or "the base squared." The meaning of "one hundred" as "ten tens" will be enhanced for those children who can also see that if the base were five, "five fives" would require a new place value. As children develop maturity in thinking about numbers, they should go on to more and more mature ways of recording their base and place ideas. (Table 12 in chap. 17, with its use of exponents, is a long way from the simple development given here, but the development of meanings at that level will depend on those developed with simple two- and three-place numeration in various bases at earlier levels.)

Counting in other bases and recording the numerals in order is another good learning activity. As pennies are counted and grouped by fives, the counting would proceed as follows: one, two, three, four, five, five and one, five and two, five and three, five and four, two fives, two fives and one, two fives and two, two fives and three, two fives and four, three fives, etc. Or five pennies might be changed for a nickel whenever possible. Then the counting might go thus: 1 penny, 2 pennies, 3 pennies, 4 pennies, 5 pennies or 1 nickel, 1 nickel and 1 penny, 1 nickel and 2 pennies, 2 nickels and 3 pennies, 2 nickels and 4 pennies, 3 nickels . . . 4 nickels and 1 penny, 4 nickels and 2 pennies, 4 nickels and 3 pennies, 4 nickels and 4 pennies, 5 nickels or 1 quarter, 1 quarter and 1 penny. . . .

Of course, counting on an abacus can be done according to any base. Suppose a limit is placed on the number of beads on each rod so that there are only six beads on a rod instead of ten. Then the counting could proceed as usual except that when the beads on the "ones" rod were used up and a change had to be made to the next rod to the left, the change would be to "sixes" rather than "tens" place.

The people who vow that bases other than ten are "too hard" or "not needed" often use such bases and do not even recognize they are doing so. One such everyday situation will serve also as an example of an opportunity for presenting the concept of the base to children, i.e., grouping pencils according to a base of twelve.

A base of twelve. Miss Whitman got some dozen-boxes of pencils from the school supply to use in developing the concept of a base of twelve. She put 57 pencils on a tabletop in front of the children, making sure that the pencils were in a randomly arranged pile with no apparent grouping. She left some of the empty boxes in sight on the table. Beginning the lesson, she asked, "How many pencils do you think I have here on the table?"

Various estimates were made, some "within range" of the correct number, some pretty far afield. One child remarked, "it's so hard to judge how many when they are all mixed up like that."

Miss Whitman responded by asking how they might be grouped so as to make the estimating of number easier. Someone quickly suggested that they could be grouped by using the boxes. This was done and the children saw that there were "4 dozen and 9 pencils," or "4 full boxes and 9 left over."

The children were asked to look the other way while each of several other arrangements was made, among them: 62 pencils in a disorderly stack; 6 boxes full of pencils, open at the end to show that each box was full; and 3 full boxes of pencils and 6 pencils more. The discussion led the children to the conclusion that in each case grouping the pencils in groups of a standard size made it much easier to see quickly how many pencils there were. The teacher used the expression "basic group of twelve" but did not press the use of the term "base."

Such a lesson could be expanded on the same or a later occasion by building twelve dozen into a gross—or even twelve gross into a great gross (if the number of pencils required does not overtax the available supply). Such an extension would of course be used only if children were ready for the idea of "a base of bases."

Children with adequate background may translate a decimal-base number of pencils into a dozen-base, or the opposite. To do so, they may actually make the groups, or they may be able to make the transition mentally without physical manipulation of objects. In either case, the exercises will help them expand their understanding of "base" and will show them that our decimal base just happens to be the one used in our written number system.

A base of four. Liquid measure often uses a base of four. Cups of water may be "grouped" by pouring the contents into quart jars (4 cups to each quart), the quarts of water grouped by pouring them into gallon containers (4 quarts to each gallon). With appropriate discussion and recording of the results, stress may be placed on "four" as the basis for grouping. Again, the advantage of grouping larger quantities in some such fashion is obvious. Children will quickly see that "it is just easier to know how much you have" if you can group the smaller measures into standard groups that contain equal numbers of the smaller units.

The regrouping of 18 cups of water by a base of four might be expressed symbolically (C = cup; Q = quart; G = gallon).

C C C C C C C C C C C C C C C C C C (1st arrangement)

Q   Q   Q   Q   C C (2nd arrangement)

G   C C (3rd arrangement)

18 cups = 4 quarts and 2 cups = 1 gallon

0 quarts 2 cups = 102_{four}

LEARNING ABOUT ZERO

The number symbol "0" is named "zero." Children should be taught this name, just as they are taught that the name of "2" is "two." The name is not important, of course, until there is occasion to develop the meaning; then the meaning has to have a name.

Zero as absence of quantity. Computational uses of zero concepts, discussed in later chapters, will be much more easily taught if the teacher also uses other situations to develop these meanings. Any activity involving scorekeeping is a setting for teaching the idea of zero as "absence of quantity." Baseball, football, or any other team sport has its scores of 4 to 0, 13 to 0, or even 0 to 0. In these sports we usually read the "0" as "nothing," but the name of the symbol is still "zero." Even the "love" of tennis is written with the zero symbol.

Let us hope the children have no (zero) experiences with teacher-administered grades of "zero" in spelling or reading or, indeed, arithmetic! In games for which each individual keeps his own score, the usual procedure is to start with a score of zero and to work up from that by ones (golf strokes), twos (baskets), threes (field goals), fives (dominoes), or various other scores. Sometimes progress is shown by adding different scores for different achievements as when, in a game, the player gets 1 point for one achievement, 2 points for another type, or 5 points for still another.

In using zero in keeping score, children are really practicing a double use of zero so far as meaning is concerned. The two meanings are not mutually exclusive, but it is well for the teacher to take note of them separately in order that she shall be sure to note both in guiding children's experiences. The first idea is that "0" means "none" or "not any." No points or credits have been earned as yet; so the score is "none," or "not any score," or "no score." In games or sports, this meaning is fairly obvious and not too difficult to comprehend. Until points are made, the score stands at 0. No doubt, this is the reason that textbook writers are so prone to use games and scorekeeping as situations in which to introduce zero, and rightfully so.

In most other situations zero as absence of quantity is a more difficult concept. This is probably at the root of the difficulty many children have with the so-called "zero combinations" such as $2 + 0$, $7 - 0$, or 3×0. These situations are so simple that to intellectualize them in this fashion is difficult. If one has 2 apples and one adds no apples, obviously one still has 2 apples, but why add at all if nothing is to be added? If one has 7¢ and spends 0¢, one still has 7¢, but why make this into a subtraction situation? If I own 0 acres of land, owning 3 times as many acres still obviously leaves me landless, but why try to make this into a multiplication situation? This matter will be treated later. It is mentioned here only to indicate unnecessary confusions that are sometimes introduced to children. These combinations are not needed until one deals with addition, subtraction, or multiplication of numbers with two places or more. When the point is reached for such work with larger numbers, stress should be placed on the situation when 0 is added, subtracted, or multiplied. In order to discuss absence of quantity intelligently with children, one almost has to start with quantity and then contrast it with lack of quantity. For example, a wagon has 4 wheels, a tricycle has 3 wheels, a bicycle has 2 wheels, a wheelbarrow has 1 wheel, a sled has 0 wheels. These statements can be drawn from the children by asking them questions. It would be ridiculous to start out by asking a

child, "How many wheels does a sled have?" Obviously, it has none. But when one starts with something that does have wheels, one can work backward from quantity to lack of quantity in building the concept of zero as representing absence of quantity.

Zero on the number line. In scoring games, zero is the starting point in counting. This holds true for both positive and negative numbers. Each starts from the 0 point. When counting apples or boys or sticks, the child counts beginning with the "one." In scores he can see that actually before there are any achievements for which points can be given, each person or each side has a score of zero. As soon as children encounter the use of temperatures that refer to degrees above or below zero, they have another practical application of this concept of zero as the starting point. Children in Montana or Maine encounter this use sooner and more frequently than those who live in Florida or California. When the use occurs, the teacher does well to make the most of it for developing the zero concept. Any use of a number line includes this same opportunity, whether it be the use of a ruler or the use of a number line in diagramming one of the fundamental processes. On the ruler, the numbered points usually begin with 1, but children can be helped to see that the left end of the ruler is the zero point. In drawing number lines on the board or encouraging children to use them in paper-and-pencil work, the teacher needs to make certain that the beginning point is not incorrectly labeled "1" instead of "0." See figure 13. In this case, to point out the error is not enough. The point to be developed is that "1" comes at the end of 1 whole inch or 1 whole mile or whatever unit is being used. The "1" is the value of the distance between "0" and "1," *not* the first point on the line. The starting point is "0."

Zero as a place holder. Zero is also a place holder. This is the zero concept, which is basic to the place-value notation we use so casually. As a place holder, it

recorded, we need a symbol to hold an empty space. If we do not have such a symbol, we cannot use our number symbols correctly in indicating how many items we have. The number shown on the abacus *(A)* is 403, *not* 43. We have

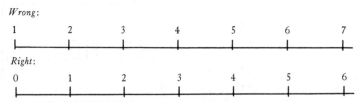

Wrong:

| 1 | 2 | 3 | 4 | 5 | 6 | 7 |

Right:

| 0 | 1 | 2 | 3 | 4 | 5 | 6 |

Figure 13. Placement of One and Zero on Number Line.

indicates absense of quantity (the idea discussed above) *in a certain place* — ones' place, tens' place, or any other place. The symbol for zero is not the only numeral that holds a place; any numeral can do the same. The numeral "0" holds the ones' place and the numeral "4" holds the tens' place in the written number "240." What is so special about zero as a place holder is that it signifies in a sense an "empty" space, whereas the other numerals signify a given quantity occupying the space. Here is the reason that the idea of zero as lack of quantity, discussed above, becomes so important in our notational scheme — an idea so obvious yet so difficult that man struggled with clumsier notational schemes for centuries upon centuries before someone conceived of a symbol to occupy an "empty" space.

How can this idea of the "empty" space be developed with a child? If he has learned to use the abacus, he knows about empty rods. If he has shown number values by manipulating tickets or slips of paper in place-value pocket charts, he knows about empty spaces. If he has spread out coins and paper money as shown in the illustration, he knows about empty spaces. NOW comes the all-important clincher! When the quantities shown in figure 14 are to be

4 hundreds, 0 tens, and 3 ones. Without the 0, we would write 43, which is not at all right. The number shown with the pocket chart *(B)* is 120, *not* 12. The value of the coins *(C)* is $1.03, *not* $.13.

Need for stress on meaning of zero. Any teacher can name dozens of similar situations in which zero as a place holder is a crucial element in a total meaning. The question is this: are these situations being used to help children learn what zero means? How much more valuable such instruction would be than the hurrying on to drills on "zero facts"! When zero facts are taught by rote, they are often reviewed and drilled and reviewed and drilled all because they do not make sense to children who have never been helped to develop adequate concepts of what zero really means and how zero is really used in our number notation.

Zero can best be defined through its uses as an indicator of absence of quantity, as a starting point of number line or scale, and as a place holder when no value is to be found in the given place. That these meanings are interrelated and interdependent will be obvious to any teacher who keeps a watchful eye for opportunities to develop them. No amount of repetition of formal definitions can take the place of *understood use* of zero concepts, in both situations involving computation and those which do not. Much more discussion of zero meanings is included in suggestions for

up all his ten fingers, the written record of the number of fingers is "10." The "1" is the same "1" that represented only one finger. In "10" it has a new meaning.

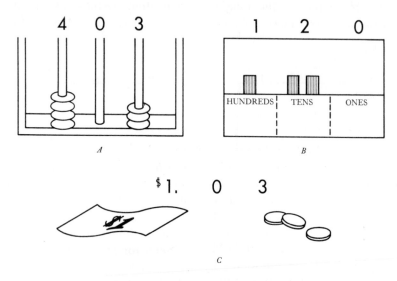

Figure 14. Zero and the Empty Place.

developing the four fundamental processes.

Children at every level of arithmetic competence in the elementary school have need for use and expansion of the meaning of zero. This is not a topic reserved for any particular level for the simple reason that anyone who uses numbers larger than 9 must use place value if he handles numbers with understanding. He cannot get beyond the meaning of the two-place numeral "10" without meeting zero. True, many children have met and passed "10" hundreds and thousands of times without understanding the function of zero, but they did not then get beyond the *meaning* of the two-place numeral "10."

Some dramatizations of place-value concepts have been suggested. If writing of the numerals accompanies or follows the dramatization of each, children have an excellent chance to see the role of zero. For example, when one child holds

It represents 1 group of ten. It can do this only when there is a zero in the ones' place so that two places are possible. Similarly, the "11" represents one set of ten fingers and one single finger more; "12" represents one set of ten and two more; and so on until we wish to show two whole sets of ten each. Again we must resort to the use of zero to put the "2" in the tens place, where it belongs if we are to have a numeral that shows 2 tens and 0 ones.

Those are the ideas to be presented. Each teacher will ask questions in her own way; different children will figure out the answers in their own ways. That is as it should be so long as the written symbols incorporating zero are seen by the learners as records of actual quantities, composed of ones and tens and hundreds and multiples of these place values. Such consideration should be encouraged at successive grade levels. As children's number ideas grow and expand, they can see broader applications of the same basic ideas. Reading and writing of Arabic numerals and numbers cannot be done with understanding by any person—young or old —who does not know the meaning and use of zero.

Learning Number System Meanings

Understanding number system involves much more than the understanding of numeration and notation as briefly reviewed in this and the preceding chapter. Extensions of the meaning of the typical number system of elementary arithmetic will be made in later chapters. Among these important extensions are these:

1. Already presented number concepts will be used within the framework of problem situations and computational patterns and procedures.

2. The development and application of number properties, expressed as laws or principles, will be presented as they affect the basic processes of addition and multiplication. These properties include commutation, association, distribution, and closure.

3. The processes of arithmetic will be presented in accordance with such system properties and in relation to one another, the processes of subtraction and division being shown as inverses of addition and multiplication, respectively.

4. With the introduction of fractions, the rational number system will be seen as a broader system than that of the whole numbers.

5. Computational procedures will be developed within problem settings of everyday use, but attention will also be directed to the ways in which computational forms and procedures depend on the structure of our number system.

This and the preceding chapter give only a partial view of numeration and notation. The ideas presented here must of necessity be developed with children in relation to the five considerations listed above before they can be seen in proper perspective. Succeeding chapters seek to give that perspective.

STUDY QUESTIONS

1. In planning learning experiences for children should the teacher think in terms of individual or group readiness for learning the particular ideas? Explain your answer.

2. Begin a listing of specific arithmetic content that you think is likely to be included in the arithmetic curriculum for some one grade (one you now teach or plan to teach). Mark the items in your list according to their appropriateness for below-average, average, and above-average learners. Continue this listing as you complete each successive chapter in this text.

3. If you are a student, keep a diary of your uses of ordinal and cardinal numbers for one week. If you are a teacher, guide your pupils in keeping such a diary (exclusive of their arithmetic lessons). At the end of the week, summarize your findings. Compare the frequency of cardinal and ordinal uses of number. Notice the comparative frequency of use of whole numbers and fractions (common and decimal).

4. Observe the number of X's in each row below. For each row, write the numerals that would record the number according to a base of ten, a base of six, a base of twelve, and a base of four.

a. X X X X X X X X X X X X X X X X X X X
b. X X X X X X X X X X X X
c. X X X X X X X X X X X X X X X X X X X X X X X

5. Use base-five numerals to express these amounts of money:

    a. 25¢   b. 12¢   c. 43¢   d. 50¢   e. $1.02

6. Read one or more of these references. Summarize the findings. Check these findings against your own observation of children's development of number concepts. Ilg, Frances; and Ames, Louise B. "Development Trends in Arithmetic," *Pedagogical Seminary and Journal of Genetic Psychology,* Vol. 79, September 1951. Martin, William E. "Quantitative Expression in Young Children," *Genetic Psychology Monographs* **44:**147-219, November 1951.

7. This schedule of the tides is taken from a newspaper. Make the necessary changes to find the times of high and low tides at Fort Morgan. You will have to recognize that time measures used here are related to a base of sixty.

Tides

(Stages shown below are calculated for mouth of Mobile River. Deduct one hour and forty minutes to find stages at latitude of Fort Morgan.)

(Central Standard Time)
April 6-13, 1958

	HIGH	LOW
Sunday	1:42 P.M.	. . . .
Monday	2:22 P.M.	12:53 A.M.
Tuesday	3:06 P.M.	2:17 A.M.
Wednesday	3:49 P.M.	3:32 A.M.
Thursday	4:36 P.M.	4:32 A.M.
Friday	5:28 P.M.	5:21 A.M.
Saturday	6:30 P.M.	5:57 A.M.
Sunday	8:03 P.M.	6:22 A.M.

CHAPTER 5

The Addition Process and
Basic Addition Facts

PRESENT-DAY ARITHMETIC deals with four fundamental processes — addition, subtraction, multiplication, and division.[1] Addition and multiplication of whole numbers[2] are basically similar in that both involve "putting together." Subtraction and division are basically similar in that both involve "taking apart." Addition and subtraction are inverse operations, as are multiplication and division. Each of the four processes can be better understood in relation to the other three. All are based on counting. All are processes of regrouping. Each will be discussed in a separate chapter to point up highlights of that particular process. This treatment should not suggest that the processes should be developed separately with children. Relatedness should be stressed with children wherever pertinent.

Addition is usually the first arithmetic process learned by children. This is appropriate since it is the most fundamental process. Multiplication is a special kind of addition. Subtraction is

the inverse process of addition and therefore closely related. Division is a taking-apart process like subtraction and therefore indirectly related to addition. A person who knows and understands addition must of necessity also know and understand many ideas that are basic to other processes as well.

What Is Addition

ADDITION IS A SPECIAL FORM
OF COUNTING

Any arithmetical problem that can be solved by adding can also be solved by counting *if time permits*. The time condition is a serious limitation on the use of one-by-one counting. If we had to count by ones to solve our addition problems, we could not operate successfully in our complex civilization. Saying the number names at a rate of 1 second for each number, it would take more than 31 years (nonstop) to count to 1 billion. Who would care to spend his lifetime counting such quantities? The need for speeding up the "counting-together" process is obvious.

In cardinal counting, the purpose is to find "how many in all." Cardinal count-

---

[1] For an interesting discussion of former classifications including more than four fundamental operations in arithmetic, see Karpinski, *The History of Arithmetic*, pp. 100-1.

[2] The discussion that follows concerning the four processes refers to positive integers. When fractions are involved, they will be specifically mentioned.

ing is a process of assigning number names to different objects, the last name assigned being the sum or total of all objects included to that point. Cardinal 2, 3, 4, 5. The right-hand group is counted 1, 2, 3. The *last* number in each case tells *how many trees in the group,* 5 in one group and 3 in the other.

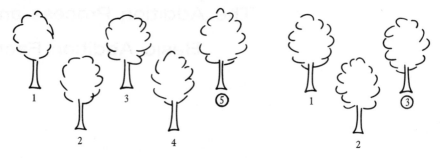

Figure 15. Counting Sub-groups Separately.

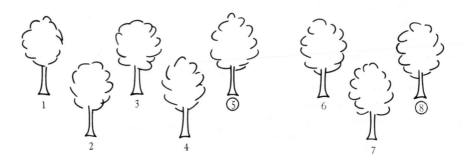

Figure 16. Re-counting to Find Total Number.

Figure 17. Partial Counting to Find Total Number.

counting may begin with the first item considered, such as the first tree in each group of trees in figure 15. The left-hand group in figure 15 is counted 1,

If we want to know how many trees in *both* groups, we may count as in figure 16, counting the left group as in figure 15 but continuing our count 6, 7, 8 instead

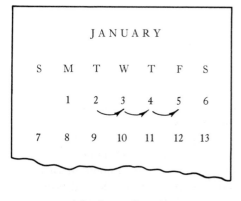

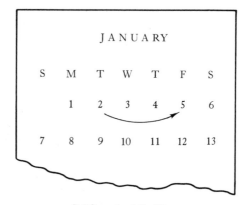

A. One-by-one Counting   *B.* "Counting in" a Three

Figure 18. Addition Involving Ordinal Numbers.

of starting over again with 1. In this way we *"count* the groups *together."*

If the "how many" of a previously counted group is already known, cardinal counting may go on from that known number, as in figure 17, without recounting of the first group. This is called "partial counting."

More efficient still is the procedure of the person who adds the two groups by simply thinking or saying, "5, 8." The person who does this is operating at a more mature level. He recognizes the size of the first group as 5, and he recognizes the size of the second group as 3, but he counts the two groups together by merely stating the "how many" of the combined quantities. He may think or say, "5, 8," or "5 trees and 3 trees are 8 trees," but those particular forms of statement are not essential. The essential of "addition as counting" is the *counting together* of the component groups contained in the new total.

In one sense, a person is "adding" every time he counts in one more item. At any place he would stop in his counting, he would have named the "how many" of the group counted to that point.

Addition may involve either regular or irregular counting. A housewife doing her grocery shopping counts 12 apples as she picks them up from the fruit counter. She may count, "2, 4, 6, 8, 10, 12" as she picks up two apples each time. If the apples are small, she may count "2, 5, 8, 10, 12," sometimes "counting in" a group of two, sometimes a group of three apples. Simple addition for adults is more likely to represent irregular counting than regular; if regular counting is possible, i.e., if many groups of the same size are to be combined, multiplication is more convenient and economical of time.

While addition is much more likely to deal with cardinal counting, it does at times involve ordinal counting. (Order is of course involved in all counting; reference here is to the *use* of the numbers in the ordinal sense.)

James wants a certain airplane model. The clerk tells him it is out of stock but that it can be ordered and will probably arrive within 3 days. "Today" is January 2. James looks at the calendar (fig. 18) and counts forward "3 days" to see that the model will probably arrive by January 5. The "2" is an ordinal number; it tells "which day." The "5" is also an ordinal number telling "which day" the order will be received. If James is mature enough in his number thinking to handle this situation by adding 3 rather than by one-by-one counting on the calendar, he probably merely thinks, "2, 5," or "January 2, January 5." The arrows in figures 18*A* and 18*B* indicate, respectively, less mature and more mature ways of moving from January 2 to January 5.

To say that addition is basically a counting process does not mean that ability to do one-by-one counting represents competence in addition. What the teacher of young children needs to remember is that they need ample experience in counting as background for competence in addition and that they need help in understanding the relation of counting and addition. Many primary-grade teachers are in too much of a hurry to have children write addition algorisms like those at the right instead of taking time to let children

$$5 + 1 = 6 \qquad \begin{array}{r} 4 \\ +2 \\ \hline 6 \end{array}$$

count meaningfully and then leading them to see that when they count by 1's or 2's or 3's, they are really adding 1's and 2's and 3's. This counting should be done orally. Laborious written counting serves so little purpose that one wonders why anyone ever requires it of children. The only writing that usually "makes sense" in these counting experiences is the recording of the result of the counting.

Every schoolroom has in it so many things that are countable and the day's events provide so many opportunities for practicing counting that no child needs to be deprived of numerous practice opportunities. There are always such things as the lunch money to be counted, the chairs needed for a group of children, enough books for those same children, the minutes on the clockface "from now until time for lunch," the thermometer on which to find what the temperature will be if it goes up 5 degrees from yesterday's high of 34, and all sorts of inventory-taking activities with books, paper, pencils, and other equipment. The point is to *use* these opportunities for practice in counting and for discussion leading to competence in adding.

The question is often asked by teachers, "How can I get children to quit counting on their fingers in order to find the sums of simple addition combinations?" The answer lies in the *why* of a child's dependence on this procedure. The cure is not in punishing him or making him feel guilty; after all, counting on one's fingers is not necessarily "bad." It is just slow and cumbersome. Children will give up their reliance on it when they become skillful in handling more efficient procedures.

Addition, then, is a special kind of counting. It is the process of "counting together" two or more quantities. The known quantities may be the same or different in size. Except when dealing with the quantity "1," addition is a quicker process than one-by-one counting. The larger the amounts to be "counted together," the greater is the saving of time in adding rather than simple counting. Incidentally, demonstrating this timesaving to children is a much more potent incentive to habituating the addition facts than any amount of appeal or threat.

ADDITION IS REGROUPING
BY COMBINING

Alice received 4 letters yesterday. Two more came for her today. She may think of these as two separate groups, those which came yesterday and those which came today. Or she may think of them as being combined into a new total group including both yesterday's and today's mail. The big question for Alice may be, "How many letters do I have to answer?" in which case she is more concerned with a regrouped total of 6 letters as having been combined into a new group of 6 letters indicated by the bracket in figure 19.

The regrouping by combination that is addition may take place as a physical "putting together" of subgroups like Alice's letters, or it may be merely a "thinking together" of subgroups like

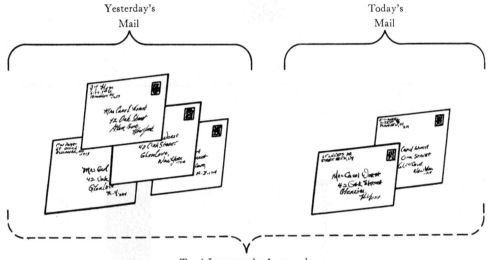

Figure 19. Addition as Regrouping by Combination.

Addition as regrouping serves the purpose of simplifying a situation. The more component or constituent groups there are, the greater is the simplification when they are regrouped into a composite or total group. That is one of the purposes of taking inventory. A business concern may have 1 to 6 typewriters in each of several offices. How much simpler it is when considering the number of typewriters in use to know that there are "17 in all" rather than to know merely that there are "1 and 2 and 6 and 4 and 1 and 3" in various offices. The quantities indicated in the two expressions are identical, but the ease of dealing with the summation "17" rather than the numerous sub-quantities is too obvious to need elaboration. The value of this simplification is more obvious in situations involving many subgroups or in situations involving larger subgroups, but it is noticeable even with basic addition combinations.

the typewriters in the different offices, but the idea of combining or "considering together" is essential. With less mature learners the physical act of putting the subgroups together is very important; with added maturity of understanding this becomes unnecessary. This maturity will vary widely according to the learner's age, mentality, and past experience with the concept. Some children in a class will need to go through the motions of combining groups, whereas others in the same class will not need such activity and may even be bored by it. What is helpful to one child may be a burden to another.

The prior concept of "addition as counting" and this concept of "addition as regrouping by combination" may and often should and do occur together. The series of illustrations in figure 20 illustrate this point. The child shown in figure 20 counts, "2 books, 5 books, 7 books," as he combines (regroups) the

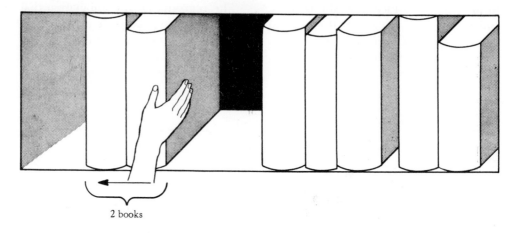

2 books

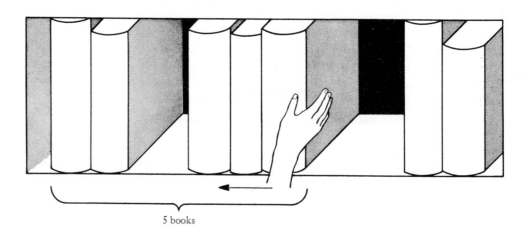

5 books

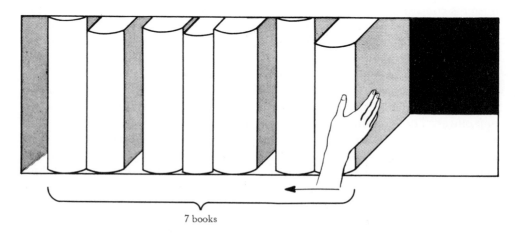

7 books

Figure 20. Adding as Both Counting and Regrouping.

three original groups of 2, 3, and 2 into a new total group of 7 books. This would be equally true if all subgroups had been the same size (regular counting) instead of different in size (irregular counting). Children should be given ample opportunity for such use of both these ideas of addition (counting together and regrouping) since each supports the other.

In elementary school arithmetic texts, addition facts are often presented in groupings by size of sum. Such a grouping of facts for the sum "8" would be: 1+7=8; 2+6=8; 3+5=8; 4+4=8; 5+3=8; 6+2=8; and 7+1=8. A total group of 8 objects (pennies, pencils, blocks) may be grouped and regrouped in all the ways suggested. The quantity "8" may be thought of as being composed of 1 and 7, or 2 and 6, and so on. The "+" sign in the written fact symbolizes the combining of the component groups (subgroups) into a composite group (total group) containing those components.

ADDITION MAY BE RELATED TO UNION OF SETS

Since the language of sets is becoming more prevalent, teachers should be aware of correct terminology for describing the addition process in those terms. Addition, as described above, is a process of regrouping by combining; the new total group (sum) then includes the original groups as subgroups of itself. This is the same idea as the *union of sets*. When two or more sets (groups) are combined to form a new set (group), the original sets are then included as subsets (subgroups) of the new total or composite set (sum). The process by which the subsets are combined to form the new set is called *union* rather than *addition,* but the idea is the fundamental addition idea.

In elementary school arithmetic, however, a special restriction is placed on addition in that the groups being combined must be distinct and separate groups. If a Scandinavian-American choral group has in it 13 people of Norwegian descent, 7 of Swedish descent, and 5 of Danish descent, one might assume that the chorus has 25 members. This would be a true sum only if no overlapping of nationalities (overlapping of subgroups or subsets) is present. If even one singer is a member of more than one of the subsets, combining the numbers for subsets gives a wrong total. If, for example, one singer is of Norwegian-Swedish ancestry and another of Danish-Norwegian ancestry, the total enrollment in the choral group would be not 25 but 23, no other exceptions being present.

In elementary arithmetic, the groups or sets to be combined by addition are assumed to be mutually exclusive. In set terminology, such sets are called *disjoint sets.* The "union-of-sets" concept includes situations in which the sets being combined are overlapping as well as nonoverlapping (disjoint). So far as our discussion of elementary school addition is concerned, we deal only with the union of disjoint sets.[3]

THE TYPICAL ADDITION STATEMENT IS A STATEMENT OF EQUALITY

A group of 3 apples and a group of 4 apples are combined into a new group of 7 apples. The 3 apples and the 4 apples *are equal to* 7 apples. The value of the new total group is *the same as* the value of the subgroups that are combined to produce the total. It is misleading to tell children, "When you add, you

[3] Children need not learn the term "disjoint sets," but teachers should recognize that this restriction applies.

get more." The supplying of the missing term in this addition sentence depends on finding a number that will make the statement of equality *true:* $3 + n = 7$, or $3 + \underline{\quad} = 7$. Current practice often uses a frame or box instead of n or the blank, thus: $3 + \square = 7$ or $3 + \triangle = 7$.

If Joe and his brother Bill added their earnings, the addition process did not increase the amount of money. True, the total is greater than either amount alone, but the essence of the adding is that the boys *put together* the two original amounts of money. The sum is not greater than what they had before they put the money together; it is *the same as* what they had before doing the adding. Joe had 2 dollars, Bill had 3 dollars. They added their resources, and the

of confusion that was sowed when they were first told that "add" means "increase" or that "when you add, your answer is a bigger number." Not only are they confused as to "bigger than what?" but they are baffled by the fact that the sum of two or more numbers may actually be smaller than any of the numbers added. A positive 5 and a negative 7 are combined (that is, added) to produce a negative 2, which result seems impossible if one believes that "add" and "increase" are synonyms. Of course a person may be just as sure of a wrong idea as of a right one. This sureness, developed through years of uncritical acceptance and practice of a wrong notion, can present a formidable block to later correct learning. Much "unlearning" must then be done—

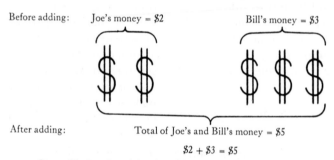

Before adding: Joe's money = $2   Bill's money = $3

After adding: Total of Joe's and Bill's money = $5

$2 + $3 = $5

Figure 21. Equality of Combined Sub-groups to Their Total.

pooled amount is 5 dollars. The 2 dollars and 3 dollars *equal* 5 dollars. The same dollars are involved before and after the addition. This is a simple statement of equality, not of an increase. Joe and Bill had 5 dollars before they added their money, but it was separated into Joe's 2 dollars and Bill's 3 dollars. We have a contradiction if we say that "adding means getting more" and then say that "2 dollars and 3 dollars *equal* 5 dollars." Figure 21 illustrates this situation. The same dollars are present before and after the adding.

When algebra students get to the operations with positive and negative numbers, many of them reap a harvest

usually a more difficult process than the learning of a correct idea in the beginning.

In some addition situations, the total is not composed of the *same* objects as those in the groups to be added. The idea of one-to-one correspondence enters into these situations. Let us suppose that we start with Joe's 2 dollars and Bill's 3 dollars (fig. 21), but with a different question to be answered. The question is: If Tom has as much money as Joe and Bill together, how many dollars does Tom have? Figure 22 represents the situation and its solution. Here the 5 dollars in the sum are not the same dollars as those in Joe's and Bill's possession. They are different dollars but correspond in one-to-one fashion to Joe's and Bill's dollars. In situations of this type it is still true that the addition statement is a statement of equality. Joe's money and Bill's money combined

particularly when the symbol "+" is used to represent the combining process in written form. The equality of the addends to the sum is expressed by the terms *equal, equals, is equal to, are,* or *is.* The common symbol for expressing

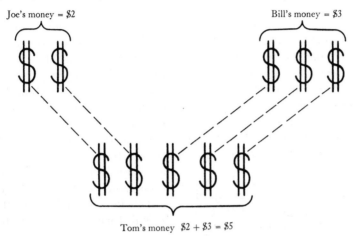

Joe's money = $2

Bill's money = $3

Tom's money $2 + $3 = $5

Figure 22. Equality of One Amount to Two Others.

are *equal* in amount to Tom's money. Joe, Bill, and Tom (each or all together) possess the same amount of money after the comparison as before it. One might ask: Then why do we add? The answer is of course that Tom does not need to add, but if Joe and Bill or anyone else is told that Tom has as much money as Joe and Bill together, he can add the known amounts of money to find out how much Tom has (an unknown amount to him).

Addition Terminology

The numbers that correspond to the groups being added are called *addends.* The number that corresponds to the group composed of all the addends is called the *sum,*[4] or *total.* The process of addition is represented by the word *and* between the addends. Sometimes the word *plus* is used in the same way as *and,*

[4] While sums may have more than one term (e.g., 4 + 2), in elementary school arithmetic the word "sum" typically refers to a single term (e.g., 6).

equality in written form is the sign "=," called the *equals sign.*

The foregoing paragraph summarises briefly all the details of common addition terminology, but such a paragraph would be of small value to a child learning how to express addition in speaking and writing about it. Children need a succession of experiences in which addition actions are discussed, stated, and recorded in correct ways. This is the only kind of firm basis for vocabulary development in any area.

The four first-grade children at one table and the five children at another table have been asked by the teacher to join her in a "reading group." How many chairs will be needed for all the children in the reading group?

If the children who participate in this situation are known by their teacher to need practice with the concept of addition and with the terminology of addition, she may take time for discussing the actions involved from an arithmetical point of view. She may ask questions such as: How many chairs will this group need? (Four.) How many chairs will the other group need? (Five.) How many chairs will both groups need? (Nine.) How many children are in the whole reading group? (Nine.) How many are four and five altogether? (Nine.) What did we do when we put four chairs and five chairs together? (We added.) What did we do when we changed a group of four children and a group of five children into a new group of nine children? (We added.)

The teacher may ask the children to see how many ways they can tell what they did. Some correct oral replies might be:

A group of 4 chairs and a group of 5 chairs make a new group of 9 chairs. (Same for children instead of chairs.)

4 chairs and 5 chairs are 9 chairs. (Same for children.)

4 chairs plus 5 chairs are 9 chairs.

4 plus 5 is 9.

When you add 4 and 5, the answer is 9.

4 plus 5 equals 9.

The important considerations here are (1) that the teacher should recognize variety of correct response, not restricting children to one set form, and (2) that the teacher should also recognize progressively more abstract forms of statement, encouraging these when she is sure that children understand that they represent the same meanings as the more detailed statements referring to actual concrete objects.

Variety of expression should also be encouraged when written records are made of an addition activity. Progressively more abstract and more condensed statements should be introduced and encouraged as children see what those statements represent in actual experiences they have had.

4 chairs and 5 chairs are 9 chairs	4 chairs +5 chairs 9 chairs
4 chairs and 5 chairs equal 9 chairs	
4 chairs + 5 chairs = 9 chairs	4
4 + 5 = 9	+5 9

The examples given do not exhaust the possibilities for correct terminology or written form. They merely suggest the possible variety. The teacher may wonder, "How long should children be expected to write out the more complete forms?" The answer is, "As long as they need to do so in order to understand fully what they are recording." This answer will necessitate different expectations from different children.

Teachers do well to note that the horizontal forms (algorisms) for addition facts fit more closely with and are perhaps a better "next step" from the simple oral statement of the fact than are the vertical algorisms. Reading a horizontal addition statement follows the same directional pattern as the child uses in his reading of verbal text; the vertical form does not.

Reading mathematical symbols like "+" and "=" should include more than learning to say the word name for the symbol. There is a big difference in understanding between the child who knows only that he should say "plus" when he sees the sign "+" and the child who replies when questioned about it by saying in his own words, "The plus sign means we put 4 chairs and 5 chairs together."

When is the "=" sign read as "is" and when as "are"? When is it read as "equals" and when as "equal"? The distinction is made on this basis: if the first part of the statement includes concrete referents, such as "chairs" or "children," the plural forms "are" and "equal" are used; if the numbers stand alone, such as "4 and 5" or "4 + 5," the expression is considered as a single combination, and the singular forms "is" and "equals" are used. In other words, "4 children and 5 children" is a plural subject demanding a plural verb; "4 and 5" is a singular subject referring to a single abstract combination and demands a singular verb.[5]

At the risk of accentuating the negative, a final word may be in order concerning the all-too-common practice of beginning arithmetic instruction with formal drill on algorisms like those below:

1	4	6	7	.2	9
+4	+6	+3	+2	+8	+5
5	10	9	9	10	14

These forms, no matter how glibly parroted or how neatly copied, are not worth the time spent on the parroting or the copying if that is what the child is doing as he is drilled on them! Worse, a child who thinks that such activity *is* addition is a child led astray. So also for parents!

The forms are not the substance; answers called in response to given number stimuli are not the desired result in learning to add. The forms have value only when they represent meanings already experienced and, later, meanings to be experienced as the abstract symbols are applied to situations in general. Correctness of symbolic representations of addition can best be judged by the user, be he child or adult. When is an addition statement true? When is an algorism correct? They are correct *when they tell the truth about the situation they are meant to describe.* The

ultimate authority for correctness is not the answer sheet on the teacher's desk or in the back of the book; the ultimate authority for correctness is the situation in which addition is about to take place or has taken place. Why is "9" the correct sum for the combination "4 + 5"? Because when the children put 4 chairs and 5 chairs together, they had a new total of 9 chairs. Any way they state that truth is correct. Condensation of form for the statement is appropriate as the condensed versions acquire meaning for the user; such meaningful condensation becomes preferred form as savings of time and effort are realized through its use, but not before then.

Rules for Addition

The addition process must obey certain principles or rules. An understanding of these rules has much to do with a person's understanding of the process and his application of the process in new situations. Two of these principles are fundamental mathematical laws stating two essential properties within our number system.[6] These are the laws of commutation and association for addition.

THE COMMUTATIVE PRINCIPLE

FOR ADDITION

The order of the addends does not affect their sum. Changing the order of the addends does not change their sum. The need for the reminder stated in this rule or law is chiefly present when additions are set down in written form. If a child holds 3 pennies in one hand and 4 pennies in the other hand, it is obvious that the total number of pennies in both

---

[5] This is a technicality of more interest to some teachers than to children. It is included only because of the frequency of teacher requests for clarification. Children need not be held to strict adherence to this distinction.

[6] Other number systems may or may not have these same properties.

hands will be the same whether he adds the 3 to the 4 or the 4 to the 3.

$$3 + 4 = 7 \qquad 4 + 3 = 7 \qquad 3 + 4 = 4 + 3$$

Stated in typical algebraic form, the law of commutation is shown by the equation: $a + b = b + a$.

Many children first encounter this principle in the writing of basic addition facts in vertical form:

$$\begin{array}{c} 3 \\ +4 \\ \hline 7 \end{array} \quad \text{and} \quad \begin{array}{c} 4 \\ +3 \\ \hline 7 \end{array}$$

When related to such vertical form, the statement that "you can turn the numbers upside down and you'll get the same answer" may be accepted from young children, but this is really not a very good statement of the idea. First, it is tied to the vertical form, which restricts its applicability. Second, the expression "upside down" is not literally true even in that algorism. Much to be preferred are such statements as these:

The same two numbers give the same sum, no matter which comes first.
The order of the numbers (addends) does not change the sum.

Any correct statement in a child's own words should be accepted. He should not be given a statement to memorize. He should rather be helped to understand the basic idea, in which case he will find a way to express it in a manner that is meaningful to him. If his expression of the idea is not correct, the teacher will recognize his need for further help with the idea of commutativity.

The name "law of commutation" or "commutative principle" need not be used with children. The word "order" should probably be stressed rather than "commutation." For those children who are capable of more advanced vocabulary, the words "commutation" and "commutative" may be related to the meaning of the verb "commute," particularly for children who already know what "commuting" means. Many have fathers who commute to work, that is, travel one direction to get to work and the opposite direction to come back home.

The importance of this rule stems from its wide applicability. A child who understands that the order of the addends may be changed without changing their sum may use this idea to help him work out nonwritten additions in the order that seems easiest for him rather than being bound to a set order. This reduces markedly the time spent in learning the basic addition facts, since "reverse facts" such as "2 + 5 = 7" and "5 + 2 = 7" may be learned together rather than as separate facts. Often a basic number fact such as "2 + 9 = 11" is harder for children to learn than the fact using the same addends in reverse order, "9 + 2 = 11." In such event, knowing that the sums are the same is a big help to the learner.

Strictly speaking, the addition operation is performed with two numbers at a time. If more than two addends are involved in an addition, it is performed in successive steps. If 2, 4, and 7 are to be added, we first add any two of the numbers, then add their sum and the third number. For each step the commutative principle holds. By extension, then, the commutative principle may be extended for any number of addends. When this is done, however, another fundamental mathematical law is also involved, the law or principle of association.

THE ASSOCIATIVE PRINCIPLE
FOR ADDITION

When three or more numbers are to be added, they may be combined or grouped without changing their over-all sum. For three addends, this means that any two addends may be added first, and then their sum may be added to the remaining (ungrouped) addend.

Figure 23 represents a situation in which the question might be: How many

sum; and "cooperative" additions in which one person derives one subtotal while another person or persons derive other subtotals.

This latter procedure has frequent applications in the schoolroom. Leaders

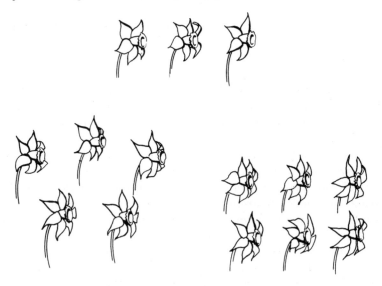

Figure 23. Association of Addends.

daffodils are shown in bloom? If no writing were required (and usually it would not be), any intelligent person should know that it does not matter where he starts or finishes in adding the 5 daffodils, 3 daffodils, and 6 daffodils. One might add the 5 daffodils and 3 daffodils first to get a subtotal of 8 daffodils; then, adding 8 daffodils and 6 daffodils, the total of 14 daffodils is found. The sum would be the same for this or any other way of "associating" or "grouping" the addends in the process of getting the grand total, so long as each addend was used once and only once.

The associative rule is applied frequently in addition in such cases as: selecting combinations with sums of 10 when adding a long column of numbers; dividing a long column into two or more parts, deriving subtotals for each, and then adding subtotals to get the final

or recorders for each table or each row (according to the seating arrangement of the class) may add to get subtotals for their respective pupil groups (attendance figures, points in a game, money collected for lunches). Each recorder may write his subtotal on the chalkboard, forming a column of figures that are then added by all the children. The teacher who is conscious of the importance of the associative concept in addition will take time to be sure that the children recognize what is being done. She might on a given occasion ask the children if this is a correct procedure and have them tell why they think so. Then they might "prove" by using different groupings of addends that they do get the same sum.

Algebraically, the law of association for addition is usually represented by the equation: $(a + b) + c = a + (b + c)$.

For elementary school children who have not had experience with letters to represent numbers, the statement can be developed with numerals for each situation. For example, in the case of the daffodils:

$$(5 + 3) + 6 = 5 + (3 + 6)$$
$$8 + 6 = 5 + 9$$
$$14 = 14$$

An interesting and worthwhile activity is the writing of the same addends in as many different groupings as possible. With only 4 addends, such an exercise would require the writing of 264 *different* expressions; so perhaps a start should be made with only 3 addends.

In such horizontally written forms or in the vertical form of column addition, it immediately becomes apparent that the principles of commutation and association often occur together. Consider the column at the right. In adding from top to bottom of the column, these additions are performed: $3 + 2 = 5$; $5 + 4 = 9$; $9 + 5 = 14$; $14 + 1 = 15$. In adding from bottom to top, these additions occur: $1 + 5 = 6$; $6 + 4 = 10$; $10 + 2 = 12$; $12 + 3 = 15$. We may interpret this situation as an application of the commutative principle—the order of the addends does not affect the sum. But we must also recognize that the addends were grouped in the process of adding in either order, and that the groupings were different. Thus the two principles operate together to provide a great number of different possible patterns of adding the five numbers (the two orders shown, as well as many others).

$$\begin{array}{r} 3 \\ 2 \\ 4 \\ 5 \\ \underline{1} \\ 15 \end{array}$$

Teachers use the associative (grouping) principle when they check their attendance registers. The teacher gets each child's total attendance for the school month or year, then adds all these sums to get the total days attended by her class. To check, she gets the class attendance for each day or month, and then adds those sums to see if she gets the same total days attended as she did by the other grouping of the same data. By varying the order of addends to be grouped (in alphabetical order of names or in some other order), the teacher also introduces the principle of commutation.

As with many other important features of our everyday existence, the commutative and associative properties of addition are not adequately appreciated; they are just taken for granted. Their importance in lightening the task of learning to add are realized when one considers how complex addition would be without these principles of operation. The more addends that are present in an addition example, the more different combinations and sequences of adding are possible. Even with only four or five addends, the number of combinations that are possible is amazing. If children in the elementary school had to learn and practice separately all these various ways of expressing the same addition, the task would be endless. So long as it is known that the order of the addends and the subgrouping of addends do not change the sum, great flexibility is permissible in handling these varied situations.

THE CLOSURE PROPERTY

The sum of any two natural (counting) numbers is another natural number. This is the closure property for addition. More attention will be given this idea with respect to subtraction, a process for which the closure property does not hold.

Other fundamental ideas not considered as basic laws of operation are nonetheless important for proper understanding of addition. One such idea is sometimes called the rule of likeness.

THE RULE OF LIKENESS

One characteristic of a group or set is some quality of likeness (the basis for membership in the group or set). In elementary school arithmetic this is usually determined in terms of the specific items of which the group is composed, e.g., trees, people, or dollars. When a group of 3 trees and another group of 5 trees are considered together to form a new group of 8 trees, it is clear that the 3, 5, and 8 all refer to the same kind of objects. One can speak of combining (adding) a group of 2 tables and a group of 4 chairs; the sum could be expressed as "2 tables + 4 chairs." The sum could not be correctly expressed as "6 tables" or as "6 chairs" because, obviously, either of those descriptions would not be true. If the number expression "2 + 4" is to be correctly replaced by the single numeral "6," the descriptions (names) of the subgroup and total group members must be the same. In this particular case, we can correctly say, "2 pieces of furniture + 4 pieces of furniture = 6 pieces of furniture."

Since this is a requirement of the particular situation in which addition is taking place, perhaps the rule of likeness can best be defined in terms of the particular problem or situation, thus: *The addends must be alike in the sense that they are being used in the particular problem situation.* If addend numerals do not refer to like things, their sum cannot be correctly stated with a single numeral.

In the algebraic sum "$2a + 3b + 4a$," the "like terms" are "$2a$" and "$4a$." Because those are like terms, we may substitute "$6a$" for "$2a + 4a$"; that is, we may substitute the number "6" for the number "$2 + 4$" since all the nu-

merals refer to like terms. The term "$3b$" must remain separate because it is an "unlike term." The "3" must continue to refer to "b," which is unlike "a"; so: $2a + 3b + 4a = 6a + 3b$.

Misinterpretations of this rule are frequent. To tell children that "apples and oranges cannot be added because they are not alike" is a half-truth that may have the same consequences as an untruth. Two apples and three oranges can indeed be added if we do not make the mistake of calling the sum "5 apples" or "5 oranges." A correct sum would be "5 apples and oranges" or "5 pieces of fruit." No violence has been done to any mathematical or object meanings. If all the addends can be correctly given some new designation that is the same for all, the numerical coefficients[7] *can* be added. This is not an exception to the rule of likeness, but a correct application of it.

If a person were measuring the width of a window and found it to be equivalent to the length of a yardstick and 4 inches more, he might correctly speak of adding 1 *yard* and 4 *inches*. His sum would also be "1 yard and 4 inches," still using the two measures *yard* and *inch*. The names of the measures are different, but the rule has not been violated since the 1 and the 4 were not added to give a meaningless number 5.

As with the oranges and apples, the form of the yard and inch measurements may be *changed* so the numbers assigned to each *can* be added. The 1 yard can be changed to 36 inches; then the numbers 36 and 4 may be added to yield a sum of 40 inches, since they now

---

[7] Elementary school children need not learn the term "coefficient" though some more mature ones will enjoy doing so. For most children, it is enough to refer merely to the *number* that goes with the name, i.e., the number that tells how many items of a given name are being considered.

have the same name. Numbers associated with different names may be added *after changing* one or both so they have the same name. Sometimes this change does not change the numbers, as when 4 boys and 5 girls are described as 4 children and 5 children, or 9 children. Sometimes, as with the yard and inches, the change to the same name necessitates a change in one or both numbers.

The rule of likeness is frequently applied in the various operations and algorisms of addition. Two of the most important relate to place value and to addition of fractions. In addition of two-place and larger numbers the rule of likeness underlies the dictum to "keep the columns straight." The quantities in the ones place must be added to other quantities in the ones place, tens to tens, and hundreds to hundreds. To confuse the columns would be to get meaningless sums. This application of the rule of likeness is basic to understanding the changing involved in "carrying."

In the addition of fractions, the use of common denominators (same names) is an application of this same rule of likeness. If fractions do not have the same denominator, they must be changed so as to have correct like denominators (names) before the numerators (numbers) are added.

The Basic Addition Facts

BASIC ADDITION FACTS DEFINED

The *basic addition facts* are numerical statements giving the sums of all possible pairs of one-digit numbers. Since we have a decimal system, we have 100 basic facts. Each of the ten number symbols 0 through 9 can be combined with each of the 9 other symbols and with itself.[8]

All the basic addition facts for our system are shown in Table 1. These facts are properly called "basic" since they are the building blocks of all later addition. Knowing these facts and understanding our "base-and-place" notational system, a person can perform any addition to secure larger sums by operating according to the principles of addition already discussed.

References in the professional literature to 81 basic facts instead of 100 come about because of the omission of all facts that include zero as an addend. Some writers have argued that these facts can be taken care of as a single generalization about the zero facts; i.e., *adding zero to another number does not change that number.* This is hardly a valid argument for omitting them from consideration as basic facts. They are truly building blocks used in later addition as are the other basic facts. Further, they are not the only facts that can be grouped under a single generalization; the same can be done for other basic facts. Generalizing about basic addition facts does not remove them from the realm of facts any more than generalization about air currents removes the facts from which the generalization was derived.

The only valid reason for omitting the zero facts from lists or charts of all

[8] If we had another base, we would have a different number of basic facts. With a base of two, only four basic addition facts are possible: $0 + 0 = 0$; $0 + 1 = 1$; $1 + 0 = 1$; and $1 + 1 = 10$. The written form of the last fact looks strange because we are accustomed to a base of ten, but $1 + 1 = 10$ in the base of two means "one plus one equals one two (the base)." With a base of eight, 64 basic facts are possible.

An excellent activity for children who are ready for it is to figure out the sets of basic addition facts with bases other than ten.

TABLE 1

Basic Addition Facts

0 +0 0	0 +1 1	0 +2 2	0 +3 3	0 +4 4	0 +5 5	0 +6 6	0 +7 7	0 +8 8	0 +9 9
1 +0 1	1 +1 2	1 +2 3	1 +3 4	1 +4 5	1 +5 6	1 +6 7	1 +7 8	1 +8 9	1 +9 10
2 +0 2	2 +1 3	2 +2 4	2 +3 5	2 +4 6	2 +5 7	2 +6 8	2 +7 9	2 +8 10	2 +9 11
3 +0 3	3 +1 4	3 +2 5	3 +3 6	3 +4 7	3 +5 8	3 +6 9	3 +7 10	3 +8 11	3 +9 12
4 +0 4	4 +1 5	4 +2 6	4 +3 7	4 +4 8	4 +5 9	4 +6 10	4 +7 11	4 +8 12	4 +9 13
5 +0 5	5 +1 6	5 +2 7	5 +3 8	5 +4 9	5 +5 10	5 +6 11	5 +7 12	5 +8 13	5 +9 14
6 +0 6	6 +1 7	6 +2 8	6 +3 9	6 +4 10	6 +5 11	6 +6 12	6 +7 13	6 +8 14	6 +9 15
7 +0 7	7 +1 8	7 +2 9	7 +3 10	7 +4 11	7 +5 12	7 +6 13	7 +7 14	7 +8 15	7 +9 16
8 +0 8	8 +1 9	8 +2 10	8 +3 11	8 +4 12	8 +5 13	8 +6 14	8 +7 15	8 +8 16	8 +9 17
9 +0 9	9 +1 10	9 +2 11	9 +3 12	9 +4 13	9 +5 14	9 +6 15	9 +7 16	9 +8 17	9 +9 18

Another possible arrangement would be with the like addends in the vertical position rather than the horizontal position.

the basic addition facts is that they are not often needed until learners come to the addition of two-place and larger numbers.

Some writers on the teaching of arithmetic draw a sharp distinction between the basic addition *facts* and basic addition *combinations*. Strictly speaking, the term "combination" refers to the pairing and indicated addition of numbers such as *4 and 5* without their sum; the same pair in reverse *(5 and 4)* is not considered a separate combination. Either order still indicates the "combination" or "combining" of those two numbers. Thus there are 55 basic addition combinations if zero combinations are included and 45 if not. The fundamental distinction between the statements of an addition *fact* and of an addition *combination* is that an addition fact is a complete declarative sentence and a combination is not a complete thought or statement of fact. It is an incomplete sentence with a subject but no predicate. The basic or primary addition facts not only make all possible combinations of one-digit numbers, but they complete the thought by also stating the sums. Below are a few of the many possible ways of stating basic addition facts. If the parts in parentheses were omitted, these "facts" would no longer be "facts" but only "combinations."

> 4 dogs and 5 dogs (are 9 dogs).
> 4 dogs plus 5 dogs (equal 9 dogs).
> 4 dogs and 5 dogs (are 9 dogs).
> 4 + 5 (= 9)   (Common usage omits
> the period in this form
> of statement.)

If boys and girls are to become skillful in the use of addition algorisms in general, they must learn the basic addition facts to the level of automatic recall. Emphasis on automatic recall should come as soon as (and not before) the learners have a good understanding of the meanings of the facts, their application, and their relationships one to another.

Basic addition facts have been organized in various ways for introduction to children in school. They have been classified as "easy" or "difficult" on the basis of drill studies or according to size-of-sum patterns. Actually, the determination of relative difficulty of number facts is by no means a simple matter, nor has this relative difficulty been accurately determined. A more fruitful basis for organization can probably be found through careful study of basic meanings and principles of the addition process and our number system, then applying these to the basic facts.[9] Individual learner differences are such that no one strict order of difficulty will ever apply to all learners.

THE BASIC ADDITION FACTS
AND COUNTING

The close relationship between the basic facts and counting is obvious not only to the advanced student of mathematics but also to the immature learner who resorts to counting out the sums on his fingers whenever he cannot find or recall the sum any other way. Since addition is a special form of counting, this relationship is not only a close one, but it is actually inherent in both concepts.

The ten basic facts in the second column of table 1 summarize in somewhat specific form the same thinking that goes on when a person counts by ones correctly and meaningfully. When setting her table for guests, the hostess (or a helper) may take plates from the shelf one by one, in which case she counts, "1, 2, 3, 4, 5, 6, 7, 8," as she adds each successive plate to those removed from the cupboard. As she places each plate with those already counted, she is really adding $1+1=2$, $2+1=3$, $3+1=4$, $4+1=5 \ldots 7+1=8$. Probably she does not take the plates down one at a time; she may take down an estimated group, by counting find that she has 7 plates, and then place 1 more plate on the table as she adds "$7 + 1 = 8$." A generalization about all the facts in which 1 is added to another number might be stated: *Adding 1 to another number is the same as counting up 1.*

Another generalization about a set of basic addition facts, also based on

[9] The method by which addition facts are learned or taught may influence difficulty ratings to an appreciable degree. See Esther J. Swenson, "Difficulty Ratings of Addition Facts as Related to Teaching Method," *Journal of Educational Research* **38:**81-85, 1944.

counting, depends for its meaning on counting by twos. Let us say that the plates in the preceding example were taken out of the cupboard two at a time. The housewife would count, "2, 4, 6, 8." She would really be adding: $2 + 2 = 4$, $4 + 2 = 6$, $6 + 2 = 8$. Knowing how to count by twos is a large part of competence in adding 2, provided the relation of counting and adding is understood by the "counter."

Addition facts are related to counting in the number line diagrams of figures 24 through 26. The same sort of dia-

Dramatization: Perhaps the schoolroom floor is covered with square tiles. The children decide to use these squares to represent city blocks. A child representing Joe walks along one of the lines between rows of tiles and steps off 1, 2, 3, 4, 5 "blocks." The same child or another one representing James steps off the next block to "James's house." He counts merely "5" for the intersection at Joe's house and then "6" for the intersection at James's house.

The teacher might ask if anyone could draw a picture on the chalkboard to show both the problem and the solution. Figure 24 is one such drawing.

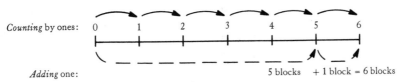

Counting by ones: 0   1   2   3   4   5   6

Adding one: 5 blocks   + 1 block = 6 blocks

Figure 24. Adding One on the Number Line.

gram might be made for any addends, two or more. These have only two addends, because they deal with basic facts. Counting is indicated by the numerals on the number line. Adding is indicated by the broken arrows and the horizontal addition algorism accompanying them.

When number lines are introduced to children, they should come in as a representation of a problem situation. To begin with, it is a good idea to have a dramatization of the addition intervening between the presentation of the problem and the number line just to make sure that the number line is a representation of experience, not a separate and unrelated exercise. Later, children will easily go directly from the problem to the number line and eventually of course handle the whole solution on an abstract basis.

Problem: Joe lives 5 blocks from school. His friend James lives on the same street 1 block farther from school. How far from school does James live?

The numbers being added correspond to segments of the line; they represent distances marked off in equal units. (In fig. 24 the arrows are broken and curved to differentiate them from the number line itself, but the actual units being added are those on the number line, which are exactly equal one to another.) The first addend in figure 24 is shown by the long broken arrow from 0 to 5. Notice that the numeral "5" comes at the end of the first arrow and at the beginning of the second one. This is where Joe lives, 5 blocks from school and at the beginning of the 1 more block that James has to go to get home. The second addend (1 block) is shown by the second broken-line arrow. The sum is the total distance marked off by both arrows; its value is also indicated by the numeral "6" at the end of the second arrow.

From the very beginning of the use of number lines with children it is important to notice the point made above, that it is the distances between points rather than the points on the line that represent the addend values. It is these distances that are being counted off on the line. And also, the line begins with 0, not with 1. The 0 is not always written in as in figure 24; if it is not written in, the numbering should begin with "1" at the *end* of the first *segment*.

Teachers will find many uses for a number line painted on the chalkboard. Having it there more or less "permanently" will make it more readily usable, and it will probably be a more accurate line than one that is hurriedly drawn for use on a single occasion.

More than one number fact can be shown on the same line, as in figure 25.

Problem: Susan is 7 years old and her brother Bill is 8 years old. Their parents have promised them that two years from now they will each receive a bicycle. How old will Susan be then? How old will Bill be?

tion facts shown on the same number line. See figure 26.

Problem Situation: The children might play store. As a variation of the usual buying and selling, a 1¢ sale might be proposed. Items with prices all the way from 1¢ to 9¢ (regular prices) might be on sale, the question being how much two items of a kind would cost at a 1¢ sale, when a second item of the same kind is sold for "1¢ more." As the price for two of a kind is given for each item (in random order) a child could indicate the "adding 1¢" process on a long line on the chalkboard. After all the possible facts have been shown, the line would look like figure 26. The same facts could be shown in horizontal fashion; a vertical line is given to indicate that vertical position is as acceptable as the more frequently seen horizontal one.

After such a line has been completed in relation to a problem situation, the teacher might ask the children to look

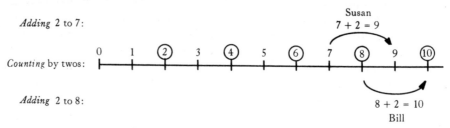

Adding 2 to 7:

Counting by twos:

Susan
7 + 2 = 9

Adding 2 to 8:

8 + 2 = 10
Bill

Figure 25. Adding Twos on a Number Line.

In figure 25 only one arrow is used for each addition. Instead of drawing an arrow for Susan's present age of 7 years, it was assumed that "7" marked the end of that number of years. The process of counting up 2 years (or adding 2 years) is shown by the arrow above the number line, beginning at Susan's present age of 7 years and ending at her age 2 years hence, 9 years. The same process is shown below the line for Bill's ages now and 2 years from now.

When children understand the uses of a number line to show addition facts, the relation between adding and counting can be emphasized by a *series* of addi-

at the line (fig. 26) from bottom to top, first reading the addition facts at the right and then merely giving the sums for those facts. She might point to the sums (*on the* line, not within the algorisms) in succession as the children read them in order.

Some child might volunteer the idea, "It sounds like counting." If not, the teacher might well ask, "What does it sound like?" She might further ask, "Counting by ones or counting by twos or how?" Obviously, giving the sums from bottom to top of figure 26 "sounds like counting by ones." This very easily leads to the generalization that "when

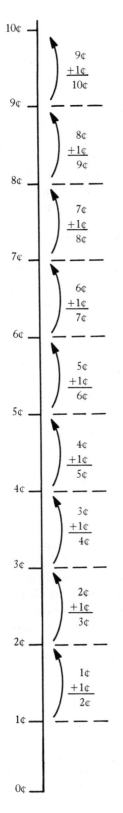

you add one, the answer is the next higher number," or "when you add one, it's like counting up one," or "adding is like counting; so if you add 1, you count up 1." The children's own wordings of the idea are important—much better than a dictated statement, which may or may not be a generalization that the children have derived from their experiences with number. It is not *their* generalization unless *they* have done the generalizing.

Deriving generalizations about sets of number facts is heavily dependent on children's prior experiences. An example of this is the relation of previous counting experiences to the development of a generalization about the addition facts that involve "adding 2."

If "adding 2" is to be related to "counting by 2," practice in counting by twos is of course important. Most primary-grade teachers do give children practice in both rational and rote counting by 2; but this is usually restricted to even numbers. Counting by 2 should include odd numbers as well; the sequence "1, 3, 5, 7, 9" is just as truly counting by twos as is "2, 4, 6, 8, 10." If the boys and girls are eventually to see that "adding 2 is like counting by 2," they cannot generalize to all addition facts with 2 as an addend unless they have done both odd and even counting by 2.

Opportunity for such practice is prevalent enough that it can be worked in naturally in the day's activities. Children distribute books and other materials. The teacher gets 1, then each of four children get 2 each—1 for himself and 1 for another pupil. The counting goes: 1, 3, 5, 7, 9. The children are playing a game on the playground in which the teacher sounds a signal every 2 minutes; the counting starts at 5 minutes past 10. The counting goes: 5, 7, 9, 11, 13, 15.

Figure 26. Adddng Ones on a Number Line.

Pictures are arranged on the bulletin board with 1 at the top and 5 groups of 2 pictures each at various places on the board. They may be counted: 1, 3, 5, 7, 9, 11. Children are lined up for a marching song. They have a leader in front followed by couples. To count the children, they may count: 1, 3, 5, 7, 9, 11, 13, 15, 17. Opportunities for even counting are still more common (counting pairs; counting couples; counting ears, eyes, hands, feet); practice with even counting by 2's should be practiced as much as necessary but not to the exclusion of odd counting by 2's.

Any of the situations mentioned in the preceding paragraph may serve as background for developing an "adding-2" generalization. The marching captain may come to the front of the room, followed by the first "couple" of children. Another child may be asked to write on the board the addition fact that has been acted out. He writes:

$$1 + 2 = 3 \quad \text{or} \quad \begin{array}{r} 1 \\ +2 \\ \hline 3 \end{array}$$

(If he writes "$2 + 1 = 3$," the teacher may indicate that he is not wrong but ask him to start with the single child in writing the number fact; this is necessary if the "adding 2" idea is to be emphasized.) Another "couple" of children join the marching column; another child writes that addition fact ($3 + 2 = 5$). This procedure is repeated until on the chalkboard the children have written:

$$\begin{array}{ccccc} 1 & 3 & 5 & 7 & 9 \\ +2 & +2 & +2 & +2 & +2 \\ \hline 3 & 5 & 7 & 9 & 11 \end{array} \quad \text{OR} \quad \begin{array}{l} 1 + 2 = 3 \\ 3 + 2 = 5 \\ 5 + 2 = 7 \\ 7 + 2 = 9 \\ 9 + 2 = 11 \end{array}$$

The 11 children then may be counted, beginning with the leader and counting by 2. The relation of the counting to the sums on the chalkboard may be noticed by the children or brought out by the teacher through questioning. If it does not seem to "ring a bell" with the children, the teacher lets it drop for the time being. Maybe they are not quite ready to "get the point." She may proceed instead to even counting by 2, asking that the marching column be counted from the end of the line to the beginning, with number facts being recorded to correspond to the counting. She may have the leader do the counting, leaving out himself. So the blackboard will come to have another set of adding-2 facts, this time with even numbers emphasized throughout. (The work with even numbers might precede that with odd numbers.)

$$\begin{array}{cccc} 2 & 4 & 6 & 8 \\ +2 & +2 & +2 & +2 \\ \hline 4 & 6 & 8 & 10 \end{array} \quad \text{OR} \quad \begin{array}{l} 2 + 2 = 4 \\ 4 + 2 = 6 \\ 6 + 2 = 8 \\ 8 + 2 = 10 \end{array}$$

If further experiences are needed by the children to develop the generalization, number lines might be used, preferably drawn by the children. Some possible ones are shown in figure 27.

The basic facts for "adding 1" and "adding 2" are particularly suited to development in relation to counting because: counting by ones and counting by twos is so commonly practiced; these addends are small enough to be readily manageable as counting intervals; and several "adding-1" or "adding-2" facts can be placed in succession on a relatively short number line. With larger addends, the representations of the facts must either overlap (which confuses the picture) or else be extended beyond the basic facts.

While discussion of "adding 1" and "adding 2" as generalizations based on counting has been limited to the basic

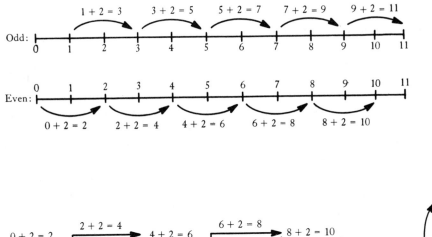

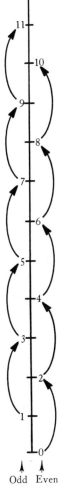

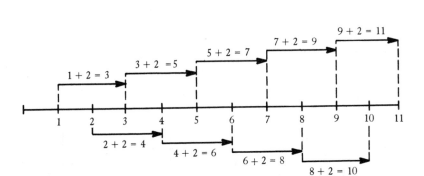

Figure 27. Various Ways of Showing the "Adding Two" Generalization on Number Lines.

facts, one of the extra "dividends" of teaching such generalizations is that they apply to any addition of 1 or 2, no matter the size of the other addend. A child may state the generalization for "adding 2" as he sees it thus: *When you add 2, you skip one number going up.* This generalization applies as truly to 25 + 2 = 27 as to 5 + 2 = 7. In "adding 2" you do "skip" 26 in one case and 6 in the other case. This general applicability of understood generalizations carries their value beyond basic addition facts.

BASIC FACTS AS REGROUPING

All addition is a matter of regrouping in the sense that two or more groups (represented by the addends) are grouped together to give a sum that is the composite of the original groups (or of groups that match the original groups in one-to-one fashion). For example, Jim has 4 marbles in one pocket and 5 in another; he puts them together (adds them) to make a new group (sum) of 9 marbles. Basic facts that have sums of more than 10 represent grouping in this same way and in another way as well. Our positional number system demands another kind of regrouping for all basic facts with sums over 10—that is, for sums larger than our base.

Let us suppose that Carl has 4 marbles in one pocket as does Jim, but in his other pocket he has 9 marbles. Carl combines (adds) his marbles and now has a new total group of 13 marbles made up of the original groups of 4 and 9, respectively. We may consider the new group as being composed of 13 ones or 13 separate marbles. It would also be correct to say (and our notational system does say) that he now has a group of 1 ten and 3 ones. Any two-digit sum for a basic addition fact is an expression of this particular meaning of regrouping, the regrouping by base and place. The size of the new standard group or collection is ten because that happens to be our number base. The place notation says that Carl now has a group of ten marbles and a group of three marbles. The word name for this sum is "thir-teen," which means "three and ten." The written notation is 13, which means 1 ten and 3 ones. Therefore, the number fact 4 + 9 = 13 really is a statement that "a group of 4 and a group of 9 are equal to a group of 10 (or 1 ten) and a group of 3." Written another way, 4 + 9 = 10 + 3. See figure 28. Thirty-six of the basic facts can be interpreted in this way. To do so not only adds meaning to those facts but also lays a foundation for later phases of addition that require similar concepts of regrouping by base and place.

The thirty-six basic facts that fit this pattern are:

2 + 9 = 11	5 + 7 = 12	6 + 9 = 15	8 + 3 = 11	9 + 2 = 11
3 + 8 = 11	5 + 8 = 13	7 + 4 = 11	8 + 4 = 12	9 + 3 = 12
3 + 9 = 12	5 + 9 = 14	7 + 5 = 12	8 + 5 = 13	9 + 4 = 13
4 + 7 = 11	6 + 5 = 11	7 + 6 = 13	8 + 6 = 14	9 + 5 = 14
4 + 8 = 12	6 + 6 = 12	7 + 7 = 14	8 + 7 = 15	9 + 6 = 15
4 + 9 = 13	6 + 7 = 13	7 + 8 = 15	8 + 8 = 16	9 + 7 = 16
5 + 6 = 11	6 + 8 = 14	7 + 9 = 16	8 + 9 = 17	9 + 8 = 17
				9 + 9 = 18

of regrouping for all basic facts with sums over 10—that is, for sums larger than our base.

Let us suppose that Carl has 4 marbles in one pocket as does Jim, but in his other pocket he has 9 marbles. Carl combines (adds) his marbles and now has a new total group of 13 marbles made up of the original groups of 4 and

Nine more facts have sums of exactly 10. An adult might view these as being easier than those with sums over 10. For children, probably the larger-than-10 sums are more helpful in the development of the concept of regrouping according to the base, since they have two groups in the new grouping as well as the original one.

Children who have really understood the meaning of the "teens" numbers have little difficulty in developing this concept. Their understanding should encompass both the meaning of the words and the written number symbols for the "teens." They should be thor-

Situations such as these might be presented:

Bess has 6 pennies and she earns 7 more pennies. If she wants to put 10¢ in her dime bank, what should she do?

Johnny buys a 6¢ pencil and 7¢ worth of candy. He spent a dime and some pennies. How many pennies?

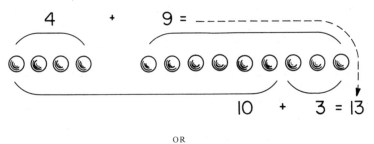

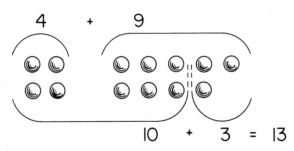

Figure 28. A Basic Addition Fact Shown as Regrouping by Base and Place.

oughly familiar before this point with these ideas, for example, that "fourteen" means "four and ten" and that "14" means "1 ten and 4 ones." If the teacher finds that her pupils do not have these ideas well in hand, she should not attempt to develop the more complex set of ideas represented by: $9 + 5 = 10 + 4 = 14$. Instead, she should work on establishing the meanings of the numerals from 11 through 18.[10]

Assuming basic understanding of the "teens" numbers, a teacher can use or devise many situations in which it will make sense for children to regroup two addends into a ten and another group.

[10] The meaning of 19 will usually be taught along with other "teens." It is omitted above because no basic addition fact has that sum.

Children should be encouraged to work out answers in as many ways as they find helpful and interesting. Particular facts to be practiced can easily be introduced by varying the numbers in the problems. *After* practice with such ideas, teachers might lead into the writing of the decimal-grouping idea (6¢ + 7¢ = 1 dime and 3 pennies = 13¢). At that point it will have much more value than if it had been dictated as a form with blanks to be filled.

LEARNING BASIC ADDITION FACTS

BY ASSOCIATION AND COMMUTATION

The commutative rule states that the order of the addends does not affect their sum; so we have here a big help in organizing the basic addition facts for study. If a child has noticed that "adding 1 is the same as counting to the next higher number," he has a scheme (pattern) for remembering 10 basic addition facts. If he also knows that "you can turn the numbers around and it won't change the sum," he therein has the clue to 9 more basic addition facts in which another number is added to 1 rather than 1 being added to the other number. These two basic ideas, then, tie together for the learner a set of 19 different basic addition facts. (The same holds true for the "adding-2" set of facts, with their reverses.) The reverse statements of basic facts still need practice, but the commutative law is very helpful in reducing the learning

task as well as in giving practice in the application of a law that will have many future applications for the learner.

The addition table shown in table 2 is an easy reference guide in which the commutative law's effects stand out rather clearly. The only addition facts that do not have reverses (0 + 0 = 0 through 9 + 9 = 18) are shown diagonally from top left to lower right. They serve to separate on the chart two reverse sets of basic addition facts. The "doubles" on the diagonal line plus either of the triangular sets (upper right or lower left of the chart) show sums for all the basic combinations; they represent 55 basic addition facts. Either set of 55 can be built up to the full 100 by application of the commutative law.

Addends↓→	0	1	2	3	4	5	6	7	8	9
0	0	1	2	3	4	5	6	7	8	9
1	1	2	3	4	5	6	7	8	9	10
2	2	3	4	5	6	7	8	9	10	11
3	3	4	5	6	7	8	9	10	11	12
4	4	5	6	7	8	9	10	11	12	13
5	5	6	7	8	9	10	11	12	13	14
6	6	7	8	9	10	11	12	13	14	15
7	7	8	9	10	11	12	13	14	15	16
8	8	9	10	11	12	13	14	15	16	17
9	9	10	11	12	13	14	15	16	17	18

Read as follows: Find the row beginning with "4."
    Find the column with "3" at the top.
    Follow that row and that column to their meeting, where the sum "7" is shown.

Table 2. Addition Chart for Basic Facts.

(If zero facts are not included among the basic facts, each set of 45 can be built up to the full 81 in the same way.)

Table 2, incidentally, is strictly a summary-type table. So far as elementary school children are concerned, it should not be presented to them ready-made. They can learn a good deal by building it for themselves. After they have been exposed in one way or another to all the facts, the building of the facts into a reference table is an interesting challenge for the more able and an aid to learning for the less able. And also, some children will see as they study the table some relationships among addition facts that they have not previously noted.

The associative law states that addends may be grouped in any manner without affecting their sum. While this law is usually considered as applying chiefly in additions involving three or more addends, it also applies when either or both of the two addends are thought of as sums of still smaller addends. In adding 5 potatoes and 8 potatoes, for example, a child might think of the 8 potatoes as being made up of subgroups of 5 potatoes and 3 potatoes. If he does not know the number fact "5 + 8 = 13" at the automatic level, he may think instead: $5 + 5 + 3 = 10 + 3 = 13$.[11] The finding of basic fact sums by "building tens" is a frequently used technique discussed earlier. While automatic mastery of basic facts is the ultimate objective, such manipulation of addends is strictly "legal" by the laws of addition.

Teachers must judge carefully how long a child should be allowed to derive sums for basic addition facts by such a procedure. What seems to an adult to be "a long way around" may at certain

levels of development actually be a "shortcut" to the sum. Children should not, however, be allowed to go on indefinitely at this level; if they seem to cling to it longer than seems necessary, the saving of time in learning the direct fact "5 + 8 = 13" should be emphasized and demonstrated.

BASIC ADDITION FACTS AND OUR DECIMAL SYSTEM

Mention has already been made of the interpretation of basic facts with sums over 10 as being a regrouping into 1 group of ten and a smaller group of ones. The reference to "building tens" in the preceding section is also particularly helpful because of our decimal, place-value notation system. (If we had a base of eight, grouping by eights would be as helpful as grouping by tens is in a decimal system.) Further examples of utilization of decimal-system characteristics in the organization of basic facts are worth considering.

The meaning of the "teens" numbers is basic to understanding the basic facts with sums of 11 through 18, as in the relations expressed thus: $8 + 7 = 8 + (2 + 5) = (8 + 2) + 5 = 10 + 5 = 15$, previously discussed. The meaning of the numbers from 11 through 18 is equally important in developing a very useful generalization for the facts designated as "adding-9" facts: *When 9 is added to another number, the sum is 1 less than if 10 had been added to the same other number.* The usefulness of this generalization is apparent to any shopper who has added the prices of a 27¢ article and a 9¢ article like this: "27, 37, 36" (first adding 10¢, then subtracting 1¢). How much easier this is than: "27, let's see, 7 and 9 are 16, remember the 6, now 20 + 10 = 30, 30 + that other number I was going to remember (I'm not sure but I think it was 6), 30 + 6? = 36?"

---

[11] In typical algebraic form, the complete process would be expressed: $5 + 8 = 5 + (5 + 3) = (5 + 5) + 3 = 10 + 3 = 13$.

The sums of 10 and the one-digit numbers 1 through 9 are not of course included in the basic addition facts, but the meaning of the numbers 11 through 19 should certainly include the concept that 11 = 1 ten and 1 one, 12 = 1 ten and 2 ones . . . 19 = 1 ten and 9 ones. From that understanding the addition form of stating the same idea is a simple step: 10 + 4 = 14. If addends can be reversed without changing the value (commutative law), 4 + 10 must have the same sum as 10 + 4, or 14. If 4 + 10 = 14, then 4 + 9 = 1 less than 14, or 13. Stated more concisely:

$$4 + 9 = 4 + (10 - 1) = (4 + 10) - 1$$
$$= 14 - 1 = 13.[12]$$

The "adding-9" facts, particularly those with larger sums, are much more easily learned by establishing this relationship to "adding 10." Why 9? Why in relation to 10? In our number system, the symbol for "10," which we read "ten," means a collection of ten, the next number above nine on the number scale. That is why. The number "9" is next to the base value, so computations involving 9 can be facilitated by recognition of its immediate proximity to the base number value. If we had a base of six in our number system, the symbol "10" would mean 1 six and 0 ones. In that case we could use for "adding 5" the same generalization used here for "adding 9." Except for the original combination, the numerals would be the same, as shown below. The meanings would vary to fit the base being used:

Base Ten: $4 + 9 = 4 + (10 - 1) = (4 + 10) - 1$
$= (10 + 4) - 1 = 10 + (4 - 1)$
$= 10 + 3 = 13$

Base Six: $4 + 5 = 4 + (10 - 1) = (4 + 10) - 1$
$= (10 + 4) - 1 = 10 + (4 - 1)$
$= 10 + 3 = 13$

The two presentations above have identical symbols for the sums as well as for the statement of the calculations, but it is not true that the sums are the same. The sum for 4 + 9 when the base is *ten* = 1 *ten* and 3 ones. The sum for 4 + 5 when the base is *six* = 1 *six* and 3 ones.

Introduction of the preceding discussion does not imply that all elementary school children will be expected to understand or to work out on their own the above place-value ideas as applied to other bases than ten. Teachers who really understand base and place should be able to do so, and many children who learn about base and place value and practice them through their early school number experiences will be able not only to follow such a discussion but also to work out similar statements for other bases. This is an excellent activity for the more mature thinkers in the arithmetic class.

Typical elementary school children (third grade or earlier) can develop a generalization for "adding 9" to fit all the basic addition facts that include 9 as an addend, but appropriate settings must be used and skillful guidance given. One teacher's way of developing this generalization is described below.

Miss Jones and her pupils had used long, narrow blocks of wood that they grouped as tens and ones in developing various addition and subtraction facts (ten "one-blocks" being stacked together and fastened with a rubber band to form a "ten-block"). Therefore, the children were already adept at grouping and regrouping the blocks. Some of the children had been using the blocks to work out sums for such combinations

---

[12] Obviously, subtraction is involved in the reasoning here. Thinking of 9 as "1 less than 10" is a subtraction (counting-backward) relation, as is the thought of 9 as "10 − 1." Persons who deal with the generalization above will surely understand these points even though they have not been specifically discussed to this point in this chapter.

as: 4 + 9; 9 + 8; 6 + 9; and 9 + 5. As is often the case, the learning of the sums for these combinations tended to become somewhat slower and more difficult as the size of addends became larger. (For example, it was more difficult to learn the sum of 4 + 9 than of 4 + 5.)

Miss Jones arranged blocks on a table in front of the children, as shown in figure 29. She asked, "What addition combination have I shown here? The

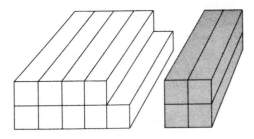

Figure 29. Addition Combination: 9 + 4.

children promptly replied, "9 + 4."

The teacher then moved only one block from the group of 4 blocks, as shown by the arrow in figure 30. She asked as she did so, "Now what addition combination do we have?" One of the children said, "Now it's 10 + 3." Miss Jones went on, "But what is another name for 10 + 3?" The children had had plenty of practice with "teen" number meanings and recognized that the answer was thirteen.

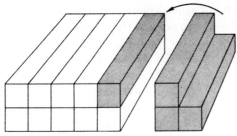

Figure 30. Addition Combination: 10 + 3.

Other combinations including 9 as one addend were similarly demonstrated, first by the teacher and then by

the children as they "got the idea" of moving 1 of the blocks from the other addend to build the group of 9 into a group of 10. After several such addition facts had been worked out, Miss Jones asked the boys and girls to write out records of what they had done, such as: 9 + 4 = 10 + 3 = 13.

Miss Jones: Can anyone tell what we have been doing in all these facts for adding 9?
Some of the answers were:
John: We changed the 9 to a 10, and we always made the other number 1 less.
Al: The sum of 9 and another number is always 10 and 1 less than the other number.
Ellen: We make the other number 1 smaller than it was and put it with the 10 that we built out of the 9 and that 1 we moved.
Bess: I see all that but I think of it this way—when you add 9 to another number, it's like adding 10 and backing up 1.

While none of these statements could pass as an ideal statement of the generalization, to each child his statement expressed a dawning relationship between "adding 9" and "adding 10."

Other procedures for developing the same idea might include: (1) buying two items, one costing 10¢ (1 dime) and the other any one-digit amount; finding the sum; then buying the same items but with the 10¢ items marked down to 9¢; noting that adding 9¢ gives a sum that is 1¢ less than if 10¢ had been added; (2) adding 9 on an abacus by adding 1 bead at a time; then doing it a "quick way" by adding 1 bead on the ten rod and removing 1 bead on the ones rod; (3) adding ten on a number line; then "backing up" 1 unit to show adding 9. Which of these or other procedures is most appropriate depends on children's backgrounds and the teacher's facility in the use of each procedure.

Since the zero concept is such an important key to the operations of our notational system, a generalization for "adding 0" is surely in order. Reference has already been made to the inclusion or exclusion of "0 facts" from the basic addition facts. The position has been taken that these are basic facts but that they are not usually needed until learners face the addition of two-place or larger numbers involving zero; e.g., $34 + 20 = 54$ uses the zero fact "$4 + 0 = 4$" in the ones place. No matter when the zero facts are introduced, they can well be generalized under a single statement: *When another number and zero are added, the sum is the other number.* Most elementary arithmetic books use a score-keeping situation to introduce the zero addition facts because it is one of the few natural situations for recording and adding a zero with other one-digit numbers. The 0 is needed in keeping a baseball score for each inning; it "holds the place" here not in the usual mathematical sense of place value but in the sense that it indicates that the team did have its inning and made no runs. This 0 is added along with other scores, but children will easily see that it "makes no difference" so far as the sum is concerned. The sum of the other numbers is the same, whether zero is added in or not. It represents *no score;* so it does not change the total score. When the team made no runs during the inning, they did not change the game score. The development of the "adding-0" generalization is easy during a discussion of such a situation.

GENERAL INTERDEPENDENCE OF
BASIC ADDITION FACTS

Many people now living remember the days when each and all of the basic addition facts were considered as quite separate and distinct entities. Textbook writers took great pains not to run the risk of making it easy for children to associate one fact with another and were very careful not to introduce on the same page any two facts that might be readily related to each other by the children. For example, presenting $2 + 4 = 6$ and $4 + 2 = 6$ on the same page would have been considered very undesirable. Fortunately, that position has gone the way it deserved to go.

The facts in which both addends are the same are often called the "doubles." (See shaded squares in table 2.) The relative ease with which they are learned (in comparison with other facts with equal-sized sums) is well known. Perhaps the frequency of use of these facts may have something to do with this; perhaps they just attract particular interest and attention by their symmetry as combinations. Be that as it may, their relations *to one another* are sometimes ignored. Noting that *the sum of each double is two more than the sum of the preceding double* or that *saying the sums of the doubles in order is like counting by twos* is worth some attention by learners who have not noticed this relationship. Applying the laws of association and commutation, one might express the adding of the "6 double" by relating it to the "5 double."

$$6 + 6 = (5 + 1) + (5 + 1) = (5 + 5) + (1 + 1)$$
$$= 10 + 2 = 12$$

Children will see this relationship if it arises in a situation where it serves their purpose to notice it. Let us say that a child knows the sum of 5 and 5; he is sure of that. He is not so sure about the sum of 6 and 6. He formerly could buy soft drinks for himself and his brother for 5¢ each. On a certain occasion, he comes to the store to buy soft drinks and finds that they now cost 6¢ each. If he does not know the sum automatically, he may reason: "My drink will cost 1¢ more and Tommy's drink will cost 1¢ more. 5¢ + 5¢ = 10¢, so now I'll have to pay 2¢ more than that. 10¢ + 2¢ = 12¢."

The wise teacher will notice such occasions and make an opportunity to guide children into noting that each double is two more than the preceding double or, for that matter, two less than the next larger double as: $4 + 4 = 2$ less than 10, because each 4 is 1 less than 5 and two 5's are 10.

A cluster of facts that were considered to be relatively difficult in the days of routine and isolated drill may be designated as "near-doubles." The larger ones, like $6 + 7 = 13$ or $8 + 9 = 17$ or $8 + 7 = 15$, were usually high on the

than $7 + 7$"; another as "$7 + 3 + 3$." Each is the expression of a correct and helpful relationship, helpful in the early stages of learning the basic addition facts and helpful also in the learner's progress toward automatic recall. Figure 31 is one learner's diagram to show his findings when he "added 1 at a time" to doubles and/or near-doubles. He used blocks in building up the combinations from $2 + 2$ through $9 + 9$, but he used X's to represent those blocks in his diagram. He wrote the number facts at the right to match the diagram for

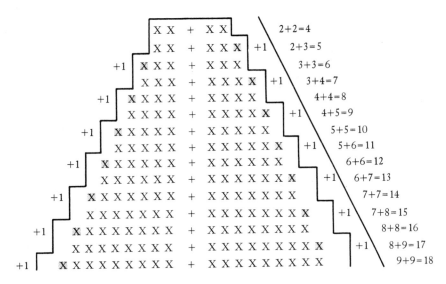

"I added one to one side every time.
I left the other side the same.
The sum got one bigger every time."

Figure 31. Doubles and Near-Doubles.

difficulty listings based on drill procedures for learning. Part of this learning difficulty may be dispersed when they are learned *in relation to* the relatively easy "doubles." For example, $6 + 7$ becomes an easier combination when the learner notices that it must have a sum "one more than the sum of 6 and 6."

Individual learners have their own "pet" relationships. One person may think of "7 and 6" as "1 more than $6 + 6$"; another may think of it as "1 less

each. The diagram should be read line by line from top to bottom. The sentences at the bottom are the boy's summary of the relationship.

RELATION OF BASIC ADDITION FACTS
AND BASIC SUBTRACTION FACTS

The preceding discussion of basic addition facts with a minimum of reference to basic subtraction facts should not be interpreted to mean that their separation is recommended either in teaching-learning procedures or in use after learning. This temporary separation results rather from the attempt to give a thorough coverage of each arithmetic process in succession (in this chapter, addition). Relationships between addition and other processes will be recognized as each later process is developed. Even with that defense, however, no discussion of basic addition facts would be adequate without mention of "fact families," a currently assumed feature of elementary school arithmetic texts.

A "number fact family" for addition and subtraction facts consists of the four related facts that deal with the same composite and the same constituent groups (total group and subgroups). The composite group might be 9; the constituent groups might be 3 and 6. The "family" of facts would then be: $3 + 6 = 9$; $6 + 3 = 9$; $9 - 3 = 6$; and $9 - 6 = 3$. A single arrangement of objects or a single drawing or diagram might demonstrate all four facts. Figure 32 might be used to represent the situation for each of the four problem statements.

Problem Statements

A. Tom has 3 green apples and 6 red apples. How many apples does Tom have?

B. Tom has 6 red apples and 3 green apples. How many apples does Tom have?

C. Tom has 9 apples, some red and some green. If 3 are green, how many apples are red?

D. Tom has 9 apples, some red and some green. If 6 are red, how many apples are green?

Number Facts

$3 + 6 = 9$
$6 + 3 = 9$
$9 - 3 = 6$
$9 - 6 = 3$

OR

3	6	9	9
+6	+3	−3	−6
9	9	6	3

Reminders about Teaching-Learning Method

Teaching method stands or falls in terms of *learning results.* Any considera-

tion of what constitutes good teaching method must relate to ideas and procedures that result in more learning, better learning, and more and better retention of what is learned.

What then are the learning results that we desire children to acquire concerning the addition process and the addition facts? Here are three results which seem to be sought by some adults for children but which are hardly desirable. The accompanying comments indicate why they may not be desirable results.

a. Ability to say quickly "15" when the teacher holds up a flash card on which appears:

$$\begin{array}{r} 7 \\ +8 \\ \hline 15 \end{array}$$

(This is by no means a guarantee that he will know when or how to add when he needs to.)

b. Ability to write answers quickly and accurately to addition combinations set down in miscellaneous order in a workbook or on the chalkboard.

(This is by no means a demonstration of ability to use addition skill in everyday affairs.)

c. Facility in looking at word problems for words like "and," "altogether," or "total" as clues telling when to add the numbers mentioned.

(This is not problem solving; it is only "clue reading.")

The suggestions and illustrations of teaching method that have been included in this chapter do not constitute a complete description of the teaching-learning activities of a teacher and her pupils as those pupils learn the addition process and the basic addition facts. No book could do that except under an extremely limited concept of what the pupils are to learn. If they are really to gain understandings, skills, and ability to use those understandings and skills wherever they apply, they must learn in situations as they arise naturally and freely within the learning environment — not in the restricted confines of a rigidly prescribed formula of either content or method.

What is meant by "situations as they arise naturally and freely within the room activities — in and out of the arithmetic "period." Fourth, she not only uses but she devises natural settings in which to introduce addition concepts and practice. Fifth, she teaches the addition process and addition facts as an integral part of the use of the addition process and addition facts in the solution of problems. The way to get learners to use skillfully what they learn is to teach it *in use*.

Shaded = red
Unshaded = green

Figure 32. Addition-Subtraction Fact Family.

learning environment"? First, this does not mean that the teacher postpones learning for children until some accidental circumstance provides a situation in which she can introduce the basic addition fact "4 + 7 = 11." She knows what she is trying to teach over-all, and she takes responsibility for seeing that appropriate selections are made from the total available content as children are ready to use it and to benefit from its use. Second, she knows that children vary widely in their readiness for specific learnings; she knows also that to force the algorisms of addition facts on all children at the same time is to set up barriers to future learning for many of them. Third, the teacher is always on the alert for opportunities to teach (that is, to help children learn). Her own knowledge and understanding of arithmetic are such that she "sees" more content in everyday classroom activities.

The following reminders are intended as guides to teachers to help them (1) to get the most benefit from teaching suggestions that have been made in this chapter and (2) to develop their own teaching procedures.

1. Be sure you know the *meanings* yourself. Do not be satisfied with teaching forms devoid of meaning.

2. Develop understandings of the process and the facts through their use in problems, both when they are first introduced and for later practice.

3. Remember that skill is more than saying or writing answers. It involves flexibility in application and knowing when to make applications.

4. The writing of addition facts should follow the experiencing of addition facts. Much of the child's early experience with number and number processes requires no writing at all. When he

does write addition facts, he should write them as a record of an activity performed or a thought set down for a purpose.

5. Use every reasonably related aspect of the learning environment as it contributes to the teaching of addition facts — no more than that, no less than that.

6. Add to the learning environment such materials and activities as will facilitate the learning of particular ideas. This is where concrete manipulative aids are helpful, not for themselves but for their constructive use. Different aids serve different purposes.

7. Strive to build continuously the concept of relatedness of the addition process to other arithmetic processes, the relatedness of addition facts to one another, the relatedness of addition facts to their uses.

The suggestions made here for the teaching of addition may be applied to the teaching of any other process in arithmetic. Similar suggestions will not be summarized for subsequent chapters, but they should be assumed by the reader as underlying discussions of method throughout the text.

STUDY QUESTIONS

1. Each X represents 1 toy: XXX XXXXXX. Describe the addition of the two groups of toys in each of these ways: (a) as combination of groups, (b) as union of sets, (c) by using numerals, (d) by drawing a picture or a series of pictures, and (e) by acting it out with manipulative materials.

2. What is the meaning of addition? Is addition independent of any written record? Why or why not?

3. Which of the following rules for addition are fundamental properties of our number system?

commutation	compensation	association
likeness	closure	

4. Demonstrate (with actual objects or with a drawing) the idea of regrouping according to the base ten for each of these basic addition statements:

$$4 + 7 = 11 \qquad 8 + 6 = 14 \qquad 9 + 5 = 14$$

5. Explain this sentence: The expressions "4 + 6," "7 + 3," "10," and "X" are different names for the same number.

6. If you buy two items costing, respectively, $.98 and $.57, how do you know the total cost without using paper and pencil? Write a sentence using numerals to tell how you did the mental calculation. Did you use the same reasoning you would use if you wrote out the addition? Why or why not? Compare notes with someone else to see how he did this exercise.

7. Try out with children some of the suggested teaching procedures reported in this chapter. Analyze for yourself how well they work.

8. Read either or both of these research studies on the teaching of addition facts. What practical applications do you see for the findings?

Thiele, C. L. *The Contribution of Generalization to the Learning of the Addition Facts.* Contributions to Education, no. 763. New York: Bureau of Publications, Teachers College, Columbia U., 1938.

Swenson, Esther J. "Organization and Generalization as Factors in Transfer and Retroactive Inhibition," *Learning Theory in School Situations,* pp. 9-39, University of Minnesota Studies in Education, No. 2. Minneapolis: U. of Minnesota, 1949.

CHAPTER 6

Addition and Larger Whole Numbers

ADDITION OF TWO-PLACE and larger numbers does not require the introduction of any new ideas. Larger numbers can be correctly added — with or without "carrying" — by applying the same ideas used in adding one-digit numbers meaningfully. In fact, correct sums can be derived even without understanding of the fundamental ideas of addition and of our positional number system, provided one knows the basic addition facts and knows where to "set down" the numerals in the written algorisms. This is a regrettable consequence (among many good ones) of a system that is so effectively simple as to be usable without being understood. If the ideas involved were so complex or difficult as to lie beyond the comprehension of the common man (or child, for that matter), this situation could be condoned. That is not, however, the case. The vast majority of children and adults can and should be able to "work arithmetic" correctly and also know what they are doing.

Two-Place Addition and Changing

The application to two-place addition of the basic concepts and principles used previously will not only be helpful in learning sound ideas of two-place addition — with and without "carrying" — but it will also be an excellent test of how well these concepts and principles were really understood in addition of smaller numbers.

BASE AND PLACE CONCEPTS IN

TWO-PLACE ADDITION

The basic addition facts with one-digit sums do not use the concepts of base and place, but those with sums of 10 through 18 do. For example, $6¢ + 7¢ = 13¢$. The "1" in the tens place signifies "1 of the base" (which in our system means "1 ten"); 6 pennies + 7 pennies = 1 "base collection" of ten and a group of 3 pennies.

In two-place addition the collections of ten are used not only in the sum but also in each addend. These base (ten) collections can be added in the same way the ones are added.[1] The basic addition facts are applicable whether ones or tens are being added. How much simpler it is to count (or add) two sizable quantities of pennies if each quantity has already been stacked in tens with only the excess unstacked, as

[1] Strictly speaking, the *tens* are "units" of a particular type just as *ones* are "units" of another type.

115

in figure 33. This same saving of time and effort is represented in the use of the base of ten in Form A, in which 2 pennies and 5 pennies are added to get a sum of 7 pennies and in which 2 *tens* of pennies and 5 *tens* of pennies are added to yield a sum of 7 *tens* of pennies. The separate pennies (ones) and the tens, or base collections, of pennies are added in identical fashion, using the basic addition fact "2 + 5 = 7."

Even greater efficiency is achieved in Form B, in which place-value notation takes care of the values of *tens* and *ones* without the use of those words. The danger in beginning with B is that children may learn to use this algorism without recognizing that "2 + 5 = 7" refers to very different values in its two occurrences in the algorism.

Zero's role as a place holder comes into sharp focus with the addition of two-place numbers. In forms like C, D, and E the zeros serve a place-holder function, which needs emphasis at this point. The three 0's in C all mean "no ones"; they also serve to keep the 2, 4, and 6 *in place* as tens. Similarly, the 0 in Form D and the 0 in Form E mean "no ones" and also keep the "2" in "20" and the "5" in "50" in their proper tens positions.

If the basic facts that include zero have not been studied previously, they should come in at this point. Algorisms C, D, and E use the facts "0 + 0 = 0," "4 + 0 = 4," and "0 + 5 = 5," respectively. If boys and girls understand the meanings of zero, these facts are easy rather than difficult. If they are taught in mechanical fashion,

Form A

2 tens and 2 ones
+5 tens and 5 ones
7 tens and 7 ones

Form B

22¢
+55¢
77¢

Form C

20¢
+40¢
60¢

Form D

34 miles
+20 miles
54 miles

Form E

50 boys
+25 boys
75 boys

they become a special source of difficulty, a situation well-documented by the large amount of discussion given to the "zero difficulties" in the literature of elementary school arithmetic.

Suggestions have been supplied in chapter 5 for the teaching of the unifying generalization for adding zero: *When zero is added to another number, the sum is the other number.* This includes of course the fact "0 + 0 = 0," but it may be wise to take special note that if we have only 0-addends, the sum will always be 0 — no matter how many 0's are added.

Algorism C is an example of "adding even tens," probably the easiest of all two-place addition situations if the children know how to handle the zeros. Teachers will do well to have the children add some tens (or dimes) without reference to any written form. The children will have no difficulty if they are competent in handling the addition facts for the numbers of tens (dimes) being added. If the writing of the algorism *follows* rather than *precedes* such activities, its meaning will be much clearer. If, for example, the children have just combined 2 dimes and 4 dimes to get a total of 6 dimes, they may first write: 2 dimes + 4 dimes = 6 dimes, using the form for any basic addition fact. Or they may write:

2 dimes
+4 dimes
6 dimes

again using words for the "dime" values. The next simple step is to the form of Algorism C. Practice with the addition of "even tens" is commonly placed at the beginning of two-place addition in elementary school texts.

THE RULE OF LIKENESS IN

TWO-PLACE ADDITION

Just as "2 feet" and "4 inches" may be added to give a sum of "2 feet 4 inches," so also "2 tens" and "4 ones" can be added to give a sum of "2 tens 4 ones." In those cases, however, the numerical coefficients are not added and should not be added unless they can be somehow changed into their equivalents with like designations. This is the rule that underlies the necessity for care in adding ones to ones and tens to tens. Only "face values" with the same "place values" can be properly added.

In Form F the "7" and "2" can be added because they both have the place value of "ones." The "3" and "5" can be added because they both have the place value of "tens." But the rule of likeness will not permit the "3" and the "2" to be added to give a sum of "5," since they do not have the same place value. The

shown in Form F, for example, could be correctly added in various ways, such as:

a. 7 (ones) + 2 (ones) = 9 (ones).
    3 (tens) + 5 (tens) = 8 (tens)
    (This is the conventional "pencil-and-paper" method.)

Form F
37
+52
89

b. 3 (tens) + 5 (tens) = 8 (tens).
    7 (ones) + 2 (ones) = 9 (ones).
    (This is often done when calculations are not written, as when a person adds sums of money while shopping.)

c. 37 + 50 = 87
    87 + 2 = 89   OR
    3 tens and 7 ones + 5 tens = 8 tens and 7 ones
    8 tens and 7 ones + 2 ones = 8 tens and 9 ones
    (This is a very common unwritten calculation.)

When the sum in each place is 9 or less, the sequence of steps or the various ways in which the addends are grouped do not matter too much except as practices are established that may help or hinder the learner's later success in adding when changing of ones to tens is necessary.

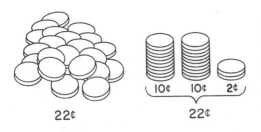

22¢   22¢

Figure 33. Ungrouped vs. Grouped Pennies.

importance of this point is often ignored when the sum in each place is 9 or less. Teachers will do well to emphasize this meaning from the beginning of instruction in two-place addition in order to lay a proper foundation for later addition when the sum of the ones is more then 9 and a place-value change becomes necessary.

COMMUTATIVE AND ASSOCIATIVE LAWS IN TWO-PLACE ADDITION

These two laws of addition allow great freedom in the sequence to be followed in performing an addition and in grouping the addends. The addition example

CHANGING ONES TO TENS

When the sums of the ones is more than 9, an intermediate step becomes necessary in adding two-place numbers. Suppose a shopkeeper is putting away his stock of Christmas cards after the holiday season. Three full boxes and an opened box of 8 cards remain on the shelf; 2 full boxes and 4 extra cards on the counter. The most likely procedure would be for the man to combine the 4 cards with the 8 cards in the opened box on the shelf. This would give a group of 12 cards. He remembers that cards are typically packed 10 to the box; so he puts only 10 in the box (now complete like the other full boxes), leaving 2 cards outside. Combining the 1 newly completed box with the 3 full boxes on the shelf and the 2 full boxes on the counter, he finds that his total supply of that variety of cards is 6 full boxes (tens) and 2 extras (ones).

Unless the shopkeeper is rather "slow with figures" he will do this without writing, except to record the sum on his inventory sheet. For purposes of discussion, it is written out as Form G. Actually, step 4 of Form G shows the complete algorism; the intermediate stages are shown merely to indicate the sequence of steps in the complete algorism.

The same procedure might well be shown with the word "tens" substituted for "boxes" in Form G. A much more efficient algorism is, however, possible with our notational system, since the boxes held 10 cards each and since our system has a base of ten along with place value. See Form H.

The intermediate steps 2 and 3 in Form G suggest one way to record the key intermediate thought step, which is required if a person has to add numbers that yield a sum larger than 9 in the ones position. These two steps are shown separately to distinguish between "changing" and "carrying." While typical arithmetic instruction of the not-too-distant past has made much

of the *carrying* of a numeral to the top of the tens-place column, that is by no means the crux of the matter. The key step is that of *regrouping* or *changing* 10 ones to 1 ten (in this case, changing 12 ones to 1 ten and 2 ones), after which placement of that ten with the other tens is required by the rule of likeness.

Our shopkeeper could, or course, think of his supply as "5 full boxes and 12 extra cards." He may not care to regroup the 12 cards into a full box of 10 and 2 extra cards. The sum "5 boxes and 12 extra cards" would be correct, but it is not the most efficient summary statement of his supply. It is so much simpler for him to record "62" as his sum, letting place-value notation eliminate the need for words as well as reducing the required number of numerals. If he were to write "5 and 12" without words to designate the tens and units, he would have a most deceptive record when he came to refer to it later. How much better for him to write the total in a form that fits our efficient positional system. So also when addition records are written, the intermediate reorganizing step, which we have called *changing* or *regrouping*, is essential for the greatest efficiency in writing out the process and the sum.

So far as the "carried" figure is concerned, it can be recorded in a variety of ways. Some of these do not necessitate "carrying" it away from the "uncarried" figure at all; as a matter of fact, it does not even need to be written anywhere, being "carried," if at all, "in our heads." So ingrained is this term that the study and practice of regrouping ones to make tens (tens to make hundreds, etc.) is more often than not subsumed under a major heading "carrying." If it is not an essential term, where did it come from? Its origin

Form G

STEP 1:

   3 boxes and 8 cards
+2 boxes and 4 cards
―――――――――――――――
               12 cards

STEP 2:

12 cards = 1 box and 2 cards

STEP 3:

 1 new box
   3 boxes and 8 cards
+2 boxes and 4 cards
―――――――――――――――
          ~~12~~ cards
           2 cards

STEP 4:

 1 new box
   3 boxes and 8 cards
+2 boxes and 4 cards
―――――――――――――――
          ~~12~~ cards
  6 boxes and 2 cards

Form H

```
  1
  3 8            3 8
+2 4   OR     +2 4
  6 2            6 2
```

probably lies in the period when the dust or line abacus was in popular and widespread use. If the computation were being done on such an abacus for $28 + 24$, 12 pebbles (or other counters) would have been shown on the "ones" line; ten of these would have been removed from the board and a single counter literally "carried" to the tens line.

Teachers and pupils will no doubt be saying "carry" in this situation for a long time to come; it is hardly an arithmetical sin to do so. Its use is not wrong; it is merely unnecessary or superfluous. What does matter is recognition that the *essential* concept that applies here is the regrouping or changing. It does matter what is said along with the term "carry." When two-place whole numbers are being added, usually the first situation in which children are exposed to the process of changing, it is definitely wrong to teach children that they simply "carry 1." This *is* a pedagogical sin—a sin of omission. It is essential for understanding that the learner knows that he is "carrying 1 *ten*." The first occasion on which one really does "carry 1" comes considerably later when fractional parts (common fractions or decimal fractions) total 1 or more.

While the idea of *changing* is an essential, that particular word is not. For children "changing" or "regrouping" is as good as any terms now in use. For more mature students of arithmetic, "reduction" or "transformation" is a correct term to use. Each of these terms refers to change in *form*, not change in value. The expressions "10 ones" and "1 ten" have the same value, but the value is expressed differently. (In addition, the change is from "10 ones" to "1 ten"; in subtraction, it is from "1 ten" to "10 ones.")

The ideas discussed above are seen in relation to children's learning of those ideas in the following detailed report of a meeting of elementary school teachers. The teachers wanted help on teaching the "carrying" process; notice that the consultant who met with them started instead with the adding of two two-place numbers that did not require changing.

Consultant: You have asked for help in teaching "carrying" to children. I hope you will be patient with me while I go back to lay a foundation for teaching carrying meaningfully. Actually, I prefer to call it changing or regrouping.

Will someone please suggest a typical classroom situation in which it becomes necessary to add two two-place numbers *without* carrying?

Teacher A: What about money? Today in school Robert brought money to pay for some notebook paper and for a ticket to the school play. He insisted on paying separately for each thing. The notebook paper cost 24¢ and the play ticket cost 35¢. I think he felt more secure with the separate amounts.

Consultant: This will make a very good problem for us. Money problems are good for emphasizing place value. The addition facts that are involved in Robert's problem are so simple that some children can get the right sum mechanically, but they may not really be paying attention to place value. It is a good idea to seize on any such opportunity to stress place value; if you do this, children will find regrouping ("carrying") much easier when they come to it.

How did you help Robert with his problem?

Teacher A: Well, to be honest about it, I didn't use it for this purpose. I just let him pay me his 24¢ and then his 35¢.

Consultant: What coins did he give you?

Teacher A: He had only dimes and pennies. I wondered if the money came out of his "piggy bank." He paid me 2 dimes and 4 pennies first, and then he paid me 3 dimes and 5 pennies.

Consultant: I'm going to give you a chance to relive this situation with Robert. Here are some "dimes" and "pennies" (toy money from the dime store). Put the price of the notebook paper on the table the way Robert did it. As you place it on the table, I will represent it on the chalkboard so all can see. I'll write a "d" for each dime and a "p" for each penny.

(Money placed on table
and symbols on board
as shown at right.)   d d   p p p p

Consultant: Now put the coins on the table to pay for the ticket.

(Money placed on
table and symbols
on board as shown
at right.)   d d d   p p p p p

Consultant: Now you are Robert. I'm going to help you add your 2 dimes 4 pennies and your 3 dimes 5 pennies. How can you act out adding them?

Teacher A: Put them all together.

Consultant: How?

Teacher A: Dimes together and pennies together. (Moves 3 dimes closer to the 2 dimes and 5 pennies closer to the 4 pennies.)

Consultant: "Robert," I noticed that you added the dimes first and the pennies last. (We'll come back to that later.) Tell me what the sum is. 4 pennies and 5 pennies = ?

Teacher A: 9 pennies.

Consultant: 2 dimes and 3 dimes = ?

Teacher A: 5 dimes.

Consultant: Was there anything harder about adding the dimes than adding the pennies?

Teachers: No.

Consultant: When you added the dimes and added the pennies, I noticed you pushed them closer together. Here on the board I am just going to draw a line around the groups that you pushed together. That will indicate the putting together (the adding).

Now we are ready to write the algorism for two-place addition. Notice that the real adding, the putting together, comes first. The writing of the record comes after the doing. This is so very important when a new step is being developed.

You tell me what to write. I will write your answers on the board as you give them to me. The children can do the same as you ask them questions about actions they have already performed. You do not need to tell *them* what to write. They can tell *you* what to write, as we will do now. (Algorism written below as answers are given.)

How much did Robert
pay for the paper? Tell
me in dimes and
pennies.------------→ 2 dimes 4 pennies
  How much did he pay
for the ticket?------→ 3 dimes 5 pennies
  4 pennies + 5 pennies
= ?------------------→
  2 dimes + 3 dimes = ?→ 5 dimes 9 pennies

I might write the record another way   24¢
too, like this: 35¢
The latter form is a shorter, quicker   59¢
way of writing the same record. It is just as meaningful as the first form *if* the children have really acted out the situation and if they have seen what the numbers mean in terms of their own prior actions. Do you suppose that sometimes children just add 4 + 5 = 9, 2 + 3 = 5 without thinking of the place values at all?

(General agreement expressed that this
often happens.)

Consultant: Why does this happen?

Teacher D: Probably because teachers don't pay enough attention to place value and don't guide the children so they pay attention to it.

Teacher A: You said you would come back to adding dimes before pennies.

Consultant: Yes, when you put the coins together, you put the dimes together first, then the pennies. In our written form for adding two-place or larger numbers we usually write the sum from right to left.

Teacher E: One of my pupils asked me if he could write the sum for the dimes first and the sum for the pennies place next. I told him he couldn't. There wasn't any carrying involved, and the answer would have been right, but I said it always had to be written from right to left.

(General discussion brought out the fact that it is common practice, when combining and counting sums of money, to count the larger denominations first (because of their greater value) and the other denominations in decreasing order of value. If the algorism is to be an exact record of what was done with the coins, left to right order might be acceptable. Some teachers were worried that the children would become confused later in "carrying" problems if they were allowed to do this.)

Consultant: Writing sums from left to right is not wrong; mental calculations often proceed in that direction. Therefore, I do not think I would tell children it is *wrong* to do it that way. If I thought children would be confused when changing (regrouping) is necessary, I think I would explain that *sometimes* the writing of addition is easier if we learn to do it from right to left and that for that reason it is good to be able to do it that way even when it is not absolutely necessary. For the more advanced learners, I think I might encourage both directions.

But we must get on to the main subject we were going to discuss today. Do you see how all this has a direct bearing on the teaching of changing or "carrying"? Do you see how paying attention to place value in the easier phases of two-place addition lays a foundation for understanding when the sum in any single place is more than 9 and has to be changed?

Teacher G: I see that, but isn't this a very slow way of teaching? Can we take time to have children act out every problem and discuss all about the ones and the tens before they write it down?

Consultant: It *is* slow so far as time spent on developing the concepts is concerned, but not to do so is very likely to prove that "haste makes waste." Plenty of time for developing understanding in the early stages will save a comparable amount of time later on. Children who know what they are doing and why we write the algorisms as we do will be spared much confusion and will need less time for practice. The amount of time to be spent will depend very heavily on the learners and how quickly they grasp the ideas involved. Certainly they should not be held back from making progress to quicker procedures when they are ready for them.

Will someone suggest a problem we might use in discussing two-place addition with "carrying"?

The purpose of including this detailed account is to suggest how important it is to lay a proper foundation for the changing or regrouping idea. The time to discuss "base and place" is not only when changing is necessary but long before that, with adequate review and use of these concepts immediately preceding the introduction of changing.

When regrouping is to be introduced, the choice of a meaningful situation is crucial. It should include some logical reason for changing the ones to tens (or pennies to dimes)—some reason beyond the demands of the written form. The children should see a reason for making the change, whether or not they would need to write out their work in a conventional form.

Such a situation was presented to a class of children by two members of the group.

One morning before school Miss Jones overheard this conversation between Jean and Ella, who were planning a small party for the next day.

Jean: Let's buy a 10¢ candy bar for each girl at the party. We can get them out of the machine at the corner drugstore.

Ella: Let's see how much money we have together. Then we can tell how many girls we can invite. I have 2 dimes and 8 pennies.

Jean: I have 37 cents. Let's just go over after school and put dimes in the machine and see how many candy bars we get. Then we'll invite only as many girls as we have candy bars, counting us.

Miss Jones recognized that here was a good opportunity to introduce the changing process in addition. She asked the girls if they would please tell their situation to the other children in their arithmetic group, a group who were ready for this new step in addition. This is what happened:

Miss Jones: Ella and Jean have told you their problem. Now let's be sure we have all the facts straight before we solve the problem. Ella, will you put your money out on the table where we can all see it?

(Ella put 2 dimes and 8 pennies on the table, dimes at the left and pennies at the right.)

Miss Jones: Now, Jean, will you please put your money on the table too? Keep it separate from Ella's until later.

> (Jean put her 3 dimes and 7 pennies on the table. The dimes were in one stack and the pennies in another.)

John: I wish Jean would put her money out like Ella did. We can see it better that way.

> (This was done. The arrangement is shown diagrammatically below.)

Ella: DIME DIME PENNY PENNY PENNY PENNY
                    PENNY PENNY PENNY PENNY

Jean: DIME DIME PENNY PENNY PENNY PENNY
          DIME   PENNY PENNY PENNY

Miss Jones: How much do the girls have to pay for *each* candy bar?

Children: One dime.

Miss Jones: Now the girls are going to put their money together. What is another way of saying that, Jim?

Jim: Add it.

Miss Jones: Before we do the adding, what could we do so we can separate the money again if we want to? The girls might decide to each keep their own money if they don't have enough for the candy bars.

Ella: We could write down how much we each have.

Miss Jones: That's a good idea. Will you go to the board and write how much you have? Jean, will you write how much you have?

> (Ella wrote: *2 dimes and 8 pennies.* Jean wrote: *37¢.*)

Miss Jones: I see you are writing your money numbers in different ways. You are both right. Boys and girls, do you have any suggestions?

Donna: I think it would be good if Ella would write 28¢ under what Jean wrote and Jean could write hers in dimes and pennies under Ella's. Then we would have the whole thing written two ways.

Miss Jones: That's an excellent idea.

> (The girls did this, forming the beginnings of two addition algorisms as shown below.)

Ellen's Form	Jean's Form
(Ella) 2 dimes and 8 pennies	37¢ (Jean)
(Jean) 3 dimes and 7 pennies	28¢ (Ella)

Miss Jones: Now what should the girls do?

John: Put the dimes together and the pennies together. (This was done.) They have 5 dimes so we know they can buy 5 candy bars. They can put 5 dimes in the machine and get out 5 candy bars.

Ella: And we have more than a dime's worth of pennies.

Miss Jones: How many pennies do you have? Do you know without counting?

Jean: Yes, 7 pennies and 8 pennies are 15 pennies. I know! We can change 10 pennies for another dime. Do you have a dime, Miss Jones?

Miss Jones: Yes, I have. Here it is. You give me 10 pennies and I'll give you 1 dime. What are you going to do with it?

Jean: I'll put it with the other dimes. Now we have 6 dimes. That will buy 6 candy bars from the machine.

Miss Jones: Maybe you can buy more than 6 bars. Can you?

Ella: No, we have only 5 pennies left. That's not enough to change for another dime.

John: Who gets the 5 extra pennies?

Jean: I think Ella ought to get them. She put in more money than I did in the beginning.

The interesting point here is that when children know what they are doing and why they are doing it, they do not need to have forms dictated to them to be rigidly followed with a "theirs not to reason why" approach. Any questions as to where and how to write the sums can be answered by referring to "what we did." The only question is: How shall we write it so it will tell the truth about what we just did?

Miss Jones in the foregoing situation or any teacher introducing her pupils to the algorism for changing should be willing to accept any correct written statement from the children. This acceptance, however, should not be the end of the story. She has a responsibility to help the children arrive at an efficient as well as a correct form. The three correct forms below indicate progress so far as elimination of detail is concerned:

a. 28¢ = 2 dimes and 8 pennies
   37¢ = 3 dimes and 7 pennies
         5 dimes and 15 pennies =
         6 dimes and 5 pennies = 65¢

b. 28¢
   37¢
   ‾‾‾
   65¢

c. ¹
   28¢
   37¢
   ‾‾‾
   65¢

Elimination of detail in written forms is desirable when, and only when, the user does not need the written details to help him in his thinking and recording of the facts. The sensible judgment on this decision is an individual matter with each learner. The teacher should encourage the use of the most efficient form the child can use with understanding and facility.

The reader should take note of the fact that in the classroom report about Ella and Jean, the word "carrying" was not used at any time. It is not needed. The word "change" was used because the changing of 10 pennies for a dime was actually done. In teaching the algorisms for the changing process, the essential term "changing" should be taught. (Some people prefer the term "regrouping," which is also good, but "changing" is better for money problems.) The term "carrying" may or may not be taught; when it is used, its use should certainly be subordinated to the use of "changing" or "regrouping." The writing of the "changed" dime or ten *with the other dimes or tens* is important because of its emphasis on place-value meanings and the rule for like values being combined with like values. When the numeral for the "changed" ten is written, it is a good practice to write it in a slightly different form from other tens for ease of identification when checking the example later. When the writing of this numeral is not needed by the learner, it should be discarded.[2]

A special case of changing in addition is that of the "extended sum".
In Form I the sum is 133. The sum in the ones place is 13 ones, which is changed to 1 ten and 3 ones. The "3" for the 3 ones is recorded at the bottom of that column;

Form I

```
  1
  6 5
+6 8
1 3 3
```

[2] This is a matter not only of learner maturity but also of the situation in which the addition is being done. See p. 136 for an adult use of the "carried" figure.

the "1" for the 1 ten is recorded at the top of the tens column in Form I. (This might have been omitted.) The sum of the tens column is also 13, but this time it means 13 tens. The "13" is recorded at the bottom, but because it occupies two places, it has to extend into the hundreds place, actually representing not only "13 tens" but also a "changed" expression as "1 hundred and 3 tens." This change is the same as that which occurs when a basic addition fact with a sum of 10 or more is written as in Form J. This form really says: 5 ones and 8 ones equal 13 ones, or 1 ten and 3 ones. The sum is extended beyond the place used by the addends.

Form J

```
  5
 +8
 13
```

In adding the numerous combinations of two two-place addends (the addends from 10 through 99), many such extended sums will be encountered. The largest sum will be 198, the sum of 99 + 99. This is another of the algoristic procedures that is so easy to perform correctly that many users of the form never stop to consider that any "changing" in terms of place value has occurred. No numeral is set down as having been "carried," but changing *has* occurred.

Teachers should take care to discuss these situations with their pupils, not only to see that the written form is correct but more fundamentally to see that the form is *correct* and *understood*.

Column Addition and Higher-Decade Facts

COLUMN ADDITION DEFINED

Form K

a	b
2	3
2	5
2	4
6	12

Column addition is really just an extension of the use of basic addition facts to encompass a series of such facts. It is a striking example of the fact that addition is a special kind of counting: regular counting as in Form

K*a* or irregular counting as in Form K*b*. The number lines in figure 34 correspond to the two columns of Form K and demonstrate the contrast between regular and irregular counting.

The longer the columns are, the more apparent it becomes that knowing the basic addition facts on the level of automatic recall is much more convenient and much faster than counting. This should be demonstrated in practice for children who resort to one-by-one counting when faced with a column of figures to be added. The saving of time and effort in adding long columns is the best incentive there is for gaining facility and speed with the basic facts.

Column addition also fits the description of addition in general as being a process of regrouping by combining. The only special feature is that more than two original groups are combined into a new total group or sum. The everyday uses of the combining of more than two groups of things come early in a person's experience. The particular combination of $3+5+4$ may apply to:

3 rabbits, 5 rabbits, and 4 rabbits in three different pens

3 marbles, 5 marbles, and 4 marbles in Jackie's pockets

3 cookies, 5 cookies, and 4 cookies of different kinds

3 pennies earned yesterday, 5 pennies donated by Aunt Clara, and 4 pennies found on the sidewalk

Actually, in the early stages of learning or "figuring out" basic addition facts, a child may have resorted to successive additions of his own accord even though he may not have written out the column algorism. If Tom does not know automatically the sum of 8 pennies and 6 pennies, he may think of it as "8 pennies and 2 pennies, that's 10, and 4 more, that's 14." In more advanced form, this might be written as: $8+6 = 8 + (2+4) = (8+2) + 4 = 10 + 4 = 14$.

NEW CONSIDERATIONS
IN COLUMN ADDITION

Two special features of column addition must be dealt with if it is to proceed

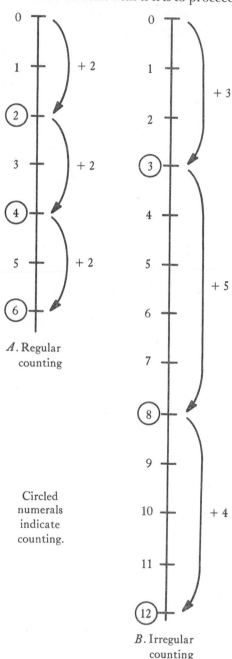

A. Regular counting

Circled numerals indicate counting.

B. Irregular counting

Figure 34. Column Addition as Regular or Irregular Counting on Number Lines.

successfully, namely, the "unseen addend" and "higher-decade facts." In Form L*a* the boldface figures indicate the *unseen addend* "8" and the *unseen fact* "8 + 3 = 11." These "unseens" are not written in the usual form for column addition. They must be "carried in mind" until the next successive sum is secured. The number of such unseen addends and unseen facts depends on the number of addends in the column. There will always be two fewer of these than the total number of addends. See Form L*a* and L*b*. Therefore, the longer the column is, the more "unseen" items must be remembered in the process of arriving at the final sum. Therein lies the major difficulty (experienced frequently even by adults) when adding lengthy columns of figures.

Primary-grade teachers often report the pleasure with which younger children engage in their first experiences with column addition, even preceding the completion of their learning of the basic addition facts. The children seem to enjoy dealing with more numbers in the same example or problem; perhaps it gives them a feeling of doing advanced work because of the greater length of the series of addends. A great deal of practice in column addition can precede the learning of the more difficult basic addition facts. Problems requiring the adding of three or more numbers also occur frequently in the everyday affairs of children; these situations should be used for introduction of the idea of column addition and for practice.

b. Four addends

$$
\left.\begin{array}{l}
2 \\
3 \quad \left.\begin{array}{l} 2+3=5 \end{array}\right\} \\
4 \quad ---\ 4 \end{array}\right\} \left.\begin{array}{l} 5+4=9 \end{array}\right\} \\
2 \quad --------\ 2 \end{array} \right\} 9+2=11
$$

4 addends: 2 unseen addends "5" and "9"
2 unseen facts
5 + 4 = 9; 9 + 2 = 11

When setting up practice exercises in column addition for children who do not know all the basic addition facts, the teacher should use particular care not to give the children a "bad taste" of column addition by introducing previously unlearned facts. For example, the column of addends at the right seems innocent enough in appearance, all addends being "5" or smaller than "5." However, if a child is to add it correctly from top to bottom, he needs to know these facts: 5 + 2 = 7; 7 + 4 = 11; and 11 + 3 = 14. If he adds it from bottom to top, he needs to know: 3 + 4 = 7; 7 + 2 = 9; and 9 + 5 = 14.[3] In this case, the downward addition may be the more difficult since it requires the use of a fact (11 + 3 = 14) that is not even included among the basic addition facts.

$$\begin{array}{r} 5 \\ 2 \\ 4 \\ 3 \\ \hline \end{array}$$

All the above column addition examples except the last involve only the basic addition facts. Only 1-digit numbers have appeared as addends, seen or unseen. Children must soon deal with unseen addends that are 2-digit numbers with facts that go beyond the basic addition facts. Because they are "unseen," these two-place addends some-

---

[3] No research evidence is available to indicate superiority for "adding down" or "adding up." Common practice in elementary school texts is to teach the downward direction for original column addition and the upward direction for checking accuracy of the sum. Hence, both are used. The point here is that different addends are used, and teachers who require children to add in both directions should note what addition facts are required for each example.

Form L

a. Three addends

$$
\begin{array}{l}
2 \\
6 \quad \left.\begin{array}{l} 2+6=8 \end{array}\right\} \quad 8+3=11 \\
3 \quad ---\ 3 \end{array}\right\} \\
\hline
11
\end{array}
$$

3 addends: 1 unseen addend "8"
1 unseen fact
8 + 3 = 11

times slip into column addition examples without either pupil or teacher noticing their presence until the children have to face up to a new and (to them) unexpected difficulty. See Form M, in which the unseen addend "13" and the unseen fact "13 + 5 = 18" appear. Since the basic facts are, by definition, those in which both addends are 1-digit numbers, $13 + 5 = 18$

Form M

$$\left.\begin{array}{r}7\\6\end{array}\right\}7+6=13\left.\begin{array}{r}\\\\\end{array}\right\}13+5=18$$
$$\begin{array}{r}5\\\hline18\end{array}---5\rfloor$$

is not a basic fact. It is a *higher-decade fact*. Column addition makes generous use of higher-decade facts; for that reason, teachers do well to guide children carefully in their learning of these facts as well as the basic addition facts.

HIGHER-DECADE ADDITION FACTS

Higher-decade addition combinations are those combinations which combine a 2-digit number with a 1-digit number. *Higher-decade facts* are those combinations with their sums. Either "13 + 5 = 18" or "5 + 13 = 18" is a higher-decade fact. The higher-decade facts that occur in the column addition process are typically stated with the 2-digit addend first (assuming that only single columns are added). When a fact does happen to be stated with the 1-digit addend first, the typical procedure is to "turn it around" according to the commutative law of addition.

As soon as column addition has unseen addends of 10 or more, higher-decade addition becomes a necessity. As already suggested, even the direction in which one adds a column of figures determines whether such 2-place addends occur. If one adds the column in Form N from top to bottom, no 2-place addends occur, but if one adds it from bottom to top, the unseen addend "12" does occur, as does the unseen combination "12 + 5," necessitating use of the unseen fact "12 + 5 = 17."[4]

Form N

$$\begin{array}{r}5\\4\\8\\\hline17\end{array}$$

There are 810 higher-decade facts if we ignore reverses.[5] From the viewpoint of ease of teaching the higher-decade facts to children, these 810 facts may be classified in three categories instead of two, namely: (1) higher-decade facts with sums that do not complete a new ten (e.g., $24 + 5 = 29$); (2) higher-decade facts with sums that exactly complete a new ten (e.g., $24 + 6 = 30$); and (3) higher-decade facts with sums that complete a ten and extend into the next decade (e.g., $24 + 7 = 31$).

Bridging is a frequently used term applying to the process of going into a new decade. When bridging is shown on a number line (fig. 35) the literal meaning of a "bridge" is easily shown. This may suggest the origin of the term. The "+8" part of the diagram "builds a bridge" across the "20" point on the scale. Children are usually delighted by this graphic representation of the concept of bridging in addition.

ADDING BY ENDINGS

Whether higher-decade facts require bridging or not, the process of deriving their sums is often referred to in arithmetic books for children as "adding by endings." The "endings" are, of course, the digits in ones place, where the focus of attention is placed by that terminology. When the adding of the units

---

[4] One might quibble over the strict interpretations of "unseen combinations" and "unseen facts," since each is partly seen and partly unseen. This is of small importance one way or another.

[5] The 810 are sometimes grouped into the 765 facts that yield 2-digit sums and the 45 facts that yield 3-digit sums.

does not total more than 9, the figure in tens place is not changed; therefore, it is appropriate to place the attention on the ones place, i.e., the "endings." The terminology may not be as accurate when the sum in ones place is 10 or more and a change in the tens figure as well as the ones figure is required. Teachers need to be familiar with the terminology whether or not they use it with children.

2," or "adding 9," he will be much more ready to figure out for himself the sums for "21+1," "29+1," "21+2," "29+2," "21 + 9," or "29 + 9." If he thinks of "adding 1" as "going on to the next larger number," he can add 1 very easily to any two-place or larger number as far as he can count. If he thinks of "adding 2" as "skipping one number as I count upward," he can add 2 very easily to any two-place or larger number

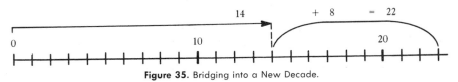

Figure 35. Bridging into a New Decade.

RELATION TO PRIOR EXPERIENCE

What a learner sees in higher-decade addition depends very heavily on his prior experiences with number. If a boy has enjoyed working out basic addition facts in terms of the ten base, this will be a big help to him in understanding and working out for himself the higher-decade facts that require bridging into the next decade. If he has learned to think of the fact "8 + 4 = 12" as meaning "8 + 4 = 10 and 2," it will not be hard for him to think of "28 + 4" as being equal to "30 and 2." If he has practiced the use of number lines, he can draw the one shown as figure 36B almost as easily as the one labeled 36A.

If a child has really grasped the generalizations about "adding 1," "adding

—again as far as he can count. If he thinks of "adding 9" as "going up ten and backing up one," he can add 9 to any two-place number within his understanding of the two-place number and its succeeding decade.

If still another child has really learned "his way around" on the hundred chart, he can work out any higher decade fact first on the chart, next by thinking of relative positions of numbers on the chart, and finally by automatic recall of specific facts.

SUGGESTIONS FOR NEW EXPERIENCES

The amount of new experience needed to make sure that a child does understand the higher-decade facts and the amount of practice he needs before

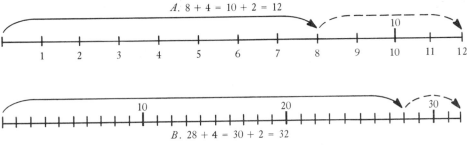

Figure 36. Basic Fact and Higher Decade Fact on Number Lines.

he masters them depend not only on prior experience with basic number facts and with number in general. They depend also on the variety and the quality of experiences provided along with the new concepts.

Beginning with a problem such as the one below, a teacher might provide children with various materials and urge them to see how many ways they could first find and then "prove" their answers to the problem.

Problem: Joe helps down at the Community Center after school. Last night someone put away the tenpins by throwing them all in a box. Joe counted 37. Later he found 7 more. How many tenpins did Joe find? Show how you would prove your answer is right.

The suggestions that follow represent a sampling of possible solutions by different learners or various solutions by the same learner.

Suggestion 1: Draw a picture of the tenpins in place ready for bowling. First there would be 3 sets of pins all set up for play and 7 pins in the fourth position. Another color could be used to draw in the 7 he found. These would finish the fourth set of tenpins and provide 4 more as the beginning of a fifth group.

Suggestion 2: Blocks could be used to represent the tenpins. Each full set would be fastened with a rubber band to set it apart as a "full ten." Three such sets and 7 "loose" blocks would show those in the first box Joe found. Then 7 more "loose" blocks could be grouped with them to make a total of 4 "full tens" and 4 extras.

Suggestion 3: A string of 100 spools could be used. The 37 pins could be shown by pushing 37 spools farther to the left on the string or wire. Another group of 7 could be set apart adjacent to the 37. The "marker" spools that show the end of each set of ten spools would help to show that 3 tens and 7 ones + 7 ones = 4 tens and 4 ones.

Suggestion 4: A hundred chart with movable "tags" or circles could be used. First the child could fill the top three rows and put 7 circles in the fourth row. Then a different color of circles could be hung so as to finish out or complete the fourth row and show 4 in the next row.

Suggestion 5: Tall blocks could be used as if they were tenpins. They could be set up as if for a game of tenpins, as in the suggested picture (suggestion 1).

Whether or not children can manage these and other ways of working out higher-decade facts depends very heavily on how much they have available in the way of simple materials with which to work and how much help they have had in *using* the materials in meaningful ways.

Another problem might stimulate learners to think of other ways to operate in proving their solutions. For instance, if the problem involved money, some children would devise solutions that used play money or other representations of coins.

SUMMARIZING EXPERIENCE ON THE ABSTRACT LEVEL

The amount of such experience that is necessary will vary widely. Eventually, all or almost all children should go on to

A:	4	14	24	34	44	54	64	74	84	94
	+2	+2	+2	+2	+2	+2	+2	+2	+2	+2
	6	16	26	36	46	56	66	76	86	96

B:	5	15	25	35	45	55	65	75	85	95
	+5	+5	+5	+5	+5	+5	+5	+5	+5	+5
	10	20	30	40	50	60	70	80	90	100

C:	6	16	26	36	46	56	66	76	86	96
	+9	+9	+9	+9	+9	+9	+9	+9	+9	+9
	15	25	35	45	55	65	75	85	95	105

higher-decade addition at the abstract level. (Unfortunately, too often they are expected to start at that level, and many of them are forced to memorize the forms without adequate understanding.) For purposes of summarizing their knowledge of higher-decade addition, sets of related facts that emphasize the "adding-by-endings" concept can be very useful. Sample sets are given below, corresponding to the three categories of higher-decade facts discussed on pages 126-128.

The teacher's skill in guiding the discussion of such summary groups and in asking questions directing attention to important considerations influences to a large degree the values derived by children from such summaries. Questions might well include these:

What is alike about all the row A facts in ones place? (Same for B and C.)

Why do you suppose that these additions are sometimes called "adding by endings"?

Look at the top number and the sum for each fact in row A. Look at the tens numbers especially. What do you notice about the number of tens in each fact? (Does it stay the same or change?) (Same for B and C.)

Why does the tens number change in rows B and C? Why does it not change in row A?

If the children have difficulty with answering such questions, they need more help. A hundred chart might be helpful. On it the pattern for each fact in a row (A, B, C) could be shown to be the same no matter where it occurs on the chart. (For example, the pattern of $6 + 9 = 15$ is the same as the pattern for $36 + 9 = 45$; the only difference is the location of the pattern on the hundred chart.)

RELATION OF HIGHER-DECADE
FACTS TO CHANGING

The sum of the higher-decade facts that require the changing of the num-

ber of tens can of course be derived by the procedure recorded in Form O. If a person is to be really proficient in the use of such a fact, he should not have to go through that rather laborious procedure for very long. When a person has to use that higher-decade fact as part of a column addition situation, he may well "lose" all or part of the "unseen" addend while going through the changing procedure. If column addition is to be done with any reasonable degree of speed and accuracy, the person doing the adding must not be tied to the thought processes of a written algorism designed for an entirely different use. The concepts of "adding by endings" and of "bridging" are much more helpful in gaining command of higher-decade addition for use in column addition. Contrast the simplicity of operation of a person who adds the numbers in Form P according to the first method below with the complicated maneuverings of a person using the second method.

Form O

```
 1
34
+7
――
41
```

Form P

```
6
5
8
6
9
7
――
41
```

First Method: 6, 11, 19, 25, 34, 41.

Second Method: $6 + 5 = 11$; $11 + 8 = 19$;

   $19 + 6$ ($9 + 6 = 15$, carry 1 ten) that's 25.

   $25 + 9$ ($5 + 9 = 14$, carry 1 ten) Let's see, how many tens did I have? Oh, now I'm all mixed up — let's just start over!

OTHER USES
OF HIGHER-DECADE FACTS

Higher-decade facts are often introduced in connection with column addition because they are so necessary for proper performance in adding columns of figures. They have other uses as well. First, they are used just as they occur. Buckingham said in 1947: "The life situations which call for adding a one-place and a two-place number are only less common than those which call for the adding of two one-place numbers."[6] Some of these uses have disappeared with the upward trend of prices. "The butcher, the baker, the candlestick maker" have fewer items for sale at 1-digit prices, but one does still frequently buy and pay for (or sell) such combinations of items as a 79¢ toothbrush and a 5¢ pencil; a quart of milk for 27¢ and a candy bar "on special" at 9¢; or a notebook for 74¢ and an eraser for 5¢. To what extent the relative scarcity of 1-digit prices is offset by the advent and increasing use of the sales tax is hard to say. Certainly the adding of the tax to 2-digit prices is an everyday (often many times a day) occurrence. Suffice it to say that higher-decade facts are useful in themselves. Mr. Average Citizen's arithmetic skills are in bad shape if, when he pays 4¢ tax on an 89¢ item, he has no better technique than to think: 89¢ plus 4¢; 9¢ plus 4¢ = 13¢; 13¢ = 1 dime and 3 pennies; 1 dime plus 8 dimes = 9 dimes; 9 dimes and 3 pennies (if he still remembers that figure) = 93¢. Also in bad shape is the salesperson who has to look up the total on a prepared chart.

Another use of higher-decade addition is in multiplication that includes changing. In multiplying 36 by 7, one must change 42 ones to 2 ones and 4 tens. Then the 4 tens must be added to the 21 tens resulting from the multiplication of 3 tens by 7. This oc-

Form Q

4

3 6

x 7

2

curs at the point suggested by Form Q. Not all the higher-decade facts are applicable in this situation, but many of them are. When needed in multiplication,

[6] Buckingham, *op. cit.*, p. 99.

it is highly desirable to have the sums of those facts "at one's fingertips."[7]

RULES OF ADDITION
APPLIED TO COLUMN ADDITION

Column addition affords some of the best illustrations of the application of the likeness, commutative, and associative rules of addition. The rules provide, in fact, the "reasons why" many of the standard column addition procedures "work" in practice. Many a child has been thoroughly grounded in the dictum to "keep the columns straight" in writing out a column addition algorism with little or no attention being paid to why; the rule of likeness is the explanation, of course. Keeping the columns straight is the mechanical means by which like addends are kept together, ones to be added to ones, tens to tens, and so on.

General practice is to add a column from top to bottom and to check it by adding from bottom to top. Since the addends may be combined in any order (commutative and associative rules) and since the combinations used in the opposite directions are not the same, this serves as an excellent check on accuracy. Another application of these rules is that one may add the columns in any order, left to right or right to left. Form R might serve as the written record for different persons who might add the constituent values in quite different orders. Bob might add the conventional way: the ones, then the tens column. Joe might add the tens first, then the ones. Bill might add tens and ones alternately. These three sequences

Form R

1 4

3 2

2 3

6 9

[7] In chap. 10 further suggestions will be made as to which addition facts need special practice preceding their use in multiplication.

are shown on the three number lines of figure 37.

Many people like to group any addends in the same column that have sums of 10, whether they come in direct sequence or not. In Form S the 3 and 7 in the ones column and the 6 and 4 in the same column would be grouped as 2 tens, then the 2 ones added for a total of 22 ones. This is a good technique if the person using it has enough competence and facility with the facts to save time rather than waste it looking for the "10" sums and then lose his place in the column as a whole. This regrouping of addends for the ones column of Form S might be shown thus:

$$3 + 6 + 7 + 2 + 4 = (3 + 7)$$
$$+ (6 + 4) + 2 = 10 + 10 + 2 = 22.$$

This is a clear example of use of the associative and commutative principles for addition.

An interesting algorism that seems to be regaining a lost popularity is that shown as Form T. The sum of the ones is written as a two-figure number at the bottom of the double column; the sum of the tens is written as a second partial sum; then the partial sums are added as are partial products in multiplication. Both commutative and associative explanations defend this procedure. It dispenses with any need for writing the "changed" or "carried" figure at the head of the tens column. The use of partial sums also serves as good background for the use of partial products in later work with multiplication.

Form S

```
2 3
4 6    3 + 7 = 10
5 7
3 2    6 + 4 = 10
2 4
―――
1 8 2
```

Form T

```
2 3
4 6
5 7
3 2
2 4
2 2
1 6
―――
1 8 2
```

CHANGING IN COLUMN ADDITION

Changing of ones to tens is done in exactly the same way in column addition as in two-place addition with only two addends. With only two addends, the number of tens that can be formed from the added ones never exceeds 1 ten, since the highest sum of a basic fact

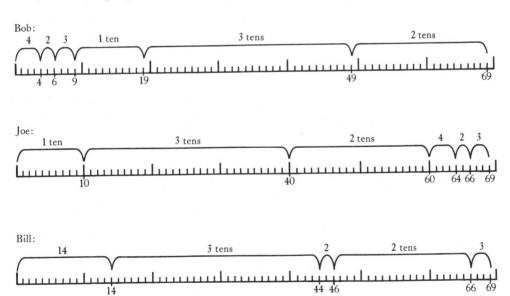

Figure 37. Different Groupings for Column Addition Addends.

is 18. With more than two addends, it is possible to form 2 or more tens, depending on the size and number of terms in the column. Sometimes this changing of 20 ones to 2 tens or of 30 ones to 3 tens needs some special attention, even though the basis for it is the same as in changing 10 ones to 1 ten.

ZERO IN COLUMN ADDITION

Zero is frequently encountered in column addition of two-place or larger addends. It is added just as in two-place addition of two addends, using the same generalization as suggested elsewhere that adding zero and another number does not change the other number. The place-holder function of zero is well demonstrated in column addition and should be recognized.

Addition of Larger Numbers

Assuming the understanding of base and place, there is nothing new about the addition of three-place, four-place, or larger numbers. The addition of these larger numbers follows exactly the same basic principles used with one-place and two-place numbers. The likeness, commutative, and associative rules apply with larger numbers exactly as with smaller ones. The basic addition facts are the same. The only difference is that the facts and the rules are applied to different place values.

Problem: In January Mr. Jones drove 2424 miles in his car. In February he drove 3737 miles. How far did he drive in January and February?

In Form U the boldface numerals to the left of the vertical dotted line are identical to the numerals at the right of that line. The addition process on either side is identical. The addition to the left of the dotted line could be con-

sidered "harder" only insofar as it may be harder to comprehend or visualize the actual distances "thousands" and "hundreds" of miles in contrast to the more readily experienced distances "tens" and "ones" of miles.

Form U

	2	4	2	4 miles
	+3	7	3	7 miles
	6	1	6	1 miles

The basic addition facts used are the same: $4+7=11$; $1+2=3$; and $3+3=6$. The sum "11" in the ones column is changed to "1 ten and 1 one" in exactly the same way that the sum "11" in the hundreds column is changed to "1 thousand and 1 hundred."

As with so many other algorisms, the ease with which they may be handled despite lack of understanding may conceal children's ignorance of what is really being done. To make sure that this is not the case, teachers should occasionally check on learners' comprehension even when they get "right answers" as well as introducing addition of larger numbers in connection with concrete or simiconcrete representations of the actual quantities. This requires starting with a problem.

The choice of a problem for initial introduction of addition of larger place values is more difficult than for smaller numbers because the larger the numbers are, the harder it is to represent them either actually, with concrete representation, or with diagrams. Money problems are about as convenient as any, as in this problem:[8]

Problem: Arthur has $24.35 in his savings account. He deposits an additional $4.75. How much will his new bank balance be?

Some children can solve this problem and handle the algorism with no help

---

[8] The problem used here is not intended as the "next one" after the last-used problem using two-place addition in this chapter. It is merely representative of the treatment of larger addends.

whatsoever. Others may need to be questioned about their procedures and why they are used. Still others may need to have the actual representations at hand as they work through the actions and then set down the algorisms as a record of those actions. Some possible actions with their accompanying algorisms are given below.

Action:

Play money is arranged on the table thus:

Already in bank: 2 $10 bills; 4 $1 bills; 3 dimes; 5 pennies.

New deposit: 4 $1 bills; 7 dimes; 5 pennies.

The 5 pennies and 5 pennies are re-grouped as 10 pennies.

The 10 pennies are changed for 1 dime, which is placed with the 3 dimes and 7 dimes, giving a total of 11 dimes.

Ten of the 11 dimes are changed for a $1 bill; the 1 remaining dime is left by itself.

The newly "changed" $1 bill is combined with the two groups of 4 $1 bills to make a new group of 9 $1 bills.

The group of 2 $10 bills remains unchanged.

The final grouping of money is: 2 $10 bills; 9 $1 bills; 1 dime; 0 pennies.

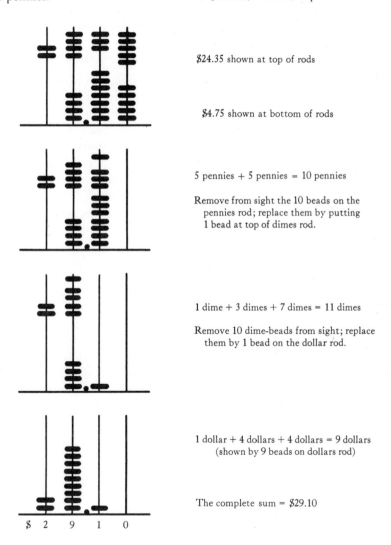

$24.35 shown at top of rods

$4.75 shown at bottom of rods

5 pennies + 5 pennies = 10 pennies

Remove from sight the 10 beads on the pennies rod; replace them by putting 1 bead at top of dimes rod.

1 dime + 3 dimes + 7 dimes = 11 dimes

Remove 10 dime-beads from sight; replace them by 1 bead on the dollar rod.

1 dollar + 4 dollars + 4 dollars = 9 dollars (shown by 9 beads on dollars rod)

The complete sum = $29.10

$ 2 9 1 0

Figure 38. Adding with Changing on the Abacus.

Possible Algorisms:

```
        1          1
2 ten-dollars 4 dollars 3 dimes 5 pennies
+              4 dollars 7 dimes 5 pennies
2 ten-dollars 9 dollars 1 dime  0 pennies = $29.10
        1   1
```

```
   $2 4. 3 5          $2 4. 3 5
   +  4. 7 5          +  4. 7 5
   $2 9. 1 0          $2 9. 1 0
```

Alternate Action (on a more abstract level):

Addition problem solved on the abacus as in figure 38.

Notice the use of the decimal point in two of the algorisms and on the base of the modified abacus. Some people may object to this use with children who have not taken up the subject of decimal fractions. This is hardly a valid objection, since "3 dimes," for example, are not being dealt with here as "3 tenths of 1 dollar" but as 3 whole coins with a certain recognized value. This use in no way detracts from correct fractional concepts dealt with later. In fact, it probably forms an excellent basis for the later work. At this level, the decimal point itself may be introduced to children as merely a marker to separate the dollars and the cents values. This interpretation should be given as soon as children deal with money values of a dollar or more in written form.

The higher level of abstraction involved in the use of the abacus as compared with the play money is obvious. The teacher will guide children to use such aids as are more nearly in keeping with the child's level of performance-with-understanding.

Other manipulative aids that are particularly helpful for dramatizing addition of large numbers are pocket charts and chains of "pop beads." (See pp. 186ff.) Since these aids are discussed more fully elsewhere, the reader can refer to those discussions and adapt the uses of the aids to fit addition of larger numbers.

Checking Addition

The checking of addition for accuracy of computation may be viewed as both an essential procedure and as a habit to be established. Its value becomes increasingly obvious as children proceed to computations involving more addends and larger addends. For example, Forms V and W involve the same number of separate additions, 15 each. With so many separate facts (basic facts and higher-decade facts) it is easy to make an error on one or more; checking becomes very important.

SOME COMMON CHECKS FOR ADDITION

One may, of course, check addition by repeating it. To avoid making the same error again (as when a child is not sure of a certain fact), a check that does not employ the same combinations is usually considered superior to one that repeats all facts in the same order.

While there is no experimental evidence to prove its superiority, the common procedure recommended in

Form V	Form W
2524576346	36
3198653427	47
5723229773	74
	22
Facts used	15
(right to left):	51
	69
6 + 7 = 13	96
1 + 4 = 5	410
5 + 2 = 7	
3 + 4 = 7	Facts used
6 + 3 = 9	(from top):
7 + 5 = 12	

1 + 5 = 6		
6 + 6 = 12	Tens	Ones
1 + 4 = 5	4 + 3 = 7	6 + 7 = 13
5 + 8 = 13	7 + 4 = 11	13 + 4 = 17
1 + 2 = 3	11 + 7 = 18	17 + 2 = 19
3 + 9 = 12	18 + 2 = 20	19 + 5 = 24
1 + 5 = 6	20 + 1 = 21	24 + 1 = 25
6 + 1 = 7	21 + 5 = 26	25 + 9 = 34
2 + 3 = 5	26 + 6 = 32	34 + 6 = 40
	32 + 9 = 41	

elementary school arithmetic texts is to add downward and check by adding upward, thus using different addition combinations. This is, of course, an application of the commutative and associative principles.

Some people like to check by varying the order and grouping of the addends in some other fashion, such as picking out combinations with sums of 10 first, then adding the remaining addends. Others use that procedure for original adding and then check by following the written order.

A check that has received a good deal of attention is "casting out 9's." If taught mechanically, it has little value except as an interesting device. Compensating errors in different columns are not caught by this check; thus it may provide

(1) Add	(2) Add digits	(3) Subtract nines	(4) Add remainders
34	3 + 4 = 7	– – – –	7
56	5 + 6 = 11	11 – 9 = 2	2
27	2 + 7 = 9	9 – 9 = 0	0
· 31	3 + 1 = 4	– – – –	4
48	4 + 8 = 12	12 – 9 = 3	3
196	1 + 9 + 6 = 16	16 – 9 =⑦	16

$$16 - 9 = ⑦$$

The sum of the remainders and the original sum reduce to the same number, 7. The addition checks.

(1) Add	(2) Add digits	(3) Add digits again
34	3 + 4 = 7	– – – 7
56	5 + 6 = 11	1 + 1 = 2
27	2 + 7 = 9	– – – 9
31	3 + 1 = 4	– – – 4
48	4 + 8 = 12	1 + 2 = 3
196	1 + 9 + 6 = 16	1 + 6 =⑦

7 + 2 + 9 + 4 + 3 = 25

2 + 5 =⑦

The two circled numerals are the same, so the addition checks.

assurance of accuracy when it is not present. If taught carefully and meaningfully, with attention to the "why's" of this check (for addition, subtraction, multiplication, or division), it has value for the insight it may stimulate into the number system.

Casting out 9's for checking addition might proceed in either of the ways outlined below. Place values are ignored in the procedure. Only face values of the digits are considered.

In the first procedure, the first step is to add the digits that are found in each addend. If any of those sums is 9 or larger than 9, 9 is subtracted from it. All the remainders (excesses) are then added. If their sum is 9 or more, 9 (or a multiple of 9) is subtracted from it. This final remainder based on casting 9's out of the addends is one of the check figures. The other check figure is found by applying the same procedure to the sum of the original addition example. Its final remainder should check with that derived from the addends.

In the second procedure, the first step is the same as that already described. The second step is different in that the digits are added again (if necessary) instead of subtracting 9's. The comparison of these two methods provides a clue to working out the "system" back of this check. Doing this is an excellent assignment for superior arithmetic students.[9]

Another alternative would be the same as the second method above except that the 9's in the bracketed column are canceled out (the 7 and 2 would be crossed out because they make a 9; the 9 would also be canceled out). This leaves only the 4 and 3, which have a sum of 7. Similarly, all 9's might be "cast out" of the original addends and sum, thus:

3 4 →3 + 6 = 9
5 6 →5 + 4 = 9
2 7 →2 + 7 = 9
3 1 →1 + 8 = 9
4 8 Only 3 and 4 are left; their sum is 7.
1 9 6 Only 1 and 6 are left; their sum is 7.

[9] Helpful references on this point are: Driscoll, Lucy E. "Casting Out Nines and Other Numbers," *Arithmetic Teacher* **5**:82-83, March 1958; Moore, Tabbie Mae, "More about Casting Out Nines," *Arithmetic Teacher* **3**:204-6, November 1956; and Ulrich, Louis E., Sr., "Casting Out Nines," *Arithmetic Teacher* **2**:77-79, October 1955.

Failure of this check to catch compensating errors has already been mentioned. For instance, if the total in one column is 1 too small and the total in another column is 1 too large, the sum of the digits in the total would be the same as if the sum had been correct. The check would "work" even though the assurance of accuracy would be false.

Because addition can so easily be checked by other means, casting out 9's is seldom used as a basic method of checking for addition; it is relatively more efficient in checking multiplication and division of larger numbers. Taught meaningfully, casting out 9's may be very revealing as related to our decimal-place-value system. In a system with a base of eight, casting out 7's would work similarly. Too often casting out 9's is taught as a routine mechanical procedure with no consideration by either teacher or pupil that it works because of the structure of our decimal notation. The check of 11's similarly derives from our decimal-place-value system.

ALGORISMS AS AN AID TO CHECKING

Closely related to addition checks are original addition algorisms that facilitate checking. The writing of the "changed" figure is one of these. In Form X, the discovery of an addition error is facilitated by the presence of the figure at the top of the hundreds column. The person who writes the "changed" 3 tens and 2 hundreds in Form X saves himself time when an error is found. Suppose that by adding the same example upward, he finds a sum of 2054 instead of 1954. He knows that one or the other sum of the hundreds column is wrong. Because he has the "2" at the head of the column,

Form X

```
2 3
1 2 4
4 3 5
5 6 8
2 5 1
1 4 9
5 2 7
─────
1 9 5 4
```

he merely reads the hundreds column to find which of the two sums is right. If the carried figure had not been entered, he would have to do more adding to correct his error.

If children have been impressed with place values, they will recognize an error in hundreds place as being more serious than one in ones place. In routine checking, this practical consideration is often neglected.

Word Problems in Addition

Stress on a problem to be solved has been emphasized throughout this chapter. New phases of the addition process have been related consistently to problem situations in which the meaning of the process could be more readily understood by the children. Algorisms have been presented as the "shorthand" written record of actions performed in solving problems that really occur and are used by the teacher and children or problems that the teacher devises as a setting for addition ideas.

Further practice in problem-solving procedures is usually needed. Children can often make up problems themselves, which they can solve individually or share with their classmates. Problems involving arithmetic of course occur quite often in other subjects of study. If children are encouraged to do so, they will notice opportunities for such arithmetic practice in relation to social studies or science. These problems may be stated orally or in writing.

When all these sources of problems have been used, children in most elementary school classrooms will still get a large proportion of their problem-solving practice from "word problems" in arithmetic books. (Unfortunately, the proportion is often higher than necessary.) Because of their common use, attention should be given to the manner in which they are used.

The writers of elementary arithmetic textbooks have improved the problems a good deal in recent years. The problems are more realistic than was sometimes true in the past. They are written in language that is more readable and understandable to children. Still, these word descriptions of problem situations are something less than a perfect substitute for real ones.

In judging textbook problems and in devising verbal problems of her own, the teacher should check these points:

1. Are the facts of the problem situation clearly stated?

2. Is the problem to be solved clearly indicated?

3. Is the situation one that children might experience?

4. When the answer is found, would it really matter (in the given situation)?

5. Are the required processes known to the children or within their ability to figure out for themselves?

6. Is attention focused on the problem to be solved in the given situation rather than on "word clues"?

The last question is a more serious one than may be immediately apparent. It strikes at the heart of children's understanding of the arithmetic processes, in this case the meaning of addition. Sometimes teachers (and textbook writers!) have been known to teach children to "solve problems" by looking for word clues. Children are told, "If it says 'together' or 'altogether' or 'how many in all,' you will know that you should add to get the right answer." This is not only unfortunate; it is downright misleading.

The real problem situations of life in which the children will (now and later) have to recognize when to add and what to add will almost never come with the question to be answered already stated. The essence of problem solving is seeing a situation in which a question needs to be answered, selecting (or finding) the necessary facts, and then applying a process that will answer the needs of the situation. The problem solver needs to ask his own questions and choose his own facts with which to solve the problem. No one stands at his shoulder and whispers, "How many altogether?" or "How many in all?" He must ask *himself* that question if that is the question demanded to resolve the difficulty.

Teachers who rely on teaching children to "read word clues" are not teaching problem solving. They are teaching "cue reading," which is something entirely different from problem solving. What children need to learn about addition problem solving is the understanding that when they need to find a total made up of two or more quantities that are to be combined to make that total, they add. *They* must recognize that a total is desired. *They* must choose the quantities to be combined.

In primary-grade texts only the pertinent facts are usually given in problem statements. In upper-grade books this is also true, but not to quite such a high degree. Textbook writers are limited as to space; they fear adding "confusing" or "unnecessary" details. Pupils and teachers will object to inclusion of irrelevancies. Since this is true, no one should rely too fully on textbook problems for problem-solving experience. A child may profit more from one realistic problem situation which he experiences fully and in which he really does choose the relevant facts and what should be done with them to solve a felt difficulty than he will profit from dozens of formal textbook problems. The textbook writers do the best they can, but that best will never take the place of the "real thing."

Most modern texts for children emphasize the translation of problem situations into open mathematical sentences or "number sentences." Teaching children to make such statements is excellent instruction in mathematical thinking. It also draws a distinction between this step and the actual computation to be done. For a problem concerning the total cost of three items, the statement might be:

$$\$1.25 + \$5.38 + \$4.79 = n$$

Even though the typical child will have to recopy the prices in vertical form to perform the addition, the formulation of the sentence is a simplified presentation of the problem to be solved. Practice with mathematical sentences in such simple addition situations will lay a foundation for later translation of more complex problem situations into their appropriate mathematical statements.

Good problem solving in addition involves knowing what addition means, when to do it, and how to do it. Every suggestion for teaching that has been made in this chapter should contribute in one way or another to that objective.

Grade Placement and Learning Sequence of Addition Concepts

Every arithmetic textbook author has to face up to the choice of content for any specific book—usually a book planned (if not labeled) for use at a specific grade level. Once chosen, the material has to be arranged in some sort of learning sequence. Preparation of state and local courses of study includes similar choices and decisions. If content is not specifically prescribed for a par-

ticular grade level, a good deal of complaint is likely to come from teachers who want to know what they "are supposed to teach" the children of a certain grade level.

Some textbook publishers have tried to dispense with grade labels on arithmetic texts, using some key by which the teacher can identify grade level without letting the children in on the secret. This practice is designed to help in assigning to the child the level of content difficulty for which he is ready to profit without the obvious grade level connotations so dear to the hearts of many teachers and parents. No great reform has followed such deletion of grade labels; some publishers have even retrogressed to their former clearly stated grade designations.

Rigid grade placement of arithmetic content stems from two classes of false assumptions, those regarding the learning abilities of children at separate grade levels and those regarding the content of arithmetic.

FALLACIES REGARDING GRADE LEVELS

The first fallacy concerning grade levels is the assumption held by too many people that they constitute the *only* way to classify pupils for instruction in school. The position is taken that grade levels have always been and always will be. One who takes this position shows his ignorance of the history of education and lacks the flexibility of thought processes necessary for progress to be possible. Grade levels in schools are relatively recent phenomena within the perspective of history. They were adopted as one way to classify large numbers of pupils into groups for instruction. It just so happens that this manner of classification worked out well enough that it became our prevailing pattern. Further, anyone who attended the hallowed "little red schoolhouse" with its single room knows that much learning cut across grade lines. Grade levels are not the law of the land and should not be treated as if they were.

The next fallacy is the uncritical assumption that the grade level classification is the *best* kind of classification. Enough experimentation has been done and is now is progress with other types of classification to lend some hope that this assumption will be more closely examined. Witness, for example, the ungraded primary school and ungraded intermediate school.

The third fallacy is a misconception as to what a "grade" is. One idea has been that it is a body of material to be learned and that promotion from one grade to another means that the children have mastered most or all of that material. For example, a child should be promoted from the third grade to the fourth grade when he has mastered the prescribed body of content for third graders in arithmetic and other areas of the curriculum. This idea does not bear close examination. It never was true and is not ever going to be true except in the minds of its believers. The thirty or more children in a typical elementary school classroom are not that much alike. Any careful examination of standardized test results or other evidences of pupils' acquisition of content will show wide variations in what they know and can do—wide variations within any one subject like arithmetic and wide variations in what each child knows and can do in different subjects such as arithmetic, science, and social studies.

Because of these demonstrated deviations from a rigid grade level of performance for all children assigned to a given grade, elementary schools in our country have moved toward the concept of promotion of most children each year. Thus the "grade" has come to mean more nearly "an age group." Some critics complain that this entails a lowering of standards, but this is not necessarily the case. It is certainly not the case if teachers are aware of individual differences and adjust their procedures and expectations accordingly. It may well be that standards of performance are raised for many children in this way.

Actually, a "grade" group of children is coming to mean realistically a group of children whose chronological ages are mostly within a spread of one year, with a few children slightly older or younger than that, e.g., a group of children between 8 and 9 years of age but with a few children younger than 8 and a few older than 9. Of course, as the school year advances, so do all the ages. The mental ages of these children vary much more widely than do their chronological ages. So also do they vary widely in knowledge and understanding and skill in arithmetic. One boy may be a very good reader and very poor in arithmetic competence, another child just the opposite. The only realistic appraisal of what a "grade" is must take these variations into account.

Because of these wide variations among the individuals in a grade group, there are no sharp lines of demarcation between successive grades. The abilities of children in a typical third-grade group overlap the abilities of children in a typical second grade and a typical fourth grade in the same school. This overlapping is more evident than the difference from grade to grade. Furthermore, the better the quality of teaching, the wider will be the spread of abilities within the class and the greater will be the variation in each successive grade.[10]

[10] Esther J. Swenson, "Rate of Progress in Learning Arithmetic," *Mathematics Teacher* **48**:70-76, February 1955.

FALLACIES REGARDING SEQUENCE OF ARITHMETIC CONTENT

Elementary school courses of study, curriculum guides, and textbooks have shown great progress in recent years in line with the preceding discussion. It has become common practice, for example, to recommend that children be encouraged to progress at their own best individual rates in reading. It has become common practice in good schools for teachers to encourage the more competent pupils in a grade group to do advanced research in reference books on a given topic in social studies or science at the same time that a less able pupil reads much easier material on the same topic. Further, certain topics or areas of study in the elementary school curriculum are much less rigidly prescribed than formerly, allowing teachers and children more freedom in adapting sequences of learning topics to fit needs, interests, and abilities of learners.

These changes have not been so evident in arithmetic instruction. The departure from rigid sequences of content has even been recommended by some authorities "except in arithmetic." Apart from the rigidity of past grade requirements, there is still the idea that arithmetic content has to be taught in a certain rather rigid order, and there is some truth in the statement that logical sequence is more important than in social studies or science. (See pp. 8-9.)

As teachers and textbook writers and curriculum makers grow in their own fundamental concepts in this area, however, they may find that they need no longer seek flexibility "*except* in arithmetic." They may seek much more flexibility in arrangement of arithmetic content than has hitherto been the rule.

Textbook writers have to arrive at a sequence of learning topics that seems reasonable to them. Teachers should become competent enough in their own control of arithmetic concepts that they can make adaptations in their use of textbook content. As teachers do become more competent, they will be less firmly tied to textbooks and can develop sequential learning experiences for and with children in terms of the demands of a situation and the abilities and past backgrounds of the learners.

ADAPTATION OF ARITHMETIC SEQUENCE BY GRADE LEVELS

Approximate indications of grade level or age level at which certain concepts or processes are typically introduced have their value, particularly to aid children who move from school to school or within a single school as children move from grade to grade. Such approximate sequences can be established in terms of an adopted series of arithmetic texts, of a local course of study, or of a combination of these and other guides. The important point here is that the teachers who agree on these sequences should view them as approximate and should think of them as being for the average learner at that grade level. Teachers should recognize not only their right to deviate but their responsibility at times to do so. It is important, however, for teachers at different grade levels, particularly adjacent grade levels, to discuss such variations with one another.

No one should build a fence around a certain piece of content and seek to exclude anyone else from its use. For example, although the process of "changing" ("carrying") in addition and subtraction is typically introduced in most third-grade books, this does not mean that the third-grade teacher should resent another teacher's working with the concept if it fits her pupils' readiness and needs for use. A second-grade child might be amply prepared for it; he should not be denied instruction because the third-grade teacher feels it "belongs" to the third grade. A fourth-grade child may not have learned the true meaning of the process of "changing"; his teacher should give him the help he needs, whether or not it is content too elementary for most of his classmates.

Anyone who is familiar with the seemingly endless reviewing that is necessary at the beginning of each school year certainly should recognize that content presented the year before may or may not have been learned in the sense that it meets the retention criterion. Overlapping of content by grade levels should be assumed since it is one of the facts of life in schools.

The best test as to appropriateness of certain content at a given level is provided by the answers to such questions as these:

1. Do the children to whom it is to be taught have adequate background for learning it?

2. Do the children to whom it is to be taught have adequate ability to appreciate its meaning?

3. Do the children to whom it is to be taught have any use for it?

4. Is it of equal or greater importance to the learners now than some other content that might be taught instead?

There is some experimental evidence to indicate that the range of performance on standardized arithmetic tests is narrower than the range of performance by the same children in reading, language skills, science, or social studies.

The usual spread is found downward from the given grade level, but fewer children rise markedly above the grade "norm," curtailing the range of scores in an upward direction. This would seem to indicate that the children have not been given the opportunity to be exposed to arithmetic content measured by the standardized tests but typically not taught until a later school grade. If this interpretation is correct, it points to a sad state of affairs in terms of challenge to the able pupil.

ADAPTATION OF ARITHMETIC SEQUENCE FOR PUPILS IN A GRADE GROUP

Perhaps elementary school teachers in the United States do more grouping of pupils for reading instruction than for any other instructional purpose. The practice of having the children in a whole class grouped into three or more reading groups is rather widely assumed. Reading materials used by the different groups are chosen not with respect to the grade label on the classroom door but in terms of the present reading ability levels of the children in the group.

A similar practice is growing for arithmetic instruction, but is not nearly common enough. Actually the children of a class are no more in need of grouping for learning to read better than they are for learning arithmetic. (At times all children in a class can and should share reading experiences, so also for arithmetic.) Since it is hardly possible that all children in a class are at the same level of competence and ability in arithmetic, it is equally impossible for instruction to proceed at optimum level if all are expected to profit from instruction that day by day presses the same content on all children at the same time and in the same amounts. Just as reading activities and materials are properly geared to different ability levels, so should arithmetic activities and materials be adapted. The number of "arithmetic groups" will vary in terms of teacher competence with group procedures and the distribution of observed pupil abilities and needs for instruction. Grouping should of course be flexible.

Grouping within the grade or class is not the whole story. Attention is still required for individual learners within the group. One child may enjoy his introduction to "changing" in addition of two-place numbers so much that he immediately wants to go on to apply the changing idea to the addition of larger numbers. Another child may not have fully grasped the meaning of the procedures. He may need to do some more "acting out" of "changing" situations while the first child is allowed to see what he can do with the larger numbers. One child may enjoy and derive much benefit from experimenting with ideas and applications of ideas such as the associative and commutative laws of addition; another may be doing well to see their simplest applications. The important point is that both are learning and making progress in their knowledge of arithmetic.

SOUND BASES FOR SEQUENCES OF LEARNING EXPERIENCES

To operate successfully within the flexible type of sequence suggested above, teachers need to have some guidelines to follow in making the decisions that need to be made.

1. Plan sequence of learning experiences in line with the learners' indi-

vidual and group *backgrounds for grasping the new learning content,* whether it be a new concept, a new process, or a skill.

2. Adapt the timetable within a sequence of learning activities so that the learners (individually and as groups) can proceed at a *pace that challenges but does not frustrate.*

3. Plan the sequence of learning experiences for a particular grade group *in relation to past and future learnings,* not only during the year in question but also over their total school history.

4. Give careful attention to the mathematical *concepts* being taught as well as the *procedures.* (This is a matter that has been too often neglected in the past, when emphasis was more on what to do and how to do it than on the basic concepts and understandings.)

5. No matter what general framework is settled upon, allow for deviations and adjustments as learning proceeds.

The foregoing are fundamental guides to good sequence. On a more superficial level but still worth careful consideration are such guides to organization of content as these:

1. In general, work with smaller numbers first, working up to larger ones as children develop competence with the smaller ones.

2. In general, work with fewer numbers in a problem at the beginning and then proceed to more complex problems.

3. In general, start with problem situations that can be readily dramatized or demonstrated with concrete materials and then proceed to those which can be handled in increasingly abstract ways.

Obviously, the preceding discussions

of problem solving and of grade placement and learning sequence of addition concepts apply not only to the teaching of addition but to all arithmetic instruction. The discussion was presented at this point in order to focus the reader's attention on these ideas early in his study of arithmetic teaching.

STUDY QUESTIONS

1. Draw a number line to show the addition of 23 and 9. Does the number line solution show "bridging"? If so, how?

2. Read the suggestions for new experiences (pp. 127-128). Collect or develop the materials needed for following one of these suggestions. Demonstrate the activity before your classmates or use it in teaching a group of children.

3. Use number lines to show several different ways of associating the addends or partial addends in adding 34 + 26. (Partial addends might be 30, 4, 20, and 6.)

4. Check the addition at the right by applying the check of casting out 9's.

$$
\begin{array}{r}
124 \\
435 \\
568 \\
527 \\
\hline
1694
\end{array}
$$

5. Suppose you have one abacus that has 10 beads on each rod and another that has a supply of 18 beads on each rod. Which one would be more helpful in teaching children the regrouping or changing of 10 ones for 1 ten in adding $24 + 48 = 72$? Why did you make that choice?

6. Read the articles mentioned on page 135. Demonstrate the basis for the casting-out-9's check for addition.

CHAPTER 7

The Subtraction Process
and the Basic Subtraction Facts

SINCE ADDITION and multiplication are both processes of combining, many modern treatments of the four fundamental processes of arithmetic discuss them fully before proceeding to their inverses, i.e., subtraction and division. Subtraction is discussed immediately after addition in this book because this represents the usual order for elementary school pupils learning arithmetic.

A complete discussion of the meaning of subtraction must include a careful look at many facets of the process. No one of these is the whole story about subtraction. Taking a look at each in turn, by itself and also in relation to other facets, leads to a development of subtraction meanings that is not only more complete but also more accurate than an oversimplified definition in a single statement.

What Is Subtraction?

SUBTRACTION IS THE INVERSE
OF ADDITION

Although we might well say that addition is the "reverse" or the "opposite" process to addition, it is better to use the term "inverse." To "invert" denotes a process that is opposite in *effect*. If two

operations are *inverse*, they undo each other. If two groups are combined (addition) and then separated (subtraction), the situation is back in original form. Subtraction has the effect of "undoing" addition. Similarly, if one amount is subtracted from another and then added to the remaining amount, the addition has the effect of "undoing" the subtraction.

Addition is a "putting-together" process. Subtraction is a "taking-apart" process. In addition there are always addends or subgroups to be combined. The result of the process is to find the total or composite group made up of the addends. In subtraction, on the other hand, the total or composite group is always known along with one of the addends. The result of the process is to find the *missing* addend.

Because addition and subtraction are inverse operations, subtraction should be taught to children in such a way as to stress that relationship. In some situations this opposite relationship may be more obvious than in others, but it is always there.

Three children want to play a game that requires 4 players. They get Tom to join them. After playing a while, Tom says, "I have to go home now. I promised to come back in half an hour." The original group of three children are disappointed. One of them says, "We're back just where we started." The representations in figure 39 show the addition and subtraction processes as inverses. (Note the directions of the arrows.)

In the three illustrations of figure 39 the composite group includes 4 children.

total is being *taken apart* (subtraction) or *separated* into the components. The intermediate situation *B* is really the conclusion of the addition process *A* and the beginning of the subtraction process *C*.

Addition and subtraction as inverse operations may be shown with subtraction being done first, followed by addi-

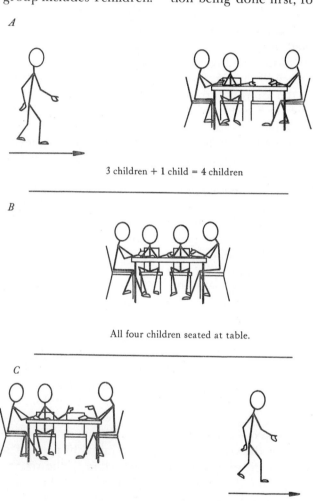

A

3 children + 1 child = 4 children

B

All four children seated at table.

C

4 children − 1 child = 3 children

Figure 39. Addition and Subtraction as Inverse Operations.

The components (addends) are 3 children and 1 child. In situation *A* the components are being *put together* (addition) to make the total. In situation *C* the

tion. Let us say that 4 children were playing their game; Tom left the group of 4, leaving 3 children playing. Alice came to take Tom's place, and again there were 4 children. Alice's coming canceled out Tom's departure.

As children arrange chairs or books or other objects in the classroom, they have many opportunities to combine and to separate, to separate and to combine. They should be encouraged frequently in working with a total group of any size (e.g., 5) to consider both the addition- and the subtraction-type actions. Say that 5 children's drawings are to be arranged in two rows on the bulletin board. As various arrangements are tried out, the children may notice that 2 pictures in the top row and three in the bottom row are 5 pictures in all; or, having placed 2 pictures in the top row, they may determine how many of the 5 pictures will be left to put in the bottom row. The same balanced emphasis on putting together and taking apart could be worked out for all the other combinations of 5 objects. The formal addition and subtraction statements might or might not be introduced with such an activity, depending on the children's past experiences and the other demands of the situation.

SUBTRACTION IS

COUNTING BACKWARD

Just as addition problems can be solved by counting, so also subtraction problems can be solved by counting. The difference is that the counting for subtraction proceeds in the opposite direction from counting for addition purposes. The child who is going to be helped by noting that subtraction is counting backward must be proficient in counting backward. The chances are that, in most primary-grade classrooms, children get much more practice in counting forward by ones, twos, threes, fives, tens, or any other interval than

they do in counting backward by the same intervals. Since subtraction is certainly not an easier process than addition (probably harder), there is no excuse for this neglect of meaningful practice in counting backward.

"One little, two little, three little Indians" has its "ten little, nine little, eight little Indians"; children enjoy not only singing this song but also acting it out, which is good arithmetic instruction on the meaning level. Children also like to count backward as well as forward in connection with counting games; all that is needed is the suggestion to do so. Some of the overemphasis on rote and rapid forward counting might well be replaced by additional practice of meaningful counting, both forward and backward.

Counting down has become an interesting—even exciting—activity for boys and girls geographically far removed from Cape Kennedy or other missile-launching sites. "Ten, nine, eight, seven, six, five, four, three, two, one, FIRE!" With "zero" substituted for "fire," the countdown can also add to the meaning of that important point on the number scale.

Opportunities for this practice are frequent enough, once the teacher is alert to their occurrence and their value. Take an activity like distributing materials, such as the scissors used in a paper-cutting activity. The teacher has a box containing 36 pairs of scissors, one for each child in the room. As a child distributes them, he may count them in usual forward fashion "to see if they are all there" or "to know how many he has given out" at any particular time or "to be sure he gives one to each child." When the same child or another one gathers up the scissors, they could be counted again from 1 to 36 or the procedure could be reversed. He could start with 36 and count backward. When he gets to zero, he has them all back — an excellent opportunity to use zero correctly too. Or the child who first gave out the scissors could have started with the known quantity "36" and counted backward as he gave them out,

on our subtraction algorism than it is an essential idea. Figure 40*A* shows addition on a number line as counting forward by threes; figure 40*B* shows subtraction as counting backward by threes. The number of steps in 40*A* and in 40*B* is the same — two each as shown in the

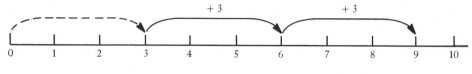

Counting: 3, 6, 9,
Adding: 3 + 3 = 6; 6 + 3 = 9
Vertical Forms:

$$\begin{array}{cc} 3 & 6 \\ +3 & +3 \\ \hline 6 & 9 \end{array} \quad \text{or} \quad \begin{array}{c} 3 \\ 3 \\ 3 \\ \hline 9 \end{array}$$

A. Addition as Counting

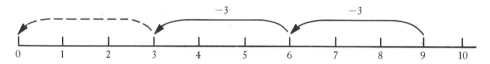

Counting: 9, 6, 3,
Subtracting: 9 − 3 = 6; 6 − 3 = 3
Vertical Forms:

$$\begin{array}{cc} 9 & 6 \\ -3 & -3 \\ \hline 6 & 3 \end{array}$$

B. Subtraction as Counting Backward

Figure 40. Addition and Subtraction as Forward and Backward Counting.

thus always knowing "how many are left in the box."

Blocks may be taken out or replaced as they are counted forward and backward by twos, threes, or any subgroup size that the children can handle so far as block size, hand size, and dexterity will allow.

The concept of subtraction as reverse counting may be more difficult for children than the concept of addition as forward counting not only because of less practice with reverse counting but also because subtraction typically involves only one written step. This is probably more a matter of dependence

algorisms, or three each if one would include algorisms for the dotted arrows (0 + 3 = 3 and 3 − 3 = 0). The column addition algorism does show the whole story of counting forward in a single algorism; we have no corresponding algorism for subtraction. However, the column addition is accomplished by successive additions, whether they are written out as such or not. The point here is that in teaching the idea of subtraction as counting backward, one should use a situation in which a *series* of *successive* subtractions is appropriate. This will make the counting relationship more obvious. (This idea will be developed further on pp. 163ff. of this chapter in connection with the teaching of the basic subtraction facts.)

Any subtraction problem can be solved by counting backward, provided one has time enough to handle the problem in that way. As children work with larger numbers, the advantage of being able to subtract quickly without laboriously "counting back" for solutions will become increasingly obvious. As with automatic control of the basic addition facts, so also the automatic level mastery of the basic subtraction facts can be motivated by demonstrating this saving of time and effort as compared with the slower counting procedure.

While cardinal numbers have been used in most of the examples above, the concept of subtraction as backward counting applies as well to ordinal uses of number. Children (and their teachers) are typically interested in knowing when vacations will begin. A particular group of children have heard that their Christmas holidays will begin 5 days before Christmas Day. If they have not reached the stage of arithmetic knowledge and skill that gives them command of "25 −

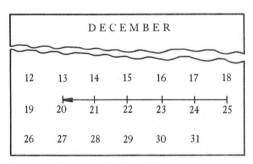

Figure 41. Subtraction with Ordinal Numbers.

5 = 20," they can figure it out by counting backward on the calendar. See figure 41. Actually the week of December 19 on the calendar as shown might be thought of as a number line. Each of the numerals represents an ordinal

or "which one?" meaning of number. The question is: Which day is 5 days before the 25th day of December? Only the "5 days" is a cardinal number concept. The "25th" and the "20th" are ordinals, as are all the dates on the calendar.

SUBTRACTION IS REGROUPING
BY SEPARATING

Norman went fishing with his father. Together they caught 9 fish, of which the father caught 5. How many did Norman catch? The answer to this question (which can be derived by subtraction) will give Norman a simpler way of telling how many fish he caught. That is, subtracting is a form of regrouping that helps Norman simplify a situation formerly described by use of two numbers into one in which only one number is needed. This simplification takes place by regrouping of the fish.

The two known facts are: the size of the total group of fish, or 9 fish, and the size of the father's catch, or 5 fish. The unknown is the size of Norman's group of fish. Notice that the father's catch of fish and Norman's catch of fish are component groups within the total catch. Norman's solution of the problem is shown in figure 42. The "given" facts are shown by the solid-line brackets. A broken line is used for the bracket indicating the solution. The subtraction process was a matter of regrouping the total group into two separate subgroups within the total, the size of one of which was already known. The unknown subgroup was found by separating the known subgroup from it.

The subgroups (known and unknown) must be mutually exclusive. Take, for example, this situation: A dog fancier has 9 dogs. Five are thoroughbred collies. Three are thoroughbred German shepherds. One is half collie and half German shepherd. In this case, we could not correctly state the problem thus: Of the 9 dogs, 4 are German shepherds.. How many are collies? Since the collies and German shepherds "overlap" in the "half-breed" dog, this would not

separated them into two subgroups, one a group of Daddy's 5 fish and the other a group of Norman's 4 fish.

These are called "open sentences":

$$9 - 5 = n \qquad 9 - 5 = \underline{\quad} \qquad 9 - 5 = \square$$

The *n* or ____ or box is used to hold the

We caught 9 fish in all.

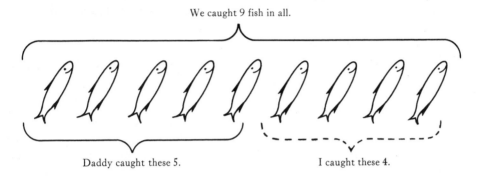

Daddy caught these 5.   I caught these 4.

9 fish − 5 fish = 4 fish

Figure 42. Subtraction as Regrouping by Separating.

fit the test of mutually exclusive subgroups within the total of 9 dogs.[1]

A STATEMENT OF SUBTRACTION
IS A STATEMENT OF EQUALITY

Just as children are sometimes misled in being told that "addition is getting more," so they are also often told that "subtraction is getting less." This too is a misleading statement.

The subtraction problem accompanying figure 42 concerns 9 fish. There were 9 fish when the problem situation was described. There were still 9 fish when the problem had been solved. The same 9 fish were present before and after the subtraction. The subtraction merely

place in the sentence until it is filled in with the missing numeral that will make the statement of equality *true*. When "4" is written instead of the place holder, the statement becomes a *closed,* or finished, sentence. The "=" sign says that "9 − 5" is *equal* to "4."

"Getting less" is *not* the essential meaning of subtraction. It is not even a part of many subtraction statements. The separation of a total composite group into two constituent groups is the essential meaning of subtraction. True, each of the constituent groups *may be* smaller than the total group; in elementary school arithmetic, this is usually true. However, when zero is involved, this is not true.[2]

Much confusion results when children have been taught the idea that subtrac-

---

[1] In elementary school arithmetic, subtraction may be described in terms of sets. The number quality of each set and subset is, however, limited to "disjoint" subsets.

[2] Zero in such situations represents the "empty set."

tion means getting less or when they have been taught to expect the answer to be a smaller number. When such children come to the use of positive and negative numbers in algebra, they are very much confused and frustrated by the fact that their answers do not come out according to their previously acquired notion of subtraction answers. This confusion need never have been built.

The conventional subtraction statement expresses an *equality,* e.g., $9-5=4$. Stated in words, "nine fish minus five fish *is equal to* four fish." The two sides of this equation must balance if the equals sign is to be correctly used. The forms "$9-5$" and "4" are merely different ways of expressing the same number.

Some modern arithmetic materials introduce the inequality sign ($\neq$) as well as the equality sign ($=$). The use of both signs requires children to weigh the situation and decide which sign is correct, e.g., $9-5=4$, but $9-5 \neq 3$. This may prevent some of the careless use of the $=$ sign without real attention to its meaning.[3]

The reading of the minus sign as "take away" adds to the confusion — may actually be the cause of the confusion in many instances. This point will be further discussed on page 155.

Subtraction has thus far been defined with four statements: Subtraction is the inverse of addition. Subtraction is counting backward. Subtraction is regrouping by separating. A statement of subtraction is a statement of equality.

[3] In this chapter subtraction statements are consistently made so that the missing term (remainder or difference) appears as the "answer" to the right of the $=$ sign. Some instructional materials place the missing term in various positions in the statement, e.g., $\_\_\_-5=4$; $9-\_\_\_=4$; and $9-5=$ $\_\_\_$. Teachers in the same school should agree on the types of statements to be used.

These are all true statements, but they are not the whole story of the meaning of subtraction. To understand subtraction fully, one must consider three different ideas of subtraction as they occur in different subtraction problems. By looking at a subtraction statement such as "$7-4=3$," one cannot recognize these separate ideas; the difference is in the application of subtraction to given problem situations.

THREE IDEAS OF SUBTRACTION

Most writers on the subject speak of three "ideas" of subtraction; perhaps it would be more accurate to speak of three "applications" or "uses" of subtraction because the distinctions among them appear only in use. The three uses to which subtraction is put in application are the take-away idea, the comparison idea, and the additive idea.

Knowing *how* to subtract is not the same as knowing *when* to subtract. Many children who recognize addition as the correct process to use in a given problem do not recognize subtraction as the correct process for another problem. Many teachers have reported the difficulty experienced by children in knowing *when* subtraction is the appropriate process to use to solve a problem. The crux of the difficulty stems from lack of clarification of the three different "when's" for applying subtraction. Many children have learned that subtraction means "take-away," and *that is all they have learned.* This is not enough, for subtraction often has comparative or additive meanings. The child who looks only for "take-away" applications is at a loss when he meets a problem demanding use of one of the other subtraction ideas. For example, he meets this problem: Jack has 14 marbles and Joe has 8 marbles. How many more does Jack have? The child who is asked to answer this question and who has been taught only the "take-away" idea of subtraction may reason as follows: "I know it isn't addition because the marbles weren't *put together*. It isn't subtraction because the marbles weren't *taken away*. What is it anyway? I don't know." He is at a loss to recognize the needed process because his notion of subtraction is limited to only one application.

An arithmetic consultant working with a group of teachers wrote the subtraction fact "9 − 3 = 6" on the chalkboard and then asked each of the teachers to write a subtraction problem in which that fact would be used for the solution. She asked them to write problems such as children might face. As the problem statements were received, they were classified into three groups: "take-away," comparison, and additive types.

Eight of the fourteen teachers wrote "take-away" problems as follows:

1. Mary had 9 Easter eggs. She broke 3. How many good eggs were left?
2. Betty had 9 cookies. She ate 3 cookies. How many cookies did Betty have then?
3. Joe had 9 rabbits in a pen. Three rabbits hopped out. How many were left in the pen?
4. Johnny went to the store. He had 9¢ in his pocket. He bought 3¢ worth of bubble gum. How much money did he have left?
5. Ben had 9 marbles. His friend came to visit him. He let him have 3 marbles. How many marbles did Ben have then?
6. Nine boys were playing ball. Three of them had to go home. How many were left playing ball?
7. Nine sparrows were sitting on a wire. Three flew away. How many were left?
8. Mother had 9 yards of cloth. She used 3 yards in sewing a dress for Sue. How much cloth did Mother have left?

Two of the submitted problems were of the comparison type, as follows:

9. Joe lived 9 blocks from school. Bill lived only 3 blocks from school. How much farther did Joe have to walk than Bill?
10. Jean had 3 pennies. Jane had 9 pennies. How many more did Jane have?

Three problems were of the additive type:

11. The reading circle needed 9 chairs. There were only 3 in place. How many more chairs were needed?
12. Buck lived 9 blocks from town. His grandmother lived 3 blocks from town on the same street. On his way home from town he stopped to visit his grandmother. How much farther did he have to walk to get home?
13. Nine boys are needed for a baseball team. Only 3 boys came out to the field. How many more boys were needed to make a full team?

Some interesting observations can be made concerning these "word problems." First, the greater relative frequency of "take-away" problems must be noted. The ratio of the three types of problems for this one group of teachers is probably fairly representative of frequency of use in and out of classrooms. Second, the frequency of use of standardized "cue words" is obvious. Six of the eight "take-away" problems used the expression "how many left?" Neither of these observations suggests anything wrong, but both of them are indicative of emphases of which teachers should be aware lest they forget to emphasize other important ideas and a variety of terminology. Both these points have a bearing on problem-solving development since too heavy reliance on one idea or one phrasing can contribute to a narrow view of subtraction in problems.

The consultant and the teachers proceeded to discuss the problems, to note the common characteristics of each type, and to consider ways in which children might act out each problem. Incidentally, acting out the different subtraction problems is the best way of clarifying the three different ideas of use for the subtraction process.

The group agreed on some summary statements for each type of problem.

1. In the "take-away" problems:
   a. The action began with a total

b. The action was one of bringing in (adding) items until a total of 9 was present.
c. The problem question asked how many had to be brought in (added).

A member of the group later worked out a summary in another form as shown below:

	TAKE-AWAY SUBTRACTION	COMPARATIVE SUBTRACTION	ADDITIVE SUBTRACTION
Given:	Total group of 9	Total group of 9	Size of total group of 9 (not present, however)
	Subgroup of 3 within total group of 9	Another group of 3	Subgroup of 3 within the group of 9 (present)
Action:	*Removing* subgroup of 3 from total of 9	*Matching* group of 3 against group of 9	*Building* up subgroup of 3 to total of 9
Result:	Other subgroup, or remainder : 6	Difference between 9 and 3 : 6	Missing subgroup : 6

group of 9 (never any more than 9).
   b. From that total group of 9, a subgroup of 3 was removed in some way (broken, eaten, ran away, spent, flew, used up).
   c. The problem question asked the size of the remaining subgroup.
2. In the comparison problems:
   a. The action began with a group of 9 and also another group of 3; so actually 12 items (pennies, blocks) were involved in the demonstration.
   b. The 9-group and the 3-group were compared with each other by matching in one-to-one fashion.
   c. The problem question asked for the difference in size of the 9-group and the 3-group. Or it asked how many in the 9-group remained unmatched with the 3-group.
3. In the additive problems:
   a. The action began with a group of 3. No other items were present at the beginning.

Although these particular summaries of the three applications of the subtraction process were made by adults, they could well be developed by children under the guidance of their teacher. Such development should come *after* the children have had ample opportunity to dramatize subtraction solutions of the various types, so that they will have a background of experience from which to draw the similarities and the differences among the three types. Upper-grade children who may not have gained as clear or complete a concept of subtraction as they should have at an earlier level also need such experiences. Developing summary statements like those above is an excellent exercise in clear thinking and a good basis for later review of the subtraction process.

The contrast in meanings of the three ideas of subtraction are also pointed up by pictures or diagrams. Problems 2, 10, and 11 are shown in figure 43. Comparison of the pictures with the summary table above will show that the same similarities and contrasts are shown in both the table and the pictures.

The contrasted ideas are shown further in figure 44 for three subtraction problems that are all well suited to presentation on a number line (problems 8, 9, and 12). The diagrams are all alike in that a total group of 9 is separated into constituent groups of 3 (known) and 6 (to be found). They are different

builds up the 3-block distance to the total known distance of 9 blocks.

All the problems pictured in figures 43 and 44 have the same written forms:

$$9 - 3 = 6, \text{ or } \begin{array}{r} 9 \\ -3 \\ \hline 6 \end{array}$$

The pictures are not needed by a child who understands the three ideas of

Problem 2 (Take Away):

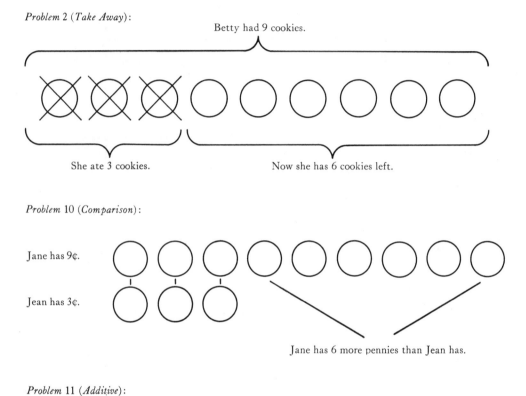

Betty had 9 cookies.

She ate 3 cookies.   Now she has 6 cookies left.

Problem 10 (Comparison):

Jane has 9¢.

Jean has 3¢.

Jane has 6 more pennies than Jean has.

Problem 11 (Additive):

3 chairs here   6 more chairs needed to make 9 in all

Figure 43. Problem Solutions for Three Subtraction Situations.

in that the take-away problem *removes* the subgroup of 3; the comparison problem *matches* a separate group of 3 against a subgroup of 3 within the total group of 9; and the additive problem

subtraction and knows the basic subtraction fact involved. On the other hand, the child who knows the basic subtraction fact "9 − 3 = 6" but thinks it always means that 3 of something is taken away from 9 of something is not prepared to handle other situations and needs very much to go through the different actions or use simple diagrams through which he can first develop and later demonstrate to others his basic understanding.

might have been worded, "When Buck gets to Grandmother's house, how many blocks does he have left to walk?" making it a "take-away" problem. If the child can demonstrate his interpretation correctly with objects or a diagram and does not have to change any of the facts

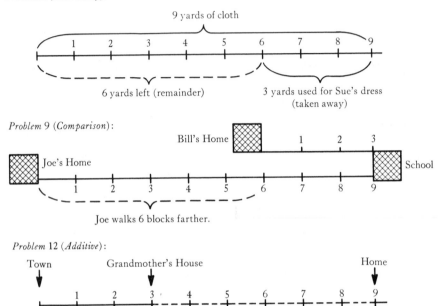

Problem 8 (*Take Away*):

9 yards of cloth

6 yards left (remainder)

3 yards used for Sue's dress (taken away)

Problem 9 (*Comparison*):

Bill's Home

Joe's Home

School

Joe walks 6 blocks farther.

Problem 12 (*Additive*):

Town   Grandmother's House   Home

Figure 44. Number Line Solutions for Three Subtraction Situations.

Pupils (and their teachers) may get into some heated arguments if they are too insistent on their own interpretations of some subtraction situations. Such arguments can best be settled by bearing in mind that the basic operation in all three cases is subtraction and that the differences may be differences of interpretation. Take, for example, problem 12 (p. 151 and fig. 44, above). The problem has been interpreted in figure 44 as additive subtraction. The question might have been asked in different fashion as, "How much farther is it from town to Buck's home than it is from town to Grandmother's house?" making it a comparison problem. Or it

of the situation, his interpretation should be accepted as correct.

Someone may ask: If different interpretations are possible for the same problem situation, why all the emphasis on three different interpretations or ideas of subtraction? The answer is simple. The object of teaching children to recognize the different possible applications of subtraction is to prepare them to meet any of those applications efficiently since they will know that any of them can be solved by subtracting.

In many elementary school classrooms, subtraction process meanings are not given the time and attention they require. The teacher knows how and when to subtract but has not thought enough about it to be as good a guide of children's learning as she should be. Because of its various interpretations, subtraction is a more difficult process than addition and deserves more attention than it sometimes gets.

Typically, the take-away idea of subtraction is taught first. Although materials for children vary on this point, usually the comparison idea is taught next. In the subtraction situations that occur in the classroom, various applications should be taken as they come, but the teacher may wish to stress one idea or another as she sees children's need for it.[4]

Subtraction Terminology

The terminology of subtraction, like the concept of subtraction, is more complex and more difficult for children to learn than is its counterpart for addition. The written algorisms for the two processes are very similar and equally simple to write. Reading those algorisms correctly is much more controversial. In fact, adults are going to have to come to some agreement on how to state subtractions before children can be expected to get the matter straight.

The algorisms are parallel for addition and subtraction, as for the "family" of basic addition facts involving the numbers 2, 4, and 6.

Horizontal Algorism		Vertical Algorism			
$2 + 4 = 6$	$4 + 2 = 6$	2	6	4	6
$6 - 4 = 2$	$6 - 2 = 4$	$+4$	-4	$+2$	-2
		6	2	6	4

[4] The classification of subtraction applications or subtraction situations into three types is the most common classification but not by any means the only one. The teacher may wish to adapt instruction to the scheme of classifying subtraction situations that appears in the materials used with the children. For example, some authors suggest four types of situations, or "how many gone" situations may be treated as distinct from "how many needed" situations.

The numerals used in any pair of addition and subtraction facts are identical, though appearing in reverse order, as would be expected since the processes are inverse. The "=" sign is the same. Only the "+" and "−" signs are different.

The plus sign (+) may be read as "and" or "plus," and it always means "put together." The minus sign (−), on the other hand, is commonly read in at least four different ways, sometimes correctly and sometimes incorrectly. The subtraction sign in the number fact "$6 - 4 = 2$" may be read as:

> 6 *minus* 4 equals 2
> 6 *take away* 4 equals 2
> 6 *less* 4 equals 2
> 4 *from* 6 equals 2

Add to this variety of subtraction terminology the fact that the equals sign (=) in subtraction algorisms is sometimes read as "leaves" in addition to being read as "equal," "equals," "are," and "is."

In the three subtraction problems below, three different applications of subtraction are expressed. Terminology may vary accordingly.

Problem A: If Alice has $6 and pays $4 for a gift, how many dollars does she still have?

Problem B: If Alice paid $6 for one dress and $4 for another, how much more did she pay for the first dress?

Problem C: If Alice wants to buy a dress priced at $6 and has only $4, how much more money does she need?

Terminology	*Correct for These Problems*
$6 *minus* $4 equals $2	A, B, C
$6 *take away* $4 leaves $2	A
$6 *less* $4 equals $2	A
$4 *from* $6 equals $2	A

Problem A is a take-away problem. Alice *takes* or *gives away* or *spends* or *pays* $4; the action is one of removing the $4 from the total of $6 in her possession.

Problem B is a comparison problem in which the $6 price of one dress is *compared with* the $4 price of the other. The $4 are matched with four of the $6. The $4 are *not* taken away.

Problem C is an additive problem; the process is one of finding the missing addend to build the $4 up to $6. Nothing is taken *from* anything else.

The conclusion from all this seems rather obvious. Children cannot be expected to go through all the preceding analysis every time they are to read a simple subtraction algorism. Why, then, do we not teach them *the correct way* of reading the algorism, which will *always* be correct, in the first grade on through the rest of arithmetic and beyond? If they are first taught the "take-away" terminologies (are even taught perhaps that the sign "−" is "the take-away sign"), they must either "unlearn" this later or run into difficulty when the subtraction problems they face *do* involve subtraction but do *not* involve *taking away.*

The recommendation that the term "minus" be taught from the beginning as the correct way to read the subtraction algorism is not intended to suggest that it must be used in all oral discussion of subtraction situations.

Primary-grade children are usually not expected to use the terms "minuend" and "subtrahend" in subtraction any more than they typically use the term "addend" in addition. Perhaps they most frequently refer to those terms in the vertical algorism as "the top number" and "the bottom number." The prefix of *"sub*trahend" gives the clue to the name of the "bottom number" in the vertical algorism, for older children as well as their teachers. That type of definition (by position in the vertical algorism) is not the most basic one. The more fundamental definitions of the terms in subtraction go back to the meaning of subtraction as a process of separating a known total group into a known subgroup and an unknown (to-be-found) subgroup. The *minuend* is the total group; it corresponds to the *sum,* or *total,* in addition. The *subtrahend* is the known subgroup within that total group, corresponding to an addend in addition. The *sub*trahend is the subgroup to be *sub*tracted. The answer is the missing subgroup, corresponding to a missing addend in addition.

The answer in subtraction has different names depending again on the problem situation for which it supplies the solution. If the problem is of the take-away type, the answer is the *remainder.* It tells the size of the subgroup that is *left* after the known subgroup is taken away. If the problem is a comparison type, the answer is called the *difference.* Here the total (minuend) is compared with another group, which is matched with a subgroup of the total to find *how much larger* the total group is or to find *how much smaller* the subgroup is. In the additive type of subtraction problem, the answer is the missing *addend.* This term is not generally used with children; they can understand the situation without that term and usually refer to the answer as "how many needed" to complete a known total.

This variety of names for answers in subtraction can be handled satisfactorily if the teacher is careful to teach the names that fit each type of problem. How does one know which name to use? One looks to the situation in which the problem arises. One uses the term that makes sense in such a problem.

Other terms that are very important as representing ideas needed as part of children's backgrounds for understanding subtraction should also be carefully taught. They include such words and phrases as: *more, less, fewer,* more than, less than, fewer than, and as many as for comparison subtraction; how many left for take away subtraction; and how many gone and how many more needed for additive subtraction.

Finally, introducing the terminology of subtraction should not be merely a phase of formal drill on the subtraction forms or algorisms of subtraction. They should develop in use in meaningful problem situations. That is not only a good place for them to develop; it is the *only* place in which they can be developed meaningfully.

Rules of Subtraction

One might suppose that subtraction, being the inverse process to addition, would follow the same rules. Caution is necessary. Subtraction does not follow the commutative or associative laws as addition does, but in each case it does have another rule that is somewhat related (in an inverse fashion). A rule of likeness applies to subtraction. The closure principle does not apply to subtraction of natural numbers.

THE SUBTRAHEND-REMAINDER RULE

Subtraction is not commutative; that is, we may not exchange the first two terms of the algorism without changing the answer. For example, we may add $2 + 4$ or $4 + 2$ to get a sum of 6 according to the commutative rule for addition; we cannot do that with subtraction. We may *not* exchange the minuend and subtrahend; for example, we cannot exchange the 6 and 2 in $6 - 2 = 4$. (The only time this would be permissible would be in the subtraction of a number from itself, e.g., $4 - 4 = 0$.)

We can, however, exchange the subtrahend and the remainder (or difference). This is as one would expect, since the *sum* in addition corresponds to the *minuend* in subtraction (the total group), and the *addends* in addition correspond to the *subtrahend* and *remainder* (or difference) in subtraction. (That is, the subtrahend-remainder rule derives from the commutative property of addition.) Figure 45 presents this relationship.

If 2 white balls and 3 black balls are to be added, it makes no difference whether they are added as $2 + 3$ or $3 + 2$. The sum will be 5. If one knows that there are 5 balls in all (black and white) and knows either that there are 2 white balls or that there are 3 black balls, he can derive the other subgroup. That is, either for addition or for subtraction, the subgroups within a total group are interchangeable as to order. The difference is that in addition both (interchangeable) subgroups are given (known), whereas in subtraction one of the subgroups is given (known) and the other is not.

The subtrahend-remainder rule in subtraction is useful in the learning of subtraction facts. This rule may be stated in various ways. Using their initial letters for the terms "minuend," "subtrahend," and "remainder," we might state the relationship thus:

$$\text{If } m - s = r, \text{ then } m - r = s$$

Using T to denote "total group" and A and B to denote the subgroups that comprise the total group, the expression of this rule would be:

$$\text{If } T - A = B, \text{ then } T - B = A$$

Often the rule is stated: $a - b = c$; so: $a - c = b$. If a child knows that $12 - 3 = 9$ and if he knows that interchanging the subtrahend and remainder will result in a different but true statement, he can figure out quite easily that $12 - 9 = 3$. Of course the child should soon get to such a level of mastery of the subtraction facts that such reliance on a known fact to derive a related unknown fact is not necessary, but in the learning stage, this is a meaningful and helpful relationship.

to draw pictures to show how it works. These pictures, if correct, will show the total group with its subgroups; the children should be able to show the "family" of addition and subtraction facts that fit the picture and should be able to point out the numerals that may be interchanged, as in figure 45.

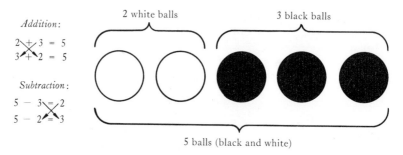

Figure 45. Commutative Law of Addition and Subtrahend-Remainder Rule of Subtraction.

Stated quite simply, *the minuend minus the remainder (or difference) equals the subtrahend.* Such a rule does not need to be given to children full-blown. They can discover it for themselves if they are given the opportunity and some guidance. Some children will discover it on their own. Some "leading questions" that may direct their attention to this relationship might be of this type:

An egg carton has spaces for 12 eggs. If there are 5 eggs in the carton, how many empty spaces will there be?
If there are 7 empty spaces, how many eggs will there be?
What is alike about these two problems?
How does one of them help you with the other one?

There are 10 boys in the scout troop. If 2 are absent, how many are present? If 8 are present, how many are absent? How does the answer to one question help you with the other question?

After a child or a group of children have formulated their own statement of this relationship, they might be tested for their understanding by being asked

ASSOCIATIVE LAW NOT APPLICABLE
TO SUBTRACTION AS TO ADDITION

The associative (or grouping) rule for addition allows the grouping of addends in any fashion without changing the sum. This will not work out for subtraction. Notice the two examples below:

Addition
$$(10 + 4) + 2 = 16$$
$$10 + (4 + 2) = 16$$
} *Same sums*

Subtraction
$$(10 - 4) - 2 = 4$$
$$10 - (4 - 2) = 8$$
} *Different remainders*

One instance of grouping subtrahends is, however, "according to rule" and is very useful. A series of successive subtrahends may be *added* and their *sum subtracted*.

$$10 - 4 - 2 = 10 - (4 + 2) = 10 - 6 = 4.$$

If Johnny has 34¢ and makes three purchases at the dime store (purchases of 5¢, 1¢, and 10¢) this association or grouping of subtrahends would be appropriate. Johnny, if he were summarizing his transactions after they were completed, might well add "5¢ + 1¢ + 10¢" and then subtract the sum "16¢" from his original 34¢. In fact, this procedure is commonly followed. It amounts to subtracting several individual subtrahends *all at once*.

$$34¢ - 5¢ - 1¢ - 10¢ =$$
$$34¢ - (5¢ + 1¢ + 10¢) = 34¢ - 16¢ = 18¢$$

Stated algebraically:
$$a - b - c - d = a - (b + c + d)$$

This rule may be stated in words: *Successive subtrahends may be subtracted by subtracting their sum.* A simpler statement for children might be: "If you have more than one number to subtract, you may add them and subtract their sum all at once."

This principle may be developed in any problem situation where it would apply. For example, children might be given this exercise, orally or in written form.

Gail bought a dozen eggs. She is going to do some baking. She will use 4 eggs for a custard and 2 eggs in a cake.
Should Gail take 4 eggs from the carton first and then 2 eggs? Or should she take out 6 eggs all at once? Does it matter? Draw a picture to prove your answer.

Figure 46 suggests an acceptable "picture proof."

THE RULE OF LIKENESS

The minuend and subtrahend in subtraction must be alike in the sense that they are being used in the particular problem at hand. In subtraction problems cited earlier in this chapter, *dollars* have been subtracted from *dollars*, *blocks* from *blocks*, *yards* from *yards*, *cookies* from *cookies*, *chairs* from *chairs*, and *boys* from *boys*. The "likeness" was represented by dollars,

blocks, yards, cookies, chairs, and boys. It would not be correct to subtract dollars from blocks, yards from cookies, or chairs from boys. On the other hand, one might correctly subtract feet from yards if one or both were first changed to the same designation: 3 yards − 2 feet = 9 feet − 2 feet = 7 feet. The "2" could not be subtracted from the "3" because those numerical coefficients did not apply to the same things. After they had the same designations, "2" could be subtracted from "9" to give a correct answer.

One characteristic of a group is a quality of likeness among the members of the group. Subtraction is a separation of a total group into constituent subgroups. Since all members of the total group must have an identifying quality in common, all members of its subgroups would have to have that same identification.

The algebraic expression "$5a - 3a$" may be changed to the single term "$2a$" because both "5" and "3" in this case refer to "a." The "$5a$" and "$3a$" are like terms. On the other hand, "$5a - 3b$" cannot be changed to a single-term expression with the coefficient "2," because the terms are unlike.

Occasionally, some confusion is caused by a problem like this one: If we know 12 people are coming to a meeting and there are only 8 chairs in the room, how many more chairs are needed? The abstract subtraction fact "$12 - 8 = 4$" fits this situation, but this does not mean "12 people − 8 chairs = 4 chairs." According to the rule of likeness (and common observation as well), this is impossible. Children enjoy reacting to the challenge of figuring out just "what went wrong here." Some skillful questioning will help if necessary. The teacher might ask: What step in our thinking is missing to give us such a silly statement? Or she might suggest that someone act out the situation — with real people and chairs or with representative objects. Or someone

to understand if the principle of like-ness had been understood and empha-sized in connection with addition and subtraction of whole numbers.

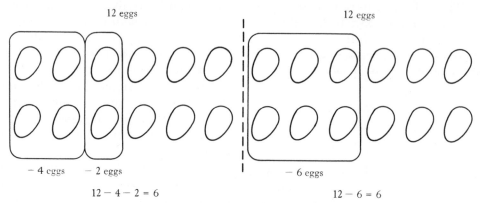

12 eggs   12 eggs

− 4 eggs   − 2 eggs   − 6 eggs

$12 - 4 - 2 = 6$ $12 - 6 = 6$

The remainder is 6 eggs in either case.

Figure 46. Subtracting the Sum of Two Successive Subtrahends.

could draw a diagram. Such activities will soon show that the missing step is this: 12 people need 12 chairs. The total of 12 chairs needed − 8 chairs now present = 4 chairs to be brought in to complete the group of 12. This is the one-to-one correspondence idea, one chair for one person.

The rule of likeness for subtraction is basic to the algorisms for subtraction of two-place and larger numbers, in which ones are subtracted from ones, tens from tens, hundreds from hundreds, and so on — like place values always being considered together. The various algorisms for subtraction of larger numbers all use this principle in one way or another, subtracting always within a given place value (name value) but sometimes changing face and place values if this can be done without changing the combined face and place value.

The rule of likeness for subtraction is also applied in the subtraction of common fractions, using common denominators (same names). The whole concept of common denominators for fractions would be very much easier for children

The Basic Subtraction Facts

BASIC SUBTRACTION FACTS DEFINED

The *basic subtraction facts* are the building blocks of subtraction just as the basic addition facts are the building blocks of addition. For every basic addition fact there is a basic subtraction fact; every addition-subtraction "fact family" includes a set of two addition and two subtraction facts,[5] such as:

Family of Basic Facts for 2, 5, and 7

2	5	7	7
+5	+2	−5	−2
7	7	2	5

Family of Basic Facts for 3, 8, and 11

3	8	11	11
+8	+3	−8	−3
11	11	3	8

Just as the basic addition facts may be defined as those which combine all the possible combinations of 1-digit num-

---

[5] Except the "doubles," for which there is only one addition fact and one corresponding subtraction fact.

TABLE 3 *

Basic Subtraction Facts

0 −0 = 0	1 −1 = 0	2 −2 = 0	3 −3 = 0	4 −4 = 0	5 −5 = 0	6 −6 = 0	7 −7 = 0	8 −8 = 0	9 −9 = 0
1 −0 = 1	2 −1 = 1	3 −2 = 1	4 −3 = 1	5 −4 = 1	6 −5 = 1	7 −6 = 1	8 −7 = 1	9 −8 = 1	10 −9 = 1
2 −0 = 2	3 −1 = 2	4 −2 = 2	5 −3 = 2	6 −4 = 2	7 −5 = 2	8 −6 = 2	9 −7 = 2	10 −8 = 2	11 −9 = 2
3 −0 = 3	4 −1 = 3	5 −2 = 3	6 −3 = 3	7 −4 = 3	8 −5 = 3	9 −6 = 3	10 −7 = 3	11 −8 = 3	12 −9 = 3
4 −0 = 4	5 −1 = 4	6 −2 = 4	7 −3 = 4	8 −4 = 4	9 −5 = 4	10 −6 = 4	11 −7 = 4	12 −8 = 4	13 −9 = 4
5 −0 = 5	6 −1 = 5	7 −2 = 5	8 −3 = 5	9 −4 = 5	10 −5 = 5	11 −6 = 5	12 −7 = 5	13 −8 = 5	14 −9 = 5
6 −0 = 6	7 −1 = 6	8 −2 = 6	9 −3 = 6	10 −4 = 6	11 −5 = 6	12 −6 = 6	13 −7 = 6	14 −8 = 6	15 −9 = 6
7 −0 = 7	8 −1 = 7	9 −2 = 7	10 −3 = 7	11 −4 = 7	12 −5 = 7	13 −6 = 7	14 −7 = 7	15 −8 = 7	16 −9 = 7
8 −0 = 8	9 −1 = 8	10 −2 = 8	11 −3 = 8	12 −4 = 8	13 −5 = 8	14 −6 = 8	15 −7 = 8	16 −8 = 8	17 −9 = 8
9 −0 = 9	10 −1 = 9	11 −2 = 9	12 −3 = 9	13 −4 = 9	14 −5 = 9	15 −6 = 9	16 −7 = 9	17 −8 = 9	18 −9 = 9

*An alternate arrangement of these facts would place the like remainders
in the vertical instead of the horizontal arrangement.

bers, so the basic subtraction facts may be described as those which have 1-digit numbers in both the subtrahend and remainder positions. Another way of saying this would be: The basic subtraction facts are those which represent either a 1-digit or a 2-digit quantity as being separated into two 1-digit quantities. As in addition there are some basic facts with 1-digit sums and some with 2-digit sums, so in subtraction there are some basic facts with 1-digit minuends and some with 2-digit minuends.

Since we have a decimal number system, we have 100 basic subtraction facts.[6] All the basic subtraction facts for our system are shown in table 3. If a person knows these facts, understands the concepts of base and place, and has control of the subtraction process as discussed in the earlier parts of this chapter, he can manage any subtraction operation

[6] If we had another base than ten, we would have a different number of basic subtraction facts. See footnote on this point for basic addition facts, p. 96.

with whole numbers, no matter how large they may be.

As with basic addition facts, some people prefer to speak of 81 basic subtraction facts, omitting from those in table 3 all the facts in which zero appears. They *are* basic facts; they are building blocks that prove very useful and necessary later. They may be omitted during the early phases of learning the basic subtraction facts, since they are usually not needed until children come to two-place subtraction examples, but they must not be ignored. When introduced, they can be rather quickly taught along with the development of two basic generalizations: (1) when zero is subtracted from another number, the number does not change; and (2) when a number is subtracted from itself, the remainder (difference) is zero.

The basic subtraction *combinations* are the same "facts" without their answers. That is, "11 − 3 = 8" is a basic subtraction fact; "11 − 3" is a basic subtraction combination.

No person can be efficient in his use of subtraction if he does not learn the basic subtraction facts to the level of automatic recall. Nor can he be efficient in subtraction applications if he does not know their meanings. Children should be introduced to subtraction facts in situations in which they can see for themselves that the fact statements are *true* in observed situations. Children can work with objects to derive the subtraction facts for themselves and then proceed to their use in enough situations to establish correct meanings. As these activities proceed, the children will be learning the facts to some degree; if more practice is needed to assure mastery, that practice may proceed on the semiconcrete and on the abstract level.

A chart such as table 3 should not be presented ready-made for children as an assignment to be memorized. It might be presented later as a basis for discovery of certain patterns of relationship that it shows. Better yet, such a chart can be made by the children, the individual facts being filled in as children work them out for themselves.

THE BASIC SUBTRACTION FACTS IN RELATION TO THE BASIC ADDITION FACTS

If children are to understand the inverse relationship of addition and subtraction, the basic subtraction facts should be taught in relation to their corresponding addition facts. This may be done according to various sequences of introducing the formal study of the facts. Subtraction facts may be presented along with their corresponding addition facts from the beginning of direct attention to the basic facts. That is, the basic facts are grouped by "families" from the beginning. Some teachers prefer to work with the addition concept and a few basic addition facts long enough for children to develop confidence in their use before the corresponding subtraction facts are presented. Once the subtraction concept and some easier facts have been introduced, successive sets of addition and subtraction facts are presented in close succession or in "families." This general plan is probably the most usual procedure. The best test of any sequence is whether or not the children seem to be understanding what they are doing. If they manage both processes well, they should continue with both. If they seem to be confused, perhaps they need more time to learn the addition concept before working with subtraction facts.

The preceding paragraph refers to the so-called "formal," or preplanned, part of the arithmetic instruction program. So far as the informal, everyday uses of arithmetic are concerned, both addition and subtraction experiences will occur long before there is any necessity to write the basic facts. The wise teacher will use such experiences but will be willing to let children operate at a level that builds their confidence in their own ability to handle such situations. Children may put groups together and take them apart, knowing very well what they are doing, without the necessity for the writing of the formal algorisms for basic facts. For example, they may arrange a group of six chairs in groups of two chairs and four chairs. They can discuss this grouping in addition and subtraction ways without mentioning those words and without using any formal algorisms:

"Two chairs here and four chairs at the table are six chairs in all."

"We have six chairs. If we put two over here, there will be four left at the table."

"We have six chairs. If only four are needed at the table, we can move two over here by the window."

"Four chairs and two chairs are six chairs. Let's put them all together."

Such discussion concerning a routine experience with subgroups and their total lays a good foundation for later arithmetic instruction, when those same observations are written out as:

2 chairs + 4 chairs = 6 chairs
4 chairs + 2 chairs = 6 chairs
6 chairs − 2 chairs = 4 chairs
6 chairs − 4 chairs = 2 chairs

OR

2 chairs	4 chairs	6 chairs	6 chairs
+4 chairs	+2 chairs	−2 chairs	−4 chairs
6 chairs	6 chairs	4 chairs	2 chairs

An excellent activity for developing the relationship between addition and subtraction facts, as well as for practicing the facts, is the playing of dominoes. See figure 47, in which one possible

"play" is outlined to show the use of the paired addition and subtraction facts: $10 - 4 = 6$ and $4 + 6 = 10$.

According to the regular rules for playing dominoes, the subtraction practice obtained would concentrate on minuends that are multiples of 5. These rules can be modified for the sake of practice; for example, one might make sums of 12 the objective if practice on minuends of 12 is desired (assuming use of a set of dominoes that go beyond the "double 6" set).

The existing relationship between basic addition and subtraction facts suggests that the sequence of planned introduction of the facts would logically coincide for the two processes. If addition facts are introduced by size of sum (for example, all addition facts with a sum of 12 introduced together), it would be logical also to introduce together the subtraction facts with the corresponding minuend (12 in this case). If addition facts are introduced in groups that encourage generalizations, such as, "Adding zero to another number does not change that number," the subtraction facts would be similarly introduced so as to build the generalization "Subtracting zero from another number does not change that number." This is not mandatory, of course, but it would seem to be consistent for an instructional program stressing relationships.

THE BASIC SUBTRACTION FACTS
AS COUNTING BACKWARD

The need for practice in counting backward has already been stressed (pp. 146-47) as background for teaching subtraction as counting backward. This counting might be reviewed in connection with some activity that would emphasize the idea, such as: walking forward and counting steps forward and then walking backward and counting backward; children counting themselves into a group and out again, with appropriate movements; building a tower of blocks as they are counted forward and then removing the blocks as they are counted backward; and doing "backward counting" on a number line.

If generalizations are to be developed for such concepts as "subtracting 1" or "subtracting 2," it is necessary to use a situation in which the same number will be subtracted more than once. The counting-backward emphasis shows up so much more clearly in a sequence of subtractions. One way to establish such a sequence is to use a problem similar to this one:

Problem: Christine's father gave her 10 tickets to the miniature golf course, which he owns. Christine uses 1 ticket each day. Show how many tickets Christine has every day until the tickets are all used up. Every time Christine uses a ticket, she subtracts. Write the subtraction story for every day.

A good aid for such a sequence of dramatizations is a strip of tickets, perforated for easy tearing. The teacher or some of the children may have such tickets; some tickets may be "left over" from a school entertainment, or they are often given as "chances" on gift merchandise in stores or shopping centers. They can easily be made of paper, with perforations run on the sewing machine. Any strip of paper may be marked off as tickets and scissors used

Situation:

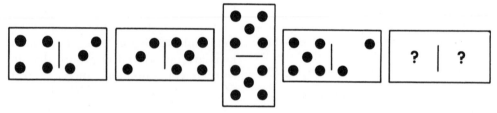

Player's Thoughts:

"How can I make the ends have a sum of 10?"
"There's a 4 on one end. $4 + ? = 10$ $10 - 4 = ?$"
"$10 - 4 = 6$. I'll put a two-six domino at the right."

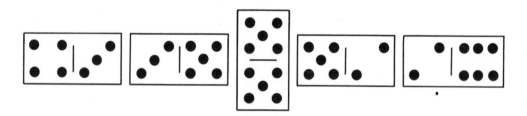

Player Verifying His Play:

"$4 + 6 = 10$"

Figure 47. Use of Paired Addition and Subtraction Facts in Playing Dominoes.

for the separation of each successive ticket.

It is very important to first perform the action of separating the daily ticket, followed immediately by the oral and written statement of the action as a subtraction fact. Either horizontal or vertical algorisms may be used, but all in the series should be in the same form.

The first two steps in the action for Christine's problem are shown in figure 48 along with the algorisms that "tell the story." After the full series of subtractions has been completed, the chalkboard will show a set of subtraction facts, which may be arranged in various ways. Two ways are shown herewith, one vertically along the margin of this page and one horizontally below.[7]

$$10 - 1 = 9$$
$$9 - 1 = 8$$
$$8 - 1 = 7$$
$$7 - 1 = 6$$
$$6 - 1 = 5$$
$$5 - 1 = 4$$
$$4 - 1 = 3$$
$$3 - 1 = 2$$
$$2 - 1 = 1$$
$$1 - 1 = 0$$

10	9	8	7	6	5	4	3	2	1
−1	−1	−1	−1	−1	−1	−1	−1	−1	−1
9	8	7	6	5	4	3	2	1	0

Even before the series is complete, some children may notice the resemblance to counting. If not, the teacher can call attention to this resemblance. She may ask, "What do you notice about the remainders?" Or she may suggest: "As I point to the remainders, I want you to read them aloud—just the remainders." After the oral reading, again some child may volunteer the generalization, or the teacher may ask further, "What did that sound like?" She is likely to get a chorus of replies, "Counting backward!"

At this point there is no necessity to formulate immediately a generalization about "subtracting 1." Some children will need more experiences before any formal statement will have adequate

meaning for them. This experience may wait until a later occasion, or the teacher may encourage further consideration of the present situation. For example, she might say, "Now I'm going to go through these actions again, more quickly this time. I will take a new strip of 10 tickets, and I will subtract them one by one. You tell me how many are left each time I subtract 1." As this is done, the pattern of counting backward will again be readily apparent if children have adequate background.

A discussion might follow concerning how easy it is to subtract 1, why it is easy, how counting backward may help, and so on until someone does, voluntarily or at the teacher's suggestion, put into words the basic relationship. Some child statements of the "subtracting 1" generalization might be:

"When you subtract 1, it's like counting backward by 1."
"When you count backward by ones, you are really subtracting ones."
"When you subtract 1, the answer is the next number going down."

A generalized understanding and statement might similarly be developed for counting backward by 2's. Christine's problem might be varied so that she takes one other child with her each day, thus subtracting 2 tickets each day.

Another situation that introduces and relates all the basic subtraction facts with 2 as a subtrahend might be one in which several children were given different sums of money from 2¢ or 3¢ through 11¢. Each child could be asked to pay 2¢ for a given item and then write the subtraction fact for what he did. These facts might be written in miscellaneous order on the chalkboard, after which the teacher could suggest their rearrangement—"all the facts with even sums on this side, all the facts with odd

---

[7] The inclusion of the fact "$1 - 1 = 0$" is optional. It depends on the teacher's judgment in light of children's past learning. The generalization may be developed with or without it.

sums on that side." (This assumes familiarity of the children with odd and even numbers.) A further suggestion, if necessary, might be that the facts should be arranged (within odd and even groupings) according to the size of the remainder, after which discussion

cluding all the following: (1) acquaintance with and understanding of the basic facts used, (2) relatedness among the various facts in each sequence, (3) relationship between subtracting and counting backward, and (4) a method for working out the remainder for any

Actions   *Facts*

First Day:

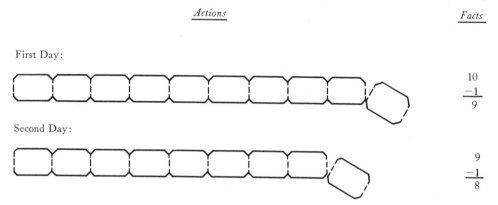

$$\begin{array}{r} 10 \\ -1 \\ \hline 9 \end{array}$$

Second Day:

$$\begin{array}{r} 9 \\ -1 \\ \hline 8 \end{array}$$

Figure 48. Acting Out a Series of Basic Facts for Subtracting One.

similar to that suggested above for the "subtracting 1" generalization might be used to help children discover and formulate the "subtracting 2" generalizations below, stated in children's words. Of course, the first two and the latter two statements relate to different discoveries inherent in the situation.

"When you subtract 2, it's like counting backward by 2 s."
"When you subtract 2, you skip one number going backward."
"When you subtract 2 from an even number, the answer is an even number."
"When you subtract 2 from an odd number, the answer is an odd number."

Reference to figure 27, chapter 5, will suggest how number lines may be used in developing the "counting by 2's" generalizations. While the illustrations there deal with "adding 2's," they can easily be adapted to show "subtracting 2's."

The outcomes of instruction like that suggested for "subtracting 1" and "subtracting 2" are varied, certainly in-

subtraction fact involving "subtracting 1" or "subtracting 2." The last point, that of transfer to other situations, is extremely important. A child who really understands that "when you subtract 2, you skip one number going backward" can subtract not only the basic facts with 2 as the subtrahend but he can also work out any other "subtracting 2" fact that is within his counting range. He can subtract "99 − 2 = 97" as well as "9 − 2 = 7." This is a tremendous advantage.

BASIC SUBTRACTION FACTS

AS REGROUPING

Since subtraction is a matter of regrouping by separation, the basic subtraction facts must represent regrouping. Even such a simple fact as "4 − 2 = 2" represents the regrouping of 4 into two subgroups of 2 each. One of the subgroups is known and the other is to be found. Children need much practice with the separation of groups if they are to understand the basic meaning of subtraction; since the basic facts must be learned before they can be used in the subtraction of larger numbers, the early instruction in the meaning of subtraction naturally uses the basic facts almost exclusively.

One special application of the concept of regrouping is found in the basic facts with minuends of 11 through 18. Take the basic fact "13 − 6 = 7." The numeral "13" already represents a grouping according to our decimal-place-value system. It means "1 group of ten and 3 ones," or a group of ten and a group of three. When we state that 13 − 6 = 7, we are really saying that the group of 10 and the group of 3 are being regrouped into a new group of 6 and another group (unknown at first but determined as 7). The question "13 − 6 = ?" really means "How can a group of 10 and a group of 3 be regrouped so one of the two new groups will be 6?" or "If a group of 10 and a group of 3 are regrouped into new groups, one of which is 6, how large will the other new group be?"

One would hardly begin the discussion of regrouping in the manner of the last paragraph with young children learning the basic subtraction facts. They need a concrete situation in which they can actually manipulate the items that make up the groups. Three such situations are provided below in three problems representing the three ideas or applications of subtraction (take-away, comparison, and additive subtraction).

Problem T (Take Away): Joel has 13¢. He spends 6¢ for candy. How much money does he have left?

Problem C (Comparison): Ethel has 13 paper dolls. Laura has 6. How many more paper dolls does Ethel have?

Problem A (Additive): Sharon is helping her mother take the ornaments off the Christmas tree. She knows how many there are because they came from two boxes, one with spaces for 10 ornaments and one with spaces for 3 ornaments. Sharon's mother has already put 6 ornaments in a box. How many more ornaments should Sharon put away?

The actions used in dramatizing the solutions of these problems will be different, but in each case the regrouping of a ten and a three into a six and a seven can be clearly shown. The picture representations in figure 49 indicate possible ways of "acting out" these problem solutions. Note that the overall concept of regrouping is enriched by using problems of different application types.

The particular type of regrouping emphasized in these problem solutions emphasizes the fact that the 6 items being subtracted (pennies, dolls, or bells) are subtracted from the subgroup 10 at the same time they are being subtracted from the total group of 13 (pennies, dolls, or bells). Therefore, an easy way to subtract 6 from 13 (before the subtraction fact itself has become automatic) is to think of subtracting 6 from 10 and then add the remainder (or difference) to the 3 ones. Although this procedure is not recommended as a permanent procedure, its use during development of the basic subtraction facts not only will facilitate learning of these facts but will increase children's facility in thinking about quantities as grouped in our base-place system.

A child who cannot follow the reasoning here probably does not have adequate background understanding of preliminary ideas (the base of ten, place value, total group, subgroups, subtraction). One very specific meaning he must possess is the meaning of the "teens" numbers, which are the minu-

Problem T:

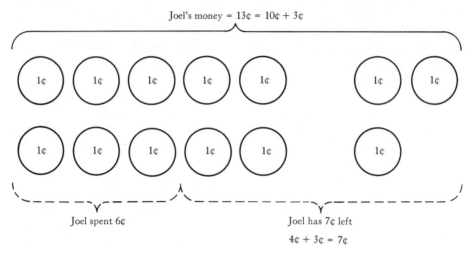

Joel's money = 13¢ = 10¢ + 3¢

Joel spent 6¢

Joel has 7¢ left

4¢ + 3¢ = 7¢

Problem C:

Ethel's dolls:

13 = 10 + 3

Laura's dolls:

Laura's dolls match up with 6 of Ethel's dolls.
10 dolls — 6 dolls = 4 dolls ◄ — — — — — —
Those 4 dolls and the other 3 dolls are 7 dolls.
13 — 6 = 4 + 3 = 7

Problem A :

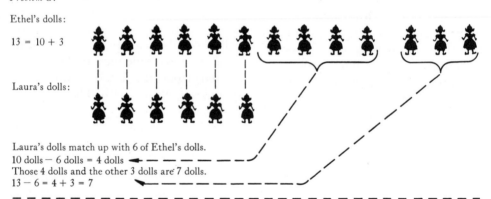

The first box holds 10.
Sharon has 6 in that box.
10 bells — 6 bells =. 4 bells needed

The second box holds 3.
3 bells needed to fill the box
4 bells + 3 bells = 7 bells needed

13 bells in all — 6 bells in box = 7 bells needed

Figure 49. Subtraction as Regrouping — Emphasis on Tens and Ones.

ends in all the basic facts that can be handled in this fashion.

The 36 basic subtraction facts which are readily regrouped as shown in figure 49 are these:

$11 - 2 = 9$	$12 - 9 = 3$	$13 - 8 = 5$	$15 - 9 = 6$
$11 - 9 = 2$	$12 - 4 = 8$	$13 - 6 = 7$	$15 - 7 = 8$
$11 - 3 = 8$	$12 - 8 = 4$	$13 - 7 = 6$	$15 - 8 = 7$
$11 - 8 = 3$	$12 - 5 = 7$	$14 - 5 = 9$	$16 - 7 = 9$
$11 - 4 = 7$	$12 - 7 = 5$	$14 - 9 = 5$	$16 - 9 = 7$
$11 - 7 = 4$	$12 - 6 = 6$	$14 - 6 = 8$	$16 - 8 = 8$
$11 - 5 = 6$	$13 - 4 = 9$	$14 - 8 = 6$	$17 - 8 = 9$
$11 - 6 = 5$	$13 - 9 = 4$	$14 - 7 = 7$	$17 - 9 = 8$
$12 - 3 = 9$	$13 - 5 = 8$	$15 - 6 = 9$	$18 - 9 = 9$

The nine-basic subtraction facts with minuends of 10 may also be taught so as to lay stress on separation of a ten into its various subgroups, but this emphasis should probably precede the regrouping scheme for 11 through 19.

USING THE RULES OF SUBTRACTION

IN LEARNING THE BASIC

SUBTRACTION FACTS

Of course, the *rule of likeness* will be used in all the problem situations within which basic facts are developed and practiced. (This is another advantage of having most of the development and much of the practice on facts done within meaningful settings instead of by routine drill procedures.) Another application of the rule of likeness is illustrated in problem T (p. 168), in which Joel had 13¢. In working this out, a child might well start with the idea that Joel had 1 dime and 3 pennies. Before he could subtract (spend) 6 pennies, he would have to change the dime to pennies. Pennies are not to be subtracted from a dime without first changing (actually or mentally) the dime to pennies so the subtraction will be done with "like" quantities. For young children, the terminology would probably empha-

size subtracting things that "have the same name."

The *subtrahend-remainder law* is used when the "reverse" subtraction facts are taught in relation to each other. Instead of separating the presentations of facts like "$12 - 4 = 8$" and "$12 - 8 = 4$," as was recommended a generation ago under strict drill theory, modern methods of teaching *use* the relationship between such pairs of facts to help children learn the facts more quickly. The children need never hear of the "subtrahend-remainder law" by that name; what they do need is the idea that the known and unknown subgroups within a known total may be interchanged. If they know any particular subtraction fact, they can use it to help them learn the fact that has the same numbers in it but with "subtracted number" and "answer" reversed.

The subtraction tables (tables 4 and 5) show the effects of the subtrahend-remainder law clearly, in addition to being useful as reference guides for children. The only subtraction facts that do not have "reverse" facts are those which have the same subtrahend and remainder (comparable to the addition "doubles"). These facts run in a diagonal line across table 4 (shaded area) and separate the chart into two triangular sections. Either of these triangles plus the diagonal central group of facts includes 55 basic subtraction facts. If one or the other triangle were missing, it could be built up by application of the subtrahend-remainder law.

Tables 4 and 5 can be built up by the children as they discover or learn for themselves the basic facts. Building such charts is a good activity for the children, since they can see many interesting interfact relationships as they do it. Either chart can be built progressively as the different facts or sets of facts are learned, or it can be built as a summary-type activity after all the facts have been developed. In any event, the learning advantages from building the been established, it is easy for both teacher and pupils to find new relationships. A very profitable activity is a search for patterns among subtraction facts, for which simple subtraction

	0	1	2	3	4	5	6	7	8	9
0	0	1	2	3	4	5	6	7	8	9
1	1	2	3	4	5	6	7	8	9	10
2	2	3	4	5	6	7	8	9	10	11
3	3	4	5	6	7	8	9	10	11	12
4	4	5	6	7	8	9	10	11	12	13
5	5	6	7	8	9	10	11	12	13	14
6	6	7	8	9	10	11	12	13	14	15
7	7	8	9	10	11	12	13	14	15	16
8	8	9	10	11	12	13	14	15	16	17
9	9	10	11	12	13	14	15	16	17	18

Example: To subtract 4 from 12, follow procedure *A* or *B*.

Procedure A:
Find "4" in top row. Go straight down to "12." Follow that row to the left.
The remainder (8) will be in the left column.

Procedure B:
Find "4" in left column.
Go to the right to "12."
Follow that column upward.
The remainder (8) will be in the top row.

Table 4. Subtraction Table for Basic Facts (Minuends within Chart).

table are much greater than those to be derived from having it presented as a completed form to be studied.

Ways of helping children to establish relationships among subtraction facts and from subtraction facts to addition facts have by no means been exhausted in the preceding discussion. Once the idea of looking for relationships has charts such as tables 4 and 5 may serve as sources of "clues."

Take, for example, table 5. Notice the "9's" running in diagonal fashion from upper left to lower right, indicating the subtraction of 9 in each case. Look at the complete subtraction facts in which 9 is subtracted. What is alike about all these facts? (18 − 9 = 9;

$17 - 9 = 8$; $16 - 9 = 7$; $15 - 9 = 6$; etc.) If the answer is not forthcoming, ask further questions, such as: What happens to the number in ones place when you subtract 9? What happens to the

table 5, such as the column of facts that always give a remainder of 8. What is alike about the subtraction facts that have a remainder of 8? (It is like subtracting a ten and adding 2 ones.)

Minuends	0	1	2	3	4	5	6	7	8	9	*Minuends*
0	0	9	8	7	6	5	4	3	2	1	10
1	1	0	9	8	7	6	5	4	3	2	11
2	2	1	0	9	8	7	6	5	4	3	12
3	3	2	1	0	9	8	7	6	5	4	13
4	4	3	2	1	0	9	8	7	6	5	14
5	5	4	3	2	1	0	9	8	7	6	15
6	6	5	4	3	2	1	0	9	8	7	16
7	7	6	5	4	3	2	1	0	9	8	17
8	8	7	6	5	4	3	2	1	0	9	18
9	9	8	7	6	5	4	3	2	1	0	

Example:

To subtract when minuend is 9 or less, as in $9 - 6 = 3$:

Find minuend (9) in left column.
Follow that row to the right to the
    subtrahend (6).
The remainder (3) will be at to the top
    of that column.

To subtract when minuend is 10 or more, as in $14 - 6 = 8$:

Find minuend (14) in right column.
Follow that row to the left to the
    subtrahend (6).
The remainder (8) will be at the top of
    that column.

Table 5. Subtraction Chart for Basic Facts (Minuends at Left and Right).

number in tens place when you subtract 9? Eventually, if the children are really ready for such reasoning, they will arrive at the generalization that "when you subtract 9, you have 1 less ten and 1 more one."

Similarly, one might call attention to a particular column of subtrahends in

In a sense, then, the tables may serve as a framework within which to discover (or rediscover) generalizations about certain groups of facts or about subtraction itself. For example, the subtrahend-remainder law is obvious in any summary chart of subtraction facts.

STUDY QUESTIONS

1. How can the inverse relation between addition and subtraction be used to help children learn basic subtraction facts?

2. This chapter (and most elementary school arithmetic texts) presents take-away, comparison, and additive subtraction as *applications* of the fundamental concept of subtraction. If these differences are apparent only when subtraction is *used* in a problem situation, why is so much attention given to them?

3. Demonstrate with objects or draw a number line to show the relation between the subtrahend-remainder law for subtraction and the commutative law for addition.

4. If you have more than one amount to subtract from a given total, does it matter which one of the subtractions is done first? Why or why not?

5. Is this a true statement? "Equal increases or decreases in the minuend and subtrahend allow the remainder to remain unchanged." Demonstrate the truth or falsity of this statement on a number line.

6. Use "34 − 17" as the basis of three word problems for children to solve. Have one problem show a take-away application of subtraction, one show a comparison application, and one show the additive idea of subtraction.

CHAPTER 8

Subtraction of Larger
Whole Numbers

MANY A CHILD has stumbled in his school progress because of stubbing his arithmetical toe on a hazard known as "borrowing"; most likely, he would not have done so had he brought to that learning task clear understandings of subtraction and of the numbers with which he was expected to deal. Except for the direction of the process, the process of *changing* or *regrouping* in subtraction (better terms for "borrowing") is fundamentally the same as *changing* or *regrouping* in addition; in either case, understanding of changing depends on understanding our place-value numeration system. Changing is generally conceded to be the most difficult phase of the subtraction of two-place and larger whole numbers; when properly introduced, it need not remain a mysterious and arbitrary ritual.

Two-Place Subtraction Without Changing

Children do not need to be shielded from two- or three-place subtraction until after they have mastered all the basic subtraction facts. The subtraction of 21¢ from a total of 42¢ may be well within the competence of a child who has not achieved automatic control of a subtraction fact like $17 - 8 = 9$.[1] In fact,

many situations arise in and out of the classroom in which young children may need to subtract two-place numbers.

The total enrollment in a class is 29; of these, 17 children have been weighed by the school nurse. If a question arises as to how many children are still to be weighed, the teacher may decide to answer such a question by merely giving the response quickly herself, by writing the algorism (such as Form A) on the board where the children can see it but without any special comment, or by encouraging them to solve the problem themselves. The demands of the particular situation (such as need for a quick response) and the teacher's knowledge of her pupils should determine the procedure to be followed.

Form A
2 9
− 1 7
1 2

Suppose the teacher purposely wrote an incomplete algorism (Form A without the remainder) on the chalkboard and then asked, "Can anyone tell me what to do next?" If the children already

[1] The sequence of topics in the present chapter is not intended to indicate formal sequence of learnings by children. It represents one of many possible logical patterns of organization of arithmetic content to cover the whole subject thoroughly for teachers, who in turn will use the material as it fits into the development and learning experiences of their pupils.

knew the two basic subtraction facts involved, they would very likely enjoy showing how well they could handle "such a big subtraction" by suggesting that $9 - 7 = 2$ and $2 - 1 = 1$, directing the teacher as to where to write the remainders. In such a case, a correct remainder could easily be obtained, but going through the formality of "getting the answer" would be no guarantee that the children understood two-place subtraction. In fact, the subtraction algorism without changing is so very easy to "work" without understanding that a large proportion of several generations of schoolchildren have been taught to work it with little or no consideration by either teacher or pupils of the base and place concepts involved.

BASE AND PLACE CONCEPTS IN TWO-PLACE SUBTRACTION

The concepts of base and place value may not be needed for manipulation of the algorism, but they are needed for meaningful two-place subtraction. They are the same concepts as those already discussed for two-place addition and for basic subtraction facts with two-place minuends. In the three subtractions below, the recognition of "16" as having a value of "1 ten and 6 ones" is the same in each case. This recognition is important in each case if subsequent, more difficult algorisms are to be handled correctly and with understanding.

Basic Fact	Two-Place Subtraction	Two-Place Addition
16	16	16
−7	−12	+12
9	4	28

Because of detailed treatments of the same ideas in other places in this text, three significant ideas for children to learn in their work in two-place subtraction without changing are merely mentioned here: (1) the meaning of "ones" and "tens" in two-place numbers, (2) the understanding that collections of tens may be subtracted just as ones are subtracted, and (3) the necessity to subtract ones from ones and tens from tens. Attention must be given to these ideas with easy two-place subtraction if children are to be properly prepared for understanding changing in subtraction later.

ZERO FACTS IN TWO-PLACE SUBTRACTION

Two-place subtraction provides the first situation in which children usually have much use for the zero subtraction facts; so this is the occasion for stress on these facts. Neither children nor adults have much, if any, need for $4 - 0 = 4$ or for $4 - 4 = 0$, and certainly not for $0 - 0 = 0$ in one-place number situations. But practice on these facts and development of the zero generalizations makes sense in two-place subtraction examples such as these:

3 4	3 4	5 0
−2 0	−2 4	−2 0
1 4	1 0	3 0

In these examples, the child can readily be led to see that "$4 - 0 = 4$" really means that when no (0) ones are subtracted from 4 ones, 4 ones remain; that "$4 - 4 = 0$" means that when 4 ones are subtracted from 4 ones, no (0) ones remain; and that "$0 - 0 = 0$" means that if there are no (0) ones at the beginning and none to be subtracted, obviously there will be no ones in the remainder. In all these cases, the place-holder function of zero should be stressed along with the "not any" meaning of the symbol 0.

THREE IDEAS IN SUBTRACTION
PROBLEMS MAINTAINED WITH
TWO-PLACE NUMBERS

Maintenance and broadening of the concepts of "take-away," comparative, and additive subtraction situations with two-place and larger numbers are rather important as part of the total program of concept development and of problem solving. Since these three applications derive from the problem situation in which subtraction is used for the solution, they *must* be learned in problem situations. Teachers who do a reasonably good job of teaching these three interpretations in easy problems using the basic subtraction facts may neglect to maintain and further clarify the same ideas with larger numbers, chiefly because their demonstration with objects, diagrams, or other aids becomes more complicated when the numbers are larger.

Clarification of take-away, comparison, and additive situations should be stressed for two-place subtraction *without* any changing because distinguishing these situations becomes more difficult when changing is involved.[2]

Figures 50 through 52 should suffice at this point to suggest ways of demonstrating the three subtraction problem situations with two-place numbers.

---

[2] The decomposition—take-away *algorism* for subtraction may become confused with the decomposition or other *situations* in which the problems arise. For example, the problem situation may be an additive one like that presented in figure 52, but if the numbers involved were $65 - 29$, the person solving the problem might use a "take-away" algorism, thus:

$$\overset{5\ \ 15}{\cancel{6}\,\cancel{5}} \\ \underline{-2\ \ 9} \\ 3\ \ 6$$

There is nothing wrong with doing this, but if the problem meanings are still not quite clear to children when the changing algorism is introduced, they may be confused.

Take-away or Decomposition Problem: Jack had saved $65. He spent $23 for a weekend trip. How much money did he have left? (Demonstration of this situation is shown in figure 50.)

Comparison Problem: While Jack saved his $65, Jim saved only $23. How much more did Jack save? (See figure 51 for demonstration of this problem situation and solution.)

Additive Subtraction Problem: Jim has $23. He wants to buy a bicycle that costs $65. How much more money does he need to pay for the bicycle? (See action indicated in figure 52.)

Changing Tens to Ones

A mother gave her first-grade son a half-dollar coin to spend at the school's Halloween carnival. She thought that he could have a good time with so much money to spend. To her surprise and dismay, he came home quite unhappy and with his half-dollar still in his pocket. He said he had not had any fun because there was nothing to buy. The mother asked, "Didn't you get any hats? Didn't you get a balloon?" His sad reply was, "No, ma'am, they didn't have anything that cost this much."

A SPECIAL DIFFICULTY

This child had plenty of money, but it was not in a form in which he was accustomed to having money to spend. He was used to being given "the right change" for purchases he made and did not understand the intricacies of paying a larger-value coin for a smaller-value item plus "change."

This is analogous to the problem that has proved to be a real difficulty for many children older than 'his boy, the problem of figuring how to subtract from a larger number that is *not in the right form* to make the process easy. With positive whole numbers it is not possible to subtract a larger face value from a smaller face value. In Form B, 29 cannot be subtracted from 24 and stay within the set of positive numbers; nor can the 9 in the ones place in either Form B or Form

rorm B Form C

  2 4   3 4

−2 9   −2 9

able to subtract 29, but the form he has learned and the rule of likeness decree that he must subtract the 9 ones from the ones number above the 9, in this case 4 ones. The solution for this example is not too hard for a child

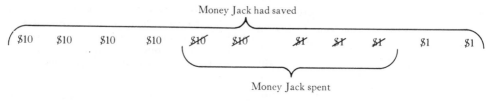

Money Jack had saved

$10 $10 $10 $10 $̶1̶0̶ $̶1̶0̶ $̶1̶ $̶1̶ $̶1̶ $1 $1

Money Jack spent

Begin with $65. Take $23 away. $42 are left.

Figure 50. Two-place Subtraction — Decomposition Situation.

C be subtracted from the 4 in the ones place. In C, however, 34 as a total quantity is large enough so that 29 can be subtracted if only the *face and place values* can be changed to a more manageable form (that is, if the quantity can be regrouped).

This is the situation that poses the difficulty. The child knows that 34 is larger than 29 and that he should be

subtracting actual objects or drawing the solution on a number line. It is the written form that poses most of the difficulty. Teachers therefore need to introduce the algorism through ample preliminary experience with (1) the demonstration of changing with objects or drawings or other aids to understanding and (2) prior development of the abstract concept of place value.

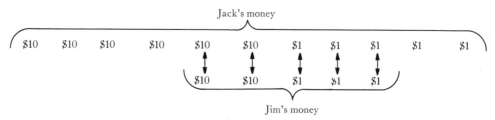

Jack's money

$10 $10 $10 $10 $10 $10 $1 $1 $1 $1 $1

$10 $10 $1 $1 $1

Jim's money

Jack has $42 more than Jim has.

Figure 51. Two-place Subtraction — Comparison Situation.

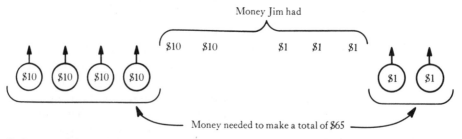

Money Jim had

$10 $10 $1 $1 $1

$10 $10 $10 $10 $1 $1

Money needed to make a total of $65

Jim has to get $42 more dollars.

Figure 52. Two-place Subtraction — Additive Situation.

THE DECOMPOSITION—
TAKE-AWAY ALGORISM

By far the most commonly used subtraction algorism in American schools is the decomposition—take-away method, commonly known as "borrowing." Some teachers and even more parents do not know it by any other name. Some authorities in arithmetic teaching have strong objections to the term as being inaccurate (since one does not really "borrow" with the intent of "paying back"). The use of the word "borrow" has dropped off markedly in children's arithmetic books (while being continued in teacher's guides and in classroom instruction). Such use of the term is probably not too dangerous, nor is it a matter worthy of lengthy argument. What does matter is that taking 1 ten —"borrowing" it—is not the complete story of what happens; nor is the term in any way essential. The essential concept is that one does "take" or "borrow" or "use" 1 of the tens so that its form but not its value may be *changed* to 10 ones, thus making possible the subtraction of 9 or any other smaller number of ones. The *changing* of the form of stating the value of the numbers is the important idea. Only the minuend is changed in form for this method, illustrated below for the subtraction of 28 from 45.

Long Form

$$4\,5 = 4 \text{ tens} + 5 \text{ ones} = 3 \text{ tens} + 15 \text{ ones}$$
$$-2\,8 = 2 \text{ tens} + 8 \text{ ones} = 2 \text{ tens} + 8 \text{ ones}$$
$$\overline{\phantom{-2\,8 = 2 \text{ tens}} 1 \text{ ten } + 7 \text{ ones} = 17}$$

Short Form with Crutches

$$\begin{array}{c} \overset{3}{\cancel{4}}\,\overset{15}{\cancel{5}} \\ -2\ 8 \\ \hline 1\ 7 \end{array}$$

According to the *decomposition—take-away* method, the basic subtraction facts used in this example are: $15 - 8 = 7$ and $3 - 2 = 1$.

Three other subtraction methods— which have seen more use in the past than at present—are decomposition-additive, equal additions-take away, and equal additions-additive. Research evidence on the comparative efficiency of the four methods is not very helpful, since method of teaching-learning as well as final method of performance and practice must be included. On the basis of ease of rationalization of the process of changing, particularly with children, as well as some research on the question, the decomposition—take-away method seems clearly preferable as the first one to be taught (for many children, the only method). On purely logical grounds, it is certainly closer to everyday experiences in subtracting by changing money or by breaking larger packs of goods into their individual parts so they can be used or distributed. It is also the easiest one for children to "discover" in well-managed introductory lessons on the process; its defense is simply that it makes sense to young learners.

Subtraction Rules
for Two-Place Subtraction

RULE OF LIKENESS

The rule of likeness applies to two-place subtraction as it does to the basic subtraction facts. Joe can subtract 17 *cents* from 29 *cents* because they are both groups of *cents*. Further, when the 17 cents are subtracted from the 29 cents, the process is made easier by subtracting the 7 *cents*, or *pennies*, in 17 from the 9 *cents*, or *pennies*, in 29 and by subtracting 1 collection of *ten cents*, or *1 dime*, in *17* from the 2 collections of *ten*, or 2 *dimes*, in *29*. The rule of likeness makes it mandatory that we subtract ones (cents) from ones and tens (dimes) from tens. Applying the rule of likeness to like place values, one might say that only "face values" with the same "place values" may be correctly subtracted. Speaking more superficially, 7 pennies may be subtracted from 9 pennies, or 1 dime from 2 dimes, because they "have the same name."

THE SUBTRAHEND-REMAINDER RULE

The subtrahend-remainder rule applies to subtraction of two-place and larger numbers chiefly as the basis for some modes of checking subtraction. (See pp. 188.) If $29-17=12$, then $29-12=17$.

Teaching Two-Place Subtraction to Children

CHOICE OF PROBLEM SITUATIONS

The use of appropriate problem situations is extremely important when introducing children to new steps or phases of any process. Within problem situations they understand, they can work out meanings and understandings for themselves in ways the teacher might never think of using. The teacher who is alert to the learning-teaching situation not only can capitalize on original discoveries and approaches children make to problems, but also can detect errors in thinking and help correct them in a way that could never have been done if the teacher did all the telling and the children's role was just that of listening and imitating.

TEACHING SUBTRACTION OF TWO-PLACE NUMBERS WITHOUT CHANGING

Most teachers and textbook writers introduce separately the subtraction of "even tens" and the subtraction of two-place numbers that are not even tens and do not require changing of tens. Since the subtraction of the tens is the same in either case and since the handling of the zeros in the two-place algorism for even tens is sometimes in question, the discussion that follows will deal with introduction of the subtraction of even tens in an actual situation.

A group of children were presented with this statement of a problem situation:

John had 90¢. He spent 40¢ for a knife. How much money did John have left after he paid for the knife?

Diagrams are inserted below to indicate actions of one child as he solved John's problem.

Randy: Well, here's John's money. John had 9 dimes. That's 90¢.

Now he pays the clerk 40¢. That's 4 dimes. He has 5 dimes left. That's 50¢.

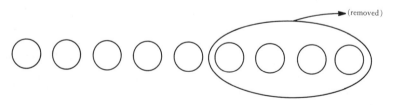
(removed)

Teacher: Can you write out the subtraction on the board?

Randy wrote on the board:

$$
\begin{array}{r}
9 \text{ dimes} \\
-4 \text{ dimes} \\
\hline
5 \text{ dimes} = 50\cent
\end{array}
$$

Teacher: Does anyone think of a different way to write this subtraction?

Alice suggested that all the "dimes numbers" should be translated into "cents numbers." After her changes, the algorism looked like this:

$$
\begin{array}{r}
9 \text{ dimes} = 9\ 0\ \cent \\
-4 \text{ dimes} = 4\ 0\ \cent \\
\hline
5 \text{ dimes} = 5\ 0\ \cent
\end{array}
$$

Joe said that it would be quickest just to write the last part (to the right of the = signs).

After general agreement that any of the suggested forms would be correct, the teacher asked if anyone could tell why the last form had zeros in it and the first one did not.

Joe: The zeros just say that John didn't have any pennies, and he didn't spend any pennies, and he didn't have any pennies left.

Teacher: But why were there no zeros in the first form that Randy wrote?

Joe: I wrote "dimes," but Alice didn't, so she had to put zeros in the pennies place to show that the "9" meant dimes.

Sue: I don't see why it has to be dimes. The problem said that John had 90¢ and spent 40¢. Maybe his money wasn't all in dimes.

Teacher: Perhaps so. What coins do you think he might have had?

With encouragement from the teacher and some help from other children, Sue put out play money representing a half-dollar, a quarter, a dime, and a nickel for John's 90¢. Then she subtracted her idea of 40¢ as a quarter, a dime, and a nickel. Her remainder was the half-dollar, which she agreed was worth 50¢,

the same as the value of Randy's remainder. Further discussion brought out the point that the final algorism told the story of Sue's solution as well as Randy's.

Sue's version of the solution is an illustration of a variation that may easily occur when pupils are freed to think through a problem situation in individual ways. While many teachers might have hesitated to introduce such a complicating feature to the discussion, its introduction by one of the children suggests its appropriateness. Actually, it brought out the fact that the expressions "90¢" and "40¢" may have many concrete representations in terms of coins, but that these "money numbers" in numeral form have generalized base-ten meanings that can be used for all combinations of coins with those *values.*

Other problems were presented to the children, as follows:

Jack had 80¢ and George had 60¢. How much more money did Jack have?

The Smith family drove 90 miles to Allentown. On the way home, they stopped for lunch after driving 30 miles. How far did they still have to drive to get home?

Pupil solutions for the comparison problem included acting out the solution by placing 8 play dimes in one row and 6 in another, drawing pictures of 8 dimes compared with 6 dimes, and using number lines showing the comparison. Solutions to the additive subtraction problem included a number line and a demonstration with wooden beads strung in sets of 10 on a string. The child who used the beads started with 3 "tens of beads," which she called "30 miles"; then she added other sets of beads—"10 miles" at a time—and counted: 40 miles, 50 miles, 60 miles, 70 miles, 80 miles, 90 miles. Finally, she had to go back and see how many tens she had added.[3]

This lesson ended with brief consideration of the algorisms for subtracting even tens. Agreement on use of the short form was arrived at in a later lesson: e.g.,

$$\begin{array}{r} 9\,0 \text{ mi.} \\ -3\,0 \text{ mi.} \\ \hline 6\,0 \text{ mi.} \end{array}$$

TEACHING SUBTRACTION
WITH CHANGING

At least one widely used third-grade arithmetic textbook presents subtraction with changing before subtraction of two-place numbers without changing. Most schools and most textbooks present subtraction with changing after children have become familiar with subtraction without changing (both with and without even tens). This was the case in the teaching-learning situation for which the description follows:

The teacher presented two problems to a group of third-grade children, suggesting that they work in pairs, doing either one or both of the problems.

The problems were stated orally by the teacher, and only notes on the essential details were written on the chalkboard for reference. (The full statements are given below, accompanied by the details written on the board.)

Problem 1: The junior scouts went to camp. Each troop had to take turns helping in the kitchen. One morning Troop 1 served cereal in individual boxes. On the shelf were 4 packs of cereal with ten boxes in each sealed pack; also, there were 2 individual boxes. There were 29 children to be served. How many boxes of cereal were left on the shelf after breakfast?
Notes on Chalkboard:
    4 packs of ten and 2 boxes
    29 children to be served

[3] Note should be taken of the use of the three subtraction ideas (decomposition, comparison, and additive subtraction) in connection with introduction of the subtraction of even tens.

Problem 2: Sue had 42¢. She went to the store and bought a toy that cost 29¢. How much money did she have left?
Notes on Chalkboard: Sue had 42¢.
                                          Sue spent 29¢.

The children were asked to show solutions by actions or drawings. The teacher observed and gave help when needed, usually by skillful questioning rather than direct suggestion. After all the children had worked out at least one solution, the group discussed the problems.

For the breakfast cereal problem, the children tended to show the 4 tens with bundles of some sort (wooden blocks grouped in tens with rubber bands, tongue depressors in tens, wooden beads in strings of ten, strips of paper perforated in tens). For this problem their drawings also tended to show the large packs as much larger than the separate boxes. See representative drawings in figure 53.

For the money problem, children tended to show "dimes" and "pennies" more abstractly, depending on abstract designations to indicate "dime" and "penny" values. They used play money, drawings of coins, and letter symbols for coins, as in the representative drawings in figure 54.

The difference in the two problems with respect to position on the concrete-to-abstract scale is of some importance to teachers. The use of the cereal box problem is particularly good for children who need to see more concretely the ten individual items that make up each of the 4 tens. The money problem is more abstract, depending on the concept of "ten times as much value" to distinguish dimes (tens) from pennies (ones). When free to select their problem and their own means of demonstrating its solution, children usually do a good job of finding their appropriate levels of operation. The assignment to solve problems more than one way, plus the teacher's observation and encouragement of individual children, provides for progression from more concrete to more abstract levels of meaning.

The different solutions also varied in the sequence of solution steps. Some children "changed a dime" or "broke a pack of ten," as soon as they saw they did not have enough "pennies" or "boxes" to subtract 9. Others subtracted the 2 "pennies" or "boxes" they had, *after* which they "changed a dime" or "broke a pack" to get the other items needed to subtract 9. After talking this over, the children decided that they were less likely "to get mixed up" if they changed a ten to ones as soon as they saw they did not have enough ones.

The teacher lent support to this view

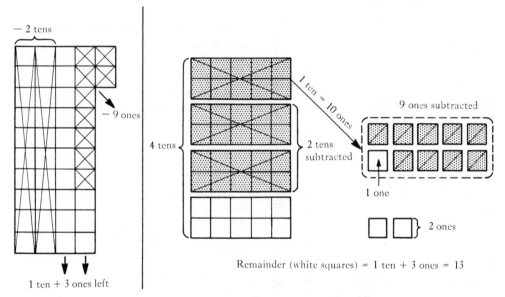

Figure 53. Subtraction with Changing (42 − 29 = 13).

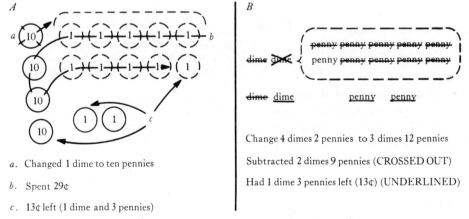

A

a. Changed 1 dime to ten pennies

b. Spent 29¢

c. 13¢ left (1 dime and 3 pennies)

B

Change 4 dimes 2 pennies to 3 dimes 12 pennies

Subtracted 2 dimes 9 pennies (CROSSED OUT)

Had 1 dime 3 pennies left (13¢) (UNDERLINED)

Figure 54. Subtraction with Changing (42¢ − 29¢ = 13¢).

because she realized that changing the ten before subtracting any ones would be a better "stepping-stone" to the written algorism. To emphasize this point, she asked two children who had used abacus solutions to demonstrate their solutions to the class.

A boy who used an abacus with ten beads on each wire acted out his solution as he explained it. An abbreviated version of his comments is shown with diagrammatic representations of the abacus for each step:

This is 42.

Then I subtracted 2 ones.

I was supposed to subtract 9 ones; so I took 1 ten and traded it for 10 ones.

Now I can subtract 7 more ones; that's 9 in all.

Now I can subtract 2 tens. The remainder is 13.

A girl had a modified abacus with 18 beads on each wire, stored in a "reserve" on the back of the frame. Her steps are shown in abbreviated form below:

I had 4 tens and 2 ones, but I need to subtract 9 ones.

I took back 1 ten and put out 10 ones with the 2 ones I had.

Then I could take away 9 ones and leave 3 ones.

I subtracted 2 tens. The answer is 1 ten and 3 ones. That's 13.

The children agreed that both abacus solutions were correct, but most of them favored the latter. They said it was easier to follow. At this point, the teacher proceeded to the introduction of the written algorism for subtraction with changing. The development of the algorism she wrote on the chalkboard is shown alongside her comments and those of the children.

Teacher: Now let's write a record of what we have done, using only number symbols. You tell me what we did and I'll write it down in "number shorthand." How much money did Sue have in the beginning?

Children: Forty-two cents.   Written Form
Teacher: How much did she   4 2 ¢
spend?   4 2 ¢
Children: Twenty-nine cents.   − 2 9 ¢

Teacher: What was the difficulty here?
Child: We didn't have enough pennies to subtract from.
Teacher: So what did you do?
Child: We took 1 of the dimes.
Teacher: Then how many dimes did you have?
Children: Three.
Teacher: I'll show that by cros-   3
sing out the "4" and putting a "3"   4̸ 2 ¢
in tens place. Now what did we do   − 2 9 ¢
with that ten?
Child: We got ten pennies for it.
Teacher: Yes, we *changed* 1 dime for 10 pennies. Then how many pennies did we have in all? 10 plus 2 equals?
Children: Twelve.

Teacher: Yes, so I cross out the "2" and put "12" in place of it to show we have 12 pennies in all. Now what?

Children: Subtract the 9 pennies.

Teacher: 12 pennies minus 9 pennies = ?

Children: 3 pennies.

Teacher: Then?

Child: 3 dimes minus 2 dimes is 1 dime.

Teacher: We write "1" in the dimes place. That finishes it. What I have written tells the story of what you did with the objects and drawings. Now shall we try to write the subtraction story some other ways?

$$\begin{array}{r} 3\ 12 \\ 4\ 2\ ¢ \\ -2\ 9\ ¢ \\ \hline \end{array}$$

$$\begin{array}{r} 3\ 12 \\ 4\ 2\ ¢ \\ -2\ 9\ ¢ \\ \hline 3\ ¢ \end{array}$$

$$\begin{array}{r} 3\ 12 \\ 4\ 2\ ¢ \\ -2\ 9\ ¢ \\ \hline 1\ 3\ ¢ \end{array}$$

Research evidence concerning the written "crutches" in the subtraction algorism seems to support their sensible use. Crutches should be used when they help to develop or maintain understanding of the process being recorded. Children who need them should be allowed (even encouraged) to use them. Those who do not need them (who may even be slowed down in their work by using them) should be encouraged to do without them. The vestigial remains of the written crutch may be observed in the way many adults make aerial gestures over their checkbooks as they perform the subtraction phases of balancing their accounts. If they need it, should not children be allowed the same latitude in their behavior?

Teachers will have their own ways of developing the "subtraction-with-changing" algorism. It is important, however, that the ways they choose be like this described procedure in three ways: (1) developing the algorism as a *record* of the children's *preceding experiences,* (2) taking time to relate each step in the written form to the comparable step in the children's preceding activities, and (3) having the children in a sense "dictate" the form as the teacher "transcribes" it into algorism form.

Higher-Decade Subtraction

HIGHER-DECADE SUBTRACTION FACTS

The higher-decade subtraction facts are the inverses of the higher-decade addition facts.

Emphasis on classification of higher-decade subtraction facts into various types can very easily be overdone so far as children are concerned. Teachers should, however, recognize various types in order to be able to provide pupils with experiences that give a broad coverage in problems and in practice exercises.

The major point of concern is whether or not a ten has to be changed to ones in order to complete the subtraction.

Hundred charts of various kinds are quite useful in helping children to work out higher-decade subtraction facts on their own and to teachers in presenting so-called "mental subtraction" in the higher decades. The charts can be used in similar fashion as for higher-decade addition.

USES OF HIGHER-DECADE SUBTRACTION FACTS

Higher-decade subtraction facts do not have any use nearly as extensive as the use of higher-decade addition facts in column addition or in multiplication.[4] It is useful, however, for itself. People do have occasion to use higher-decade subtraction directly in such everyday situations as comparing prices at the supermarket or from store to store. One brand of coffee sells for 91¢ per pound, another brand for 83¢; the homemaker when shopping should be able to tell

[4] Some use can be made of higher-decade subtraction in the long-division process, but this use is not nearly as frequent as the mentioned uses of higher-decade addition.

the difference in prices without searching in her purse for a pencil and paper. A common sales promotion practice is to advertise prices as "8¢ off" or "25¢ off." Again, higher-decade subtraction is useful. Children frequently have total cash balances on hand of less than one dollar. In making a purchase they must often consider how much they will have left if they purchase a given item at a given price, e.g., 83¢ (on hand) minus 75¢ (for a toy) or 45¢ (on hand) for a 6¢ candy bar.

The practice of higher-decade subtraction facts, with both one-digit and two-digit subtrahends, should have obvious carry-over into two-place subtraction—particularly in two-place subtraction without writing and even in the written algorism with changing. A person who develops command of the higher-decade subtraction facts thereby reduces or eliminates his need for "crutches" (or of any writing) in the subtraction algorism for two-place or larger numbers. For instance, he will be able to think of "53 − 46" as having a difference of 7 without any formal written algorism, or he may handle without writing such an example as "453 − 308." Higher-decade subtraction facts are also used in so-called "short division."

TEACHING HIGHER-DECADE
SUBTRACTION FACTS TO CHILDREN

The teaching of higher-decade subtraction facts should begin with problems. Suppose a certain brand of toothpaste is being advertised as "on special," marked down 9¢ from its usual price of 45¢. The following suggested activities might be initiated either by the children or by the teacher, but the children should work out the solution of the problem with only as much help as is really needed.

1. Wooden blocks or sticks fastened in sets of ten might be provided. With these the children could arrange 4 sets of ten blocks each and 5 separate blocks. Nine could be subtracted by first "breaking one ten" into 10 separate blocks and then removing 9 blocks.

2. A number line could be drawn, or the children could use one that is mounted on the wall or chalkboard for easy reference. The solution might be worked out either vertically or horizontally, as shown in figures 55 and 56.

3. A hundred chart could be used in various ways. One child might use it to count backward 9 spaces to 36; another might simply move "back 10" (movement straight up to the next row, to "35"), then "forward 1" to 36. The reasoning in the latter case might be that "subtracting 9 is like subtracting 10 and adding 1," applying a generalization learned with the basic subtraction facts.

Figure 55. Bridging Downward in Subtraction on a Vertical Number Line.

4. The problem might be related to the idea of "subtracting by endings."

(See adding by endings, pp. 126-27.) In this case the higher-decade subtraction fact would be related to the basic subtraction fact that "has the same ending," thus:

15	25	35	45	55	65	75	85	95
−9	−9	−9	−9	−9	−9	−9	−9	−9
6	16	26	36	46	56	66	76	86

Attention should be directed not only to the numerals in ones place but also to the change in tens place.

Supposing some such assortment of activities as these had been experienced by the children; the teacher might well use these solutions as the basis for a comparison and general discussion of the "big idea" in each solution. This would point up the changing of a ten in each case, whether it be the bridging down into the next decade used on the number line or the hundred chart or the "breaking" of a set of ten blocks, or the changing of the "tens number" in the set of written facts for subtracting by endings. From such a discussion some children might clarify their concepts; some might get ideas of different ways to solve future related problems; and some might decide that "it would just be quicker if I would learn those subtraction facts so I would know the answer without taking so much time." For the last-mentioned, the time is ripe for practice on higher-decade subtraction facts.

One way (among several possible ways) of dealing with the higher-decade subtraction facts that involve the subtraction of a two-digit number from a two-digit number is to use these facts as a review of place-value concepts and basic facts. Children may be challenged to see how many different ways they can "think out" the answers to subtraction examples such as these:

$$(1) \quad \begin{array}{r} 56 \\ -52 \\ \hline \end{array} \qquad (2) \quad \begin{array}{r} 34 \\ -28 \\ \hline \end{array}$$

A few possible thought sequences might be:

$$(1) \quad 50 - 50 = 0$$
$$6 - 2 = 4$$
OR
$$56 - 50 = 6$$
$$6 - 2 = 4$$
OR
$$(50 + 6) - (50 + 2) = (50 - 50) + (6 - 2) = 4$$

$$(2) \quad 34 - 20 = 14; \; 14 - 8 = 6$$
OR
$$34 - 28 = (20 + 14) - (20 + 8)$$
$$= (20 - 20) + (14 - 8) = 6$$

Subtraction of Larger Numbers

HANDLING LARGER NUMBERS IN SUBTRACTION

Subtraction of large numbers uses the same basic concepts of the meaning of subtraction, the same basic subtraction facts, the same concepts of relative place value, and the same rules of operation as have already been learned in practice with subtraction of smaller numbers.

Anyone who understands subtraction thus far should usually have little more difficulty in subtracting thousands or millions or billions than he has had in subtracting tens or ones so far as the mechanics of the computations are concerned. Extension of subtraction to these larger quantities, assuming satisfactory performance with the subtraction process to this point, hinges chiefly on the extension of the child's familiarity with the larger place values. This extension includes being able to read and write these numerals with understanding.

Understanding the notational system and the computational scheme is not the whole story of understanding the larger numbers. Not only elementary school children but also most of their teachers and parents have had limited first-hand experience beyond thousands.

Nevertheless, experiences are needed to help children grasp somewhat more fully the significance of the different place values. Showing them on the abacus or writing them with numerals is by no means the same as understanding these values. Problems with money are often used since so many of the problems using larger numbers deal with

for each ten. The chains of 100 beads were then looped together with a loosely knotted string into thousands. This assembly job was a good learning experience for the children because of the emphasis on 10 ones in 1 ten, 10 tens in 1 hundred, and 10 hundreds in 1 thousand. Once assembled, the beads did give a striking contrast in the rela-

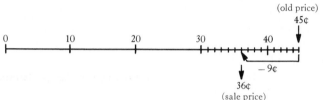

Figure 56. Bridging Downward in Subtraction on a Horizontal Number Line.

money situations, but the relative value of $2000, $200, $20, and $2 has to be gained through experiences that teach what these sums will buy, relatively speaking.

While it is easy enough to have a set of ten blocks to contrast with a single block or even a bundle of a hundred sticks or tongue depressors to contrast with a bundle of ten, one soon reaches the point at which the individual items lose their identity in the larger groups or the larger groups become unwieldy, space-consuming, and difficult to handle.

One teacher hit upon a concrete aid that she found to be very effective in dealing with larger quantities. Reading a newspaper advertisement for "pop bead" necklaces, she ordered a gross of them. When they arrived, she found that each necklace had 60 beads, so she found herself in possession of 8640 pop beads, all in one fair-sized cardboard carton. Her pupils helped her to re-assemble the beads into sets of 10 beads each. These were recombined into closed chains of 100, the tens still evident through use of alternating colors

tive values of, for example, 2 ones, 2 tens, or 2 hundreds. (See fig. 57.)

Once assembled, the beads proved to be very useful in helping children extend their comprehension of place values and also in connection with the arithmetical processes using larger numbers.

SUBTRACTION OF LARGER NUMBERS
WITH ZEROS IN THE MINUEND

The beads were used by this teacher and her pupils for subtraction of various larger subtraction examples, such as this rather incomplete sampling of different place-value situations.

3 4 6	8 5 2	5 6 1	8 0 2	1 2 8 0	6 7 8 2
−1 2 4	−5 3 8	−2 7 6	−1 7 0	−4 5 3	−1 8 8 4

Because a later example illustrates both the practice with larger numbers and one particularly "tricky" zero situation in the minuend, a detailed description will be given of that particular lesson.

Subgroups of an arithmetic class were each given a box of 2000 pop beads, assembled as described earlier. The same problem was presented to all four groups:

Your box has 2000 beads in it. If you take out 576 beads, how many beads will be left in the box?

One pupil wrote on the chalkboard the form for the intended subtraction:

$$\begin{array}{r} 2\ 0\ 0\ 0 \text{ beads} \\ -5\ 7\ 6 \text{ beads} \\ \hline \end{array}$$

Teacher and pupils agreed that the form did describe the situation; then the pupils were challenged to work out the solution with the beads and also with a written algorism. Each subgroup went to work with its box of 2000 beads.

After encountering some "detours" and "blind alleys" and being assisted by the teacher's skillful questioning at crucial points, all the groups were able to derive a correct remainder of 1424 beads; but they varied rather widely as to method of handling the materials and as to algorisms written. Abbreviated accounts of the work done are given for three groups:

Group A: We just took off 1 ten and took 6 beads away from it. We kept the 6 beads and put 4 back in the box.

We had 9 tens left in the chain we broke. We took away 7 tens and put 2 tens back in the box.

We had used up one whole chain of 1 hundred; so we had 9 hundreds that were not tied up in a thousand. We subtracted 5 hundreds and put 4 hundreds back in the

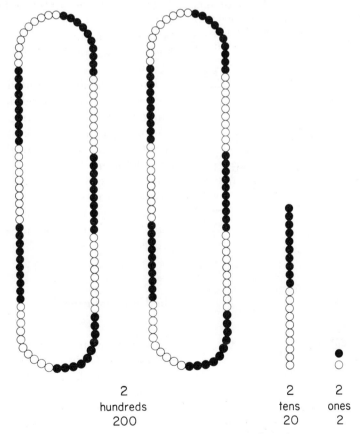

2		2	2
hundreds		tens	ones
200		20	2

Figure 57. Pop Beads Arranged to Show Place Value.

box. That gave us 576 beads we were supposed to get.

Then we counted what was left in the box. We had 1 whole thousand, 4 hundreds, 2 tens, and 4 loose beads. That's 1 thousand, 4 hundred, twenty-four.

We got mixed up when we tried to write it out with numbers all in one example, so we wrote it in parts, like this:

10 ones	9 tens	9 hundreds	2 thousands
−6 ones	−7 tens	−5 hundreds	−1 thousand
4 ones	2 tens	4 hundreds	1 thousand

Joe said that was backward of the way it should be written; so we turned it around:

2 thousand	9 hundred	9 tens	10 ones
−1 thousand	−5 hundred	−7 tens	−6 ones
1 thousand	4 hundred	2 tens	4 ones

We are pretty sure that's right, but we don't know how to write it if we leave the words out.

Group B: We knew we had to have some tens, but there weren't any separate tens. Somebody said, "There are lots of tens; 2 thousand is 200 tens." So we took 1 ten and that left 199 tens.

We had 10 beads and took 6 beads away. That left 4 beads. This is what we wrote:

Then it was easy from there. We had 9 tens and subtracted 7 tens and wrote 2 in the tens place on paper.

$$\begin{array}{r} 1\,9\,9\,10 \\ 2\,0\,0\,\cancel{0} \\ -5\,7\,6 \\ \hline 4 \end{array}$$

Then we subtracted 5 hundreds from the 9 hundred chains we had. That left 4 hundreds, and we wrote it in the hundreds place on paper.

We didn't need to do anything to the 1 thousand bundle, so we just wrote 1 thousand in the answer.

$$\begin{array}{r} 1\,9\,9\,10 \\ 2\,0\,0\,\cancel{0} \\ -5\,7\,6 \\ \hline 1\,4\,2\,4 \end{array}$$

Group C:

We still hadn't subtracted anything, but it was easy to take 6 ones and 7 tens and 5 hundreds. We had 1424 left. We wrote our subtraction this way:

$$\begin{array}{r} 1000 + 900 + 90 + 10 \\ - \qquad 500 + 70 + \;6 \\ \hline 1000 + 400 + 20 + \;\;4 = 1424 \end{array}$$

Perhaps individual children in each group varied as much in their thinking about this problem as the groups varied. Some of them no doubt needed a good deal more experience with such a difficult type of subtraction problem. The children decided that everybody had done some good thinking and were pleased that everybody got the right answer to the teacher's problem question. They decided that the algorism worked out by group B was the simplest. (This does not mean that it needed to be adopted immediately by all or that it had to be accepted as "best" for all time to come.)

The probability is rather high that even group A, though admitting being "mixed up" about writing a concise algorism for their work, knew more about the real meaning of this subtraction situation than a large majority of children who have been presented with a typical shortened subtraction algorism and expected to learn it as a formal, rote, and "theirs-not-to-reason-why" procedure.

Checking Subtraction

Various means are used for checking subtraction. Children should of course be taught the habit of checking their subtractions. The addition forms of checking are perhaps most common, but subtraction and "excess" methods are also available.

CHECKING BY REPEATING SUBTRACTION

As with any process, one may check one's subtraction accuracy by simply repeating the subtraction. For the subtraction example $48 - 32 = 16$ the check might be a simple repetition of the process, using the same algorism and the same number facts (Check A).

Check A:	4 8	Facts Used
	−3 2	$8 - 2 = 6$
	1 6	$4 - 3 = 1$

Check B:	4 8	Facts Used
	−1 6	$8 - 6 = 2$
	3 2	$4 - 1 = 3$

Check B, based on the subtrahend-remainder rule, uses different facts in the check from those used in the original subtraction; this is really the same procedure as checking the accuracy of one basic subtraction fact against its reverse.

CHECKING BY ADDING

Numerous checks are based on the concept of subtraction as the inverse of addition. If the subtraction is correct, the subtrahend plus the remainder should equal the minuend. The variants are merely matters of form in arranging the items to be added in making the check. These differences are shown in Checks C, D, E, and F for the subtraction $48 - 32 = 16$.

Check C	Check D	Check E	Check F	
32	16	~~48~~	48	Add upward:
+16	+32	−32 ↑	−32	$6 + 2 = 8$
48	48	16 ↑	16	$1 + 3 = 4$
		48		

Checks C and D require copying the addends; Checks E and F use the original subtraction algorism. The first two checks above are more frequently found in children's texts. Some people object to E because if the minus sign has been written in front of the subtrahend (e.g., -32), the written form would be wrong, with $-32 + 16$ said to equal 48. Another objection to the same form is that it "hides" the remainder in the algorism and copying errors may ensue. Form F has some advantages in that it does not require taking time to recopy any numerals. The upward adding also dramatizes the "building back up" to the original total.

CHECKING BY "EXCESS" METHODS

Casting out 9's is the more commonly used "excess" method, though a similar check uses 11's. Check G demonstrates the casting-out-9's procedure using two ways of deriving the "excess."

	Check G			Excess
4 5 7	$4+5+7=16$	$16-9=7$	~~45~~7	7
−1 6 7	$1+6+7=14$	$14-9=5$	−1 6 7	−5
2 9 0	$2+9+0=11$	$11-9=2$	2~~9~~0	2

In the first procedure in G, the digits in each term (minuend, subtrahend, and remainder) are added, and then 9 (or a multiple of 9) is subtracted from each. (Some people also add the digits of these term sums instead of using the subtraction of 9's. The result is the same.) The excesses are then checked. The subtraction is checked as being correct because the excess 7 minus the excess 5 equals the excess 2. In the next procedure in G any 9's or digits that have a sum of 9 are "scratched" to get the excess, as for the 4 and 5 in the minuend and the 9 in the remainder. This is just another way of subtracting 9's.

Sometimes the procedure as described yields a smaller check figure for the minuend than for the subtrahend, as in the example below:

4 5 2	$4+5+2=11$	$1+1=2$	2 is smaller than
−1 6 7	$1+6+7=14$	$1+4=5$	the 5 to be sub-
2 8 5	$2+8+5=15$	$1+5=6$	tracted!

Ways of handling this situation vary; two are shown below:

a. Restore one of the "cast-out" 9's to the minuend, bringing it back up to "11." Then $11 - 5 = 6$; it checks.

b. Add the subtrahend and remainder check figures: $5 + 6 = 11$. Now add the digits of the "11" $(1 + 1 = 2)$. The resulting sum should be the same as the minuend check figure (in this case, 2).

Merely as a check on the subtraction, casting out 9's is a cumbersome procedure besides not being the most reliable.

(See pp. 135-36.) Its current revival is related to emphasis on our decimal-place-value system. Children who can profit from exploring bypaths in arithmetic will enjoy this check, particularly if they are encouraged to "figure out why it works." Doing the latter might well be a step toward finding what one would have to "cast out" to have the same check for computations with numbers in other bases than ten. Of course, a real study of casting out 9's will also reveal the relation of the check to divisibility by 9.

STUDY QUESTIONS

1. Read the article by Glenadine Gibb, "Take-away Is Not Enough!" *The Arithmetic Teacher* **1**:7-10, April 1954. How does its discussion compare with the ideas of subtraction presented in this chapter?

2. The decomposition—take-away procedure is developed in this text and in most elementary school materials. Look up other algorisms for showing subtraction with changing such as the decomposition-additive method, the equal additions—take-away method, and the equal additions—additive method. Explain not only how to do these methods but the logic back of them.

3. Subtract, using no writing: $63 - 48$; $85 - 47$; $58 - 29$. Now write the record of what you thought in performing these subtractions mentally.

4. Demonstrate on an abacus these subtractions: $384 - 126$; $384 - 195$; $1054 - 728$; $2001 - 1444$. Which type of abacus works better for these demonstrations, one with 9 or 10 beads on each rod or one of the modified forms with 18 beads on each rod? Why? Would it be better to have 18 or 20 beads on each rod? Why?

5. Show these higher-decade subtraction facts on number line drawings: $42 - 4 = 38$. $30 - 4 = 26$; $28 - 6 = 22$. Which use bridging?

6. Check this subtraction by casting out 9's: $356 - 147 = 209$. Why does this check work?

CHAPTER 9

The Multiplication Process
and the Basic Multiplication Facts

THE CLERK WHO has just sold 3 pairs of hose at $1.19 per pair, the customer who is debating whether to buy 4 or 5 place settings of silver at $15.75 per setting, the bank teller who is checking the bag of money brought in with attached deposit slip, the housewife who is figuring the needed amount of sugar for 3 batches of cookies requiring 2 cups each, the stock clerk taking inventory, the child who wonders how many marbles he has in 2 bags with 24 in each, the treasurer of a large corporation and

Perhaps if teachers and parents took the process less for granted and considered more carefully just what multiplication is, they would do a better job of helping children understand it.

MULTIPLICATION IS BASED ON
A SPECIAL FORM OF COUNTING

The special kind of counting that is done more quickly if one is adept at multiplying is that form known as regular counting—counting by equal-sized

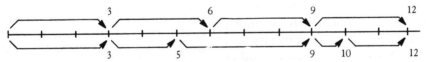

Figure 58. Regular and Irregular Counting.

all his staff of accountants—all need to be quick and accurate in multiplication. Be it done with or without pencil and paper, with or without benefit of calculating machine or mechanical brain, the uses of multiplication are legion, perhaps more frequent even than the uses of the fundamental process of simple addition from which it stems.

What Is Multiplication?

Adults more or less take multiplication for granted, except when Jack and Jill are doing homework on "the tables."

intervals. The arrows *above* the number line in figure 58 show how regular counting proceeds, in contrast to irregular counting, shown *below* the same line.

Buckingham says, "... multiplication by a whole number may be thought of as counting the multiplicand as many times as the multiplier specifies."[1]

When children learn to count by twos, threes, fives, or other whole numbers, they are accomplishing the same task that is done more quickly by knowing the multiplication facts. Their "multiple-

[1] Buckingham, *op. cit.*, p. 67.

counting" experiences are excellent background for later multiplication of a more formal kind. In fact, some children who are hurried into memorization of multiplication facts and tables would learn them more easily if time were first allowed for them to develop their skills in multiple counting.

The idea that multiplication is regular counting is demonstrated rather clearly by the close similarity of table 6 (a multiple-counting chart) and table 7

1	2	3	4	5	6	7	8	9	10
2	4	6	8	10	12	14	16	18	20
3	6	9	12	15	18	21	24	27	30
4	8	12	16	20	24	28	32	36	40
5	10	15	20	25	30	35	40	45	50
6	12	18	24	30	36	42	48	54	60
7	14	21	28	35	42	49	56	63	70
8	16	24	32	40	48	56	64	72	80
9	18	27	36	45	54	63	72	81	90

To count by any number (1–9) follow the row which begins with that number.

Table 6. Counting Chart.

(a multiplication chart). These two charts are identical except for the top row and left column of factors in table 7 and the extension of the counting chart to include the even tens numbers in the extreme right column. Neither of these variations is an essential of the type of chart in which it occurs. Either chart may be used for regular counting or for recording and practicing multiplication facts because multiplication *is* counting by multiples of the first number in the counting series.

MULTIPLICATION IS A
SPECIAL FORM OF ADDITION

It is regrouping by combining groups of equal size. Both the forms of counting represented in figure 58 show addition; only the regular counting shown there is muliplication, because that one indi-

cates counting by *equal* intervals of 3. Any multiplication problem with whole numbers can be solved by counting or by adding; sometimes it is also just as quick to count or add as it is to multiply. One can count 6 eggs in a carton just as quickly by thinking, "3 + 3 = 6," or "3, 6," as to think, "2 × 3 = 6." When the number of equal-size groups becomes greater, multiplication is a great time-saver. To add 234 + 234 + 234 + 234 + 234 + 234 + 234 + 234 + 234 takes much more time than multiplying 9 × 234 (after the human computer has mastered multiplication, of course). As the multiplier grows in size, so does the value of multiplication as a time-saver increase. This is the reason that multiplication is often referred to as "high-powered addition."

This definition of multiplication applies to the multiplication of fractions when the multiplier is a whole number. Some modification becomes necessary with multipliers that are expressed as either common or decimal fractions.

Multiplication of whole numbers may be called a variation of addition. Swain calls it "extended addition."[2] Addition is not always multiplication, since the subgroups being combined by addition to build a total group are not necessarily of equal size. This contrast necessitates a contrast in the statements and the algorisms of the two processes.

An addition statement or algorism must give the sizes of each of the groups or sets being combined, whether they be of the same or different sizes. The number of groups being combined is not an essential of the statement, though it is readily noted. One need not say, "Add *four* groups of 3, 5, 4, and 6." One says only, "Add 3, 5, 4, and 6." In multiplication, since all groups or sets being

[2] Robert L. Swain, *Understanding Arithmetic,* New York: Rinehart, 1957, p. 53.

combined are the same size, one states the size of the equal groups only once, but it then becomes necessary to tell also how many such groups are being put together. The two algorisms below tell the same story; but the addition algorism tells the subgroup size *4 times,* whereas the multiplication algorism gives the size of the subgroups only

This concept of multiplication is a neglected one and merits more attention than it usually receives in arithmetic instruction. Teachers tend to introduce multiplication as regular counting or as a special case of addition

Factors ⟶	1	2	3	4	5	6	7	8	9	
1	1	2	3	4	5	6	7	8	9	
2	2	4	6	8	10	12	14	16	18	
3	3	6	9	12	15	18	21	24	27	
4	4	8	12	16	20	24	28	32	36	*Products*
5	5	10	15	20	25	30	35	40	45	⟵
6	6	12	18	24	30	36	42	48	54	
7	7	14	21	28	35	42	49	56	63	
8	8	16	24	32	40	48	56	64	72	
9	9	18	27	36	45	54	63	72	81	

Products

Choose a factor in left column and a factor in top row.
Follow the corresponding row and column to find their product.

Table 7. Multiplication Chart.

once, stating in an extra term that this group is being used *4 times.* The greater the number of groups being put together, the greater is the saving of time in writing the multiplication algorism, to say nothing of time saved in computation. The meanings of the two terms in the multiplication algorism are discussed further on pages 196-98.

Addition Algorism
63
63
63
63
———
252

Multiplication Algorism
63
×4
———
252

and then proceed to work with problems in which the ratio-to-one idea is used but never attended to as such. Some simple problems serve to contrast the addition and ratio-to-one ideas.

Problem A: Two window boxes will hold 4 plants each. How many plants are needed for the 2 window boxes?

Problem R: One window box holds 4 plants. The box at the other window holds 2 times as many plants. How many plants does the second box hold?

Problem A is illustrated in figure 59. It fits very well the addition idea: "4 plants + 4 plants = 8 plants," or "2 fours = 8."

Figure 60 fits problem R. The second window box has 2 plants for every 1 in the first box. This is two-to-one correspondence. We say the second box has "2 times as many" plants as the first. As a multiplication statement, we say: "2 times 4 plants = 8 plants."

In the first problem we deal with 8 plants, first presented as 2 sets of 4 plants each. In the second problem we deal with 12 plants in all, 4 (known number) in the first box and 8 (unknown number) in the second. But we are asked about the second box only, and that by comparison with the first. It might be stated as a proportion, thus:

$$2 : 1 :: n : 4 \qquad \text{OR} \qquad 1 : 2 = 4 : n$$

For children, the terminology that best fits problem A is "2 fours are 8"; for problem R it is better to say: "2 times 4 = 8." Therefore, the teacher would do well to use addition-type multiplication situations at first with the "2 fours" terminology and then go on later to ratio-to-one-type problem situations, introducing the "2 times 4" terminology.[3]

Either type of problem may of course be converted into the other type. Problem A may be so worded that one speaks of needing "twice as many" or "2 times as many" plants for two boxes as for one box. Problem R *may* be solved by thinking that if the second box holds twice as many plants, one could find the right total by adding 2 fours. Eventually, children learn to use the "times" terminology for all multiplication situations, those in which a given addend is added as many times as the multiplier indicates

and those in which the product is that many times some other group.[4]

The ratio-to-one idea is common in child and adult experience. People walk 2 times as far today as yesterday, pay 3 times as much for one article as for another, secure 4 times as many chairs for one group as for another.

The ratio-to-one idea is a comparing idea. It applies to multiplication of both whole numbers and fractions, whereas the addition idea typically applies to fractions only when the multiplier is a whole number.

MULTIPLICATION IS A
RECTANGULAR-ARRAY IDEA

This idea of multiplication is particularly important in the mathematics of sets.[5] Suppose we consider an arrangement of asterisks in rows and columns as below. We have there two disjoint sets, a set of 2 rows and a set of 4 columns. We might also say that there are

```
*   *   *   *
*   *   *   *
```

2 rows of 4 asterisks each (or 4 columns of 2 asterisks each). The product of the numbers 2 and 4 is 8, which is the cardinal number of asterisks in the complete array.

The same diagram might also represent a situation that involves the pairing of items in two sets so as to show all the

---

[3] See Buckingham, *op. cit.*, pp. 64.67, and ∴ Houston Banks, *Learning and Teaching Arithmetic*, Boston: Allyn, 1959, pp. 140-141.

[4] Strictly speaking, the ratio-to-one idea may be applied to situations in which the "*other* group" is completely independent of the product group, as in figure 60, or to situations in which the "*other* group" is also a subgroup of the product group, as when a boy says that his earnings for the week are 4 times his Saturday earnings.

[5] The use of arrays in the development of multiplication is heavily stressed in some of the newer experimental materials such as the intermediate-grade arithmetic materials developed by the School Mathematics Study Group.

possible pairings; e.g., 2 sizes of books, which we shall designate simply as "large" and "small," may be paired with 4 possible colors of book covers: green, red, yellow, and brown. There are 8 possible pairings of size and color, thus:

	Small	Large
Green	*	*
Red	*	*
Yellow	*	*
Brown	*	*

While the defining of multiplication in set terms is relatively new, the idea of

such as egg cartons or boxes containing Christmas tree ornaments.

A STATEMENT OF MULTIPLICATION IS A STATEMENT OF EQUALITY

Although the word "multiply" is frequently used in everyday conversation to mean "increase," as when we complain that our everyday problems of living are multiplied by one condition or another, this is not the fundamental

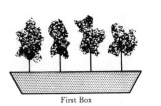
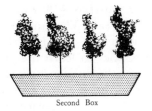

Figure 59. Multiplication as an Additive Idea.

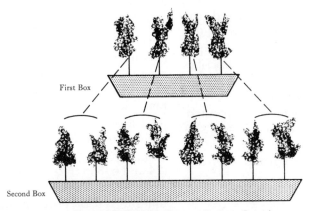

Figure 60. Multiplication as a Ratio-to-One Idea.

the rectangular array for showing the multiplication idea is very common, both in elementary school arithmetic instruction and in everyday affairs. One of the most common applications of this idea is in situations involving rectangular areas. Seating arrangements that specify an equal number of seats per row use this idea. Objects are often sold in boxes that have arrays of compartments,

or even an essential meaning of multiplication in arithmetic. In multiplying by a proper fraction, one certainly does not create a product that is larger than the multiplicand. When multiplying by 1, one gets a product that is identical with the multiplicand. When the multiplier is a whole number larger than 1, the product is larger than the multiplicand; but even then the multiplication process is not necessarily responsible for any increase of quantity.

Take, for example, a situation like this: A man is 4 times as heavy as his 42-pound child. The father's greater weight is not achieved by the multiplication 4×42 pounds = 168 pounds. Rather, the multiplication helps us find out what the father's already existent weight is. We have been told only that he weighed 4 times as much as a child weighing 42 pounds. Without needing to inquire what the father's weight was, we learned it by multiplying.

A housewife purchases 3 cans of beans at 35¢ per can. The unit price "35¢" is not increased to $1.05. She multiplies "3 × 35¢" to learn the *price of 3 items*. Before the answer is known, a place holder "n" or $\square$ might be used in an open sentence. The replacement for "n" or $\square$ must satisfy the condition of being equal to "3 × 35¢." $3 \times 35¢ = n$, or $3 \times 35¢ = \square$ becomes a closed true statement when the substitution "$1.05" is made because "3 × 35¢ does equal "$1.05". The term "3 × 35¢" describes 3 groups of 35 each; the term "$1.05" described the *same* 3 groups of 35¢ each, now combined rather than separated. The multiplication fact $3 \times 5 = 15$ says that 3 groups of 5 items each have the *same* total quantity as 1 group of ten and a group of 5 ones.

Multiplication Terminology

Too frequently, perhaps, the terminology that accompanies multiplication algorisms is defined according to placement in the algorism rather than according to basic meanings. Thus the *multiplicand* is defined as "the top number," the *multiplier* as "the bottom number before you multiply" or as "the number after the ×," and the *product* as "the bottom number when you are through multiplying" or as "the answer."

Most of these descriptions relate to vertical algorisms:

$$\begin{array}{rl} 8 & \text{---- multiplicand ----} \quad 3\ 2\ 4 \\ \times\ 3 & \text{---- multiplier} \quad\text{----} \quad \times\ 2 \\ \hline 2\ 4 & \text{---- product} \quad\text{----} \quad 6\ 4\ 8 \end{array}$$

They are of little help in naming the terms in the horizontal algorisms:

$$3 \times 8 = 24 \qquad 2 \times 3\ 2\ 4 = 6\ 4\ 8$$

A more serious deficiency of such definitions is that they are not based on the meanings of the terms as they relate to problem situations or the multiplication process. When multiplication is thought of as a condensed version of addition, i.e., as a process of combining a given number of equal groups to form a total group, this parallel is in order:

Addition	Multiplication
$\left.\begin{array}{l} 8 \\ 8 \\ 8 \end{array}\right\}$ addends $\left\{\begin{array}{l} 3\ 2\ 4 \\ 3\ 2\ 4 \end{array}\right.$	$\begin{array}{l} 8 \text{ ---multiplicand--- } 324 \\ \times 3 \text{ ----multiplier---- } \times 2 \\ \hline 24 \text{ ---- product ---- } 648 \end{array}$
$\overline{24}$---sum---$6\ 4\ 8$	

The *addends* in addition are the numbers telling the sizes of groups to be combined; this is also what the *multiplicand* tells. The numbers "8" and "324" tell the sizes of the groups to be combined in the two examples above. The total group that results from the combining process is called the *sum* in addition and the *product* in multiplication (24 and 648 in the examples).[6] The final comparison is the one children sometimes miss if they are not helped to see it. In the addition algorism *the addends are shown as many times* as the groups are used (*three* 8's or *two* 324's). The multiplicand, however, is shown only once in the multiplication algorism; the *multiplier tells how many times* that size group is *used*. The "×3" and "×2" in the algorisms above save us a little time in that they take the place of writing the

[6] Actually, "3 × 8" is an expression of a *product*, as is "2 × 324." In the elementary school, however, the term "product" is usually reserved for the "answer" in multiplication.

same addend repeatedly. Of course, the saving of time is negligible in these examples; it would be very important if the multiplier were 835.

With the terminology commonly used when children are introduced to multiplication, the addition algorisms under discussion could be read as "three 8's are 24" and "two 324's are 648." The corresponding multiplication algorisms *could be read that same way.* It might be a good idea for teachers to experiment with this form of reading multiplication examples with larger numbers as well as with simple multiplication facts, for it is at this point that confusion sometimes arises.[7]

The point of confusion is the order of reading the vertical algorism, an order that does not correspond to our typical top-to-bottom reading direction. In the horizontal algorism ($3 \times 8 = 24$) this difficulty does not arise. The spoken form "3 times 8 equals 24" fits very neatly with "$3 \times 8 = 24$"; but in the vertical algorism one must begin with the "×3" (written backward in terms of our typical reading pattern), go upward to "8," and then skip downward to the product, thus:

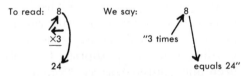

In any multiplication algorism the multiplication sign "×" may be read "times." It belongs with the multiplier. In "$3 \times 8 = 24$," this is easily read "*3 times* 8 equals 24." In the vertical form, one must read backward to make "×3" say "3 times"; but that *is* correct form. Another correct form of reading the

same vertical algorism is "8 *multiplied by 3* equals 24." This allows the reader to proceed in top-to-bottom and left-to-right order, since "multiplied by" takes the place of "times."

The essential idea is that the multiplier is the term that designates the number of equal groups being combined (or the number of times the equal groups are used). It must not be associated with the name of any concrete item. The multiplicand, on the other hand, refers to the number of items in each equal group, and it may be associated with the name of those items. In a concrete multiplication situation, the multiplicand refers to the concrete items that make up the equal groups. The product, since it is composed of the same groups designated by the multiplicand, may also be associated with the name applied to the multiplicand. This leads to the necessity for distinguishing between the meanings in actual situations of such related multiplications as 3×4 and 4×3. The array of eggs in a dozen-carton may be thought of as 3 rows of 4 eggs each or as 4 rows of 3 eggs each. Some examples of correct terminology to go with each situation are indicated for each diagram.[8]

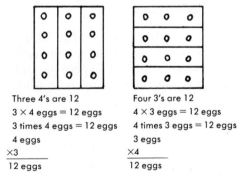

Three 4's are 12
3×4 eggs $= 12$ eggs
3 times 4 eggs $= 12$ eggs

4 eggs
×3
___
12 eggs

Four 3's are 12
4×3 eggs $= 12$ eggs
4 times 3 eggs $= 12$ eggs

3 eggs
×4
___
12 eggs

---

[7] This form is not being suggested for any and all occasions. The teacher will recognize when it is appropriate, e.g., when the multiplication problem being solved is clearly of the type that is "addition."

[8] Strictly speaking, all numbers are abstract, though the term "concrete number" has been widely used in arithmetic to refer to numbers linked with names for objects. Of course, the numbers, not the names, are multiplied. The product number is interpreted in terms of the same units to which the multiplicand refers.

The word "factors" has not been widely used in elementary school arithmetic, but its use is increasing. This use should be encouraged. Both the multiplicand and the multiplier are *factors;* they are the "makers" of the product. This term is used most appropriately when both multiplicand and multiplier are expressed as abstract numbers.

If we think of multiplication as the combining of equal-sized sets, the two numbers to be multiplied (the factors) are the number of sets and the number of elements in each equivalent set. Conventionally, the factor that is stated first (like the "3" in "3 × 4") tells the number of equal sets, and the factor that is stated second (like the "4" in "3 × 4") tells the number of elements within each set.

When the multiplier is a two-place or larger number, we usually have *partial products* as well as a total product. In the example at the right, the partial products are 92 ones and 23 tens. The partial products are added, and their sum is the final product. This also will be discussed further in relation to rules of the multiplication process.

$$\begin{array}{r} 2\ 3 \\ \times 1\ 4 \\ \hline 9\ 2 \\ 2\ 3 \\ \hline 3\ 2\ 2 \end{array}$$

Rules for Multiplication

The rules that apply to the addition process apply also to the multiplication process, as would be expected. Multiplication has one more rule (distribution).

THE COMMUTATIVE PRINCIPLE

FOR MULTIPLICATION

The order of the factors in multiplication does not affect their product. At the manipulation-of-algorisms level this may appear to be exactly parallel to the commutative (or order) rule for addition. At the level of elementary multiplication problem situations, this is not the case. The rule as stated above is true only when the factors are divorced from the concrete situations from which the multiplication problem arises.

In algebraic form, the principle may be stated: $a \cdot b = b \cdot a$.

The two illustrations on page 197 are different situations, though they have the same abstract factors (3 and 4) and the same product (12). We must recognize that, although "3 × 4 eggs" and "4 × 3 eggs" do have the same product, they are not the same situations. When a child gets to multiplication facts that are more difficult, e.g., "3 × 8 = 24" and "8 × 3 = 24," the teacher would certainly allow him (and encourage him) to have the help he gets from applying the commutative rule and using the fact he knows better to help with the other fact. But he should be made and kept aware of the differences in the concrete situations to which the two facts apply. Adequate experience with actual objects, diagrams, and demonstrations will make this distinction real.

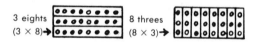

3 eights (3 × 8)➜   8 threes (8 × 3)➜

After such experiences, children can make their own statement of the rule in much less formal terms. Some such wording as this is appropriate for children and entirely correct: "3 times 8" and "8 times 3" are not the same, but they give the same answer.

The merits of introducing the commutative principle in relation to the rectangular-array idea are obvious. Whether one looks at a 2 × 4 array of chairs as "2 × 4 chairs" or "4 × 2 chairs" one can easily show they give the same product, just as for "3 × 4 eggs" or "4 × 3 eggs."

If this clear understanding is developed for the basic multiplication facts, the learning-teaching task will be much simpler when children get to problems such as this:

In a class of 32 children, each child made a ribbon bookmark 3 inches long. How much ribbon was needed?

Forms A and C are correct, including "inches" as the name of multiplicand and product. Algorisms B and D are also correct, because 32 × 3 = 3 × 32 = 96; but the "inches" labels are omitted when the factors are reversed. It would be wrong to write "3 inches times" anything, since the multiplier must be an abstract number without a concrete designation. If the name (inches) is omitted after the 3, it should also be omitted after the numerical product of 96. A separate oral or written statement may indicate that "96 inches of ribbon will be needed."

A: 32 × 3 inches = 96 inches.
B: 3 × 32 = 96
C: 3 inches   D: 32
    ×32   ×3
     6   96
   90
   96 inches

One could challenge the position taken here, arguing that "32 × 3 inches = 3 × 32 inches." This is true and would allow the label "inches" to be written for both the multiplicand and product in the commuted algorism. The omission of word labels with the commuted form is, however, simpler and less likely to lead to careless use of labels. Actually, adults seldom include labels (except for money numbers) in their written algorisms anyway, once they have departed the surveillance of their elementary school teachers. Most mathematicians object strongly to any use of word labels.

When multipliers of 3, 4, and more digits are used with smaller multiplicands, the reversal of the factors according to the commutative rule is a great time-saver for calculations either with or without pencil and paper. When two-place and larger multipliers are first used, the rule is most helpful, as will be shown in chapter 10.

THE ASSOCIATIVE PRINCIPLE FOR MULTIPLICATION

The factors in multiplication may be grouped in any order. That is, *when more than one multiplication is to be performed, they may be performed in any order.*

A typical application of this rule is apparent in this problem:

Two boys each earn $3 a day for 4 days. How much money do both boys earn in all?

In many elementary texts, this is called a "two-step problem." One child may think: "2 boys earn 2 × $3 each day. 2 × $3 = $6. In four days they will earn 4 × $6, or $24." Another child may think: "In 4 days, each boy will earn 4 × $3, or $12. Both boys will earn 2 × $12, or $24." Either line of reasoning is correct.

Stated in more abbreviated fashion and with parentheses enclosing the first step in each case, the solutions could be written:

$$4 \times (2 \times \$3) = 4 \times \$6 = \$24$$
OR
$$2 \times (4 \times \$3) = 2 \times \$12 = \$24$$

In algebraic form, any of the following statements is an expression of the associative principle for multiplication:

$$(a \cdot b) \cdot c = a \cdot (b \cdot c)$$
$$a \cdot b \cdot c = a \cdot (b \cdot c)$$
$$a \cdot b \cdot c = (a \cdot b) \cdot c$$

When one or more of the numbers involved in such a problem are large, the problem solver may multiply the easy multiplication step without resorting to a written form and then write only the last step involving the larger numbers.

In a very interesting and useful application of the associative rule of multiplication, the multiplicand, the multiplier, or both are broken down into their factors and then the factors are associated and commuted in a variety of ways, such as:

$8 \times 9 = 2 \times 4 \times 3 \times 3 = (2 \times 3)(3 \times 4) = 6 \times 12 = 72$
$15 \times 24 = (3 \times 5) \times (4 \times 6) = (3 \times 4) \times (5 \times 6) =$
$12 \times 30 = 30 \times 12 = 360$

The usefulness of this rule for doing calculations without written aid is apparent. A man is driving down the road and wishes to figure out how far he can drive before he needs to stop for gas. He estimates that he can drive about 17 miles per gallon, and his gas gauge indicates that he has about 12 gallons in the tank. He may find it easier to use 1-digit multipliers, so he thinks of 12 as 3×4. He multiplies 4×17 to get 68, then multiplies 3×68 to get a product of 204, and knows that he should probably stop for gas before he drives 200 more miles. $12 \times 17 = 3 \times (4 \times 17) = 3 \times 68 = 204$.

The applications related to place values will be developed later, but one example may be cited here: $20 \times 45 = 2 \times 10 \times 45 = 10 \times (2 \times 45) = 10 \times 90 = 900$.

THE DISTRIBUTIVE PRINCIPLE
FOR MULTIPLICATION

Multiplication is distributive with respect to addition. Since subtraction is the inverse of addition, it is also true that *multiplication is distributive with respect to subtraction.*

Frank asked Bill and Joe how many marbles they had together. Bill said, "I have 4 and Joe has 5; that's 9 together." Frank said, "I have 6 times as many as you have together. Do you know how many I have?" Bill and Joe both got the right answer, but they did it differently.

Bill thought, "$6 \times 9 = 54$." Joe thought, "$6 \times 4 = 24$ and $6 \times 5 = 30. 24 + 30 = 54$."

Diagrams of the two ways of solving this simple problem show that Bill was dealing with 6 groups of 9 marbles each. Joe thought of Bill's 4 marbles and his 5 marbles separately, multiplied each group by 6, and then added. He was using the distributive principle.

In summary form, $6 \times 9 = 6 \times (4 + 5) = (6 \times 4) + (6 \times 5) = 24 + 30 = 54$.

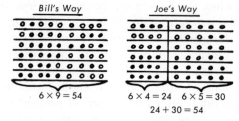

Bill's Way   Joe's Way

$6 \times 9 = 54$ $6 \times 4 = 24$ $6 \times 5 = 30$
$24 + 30 = 54$

The typical algorisms for multiplication of two-place and larger numbers use the distributive law repeatedly. When multiplying 2×34, the thought process is somewhat like this: $2 \times 30 = 60$; $2 \times 4 = 8$; $60 + 8 = 68$, working from left to right in the horizontal algorism, or $2 \times 4 = 8$; $2 \times 30 = 60$; $60 + 8 = 68$, working from right to left in the vertical algorism.

By commutation, the distributive rule is also applied to two-place and larger numbers when they occur in the multiplier. This is the whole basis of algorisms with "partial products."

The distributive law for multiplication with respect to subtraction is frequently used when one is shopping, owing to the frequency of prices like 49¢ and 98¢. The total price of three items at 49¢ each is usually computed somewhat as follows: $3 \times 50¢ = \$1.50$; $3 \times 1¢ = 3¢$; $\$1.50 - 3¢ = \$1.47$, though the mature calculator probably would report that he thought only, "$\$1.50, \$1.47$."

In summary form: $3 \times (50¢ - 1¢) = (3 \times 50¢) - (3 \times 1¢) = \$1.50 - 3¢ = \$1.47$.

The algebraic formulation of the distributive principle may be written:

$$a \cdot (b + c) = a \cdot b + a \cdot c$$
$$\text{OR}$$
$$(b + c) \cdot a = b \cdot a + c \cdot a$$

THE RULE OF LIKENESS

The multiplicand and the product must be alike in the sense that they are being used in a particular situation. The equal groups that are combined in multiplication of whole numbers constitute the total group or product; obviously, they must "have the same name" in concrete situations or even in those dealing with abstract items that are named. In figures 59 and 60 the subgroup is made up of 4 *plants;* so the product group must also be *plants.* This is true whether the multiplication situation is just a different version of an addition situation or whether it is a ratio-to-one situation. In the first case, the 8 plants represented by the product are the identical plants in the subgroup (represented by addends or multiplicand). In the latter case, the *plants* to which the product refers are in a 2-to-1 ratio to the *plants* to which the multiplicand refers.

Because of this rule, labeled algorisms should show the same name for the multiplicand and the product. The multiplier is never appropriately associated with a "concrete" label.[9]

THE PRINCIPLE OF CLOSURE
FOR MULTIPLICATION

The term "closure" need not be developed in the elementary school arithmetic program, but a complete description of the multiplication process should include it. The natural numbers are said to be closed with respect to multiplication as they are for addition. This simply means that any two natural numbers, when multiplied, will give a product that is also a natural number.

The principle of closure, like many other things, is appreciated most when it is absent. The principle of closure does not hold for division; one cannot take just any natural number, divide it by any other natural number, and expect to get some other natural number. Coming back to multiplication, we can take any natural number, multiply it by any other natural number, and get some other natural number.[10]

The Basic Multiplication Facts

BASIC MULTIPLICATION
FACTS DEFINED

The basic multiplication facts are numerical statements in which a 1-digit number is multiplied by a 1-digit number. In other words, both factors are 1-digit numbers. Without the products given, we have "multiplication combinations." Giving the product completes the multiplication statement.

All the basic multiplication facts are shown in table 8. They are the only facts that are absolutely necessary to perform multiplications in our decimal-number system; so they are called "basic." Anybody who knows all these facts and understands our notational system can perform the multiplication of numbers of any size by applying the rules of multiplication discussed in the preceding section. The facts should be learned to the level of automatic recall.

Table 8 includes 100 basic multiplication facts. As with basic addition facts,

---

[9] The rule of likeness is not a mathematical principle or law. It is a practical rule of application in problem situations.

[10] The same statement could be made if "whole number" is substituted for the term "natural number" throughout the statement.

TABLE 8

Basic Multiplication Facts

0	1	2	3	4	5	6	7	8	9
×0	×0	×0	×0	×0	×0	×0	×0	×0	×0
0	0	0	0	0	0	0	0	0	0
0	1	2	3	4	5	6	7	8	9
×1	×1	×1	×1	×1	×1	×1	×1	×1	×1
0	1	2	3	4	5	6	7	8	9
0	1	2	3	4	5	6	7	8	9
×2	×2	×2	×2	×2	×2	×2	×2	×2	×2
0	2	4	6	8	10	12	14	16	18
0	1	2	3	4	5	6	7	8	9
×3	×3	×3	×3	×3	×3	×3	×3	×3	×3
0	3	6	9	12	15	18	21	24	27
0	1	2	3	4	5	6	7	8	9
×4	×4	×4	×4	×4	×4	×4	×4	×4	×4
0	4	8	12	16	20	24	28	32	36
0	1	2	3	4	5	6	7	8	9
×5	×5	×5	×5	×5	×5	×5	×5	×5	×5
0	5	10	15	20	25	30	35	40	45
0	1	2	3	4	5	6	7	8	9
×6	×6	×6	×6	×6	×6	×6	×6	×6	×6
0	6	12	18	24	30	36	42	48	54
0	1	2	3	4	5	6	7	8	9
×7	×7	×7	×7	×7	×7	×7	×7	×7	×7
0	7	14	21	28	35	42	49	56	63
0	1	2	3	4	5	6	7	8	9
×8	×8	×8	×8	×8	×8	×8	×8	×8	×8
0	8	16	24	32	40	48	56	64	72
0	1	2	3	4	5	6	7	8	9
×9	×9	×9	×9	×9	×9	×9	×9	×9	×9
0	9	18	27	36	45	54	63	72	81

the facts including zero are often omitted in multiplication charts, leaving only 81 facts. The so-called "zero facts" are not usually needed in elementary school arithmetic unless one multiplies two-place or larger numbers. When such situations are encountered, the zero facts can be taught rather easily in relation to the generalization that "multiplying any number by zero gives a product of zero" and the generalization that "multiplying zero by any other number gives a product of zero." When the first occasion presents itself for multiplying zero or multiplying by zero, the needed generalizations can be developed.

The multiplication facts with 1 as a factor may also be taught as soon as they are needed in two-place multiplication. They have no use prior to that point. Again, a generalization or two should be the heart of the teaching: "Any number times 1 equals that number," and "Any number taken only 1 time is that same number." Adults who deal with the "1 facts" as though they were easy are making a mistake. The concept involved is "so easy it is difficult." Obviously five

1's are 5; that is an elementary meaning of 5. $1+1+1+1+1=5$. Obviously, if 5 things are used (1 time), 5 things are used. One five = 5. A 5 is a 5 is a 5, to Gertrude Stein or anyone else. The multiplication process is not apparent in such situations; therefore, the "1's facts" should be postponed until the multiplication concept is well-developed. To try to teach multiplication first with 1's would be folly.

Omitting the facts for 0 and for 1 in the early stages leaves 64 multiplication facts to be learned. These may be organized in various ways for presentation to children, the traditional arrangement being in "tables." Any column or any row of facts in table 8 is a multiplication table. Teachers often ask whether or not they should "teach the tables." Parents ask why children do not start multiplication by memorizing the tables. The tables of multiplication have their proper place in arithmetic teaching, but it is not as formal first exercises in multiplication. They should not be given "ready-made" to children who are ready for multiplication. The instructional procedure for the facts should more nearly *end* with tables rather than beginning with them. Children can build their own multiplication tables and charts if multiplication is meaningfully taught.

TEACHING BASIC MULTIPLICATION
FACTS AS COUNTING

Many of the same counting experiences that build readiness for addition also lead toward multiplication, specifically, those which involve regular counting. Some counting opportunities are part of regular classroom activities: counting the children for attendance reports, counting teams in games, counting couples as they walk to the lunchroom or auditorium, counting fours or

sixes as children are seated at tables; giving 2 sheets of construction paper to each child and counting by 2's to keep track of the amount distributed, counting the lunch money (nickels by 5's, dimes by 10's), and counting the milk money (4¢ per bottle). Some counting opportunities are brought in specifically for counting practice: counting on a counting frame, a twenty board, a hundred board, the abacus; counting materials provided by the teacher such as pictures of cloverleaves to be counted by 3's; paper clips fastened in equal groups of any number; and buttons as sold on cards in 2's, 3's, 4's, or other quantities.

Any such regular counting is background for the multiplication concept, but that does not mean that each time a teacher thinks of this relation she must pounce on it and call it multiplication. When counting facility has been established, intermediate steps are in order, such as use of the terminology "2 fours" or "5 twos." The teacher may ask:

"How many clovers (or clover stems) are shown?"   (4)
"How many cloverleaves?"
"Count them by threes."   (3, 6, 9, 12)
"Four 3's are how many?"   (12)

This is enough. Children need time to "absorb" their experiences. Writing the multiplication fact as "$4 \times 3 = 12$" can usually wait until the children have accustomed themselves to simple regular counting to find how many, then to the terminology of "three 4's are 12." First- and second-grade children may well have many such experiences and not need to be introduced to "multiply" or "4 times 3 equals 12" until they are older.

When the teacher (at any grade level) judges some children to be ready for the more formal terminology, all that will be new to the children is the new name of what they have done—a new way of talking about a familiar experience. The written forms may wait even longer or be introduced along with the new spoken terminology, but sometimes teachers are tempted to be too eager to get to written arithmetic when children's needs might be better served by having ample experience at the concrete and semiconcrete levels.

With children whose number concepts are more advanced, a teacher may decide to use more abstract counting devices such as the counting frame or abacus. Various counting devices are available or readily made that have 100 items: for example, 100 wooden beads or spools on a rigid wire on which they can be grouped in various ways or 100 pegs on a pegboard in 10 rows of 10 pegs each. Golf tees on perforated ceiling board are excellent for this purpose.

The hundred board with removable tags may be arranged so that it facilitates counting by various 1-digit numbers and has a "built-in" checking device. On the outward-facing side of the tags are the numerals from 1 to 100 arranged as usual. On the back of each tag which is a multiple of any number from 2 through 9 the appropriate numerals are written. For example, on the back side of the "12" tag will be small numerals for 2, 3, 4, and 6 because 12 is a multiple of those numbers. (See fig. 61.) The "15" tag will have only 2 numerals on the back, 3 and 5. The "11" tag will have no numerals on the back because it is a prime number.

As a child counts by 4's, he turns over the tags as he calls the numbers—4, 8, 12, 16. . . . He knows that if he is counting correctly, there will be a small "4" on the back of each tag he turns except the "4" tag itself. See figure 62.

If this device is to work smoothly and not be so cumbersome as to interfere with the counting, the tags must be easily turned. If they are attached by short strings, they will turn easily. This type of counting board is well worth the time spent on constructing it, because it can be used not only as a regular hundred board but also for counting as described here and for practice on

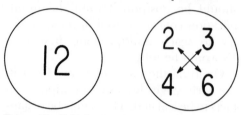

Figure 61. Multiplication Factor Tag for Use on a Hundred Board.

multiplication facts. For the latter use, tags with products on one side and factors on the other side may be turned to show the factors; the child then says the product and checks himself by turning the product side outward. The arrows indicate the factors to be multiplied together to get the product.

Regular counting on the number line is also either a preliminary to multiplying or a form of demonstrating multiplication.

TEACHING MULTIPLICATION FACTS
AS REGROUPING

Each number fact with a product of 10 or more uses regrouping to fit the idea of changing ones to make new groups of ten, the number base of our system. The combination "3 fours" or "3 × 4" is a description of one way of grouping that many items—three groups of 4 items each. When the combination is completed to become "3 fours are 12" or "3 × 4 = 12," the items are represented as being regrouped to become 1 group of ten and another group of two, or 1 ten and 2 ones. We say that 4 nickels = 2 dimes; so also $4 \times 5¢ = 2 \times 10¢ = 20¢$. The diagram below shows 3 groups of 5 each, regrouped as 1 ten and 5.

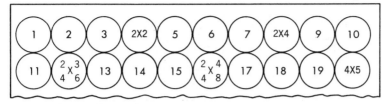

Figure 62. Part of a Hundred Board Showing Products for 4.

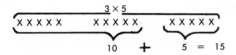

$$10 \quad + \quad 5 \quad = \quad 15$$

The number of players on a baseball field is reported with equal accuracy whether we say there are "2 × 9 players" or "18 players." The ability to revise various groupings to the decimal base is, however, of great value when one wishes to compare various combinations. Each can be translated to the standard base, and they can be more easily compared. The quantities "6 × 7" and "5 × 9" are difficult to judge as to relative size because of their different types of grouping. When they are both converted to basic collections of ten, they are readily and quickly compared, as seen in the diagram:

"ten-groups." The multiplication facts for 2's with sums of 10 or more can be handled the same way, the process being easier with 2's and 5's because "even tens" are derived. After these experiences, children can proceed to the same type of activities with groups that do not convert to "even tens."

Fitting of cubes into a 10 × 10 cube holder, as in figure 63, is a good activity for this purpose. At first, the original groups (e.g., 4 sevens) may be better recalled if each group is a different color (e.g., 7 red, 7 white, 7 yellow, 7 blue). The 4 sevens are arranged to fill complete rows (tens) in the cube holder. After the arrangement, the child can "read" the complete multiplication fact from it. The colors remind him that he started with 4 sevens; the new grouping

```
* * * * * * *          * *    * *    * *    * *    *
* * * * * * *          * *    * *    * *    * *    *
* * * * * * *     =    * *    * *    * *    * *
* * * * * * *          * *    * *    * *    * *
* * * * * * *          * *    * *    * *    * *
* * * * * * *
```
$$6 \times 7 = (4 \times 10) + 2 = 42$$

```
* * * * * * * * *          * *    * *    * *    * *    *
* * * * * * * * *          * *    * *    * *    * *    *
* * * * * * * * *     =    * *    * *    * *    * *    *
* * * * * * * * *          * *    * *    * *    * *    *
* * * * * * * * *          * *    * *    * *    * *    *
```
$$5 \times 9 = (4 \times 10) + 5 = 45$$

This idea of regrouping by tens is particularly appropriate for introduction with the multiplication of 5's. Counting by 5's or adding successive 5's (on a number chart, on a 100-spool wire, or even on the abacus) dramatizes the transfer from "five-groups" to

shows him that $4 \times 7 = 2$ tens and 8, or 28.

The long "stick blocks" are also good for practice with regrouping. Notice figure 64. The following practice exercise arranged for children working in pairs is a good example:

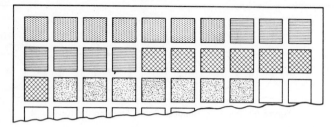

Figure 63. Cube Arangement to Show: 4 × 7 = (2 × 10) + 8 = 28.

Use your stick blocks. Take turns using the blocks. Player A will put out blocks to fit the multiplication combination. Player B will regroup them to show *tens* and *ones*. Then player B will put out the blocks for the next combination, and player A will change it to *tens* and *ones*. Check on each other to be sure you are correct.

When you have used the blocks for all the combinations, write in the products on this sheet. Do this without the blocks if you can.

3 × 6 =___tens and___ones =___   8 × 2 =___
6 × 4 =___tens and___ones =___   6 × 5 =___
7 × 3 =___tens and___ones =___   9 × 3 =___
6 × 2 =___tens and___ones =___   4 × 6 =___
5 × 3 =___tens and___ones =___   5 × 5 =___

THE RULES OF MULTIPLICATION APPLIED IN LEARNING MULTIPLICATION FACTS

While the children may not be aware of formal laws of mathematics, they may frequently use the rules of multiplication as they discover and practice multiplication facts. The rule of likeness will be used repeatedly as they work with equal groups, as they count by regular intervals, and as they regroup objects and draw pictures of grouped items. Eight "couples" of children for a game

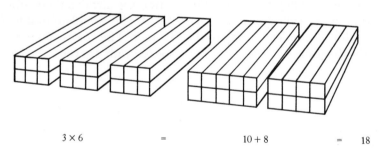

3 × 6   =   10 + 8   =   18

Figure 64. Regrouping Blocks to Show: 3 × 6 = 10 + 8 = 18.

Of course, the main purpose of such an activity is to help children discover multiplication facts for themselves and understand (in terms of regrouping by tens) what a multiplication fact statement really "says."

Regrouping the blocks may also emphasize other aspects of the multiplication process, such as the application of the rules of multiplication, particularly commutativity, associativity, and distributivity.

will be discussed as 8 groups of 2 *children* each making up a total group of 16 *children*. Three groups of 6 *blocks* each will be regrouped as 18 *blocks*. Six sets of 4 *chairs* at each table will be rearranged in a circle for the whole class in a total group of 24 *chairs*. This likeness characteristic of the equal subgroup and the total group should be pointed out before, during, and after development of the algorisms for multiplication facts.

Omitting the "0" and "1" multiplication facts and the facts in which both factors are the same (e.g., $4 \times 4 = 16$), there are 56 basic multiplication facts all of which are tied in with the commutative principle. As with the learning of addition "reverses," the discovery and use of this principle can be a big boon to the learner on his way toward automatic control of these facts. In the case of the multiplication facts, however, the teacher needs to make sure that the children see not only the *relationship* of the pairs of facts having the same factors but also their *contrasted* meanings.

The counting activity described in relation to figure 61, with factors of a number shown on the reverse side, may well call attention to pairs of multiplication facts with the same factors and products.

Children who need help on noting the existence of pairs of reverse facts may enjoy arranging marbles on a Chinese checkers board, or corks may be used if one prefers their silence and greater likelihood of staying in place. One or two children could be given 16 marbles or corks and told to arrange them in equal groups as many ways as they can. The presence of one "non-reversible" fact ($4 \times 4 = 16$) in the group will merely emphasize the reversal of 2×8 and 8×2. As they achieve control of easier facts, children can do the same thing with larger groups of marbles. (Obviously, this is also preparation for learning division facts.) Further, in playing this game, children will no doubt hit upon arrangements of equal groups that employ other principles than commutation.

Two boys had laid out 12 checkers so as to show 4 threes, 3 fours, 2 sixes, and 6 twos. They were quite proud of themselves at finding so many arrangements. Their teacher suggested that they might find even more if they worked at it. After a few minutes one of the boys went to the teacher to ask, "Is it all right to have groups inside of groups?" She said, "Yes, I think you are on the right track." The boys stayed with the problem until they had worked out the arrangements shown below with the boys' verbal descriptions:

"3 sets of two 2's" "2 sets of two 3's" "2 sets of three 2's"

Pleased with themselves, the boys were eager to try their new-found skill in regrouping other totals. When she was sure they had the concept of "equal groups within equal groups" well in hand (or mind), the teacher helped the boys to work out multiplication statements: $3 \times 2 \times 2 = 12$; $2 \times 2 \times 3 = 12$; $2 \times 3 \times 2 = 12$.

Other children had become interested in what was going on, and wanted to do it too. One of these newcomers to the activity had his own bright idea. After watching while one of the first two boys demonstrated, he said, "You know, that would help you figure out new facts you didn't know—those with big numbers like 6 and 8. Let's take more marbles."

The teacher suggested 24 as a total because she knew this boy had been struggling with $3 \times 8 = 24$. Before he left the "game," he had found that 3×8 could be rearranged in a pattern of $2 \times 3 \times 4$. Although he could not have written the record like this, he was actually both commuting and associating factors thus:

$3 \times 8 = 3 \times (4 \times 2) = 3 \times 4 \times 2 = 2 \times 3 \times 4 = (2 \times 3) \times 4$

The teacher was satisfied to let the matter rest when the boy saw for himself that he had changed 3×8 into 6×4.

She knew that he would go on from there as he had more experiences with experimental groupings within a total. She was also pleased to think how much all the boys were learning from this experience, which would help them with division facts at a later date, to say nothing of "factoring."

A teacher who wonders why she should know about commutativity and associativity should find the answer in observing how such principles can operate (unnamed) in children's thinking, laying sure foundations for later understandings.

The principle of distributivity also comes in for its share of credit in helping boys and girls to figure out unknown products for larger combinations.

Ellen was asked by her teacher to get enough construction paper so that each child at her table would have 6 sheets. Ellen said, "There are 6 people at our table. I can give everybody 3 sheets first, and then 3 more sheets each. 6×3 sheets $= 18$ sheets. I'll use 18 sheets twice. $18 + 18 = 36$. I need to get 36 sheets of paper to have enough."

Charles was planning a wiener roast for some of his friends. He had invited 3 girls and 3 boys, and he knew that with himself there would be 3 girls and 4 boys at the wiener roast. His mother suggested that he ought to have at least 3 wieners for each child. How many wieners did he need to buy? Charles did not know how much 7 threes would be, but he thought, "The 3 girls will eat 3×3 wieners; that's 9 wieners. The 4 boys will eat 4×3 wieners; that's 12 wieners, $9 + 12 = 21$; so I need to buy at least 21 wieners."

Both of these children were using the distributive principle. Ellen was changing "6 sheets" to "3 sheets $+ 3$ sheets," multiplying each by 6 and then adding

the two products. Charles was actually distributing the multiplier (using both distributivity and commutativity). In formal mathematical statements (not needed by the children at this stage) this is what they did.

Ellen: $6 \times 6 = 6 \times (3 + 3) = (6 \times 3) + (6 \times 3) =$
           $18 + 18 = 36$

Charles: $7 \times 3 = (3 + 4) \times 3 = (3 \times 3) + (4 \times 3) =$
             $9 + 12 = 21$

The rule of distribution is very usable with multiplication facts that are beyond the present control of children. If they are encouraged to use it with the basic facts, they will the more readily see its applications in multiplication of larger numbers.

Children's prior understandings of the decimal-place-value system will also help them to use the distributive rule to derive products. They find it easy to multiply tens, since "6×10," for example, simply means "6 tens," or "60." When called on to figure out the product of 6×8, they can be helped by questions such as these: How many are 6×10? (60) How much difference is there between 8 and 10? (2) If $6 \times 10 = 60$, how much less would 6×8 be? (6 twos, 12) What is $60 - 12$? (48) (Note the use of the distributive rule with respect to subtraction, also the use of the higher-decade subtraction fact $60 - 12$.)

INTERDEPENDENCE OF BASIC FACTS

During the experiences children have with the multiplication facts before and after learning them to a level of automatic recall, they need and should have help in relating the facts to one another. For too long and in far too many places the only relationships to receive much stress are those which exist in the multiplication tables, and sometimes even that stress has been a relatively formal organization by proximity rather than by meanings.

A list of some relationships that may be used in building up the meanings of multiplication facts may emphasize the availability of different patterns of relatedness:

a. Relation to regular counting: 4, 8, 12, 16; $4 \times 4 = 16$

b. Relation to addition: $4 + 4 + 4 + 4$; 4 fours; $4 \times 4 = 16$

c. Relation to subtraction: "I know my mother said that the 3 of us used up a dozen eggs in 4 days." $12 - 3 - 3 - 3 - 3 = 0$; 4 threes are 12; $4 \times 3 = 12$

d. Relation to division facts: $15 \div 3 = 5$; $5 \times 3 = 15$

e. Relation between "reverse" facts: $8 \times 9 = 72$; $9 \times 8 = 72$

f. Relation between facts having the same product:

$$\overset{\div 2}{6 \times 4 = 24} \quad 3 \times 8 = 24 \quad \text{OR} \quad \overset{}{6 \times 4 = 24}$$
$$\underset{\times 2}{\qquad}$$

and $4 \times 6 = 24$

g. Relation to "component facts":

$$2 \times 8 = 16$$
$$3 \times 8 = 24$$
$$\overline{5 \times 8 = 40}$$

h. Relations in factoring schemes: $6 \times 8 = 2 \times 3 \times 4 \times 2$

i. Relations among facts with the same multiplicand: tables of twos, threes, etc.

j. Relations among facts with the same multipliers: tables of "2 times," "3 times," etc.

k. Patterns within tables (next section)

These are by no means the only relations that may be discovered and used in thinking about the multiplication facts.

PATTERNS IN THE MULTIPLICATION TABLES

Anyone who wants evidence of the *systematic* characteristics of the number *system* has only to study the multiplication tables, or the order of the products in those tables. Some of these patterns may be pointed out to children; some can be found by them with a little skillful questioning by the teacher; and the rest can then be found by the children themselves—once they get the notion that such patterns do exist. The search for patterns is an interesting activity and also one that may help children in their progress toward automatic recall and use of facts as needed.

The reader may wish to refer to tables 6 through 8. Only the products are given in the "Table of Nines" below.

This patterning of the nines table has been used so often as a "stunt" or "trick" that its chief value is lost. As children are led to figure out "why it works," they get the real benefit from it. Children who enjoy this may wish to explore further the checking of computations by casting out 9's, also the rationale of that procedure.

Table of Nines	Suggestions for Treatment
9	Read down the ones column: 9, 8, 7, 6, 5, 4, 3, 2, 1 (backward counting)
18	Read down the tens column: 1, 2, 3, 4, 5, 6, 7, 8 (forward counting)
27	Why does it work that way? (Each step is really adding one more 9. Adding 9 has
36	the same effect as adding 10 and subtracting 1. Following the arrows, we really
45	add 1 ten, subtract 1 one, add 1 ten, subtract 1 one, repeatedly.)
54	
63	
72	
81	

$$9$$
$$\swarrow$$
$$1 \rightarrow 8$$
$$\swarrow$$
$$2 \rightarrow 7$$
$$\swarrow$$
$$3 \rightarrow 6$$

Ignoring place value, add the digits for each product. You get:

$$1 + 8 = 9$$
$$2 + 7 = 9$$
$$3 + 6 = 9$$
$$4 + 5 = 9$$
Etc.

Why are the sums of the digits always 9?

You are adding 1 to one addend and subtracting 1 from the other addend at each step. Having started with 9 as the sum, all successive sums stay at 9.

Other patterns to look for include:

Table of Twos: Even counting pattern; even numbers in ones place in their counting order; sequence repeated as far as one wishes to extend the table. Why?

Table of Threes: Sum of digits always 3 or a multiple of $3 - 3, 6, 9, 3, 6, 9$, etc. Why?

Table of Fours: All even digits in ones column. Why? Sequence always the same, 4, 8, 2, 6, 0, 4, 8, 2, 6, etc. Why?

Table of Fives: Ones-column digits always 0 or 5, occurring alternately. Why? Alternate products beginning with 5 have digit sums that steadily increase by 1 each time. Why? Alternate products beginning with 10 have digit sums that steadily increase by 1 each time. Why?

Table of Sixes: Even digits in ones column. Why? Sequence always 6, 2, 8, 4, 0. Why?

Table of Sevens: Every possible digit in ones place. Why? (Same for threes and nines.)

Table of Eights: Ones digits always even numbers in this order: 8, 6, 4, 2, 0. Why? Sums of digits in ‾descending order (when sum is a two-digit number, those two digits must be added). Why?

Other patterns not inherent in the tables as such may be discovered in the multiplication chart, such as the pattern of the squares on the "top left to lower right" diagonal (ones digits in symmetrical arrangement, ascending and descending). For the child who needs to be challenged, the search for these patterns provides excellent assignments, particularly with the "why" questions to be answered.

LEARNING SEQUENCE FOR THE BASIC MULTIPLICATION FACTS

No one fixed sequence for teaching the multiplication facts can be strenuously defended, on grounds of either research evidence or practical observation or learning theory. "Teaching order" is not going to be the same as individual "learning order" anyway. Tentative recommendations are, however, appropriate if teachers understand their responsibility for making modifications in the light of their own appraisals of learners and situations.

Some factors that must condition sequence in any teaching program (of multiplication facts or anything else) are:

1. *Individual differences in learners.*
To expect all children to learn multiplication facts in exactly the same sequence or at the same rate is unrealistic. To hold to this view reveals either ignorance or unwillingness to adjust to what is known about human variation.

2. *Opportunities for experience with multiplication situations.* Here too, wide variation exists in opportunities for both children's in-school and out-of-school experiences. A newsboy who handles nickel transactions daily already knows "the fives." A school situation in which children purchase 6¢ items or are frequently seated in groups of 6 may make "the sixes" easier than some smaller group. Experiences vary as to

what is experienced, how often it is experienced, how recently it has been experienced, how impressive the experience was, and how well it ties in with different children's purposes.

3. *Local courses of study and textbooks in use.* The less security the teacher feels in making judgments on matters of sequence, the more she will rely on local courses of study, textbooks, and other printed materials. While no instructional program should consist of slavish adherence to any text, many situations do arise in which apparently equivalent arguments could be offered for different orders of presentation; at such time, it seems sensible to follow local courses of study or locally adopted texts (the latter often serving in practice as courses of study).

Assuming that such considerations as these will be kept in mind, it is safe to recommend an over-all sequence in which the first experiences are with a relatively easy, miscellaneous group of multiplication facts occurring incidentally and in planned situations. A teacher who uses purposefully the occasions that arise incidentally will necessarily call attention to miscellaneous facts (though perhaps not as formally stated facts). Planned presentation of the grouping of objects into equal-sized groups should also cut across "the twos," "the fours," and so on. The main purpose at the beginning is not the presentation of *certain facts* of multiplication but the presentation of the *idea* or *concept* of multiplication as the combining of equal groups into a new total group that includes them. This can more easily be done if emphasis on particular groups does not come too soon.

After adequate preliminary work with miscellaneous combinations has laid a basis for the multiplication concept, the expansion of that concept can proceed with organized groups of facts. These groups may be organized to promote exploration of all the facts that can be found for a given product (e.g., all facts with products of 6 or 8 or 12) or all the facts with a given multiplicand (e.g., the twos, the threes, and so on). The latter is the usual procedure. The general sequence should usually be from smaller to larger numbers, but exceptions to this size sequence are also desirable. Some writers prefer to start with the "twos" or the "fives" because of their frequency of use and the ease of counting by these amounts. Some prefer starting with the "threes." Although order may vary from a rigid sequence of twos, threes, fours, fives, sixes, sevens, eights, and nines, the "0 facts" and "1 facts" should definitely be postponed until needed in two-place multiplication.

When organized presentation of groups of facts is undertaken, it should not consist of a formal presentation of the tables of facts. The purposes are to expand and clarify the multiplication concept and how it works and to build understanding of the separate multiplication facts and their relations to one another. One of the earliest activities is the building up of sets of facts with manipulative materials. If blocks are used, two obvious ways are shown in figure 65. In each case, the equal subgroups are added one by one until 9 (or more) groups have been used. At the left in figure 65, the groups are added at one side. At the right in figure 65, the groups are added by stacking them one on top of the other. As the groups are built up, the children may be asked to describe each new total successively, as: 2 fours, 3 fours, 4 fours, . . . 9 fours; later, 2×4, 3×4, 4×4, . . . 9×4. The same actions may be described in terms of column addition also, building the relation between addition and multiplication.[11]

The question is sure to arise as to whether the "reverse" facts are to be introduced together or in close prox-

"nines," there will be 8 new facts in each set.[13] If the reverses are presented together and the sequential order from "twos" through "nines" is followed, the number of facts in each new set will be: 15 new facts for "2," 13 new facts for

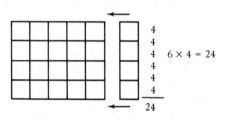

5 fours being built up to 6 fours

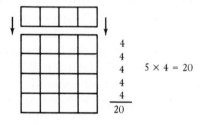

4 fours being built up to 5 fours

Figure 65. Building Multiplication Tables.

imity. If organization is according to size of product, such "reverses" as $4 \times 6 = 24$ and $6 \times 4 = 24$ will, of course, be presented together. If the grouping corresponds to later conventional tables, the question is very real. In the illustration above, for example, should children simultaneously or in close sequence be introduced to building relations for fours (2 fours, 3 fours, 4 fours, 5 fours, etc.) and for their reverses (4 twos, 4 threes, 4 fours, 4 fives, etc.)? No one disagrees about the eventual need for the relation to be built; the problem is one of timing. Should the reverses be introduced in relation to each other, or should the relation be discovered later?[12]

This question affects the relative number of facts to be presented for each step in the organizational pattern. If the reverses are not introduced together and if the facts are presented sequentially from the "twos" through the

"3," 11 new facts for "4," 9 new facts for "5," 7 for "6," 5 for "7," 3 for "8," and only 1 new fact for "9."

2 × 2 = 4	2 × 2 = 4	2 × 3 = 6	3 × 2 = 6
3 × 2 = 6	2 × 3 = 6	3 × 3 = 9	3 × 3 = 9
4 × 2 = 8	2 × 4 = 8	4 × 3 = 12	3 × 4 = 12
5 × 2 = 10	2 × 5 = 10	5 × 3 = 15	3 × 5 = 15
6 × 2 = 12	2 × 6 = 12	6 × 3 = 18	3 × 6 = 18
7 × 2 = 14	2 × 7 = 14	7 × 3 = 21	3 × 7 = 21
8 × 2 = 16	2 × 8 = 16	8 × 3 = 24	3 × 8 = 24
9 × 2 = 18	2 × 9 = 18	9 × 3 = 27	3 × 9 = 27

2 × 4 = 8	4 × 2 = 8	2 × 5 = 10	5 × 2 = 10
3 × 4 = 12	4 × 3 = 12	3 × 5 = 15	5 × 3 = 15
4 × 4 = 16	4 × 4 = 16	4 × 5 = 20	5 × 4 = 20
5 × 4 = 20	4 × 5 = 20	5 × 5 = 25	5 × 5 = 25
6 × 4 = 24	4 × 6 = 24	6 × 5 = 30	5 × 6 = 30
7 × 4 = 28	4 × 7 = 28	7 × 5 = 35	5 × 7 = 35
8 × 4 = 32	4 × 8 = 32	8 × 5 = 40	5 × 8 = 40
9 × 4 = 36	4 × 9 = 36	9 × 5 = 45	5 × 9 = 45

2 × 6 = 12	6 × 2 = 12	2 × 7 = 14	7 × 2 = 14
3 × 6 = 18	6 × 3 = 18	3 × 7 = 21	7 × 3 = 21
4 × 6 = 24	6 × 4 = 24	4 × 7 = 28	7 × 4 = 28
5 × 6 = 30	6 × 5 = 30	5 × 7 = 35	7 × 5 × 35
6 × 6 = 36	6 × 6 = 36	6 × 7 = 42	7 × 6 = 42
7 × 6 = 42	6 × 7 = 42	7 × 7 = 49	7 × 7 = 49
8 × 6 = 48	6 × 8 = 48	8 × 7 = 56	7 × 8 = 56
9 × 6 = 54	6 × 9 = 54	9 × 7 = 63	7 × 9 = 63

[11] Such a table-building activity as this will usually precede such activities as the discovery of patterns among multiplication facts.

[12] Presenting related facts and related tables together is recommended on the basis of logic, though research evidence is lacking.

[13] Facts for 1 and 0 will come later.

2 × 8 = 16	8 × 2 = 16	2 × 9 = 18	9 × 2 = 18
3 × 8 = 24	8 × 3 = 24	3 × 9 = 27	9 × 3 = 27
4 × 8 = 32	8 × 4 = 32	4 × 9 = 36	9 × 4 = 36
5 × 8 = 40	8 × 5 = 40	5 × 9 = 45	9 × 5 = 45
6 × 8 = 48	8 × 6 = 48	6 × 9 = 54	9 × 6 = 54
7 × 8 = 56	8 × 7 = 56	7 × 9 = 63	9 × 7 = 63
8 × 8 = 64	8 × 8 = 64	8 × 9 = 72	9 × 8 = 72
9 × 8 = 72	**8 × 9 = 72**	**9 × 9 = 81**	9 × 9 = 81

New facts for each table shown in **bold face;** previously used facts shown in regular type.

In either case, the total of 64 facts are presented. When reverse sets of facts are introduced together, the number of new facts in each set is smaller and smaller; this seems desirable, since the larger and usually more difficult facts get attention and practice along the way. As the children study the new sets of facts, they merely review familiar ones and meet a decreasing number of totally new ones. Admittedly, before the whole sequence is complete under either scheme, children will tend to discover and use the commutative principle that relates the reverse multiplication facts.

The benefits children derive from building the tables themselves are great. If relations among facts are constantly encouraged in the various ways that have been suggested, children will enjoy the rearrangement of the facts into the systematic sequence of the table form and will use them more intelligently because of knowing how they "came to be." This is not to say that organization into tables must wait until every fact is mastered, but neither should they be introduced before the learner has built up acquaintance and experience with a sizable number of facts. Practice with tables should be summarization of facts known. The counting chart and product chart (tables 6 and 7) are in a sense "tables of tables" since they may be used to summarize all the tables.

All the basic facts for multiplication do not need to be taught before any two-place or three-place numbers are used in multiplication problems. In fact, with the background of experience children usually have in adding larger numbers before they do much work in multiplication, they can readily make the transfer to use of larger multiplicands without changing, or even with changing if the changing procedure in addition has been well understood.

Although multiplication and division are presented in separate chapters in this book, no separation in the learning sequence is intended. After children have gained a reasonable introductory knowledge of the multiplication process and are beginning to master some multiplication facts, they should benefit from developing related division facts in "multiplication-division families" comparable to "addition-subtraction families." In chapter 11 this point will be developed more fully.

The sequence of forms used for stating multiplication facts should probably follow that suggested in the local course of study or adopted basic text. The reason for this recommendation is that it will facilitate children's progress as they move from teacher to teacher. If there is confusion in what is expected by different teachers, the child suffers. This applies to both oral and written forms of stating multiplication facts. Oral statements should normally precede written statements because of the opportunities to discuss and revise and vary oral statements before coming to the usual final stage of *saying* only what is acceptable for *written* forms.

All along the way, practice with multiplication facts is necessary: practice in real multiplication situations, practice in purposely planned classroom situations that demonstrate meanings, practice in the setting of verbal problems, practice in dramatizing or drawing pictures to show meanings already gained, practice in organized patterns such as the tables, and practice on individual facts in games, exercises, and contrived situations of one kind or another. The almost inevitable flash-card type of practice need not be described, except to suggest that it certainly belongs late in the sequence of types of practice listed and that teachers should use variations of flash-card style.[14]

[14] One useful variation is that which has all the various combinations for a certain product on one side of the card, instead of having only one fact. The child tries to tell all the combinations for a given product.

A teacher should help children work individually from discovery to mastery of multiplication facts. The work with concrete manipulative materials looms large at first and tapers off as it is no longer needed. The use of abstract ideas and forms begins after some concrete experience and should steadily increase as meanings are developed. So-called "semiconcrete" or diagrammatic representations are transitional between concrete and abstract levels. Word problems are used continuously as the settings for use of meanings. Most important, all of these should be embedded in a context of meanings derived from experiences the learners can understand.

STUDY QUESTIONS

1. Write out three word problems suitable for use with children and using $4 \times 5 = 20$ for their solution. Make one problem fit each of these ideas of multiplication: (a) multiplication as an extension of addition, (b) multiplication as a ratio-to-one idea, and (c) multiplication as shown by an array.

2. Draw some sort of drawing (e.g., number line, picture of objects, area drawing) to show the meaning of each problem situation you posed in question 1 and to show the solution.

3. What are some recent uses you have made of the commutative or associative principles for multiplication?

4. Our notational system involves the idea of multiplication within each place-value position (the face value × the place value). Using this idea, express these numerals as sums of products: 246; 378; 1032; 9870.

5. What are the factors of 24? 28? 15? 36? 81? 64? 42?

6. If children are to be able to build their own multiplication tables, what prior experiences do they need?

Multiplication of Larger Numbers

THE MULTIPLICATION OF larger numbers involves little that is new beyond the basic concepts that should be developed in connection with the basic multiplication facts. Of particular importance for the multiplication of larger numbers are concepts of place value and the distributive principle.

Place Value and the Distributive Principle in Multiplication

PLACE VALUE IN MULTIPLICATION
OF LARGER NUMBERS

Some attention has been given to place values in two-place products of basic multiplication facts, e.g., $4 \times 8 =$ a regrouping into 3 tens and 2 ones. The factors of the basic facts, by definition, are 1-digit numbers; their products, however, may be 1-digit or 2-digit numbers.

When either of the factors in multiplication has more than one digit, place value *must* be clearly understood if the multiplication is to be clearly understood. In multiplying 4×22, one multiplies 4×2 *ones* and 4×2 *tens*. In multiplying 14×22, one multiplies 4×2 *ones*, 4×2 *tens*, 10 (or 1*ten*) $\times 2$ *ones*, and 10 (or 1*ten*) $\times 2$ *tens*. In other words, the

basic multiplication facts are used, but the correct answer will be derived *only* *if* those basic facts are properly related to the *place values* of the numbers being multiplied, thus:

		2 2
Basic Facts Used	Place Values Represented	×1 4
$4 \times 2 = 8$	4×2 ones = 8 ones- - - - - - -	8
$4 \times 2 = 8$	4×2 tens = 8 tens- - - - - - -	8 0
$1 \times 2 = 2$	1 ten $\times 2$ ones = 2 tens- - - - -	2 0
$1 \times 2 = 2$	1 ten $\times 2$ tens = 2 hundreds	2 0 0
	Sum of partial products	3 0 8

This place-value situation is also shown in the common algorism (Form A), but it is not as obviously emphasized. Children are too often taught only "where to write" the digits in the products without the basic reasons for writing them in those places.

Form A
```
    2 2
   ×1 4
    8 8
    2 2
    3 0 8
```

THE DISTRIBUTIVE PRINCIPLE

The distributive principle is the other most fundamental basis for the multiplication algorism. It is used in the example above. The multiplication of 22 by 14 is not performed all at once; rather, the basic facts and place value are used so that the multiplication is *distributed* as to both the multiplier and the multiplicand. Instead of having to learn the product of 14 and 24, one can derive it "piece by piece" by thinking of 22 as $20+2$ and 14 as $10+4$.

$$14 \times 22 = (10+4) \times (20+2) = (4 \times 2) + (4 \times 20)$$
$$+ (10 \times 2) + (10 \times 20) = 8 + 80 + 20 + 200 = 308$$

Multiplicands of Two or More Places

CHANGING AND ITS EFFECTS

When no changing (carrying) is involved, the multiplication algorism for two-place or larger multiplicands introduces no complications. When, for example, a boy purchases 3 toys being sold for 21¢ each, he may think of paying "3 times 1 cent" and "3 times 2 dimes," using the distributive principle and moving from right to left in the algorism (Form B). Of course, he could just as easily work from left to right, thinking first "3 times 2 dimes = 6 dimes," then "3 times 1 penny = 3 pennies." (In fact, he is probably more likely to follow the latter pattern.) When no changing of pennies to dimes is involved, direction of thinking and writing about the different place values makes no difference. Our defense for teaching right-to-left direction for such a multiplication example is that it starts the child on building a direction habit that will be useful when he comes to later examples in which changing is needed.

Form B
```
  2 1 ¢
  ×  3
  ────
  6 3 ¢
   ←
   OR
   →
```

If the price of the toy is 24¢, the left-to-right direction does become important. Let us suppose that the child multiplies the dimes first, as shown in Form C, and records the "6 dimes" in the appropriate place in the product. When he multiplies "3 times 4 pennies" to get a product of "12 pennies," he should not write "12" after the "6." (He may do so, but he will have a wrong product of

Form C
```
  2 4 ¢
  ×  3
  ────
  6   ¢
```

"612.") This difficulty may be resolved in various ways, four of which are shown below:

Form D	Form E	Form F	Form G
		1	
2 4 ¢	2 4 ¢	2 4 ¢	2 4 ¢
× 3	× 3	× 3	× 3
6 0 ¢	1 2 ¢	7 2 ¢	7 2 ¢
1 2 ¢	6 0 ¢	←	←
7 2 ¢	7 2 ¢		

Forms D and E are obvious. They also have the merit of making very clear that "$3 \times 4¢ = 12¢$" and that "3×2 dimes $= 6$ dimes (or 60¢)." They are not as compact and efficient as F and G for general later use. Form F is the usual algorism with the "carried figure" shown as a crutch, and Form G is the typical algorism used by most people. Sequence of multiplying the two-place values is interchanged in D and E; because of the completeness of the record, this causes no trouble. Sequence in F and G is right to left; to change the sequence to left to right would introduce the difficulty of having to erase, cross out, or in some other manner modify the "6" first obtained for the tens, or left-hand, numeral in the product.

All this discussion is purely academic if one is not concerned about the meanings of base and place. If one cares only for a routine to be followed, one simply starts with Form F or G and teaches it by a formal set of steps. To do this is not only to teach this particular type of example without meaning; it is also a hindrance to understanding of later, more complex algorisms.

If it were not for the effects of changing place values, multiplication facts with two-place products could be used as easily as those with one-place products. The significance of this distinction increases as the number of places in the multiplicand increases.

USE OF ADDITION

IN MULTIPLICATION

When it becomes necessary to use changing (carrying) in the typical multiplication algorism, it also becomes necessary to use addition. In the immediately preceding example, one needs to use the simple basic fact "$6 + 1 = 7$" (that is, 6 dimes + 1 dime = 7 dimes). When larger numbers are involved, as in Form H, basic addition facts do not suffice. The full sequence of thought steps is listed here with an "x" preceding each one that uses a higher-decade addition fact:

Form H

```
  4 5 6
  × 7
  3 1 9 2
```

7×6 ones = 42 ones

42 ones = 4 tens and 2 ones (remember the 4 tens)

7×5 tens = 35 tens

x 35 tens + 4 (changed) tens = 39 tens

39 tens = 3 hundreds and 9 tens (remember the 3 hundreds)

7×4 hundreds = 28 hundreds

x 28 hundreds + 3 (changed) hundreds = 31 hundreds

31 hundreds = 3 thousands and 1 hundred

This need to use addition (particularly when it is higher-decade addition) as part of the multiplication process is often the cause of considerable difficulty, both to children learning the process and also to persons using the process after they understand it. First, it is easy to forget about the "changed and carried" number, particularly since its use is postponed by the need to find the next product before it is added. Written crutches may be used to prevent such forgetting, as in Form I, but a second difficulty arises when one has a multiplier with more than one figure. If, for example, the multiplier had been 57 instead of 7, all the "carried" figures for multiplying by 7 would have to be erased, crossed out, or at any rate ignored, if they were not to interfere

Form I

```
  3 4
  4 5 6
  × 7
```

with a new set of "carried" figures for multiplying by the 5 in the tens place of the multiplier. Third, if the person does not have the higher-decade addition facts well in hand, at best he is slowed down in completing the multiplication example, and at worst he introduces errors into the product or becomes so involved with the addition that he gets "mixed up" in his multiplication.

Teachers need to pay very special attention to this point in order to forestall the difficulty as far as possible and deal effectively with it when it occurs.

The difficulty is certainly prevented from occurring in Form J (similar to Forms D and E on p. 216). No "carried" figures are needed (except the 1 thousand in the last step, too easy to cause much trouble); each numeral indicates its value by its placement in the partial products, and the adding of numbers having the same place value

Form J

```
  4 5 6
  × 7
  4 2
  3 5
  2 8
  3 1 9 2
```

is accomplished all at once (as a final step). As an introductory form or as a form of remedial work for children who are having difficulty with their handling of "changed and carried" figures, this form has much to recommend it. As a final standard form, it is time-consuming and inefficient. The decision to choose it must be based on the user's ability to use it as contrasted with his ability to use the more concise form. All children will probably benefit from at least seeing this form and recognizing that it tells in detail what the more compact algorism tells more briefly.

Crutches may be used insofar as their use seems to help rather than to hinder; they should be considered temporary helps, not permanent fixtures in the child's multiplication procedures. Crutches may be written above the multiplicand (as shown in Form I) or at the side to avoid confusion of successive different crutches.

Another big help with this phase of the process is provided by careful review of higher-decade addition facts. The child who is doing this type of multiplication will most likely have no trouble with simple additions such as "$6 + 1 = 7$" or "$7 + 2 = 9$." Before he gets to multiplications with larger multipliers, which will introduce higher-decade addition facts, a quick survey test of his competence with these facts is in order. If the results of such a test so indicate, practice should be provided on those higher-decade addition facts which occur in multiplication. This suggests that the teacher should select for special practice those facts (e.g., $48 + 5 = 53$) which do occur in multiplication examples and omit (for this purpose) those which cannot occur (e.g., $34 + 9 = 43$).[1] In fact, a very good activity for children who need extra assignments to challenge their interest and use their abilities would be the construction of a complete set of higher-decade addition facts that can occur in multiplication examples.

In regard to the difficulty of needing to use multiplication and addition interchangeably, this must be learned through practice. The suggestions for working gradually into habitual use of the two interchangeably should reduce but not eliminate the need for practice. Much of the practice will, of course, occur in multiplication problems

[1] Since the largest product of a basic fact of multiplication is 81, the digit 9 cannot occur as a "carried figure"; all higher-decade addition facts including 9 as the second addend are therefore eliminated from consideration. The fact "$48 + 5 = 53$" is appropriate because in multiplying 8×67, one would "carry" 5 tens and add them to the 48 tens secured by multiplying 8×6 tens. One would not ever use "$47 + 2 = 49$" in multiplication because 47 is not the product of any basic multiplication fact.

and exercises being done for other purposes as well.

MULTIPLYING EVEN TENS

A logical early step in teaching children to multiply two-place numbers by a one-place number is to multiply even tens. A realistic problem situation might deal with "ready-mix" biscuits that come in cans containing 10 biscuits each. Little difficulty will be met in helping children see that 5 cans of biscuits will hold 50 biscuits, that is, "5×1 ten $= 5$ tens," or "$5 \times 10 = 50$." If the children know the meaning of 10 and the meaning of 50, there is nothing new here except the form of statement that 5 tens are fifty. The vertical algorism may be new. It should, of course, be made clear that all the forms below are just different ways of stating the same fact:

		1 ten	10
5 tens = fifty	5×1 ten = 5 tens	$\times 5$	$\times 5$
5 tens = 50	$5 \times 10 = 50$	5 tens	50

Similarly, money values may be used, starting with "even dimes." If an article costs 20¢ (2 dimes), how much will 3 such articles cost? Again, the important point here is to establish the equivalence of all these forms, some familiar, some new, but all leading to the vertical form that will be a part of the multiplication toward which this work is leading:

			2 dimes	20¢
3×2 dimes	2 dimes	20¢	$\times 3$	$\times 3$
= 6 dimes	2 dimes	20¢	6 dimes	60¢
	2 dimes	20¢		
$3 \times 20¢ = 60¢$	6 dimes	60¢		

Children should already be familiar with counting by tens. In order to relate the multiplication of tens to counting by tens, the problems may also be solved by that procedure. For the first example above, the children may simply count: 10, 20, 30, 40, 50. For the second, the counting will go: 20, 40, 60.

The interpretation of the vertical algorism (last of each group above) should stress *place values,* but not the idea of multiplying zero. It is not necessary to multiply 5×0 or 3×0, though that might be done. The essential interpretation is that when *tens* are multiplied, the product must also be *tens* (by the rule of likeness) and that the zeros make it possible to show that tens rather than ones are being multiplied. The product "2×30" might be restated as: $2 \times (3 \times 10)$ or $(2 \times 3) \times 10$.

The introduction of the multiplication of even tens may occur well in advance of any formal presentation of two-place multiplicands. The situations in which even tens are multiplied are frequent with money numbers, and children are not likely to find difficulty with this process. The teacher's task is to *use* such situations to lay a foundation for later work in multiplying two-place numbers that are not even tens.

MULTIPLYING OTHER TWO-PLACE
NUMBERS BY ONE-PLACE
MULTIPLIERS

The multiplication of two-place numbers by one-place multipliers may be introduced before the children have mastered all the basic multiplication facts. They often like to use larger numbers and have many everyday uses for them. Larger multiplication facts such as $6 \times 8 = 48$ and $9 \times 7 = 63$ were not needed by a third-grade class who wanted to know how many hamburger buns there were in 4 packages of a dozen each.

Many boys and girls at this level can solve such a problem immediately by use of abstract methods. Some need to use concrete or semiconcrete aids in their solutions. One subgroup in this particular class began their solution with concrete objects, using 12 blocks to represent 12 buns in each package. Because these children had become habituated to thinking of two-place numbers made up of tens and ones, they arranged each set of 12 blocks as 1 ten and 2. To show 4 packages of buns, this arrangement of blocks was repeated four times, as shown in figure 66. The abstract forms at the right show some ways in which different children made abstract records of what they had done with the blocks.

Notice the opportunities provided for building and strengthening such basic ideas as: (1) the relation of multiplication to addition, (2) place values in multiplication, (3) the distributive principle in multiplication, and (4) the rule of likeness. Such building and strengthening takes place better through meaningful use than through formal, adult-type statements. Therefore, children's own wording of meanings involved, when correct, should be encouraged. Examples from the above situation are:

Relation of multiplication and addition: "I like to add first; then I feel more sure about the multiplication answer. I know the answer is supposed to be the same if I do it right."

Place values in multiplication: "When you multiply ones times tens, the answer will be tens."

Distributive principle: "You don't have to multiply a big number all at once. You can multiply it a part at a time, like the 2 ones and the 1 ten."

MULTIPLYING WITH CHANGING

When children have developed some skill and adequate understanding of situations that do not require changing, this step may be introduced. The opportunity may occur rather informally, as with a group of children who had assembled egg cartons and were using them in various ways in the arithmetic program. One alert youngster figured out that he could use a string to help him figure out the number of "eggs" in several dozen. The illustration for 8 dozen in figure 67, with his verbal comments, indicates a good deal of understanding for a child who had not been introduced to the formal algorism for the multiplication of 8 × 12 with changing ("carrying").

When the teacher plans for the introduction of changing or regrouping in multiplication, she should consider the readiness of the learners for this concept. She should review mentally (and if necessary by testing) their competence with any basic multiplication facts to be used, with the multiplication algorisms used to date, with place value and changing in addition, and with the basic

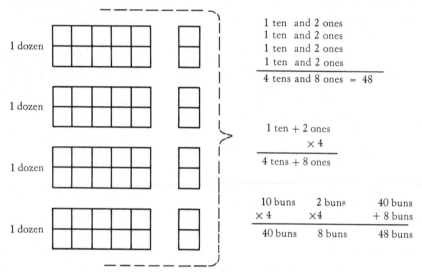

Figure 66. Introducing a Two-place Multiplicand.

"See, I put a string like this so it cuts off 2 eggs in each dozen. Then I have 8 tens and 8 twos. Eight tens are 80; I know that. Eight twos are 16; I know that. Then I just add 80 and 16. That's 96, so 8 dozen would be the same as 96."

Such an experience may be used as the basis for asking children to see how many ways they can write a record of the experience, leading to the more efficient abstract forms, or additional activities may be introduced first. Some systematic, planned work will be necessary.[2]

[2] Some people may object to the use of a multiplicand including "1" in the tens place at such an early point. The emphasis is not on "multiplying 1," but on multiplying *tens*. If anyone objects, he may hold multiplication of dozens or any other "teen" multiplicand until later, applying the same principles to multiplicands of 20 or more.

meanings of multiplication and the rules that apply to the process in general. Then she should set up or use some existing situation in which children can work out solutions to a multiplication problem that will use changing of ones to tens in its solution.

Such a problem may well involve money, both because the changing concept is familiar in connection with money and because such problems are more likely to occur in children's everyday experience.

Problem: Notebook covers at the school supply store are 24¢ each. Four covers are needed for holding the loose-leaf reports the class is making on a social studies project. How much will the 4 notebook covers cost?

This problem may be worked out in several ways, both with play coins or other manipulative aids and in abstract terms. Which are used must depend on the children's levels of security and understanding. Some reasonable possibilities follow.

Children might work in pairs, using play money. They might lay out 4 times will be worth 96¢ just as they are; but the changing idea will be emphasized if children are encouraged actually to change ten of the 16 pennies for 1 dime, place it with the 8 dimes, and thus get a final grouping of 9 dimes and 6 pennies.

Some books for teachers and text-

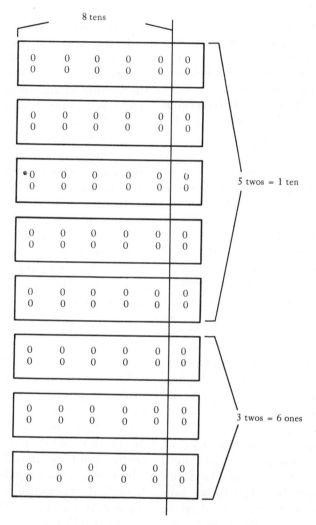

8 tens + 1 ten + 6 ones = 96

Figure 67. Demonstration: 8 dozen = 9 tens 6 ones.

the price of a notebook cover (24¢) in dimes and pennies. They would then have an arrangement of 4 sets of 4 pennies each, equal to 16¢, and an arrangement of 4 sets of 2 dimes each, 8 dimes, or 80¢. The 8 dimes and the 16 pennies books for children place heavy reliance on the use of pocket charts showing place values. Such a device might be used at this point to demonstrate the changing. In 4 successive "rows" on the pocket chart the children might arrange tickets to show 2 dimes (tens) and 4 pennies (ones). (See fig. 68*A*.) Then the quantities may be regrouped as in figure 68*B*, showing 8 dimes (tens) and 16 pennies (ones). The changing step is completed by changing 10 of the ones in *B* for 1 ten, as shown in figure 68*C*. Finally, the whole product may be shown as in figure 68*D*. Some of the steps may be omitted if children do not need them to clarify the process. Finally, the written forms should be developed as *records* of what was done.

Some users of pocket charts prefer to show changing of 10 ones to 1 ten by making a bundle of the 10 tickets and placing this bundle in the tens section of the chart. In this case, the original tens should each also be shown by bundles of 10 single tickets. The bundles to show ten are probably more appropriate in earlier stages of learning, with a transfer to the more abstract showing of tens by place value alone as soon as possible.

The same problem might be demonstrated on any form of abacus, though the changing step is somewhat more difficult on the abacus if it has 10 beads or less on each rod.

After the children have had ample opportunity to act out the multiplication process with changing, they should be asked to write the solution in the form of an algorism. Similar examples requiring changing should also be written out in various ways that appeal to different children, or the boys and girls may simply be asked to see how many different ways they can think of to write the solutions. Thus, for 3×27, they might work out such forms as K1-8:

$$
\begin{array}{ll}
\text{K1: } & 27 \\
& 27 \\
& 27 \\ \hline
& 21 \\
& 6 \\ \hline
& 81
\end{array}
\qquad
\begin{array}{l}
\overset{2}{\ } \\
\text{K2: } 27 \\
\ 27 \\
\ 27 \\ \hline
\ 81
\end{array}
\qquad
\begin{array}{l}
\text{K3: } 20 \quad 7 \\
\underline{\times 3} \ \underline{\times 3} \\
60 \quad 21 \\
\quad 21 \swarrow \\ \hline
\quad 81
\end{array}
\qquad
\begin{array}{l}
\text{K4: } 27 \\
\underline{\times 3} \\
60 \\
21 \\ \hline
81
\end{array}
$$

$$
\begin{array}{l}
\text{K5: } 27 \\
\underline{\times 3} \\
6 \\
21 \\ \hline
81
\end{array}
\qquad
\begin{array}{l}
\text{K6: } 27 \\
\underline{\times 3} \\
21 \\
6 \\ \hline
81
\end{array}
\qquad
\begin{array}{l}
\overset{2}{\ } \\
\text{K7: } 27 \\
\underline{\times 3} \\
81
\end{array}
\qquad
\begin{array}{l}
\text{K8: } 27 \\
\underline{\times 3} \\
81
\end{array}
$$

The children's discussion and comparison of such forms provides opportunity for clarifying various relationships of addition and multiplication, place value and changing, and rules of multiplication. Perhaps few of the forms shown will be retained as the final form. If the writing of the changed (carried) 2 tens were omitted from From K7, it would be the same as the most concise form (K8); the use of the abbreviated form should be encouraged as soon as the teacher believes that an individual child is ready for its correct and meaningful use. Certainly it would be well to develop some competence in this "crutchless" form before children are expected to do multiplication with 2-place or larger multipliers in problems that require changing in the same place more than once.

MULTIPLICANDS OF MORE
THAN TWO PLACES

No new ideas are needed for the multiplication of 3-place or larger multiplicands. In fact, some examples with 3-place multiplicands (such as 3×232) are much easier than some with 2-place multiplicands (such as 9×47). Children who multiply such numbers will already have had experience with addition of 3-place and larger addends; they will not be troubled by the use of the same ideas in multiplying 3-place multiplicands as those used in multiplying 2-place numbers. True, sometimes they will have to change ("carry") twice or more with larger numbers, but they have already done this with addition. The fundamental point here is that the basic

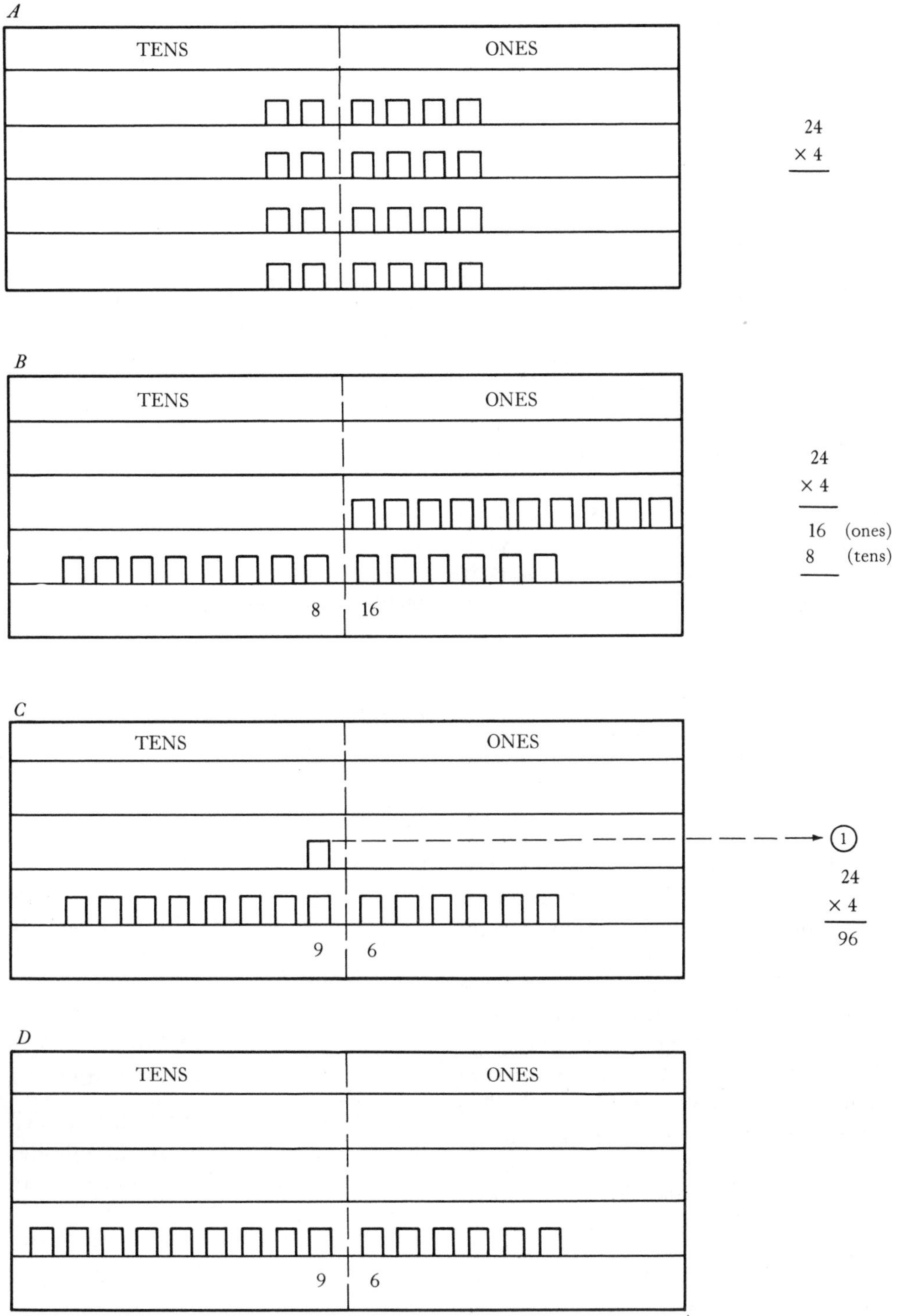

A

24
× 4

B

24
× 4
———
16   (ones)
8   (tens)
———

C

24
× 4
———
96

D

Figure 68. Multiplication Using a Pocket Chart.

meanings are the same; the only difference is their application in more places.

Some mention should perhaps be made of the use of 0's and 1's in larger multiplicands. The emphasis should be on generalizations based on meanings of these numerals rather than on basic multiplication facts or on "multiplying 0" or "multiplying 1." In L1-4, the treatment should rely on meanings already built. In L1 and L2 (short and long forms for the same example) there are *no tens* in the multiplicand. Therefore, there are *no tens* in the product. Just as a 0 is used to show no tens in the multiplicand, 0 is used to show no tens in the product. In Forms L3 and L4 (short and long forms for the same example), there are again no tens in the multiplicand;

L1	L2	L3	L4
3 0 4	3 0 4	3 0 4	3 0 4
× 2	× 2	× 6	× 6
6 0 8	8	1 8 2 4	2 4
	3 0 0		1 8 0 0
	3 0 8		1 8 2 4

but the multiplication of 6×4 ones yields 24 ones, or 2 tens and 4 ones. The 2 tens must be written in the product. Because the "2" holds the tens place in L3 and L4, no 0 is needed to hold the tens place as in L1 and L2. (There is really no need to go through the formality of thinking: 6×0=0; 0+2=2. If, however, either the teacher or the learner feels more secure with such a procedure, perhaps he should use it until it no longer seems necessary.) The main point is that "what to do about zero" is decided in terms of the particular situation.

Similarly, in Forms M1-6, "what to do about 1" in the multiplicand is just a matter of understandings. In Forms M1 and M2, the "1" in tens place means 1

ten; if anyone prefers to think "3 times 1 ten = 3 tens," it is not wrong to do so. Such formality is not necessary; just note that *3 tens* are called for. The formal basic fact statement is like saying "3 tens = 3 tens." The same could be said of the 3 hundreds in Forms M3 and M4. In Forms M5 and M6, the additional step of "adding in" the "changed 1 ten" with the "3 tens" is the only new point. It will hardly be new if children have understood preceding work.

M1	M2	M3	M4	M5	M6
3 1 2	3 1 2	1 2 2	1 2 2	3 1 4	3 1 4
× 3	× 3	× 3	× 3	× 3	× 3
9 3 6	6	3 6 6	6	9 4 2	1 2
	3 0		6 0		3 0
	9 0 0		3 0 0		9 0 0
	9 3 6		3 6 6		9 4 2

Multipliers of Two or More Places

As multiplication has been typically taught for several past generations, the introduction of two-place and larger multipliers has usually been one of the big steps as far as the teaching of the formal algorism is concerned. The use of partial products has usually been encountered first at this point. According to modern approaches, the use of two-place multipliers is not so likely to be different from meanings and procedures already in use.

PARTIAL PRODUCTS

AND THEIR PLACEMENT

With one-digit multipliers partial products are not necessary, though they may be used as shown above. With two-place or larger multipliers, they do usually become necessary.[3] In multi-

[3] One might argue that partial products are not absolutely necessary when using all two-place multipliers. One might multiply 25 × 42 by thinking: "4200 ÷ 4"; but this is an exception rather than a typical written performance.

plying 14×22, one separates the multiplier into its component parts, 10 and 4, and then multiplies to get two separate products ("$4 \times 22 = 88$" and "$10 \times 22 = 220$"). The partial products "88" and "220" must then be added to get the total product of 14×22. The typical algorism is shown as Form N1. Form N2 shows three separate steps. Form N3 has the advantage of compact form (as in N1) but is more explicit than N1 in showing the complete second partial product. It also removes any question as to "moving over" to write "22" in the tens place.

N1	N2			N3
2 2	2 2	2 2	8 8	2 2
× 1 4	× 4	× 1 0	+2 2 0	× 1 4
8 8	8 8	2 2 0	3 0 8	8 8
2 2				2 2 0
3 0 8				3 0 8

An approximate oral statement of how most adults learned to perform this simple two-place multiplication would go something like this: "$4 \times 2 = 8$. $4 \times 2 = 8$. Move over (to write the next product). $1 \times 2 = 2$. $1 \times 2 = 2$. Bring down the 8. $8 + 2 = 10$. Write the 0. Carry the 1. $1 + 2 = 3$."

Conceivably, a person going through that ritual may know what are the meanings with which he deals. Chances are quite high, however, that a majority of those who learned to parrot it did not (and perhaps still do not) relate the form to the place value and other meanings involved.

Children learn placement of the partial products not in terms of "moving over" for each successive partial product but rather in terms of understanding that a two-place or larger multiplier is multiplied in a series of steps. Typically, we multiply first by the number represented in ones place of the multiplier, then by the number in tens

place, and so on. Finally, all the partial products are added to give the total. Actually, the concept of place value and understanding of the distributive rule of multiplication are involved.

DEVELOPING A MULTIPLICATION PROBLEM ABOUT MONEY

A simple illustrative problem should indicate the occurrence of several previously used meanings within the computational procedure for two-place or larger multipliers.

Problem: Twelve children are going on a picnic. If they take box lunches prepared in the school cafeteria at a cost of 34¢ each, what is the total cost of the 12 lunches?[4]

First the teacher might ask the children to find in any way they wish the total cost of the lunches. Some children might add; some might use the series of steps shown in Form N2. These and other ways of working the problem would then appropriately be discussed. Finally, the teacher who is trying to work toward the shorter typical algorism but without neglecting any of the meanings involved might proceed somewhat as follows.

Teacher: Let's work the problem now with play money. I am going to ask 12 of you to lay out 34¢ each on your desks. Using only dimes and pennies, how can you show 34¢ most easily?
Children: With 3 dimes and 4 pennies.
Teacher: You have already found the answer in several ways. I am going to suggest another way. I am going to ask 10 children to sit together here at your left and 2 children to sit alone over here at your right. Take your 34¢ with you, please.
(Children move so that there is an obvious grouping of ten children at the left and 2 children at the right.)
Teacher: Why do you suppose I asked you to sit in a group of 10 and a group of 2?

[4] The discussion of this particular problem is not necessarily intended to represent the first experience of children with two-place multipliers.

Child: Because 12 means 1 ten and 2 ones.

Teacher: Now I am going to take all the pennies from the two children. Without looking in my hand, how many pennies do you think I have?

Children: Eight.

Teacher: How do you know?

Children: Because $2 \times 4 = 8$.

Teacher: I am going to put the eight pennies down here on the table. (To the right as the children look at the table.) Now I am going to take all the dimes from the same two children. How many dimes will I get?

Children: Six.

Teacher: Yes, 2×3 dimes $= 6$ dimes. How many *cents* would you say that is?

Children: Sixty cents.

Teacher: I'll put the dimes here with the 8 pennies. You see that the lunches for the two children will cost 6 dimes and 8 pennies, or 68¢. Now let's get the money for the 10 lunches. I will gather up the pennies from all ten children. How many pennies will I get?

Children: Forty.

Teacher: How do you know?

Children: Ten fours are forty. (Or: $10 \times 4 = 40$.)

Teacher: Yes, I have forty pennies. I am going to keep these separate from the other pennies I got from the two children. I have so many pennies that it is hard to see how many. What could I do to make it easier to see that I have 40 pennies?

Children: Stack them by groups of ten. (Or: Change them for 4 dimes.)

Teacher: Now I am going to take all the dimes. How many dimes does each child have?

Children: Three dimes each.

Teacher: And I am taking 3 dimes from each of the ten children. How many will that be? 10×3 dimes $=$ how many dimes?

Children: Thirty dimes.

Teacher: Again I have so many coins that it is hard to see how many. What should I do to make it easier?

Children: Stack them in groups of ten each. (Or: Change every ten dimes for a dollar.)

Teacher: Here is the money for the 12 lunches, or 12×34¢. (Arrangement on the table as viewed by the children shown in fig. 69.)

Teacher: Now we can write a record of what we have just done. You tell me what we multiplied each time and what I should write on the board. (To one of the two children): Tell me the first step.

Child: 2×4 pennies $= 8$ pennies (cents).

Teacher: Yes, so I'll write: -------- $.08
(To other child of the two.) Then what?

Child: You took our dimes. 2×3 dimes $= 6$ dimes. That's 60¢.

Teacher: I'll write that under the $.08
8 cents: .60
Now one of the ten children, tell me what we did next.

Child: You took 10 sets of 4 pennies each. 10×4¢ $= 40$¢. You should write 40 cents. $.08
                                      .60
Teacher: That's right. I'll write 40¢   .40
under 60¢. Now, someone else tell me what we did last.

Child: You took 10 groups of 3 dimes each. 10×3 dimes $= 30$ dimes.

Teacher: Yes, 30 dimes. What is another way to say it?

Child: Three dollars.

Teacher: I will write that last, under $.08
the other sums of money. Maybe I   .60
should say "under the other products."   .40
Does it mean either 30 dimes or 3   3.00
dollars, the way I have written it? (Discussion should indicate that it does.)

Teacher: Here are all the products. What should we do now?

Children: Add them to get the total.   ⌈ $.08
(Teacher draws line under last item | .60
and adds the column.) --------------⟨   .40
Teacher: This sum is 4 dollars and | 3.00
8 pennies. Is that what I have?   ⌊$4.08

(Further discussion would develop the point that the 6 dimes and the 4 dimes have a sum of 10 dimes, which can be changed to 1 more dollar, or 1 new stack of 10 dimes.)

From this point, the teacher might proceed to further discussion and a shorter way of writing the same record of the experience. The pennies and the dimes for the lunches of the 2 children would then be combined as 6 dimes and 8 pennies. The pennies and dimes for the lunches of the 10 children would next be combined to show 30 dimes and

40 pennies, or 3 dollars and 4 dimes. Finally, all pennies, dimes, and dollars would be combined to get the total cost of the 12 lunches at 34¢ each:

$.68
3.40
$4.08

The final step would be the complete

DEVELOPING A MULTIPLICATION
PROBLEM ABOUT AREA

An area problem is a good one for demonstrating that a problem setting may lend meaning to the computation form at the same time that the computational procedure lends meaning to the problem situation.[5]

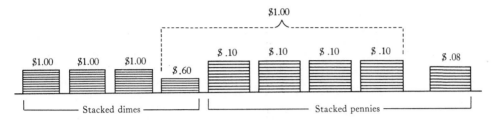

$1.00

$1.00 $1.00 $1.00 $ .60 $ .10 $ .10 $ .10 $ .10 $ .08

└──── Stacked dimes ────┘ └────── Stacked pennies ──────┘

Figure 69. Money for 12 Lunches, Regrouped as $4.08.

multiplication algorism, which so many people have learned as a series of memorized steps instead of as a record of experiences and meanings:

$$\begin{array}{r} \$\quad .3\ 4 \\ \times\ 1\ 2 \\ \hline 6\ 8 \\ 3\ 4 \\ \hline \$\ 4\,.0\ 8 \end{array}$$

Some teachers may object to the insertion of the decimal points in the record as suggested in earlier steps in this fictitious account since they do not occur in the typical short-cut algorism. They may of course be omitted throughout, but using them in the "full-account" algorisms should lend more meaning to the final short one in which they are omitted in partial products.

A discussion of the placement of the partial products in the final algorism should focus on *why* they are written where they are. Any doubts as to placement of any numeral can be resolved in convincing manner by referring back to the activity in which the whole solution was acted out with coins.

Problem. A room is covered with square tiles. There are 33 tiles in each row and 22 rows of them. How many tiles did it take to cover the whole floor? (This is another way of asking: What is the area of the floor, units of area being expressed in terms of the particular tile being used?)

One teacher used this problem with her fourth-grade pupils, both to help them understand area as "surface covered" and also to help them develop understanding of the multiplication of two-place numbers. She used a flannel board on which she placed pieces of felt in different colors to emphasize the different parts of the total product. Starting with the incomplete algorism for multiplication, she asked the pupils to suggest what she should do with the felt squares and then asked them to tell her what to write on the chalkboard to represent what had been done on the flannel board. The beginning form was:

$$\begin{array}{r} 33\ \text{squares} \\ \times 22 \\ \hline \end{array}$$

[5] The concept of area is discussed further in the chapter on measurement, chapter 19.

Teacher: What is the first multiplication fact I use?

Answer: 2 × 3 = 6.

Teacher: 2 × 3 what?

Answer: 2 × 3 squares = 6 squares.

Teacher: How can I show just that much on the flannel board, using these felt squares to represent the floor tiles?

The children suggested that 6 squares be placed on the flannel board in this arrangement:

Teacher: What should I write on the board to show that we have shown 2 threes?

Answer: Write "6" in the ones place.

Teacher: Now what is the next multiplication we do?

One child suggested that this was also 2 × 3 = 6. Another child said it was 2 × 3 tens of squares. Still another said it was really 2 × 30 squares. The teacher gave them a chance to see that either of the last two responses was correct. Then she asked the child who had said "2 × 30" to come up and select some flannel pieces that would represent "2 × 30." He hesitated but finally chose 6 strips of felt that had been marked to show 10 squares in a row. He said, "Two thirties would be 2 groups of 3 tens like these, or 6 tens of squares."

Teacher: Do you know where to place them on the flannel board so they will look like 2 thirties, or 2 sets of 3 tens each?

With some help from other children and the teacher, he eventually placed the strips of felt in rows to the left of the first six squares.

Another preferred to write the new "6" on a new line, thus:

```
33 squares
×22
─────────
 6 squares
60 squares
```

Both forms were accepted.

Teacher: Now we are going to multiply again, using the numbers 2 and 3. Who can tell me what we are really multiplying this time?

After due consideration, the group agreed that the next multiplication was really "20 threes" or "2 tens of threes." One child, however, said, "Well, in multiplication you can turn the numbers around if you want to and still get the right answer. You could say that '20 threes' is the same as '3 twenties.'"

Some of the children were puzzled by this explanation, but the teacher accepted it and asked this boy to choose pieces of felt that would show the right number of squares for this multiplication step. He chose 6 tens, just as the preceding boy had done, "because 3 twenties are sixty or 6 tens." (Actually, the teacher had also supplied enough strips of "threes" that he could have selected "20 threes" if he had so chosen. Later, the group did the solution again using this arrangement.)

Teacher: Where do you think you should put those 6 tens? Where do you think they belong on the flannel board?

With some help from others, the boy placed them as shown on page 229.

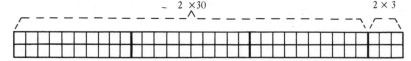

Teacher: Now what should I write on the board to show that we used 6 tens to show 2 groups of 3 tens each?

The children already had some acquaintance with the multiplication algorism. One suggested this arrangement:

```
33 squares
×22
─────────
66
```

The third numeral "6" was recorded in both algorisms, respectively:

```
33 squares        33 squares
×22               ×22
─────────         ─────────
66                 6 squares
 6                60 squares
                  60 squares
```

Teacher: We have only one more multiplication to do. Can someone tell me what

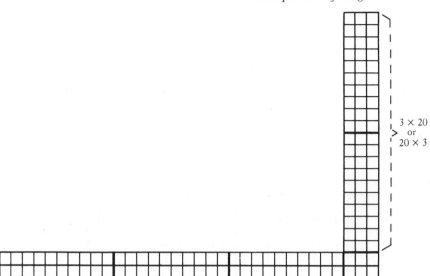

3 × 20
or
20 × 3

I should do on the flannel board and what I should write on the board?

Child: We multiply 2 × 3 again, but it's 2 tens × 3 tens. It's 20 times 30.

Teacher: How can I show 20 × 30?

Another child: Well, 10 × 10 is 100. This would be 6 times as much; so it would be 600.

Teacher: I have some pieces of felt that show 100's. Where should I put them?

The children decided that the 6 hundreds should be placed in the space that would complete the rectangle. Though these squares were not marked into smaller-unit squares, it was clear to the boys and girls that these were 10 spaces high and 10 spaces wide, or 100 squares over-all. The completed rectangle representing the tiled floor is shown in figure 70.[6]

Teacher: Now what will I write on the board to show the 6 big blocks of 100 squares each?

The two algorisms were completed thus:

33 squares	33 squares	
×22	×22	
66	6 squares	(2 threes = 6)
66	60 squares	(2 thirties = 60)
726 squares	60 squares	(20 threes = 60)
	600 squares	(20 thirties = 600)
	726 squares	

[6] Fig. 70 is a good illustration of the array idea of multiplication.

One child suggested the addition of the parenthetical notations shown with the right-hand algorism "to show how we got each part."

Teacher: But we put up only 6 big squares to show 100 each. The product says we have 7 hundreds. Where is the seventh hundred?

The children worked on this until they saw that 10 tens (of the total of 12 tens) were considered as being regrouped into 1 hundred. To prove the point, one child actually moved 4 felt "tens" from the lower left so they were next to the 6 "tens" at the upper right, making 10 tens or 1 hundred.

This problem solution is particularly impressive to children because all the partial products use the numeral "6." Each "6" is different in meaning. They all have the same "face" value, but their place values differ. The pupils enjoyed this activity so much that they wanted to do it again the next day. In the subsequent experience no doubt some children understood more than during the first experience. Some enjoyed seeing variations of arrangement that were possible, also expanding their concepts of two-place multiplication, the "why" of placement of partial products, and the meaning of area.

USE OF THE PLACE-VALUE CONCEPT
AND RULES OF MULTIPLICATION

The rules of multiplication are all apparent to the observer who is conscious of their meanings and uses. For example, the rule of likeness is shown when 2×4 *pennies* $= 8$ *pennies* while 2×3 *dimes* $= 6$ *dimes,* the likeness of

The associative principle is not so obvious in these particular problems, but one might say that it is operative in the last partial product concerning the area problem. Though the children did not set it forth in this fashion, this is what actually happened: 2 tens $\times$ 3 tens $= (2 \times 10)\ (3 \times 10) = 2 \times 10 \times 3 \times 10 = 2 \times 3 \times 10 \times 10 = (2 \times 3)\ (10 \times 10) = 6 \times$

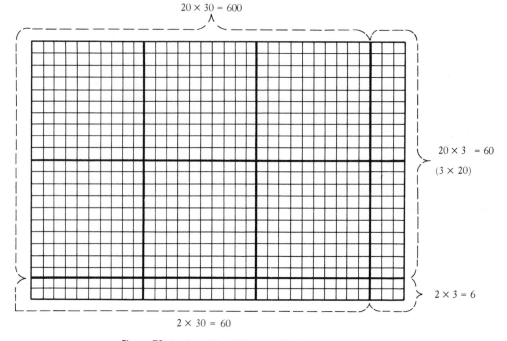

$20 \times 30 = 600$

$20 \times 3\ \ = 60$

(3×20)

$2 \times 3 = 6$

$2 \times 30 = 60$

Figure 70. An Area 22 x 33 Showing the Distributive Principle.

multiplicand and product being shown in respect to having "the same name" and also being written so as to have the same place value indicated by that same name.

The commutative principle is shown in the child's remark that "you can turn the numbers around if you want to and still get the right answer. You could say that '20 threes' is the same as '3 twenties.' "

The distributive principle is, of course, basic to the two-place multiplication algorism in which the numbers are multiplied part by part and then added to get the total product.

$100 = 600$. By commutation and association, the 2 tens $\times$ 3 tens become 6 hundreds, as was shown by the large felt squares representing a hundred each.

Pointing out that the rules of multiplication are operative in the solutions of these simple multiplication problems should not be interpreted as a recommendation that fourth-grade children should be expected to use the terminology of the immediately preceding paragraphs. Adults who teach children should know the rules well enough to recognize their use and to lead children into their use as was done in both the teaching situations described. The children showed that they were developing the meanings of these principles of operation; that is enough at this level. The "grown-up" terminology can wait so long as the basic concepts are being built.

CHANGING IN MULTIPLICATION

OF STILL LARGER NUMBERS

As with smaller numbers, changing (carrying) in multiplication of larger numbers works exactly the same as changing (carrying) in addition. The teacher who is introducing changing with two-place and larger multipliers does well to take time to emphasize first the parallel between changing in addition and changing with one-place multipliers. Whether a person is adding *seven 456's* or multiplying 7×456, he must change ones for tens and tens for hundreds in just the same way. The parallel is apparent in a study of Forms O (1-4):

Form O-1	Form O-2	Form O-3	Form O-4
3 4	3 4		
4 5 6	4 5 6	4 5 6	4 5 6
4 5 6	× 7	4 5 6	× 7
4 5 6	3 1 9 2	4 5 6	4 2
4 5 6		4 5 6	3 5
4 5 6		4 5 6	2 8
4 5 6		4 5 6	3 1 9 2
4 5 6		4 5 6	
3 1 9 2		4 2	
		3 5	
		2 8	
		3 1 9 2	

In Forms O-1 and O-2, the changing is shown with conventional "crutches" or "carried figures," identically the same for addition and multiplication. In Forms O-3 and O-4, the "crutches" are shown as partial sums and products. No matter the form in which the changing is recorded, the actual steps are the same for all four forms. Those steps are:

7×6 ones $= 42$ ones. CHANGE 42 ones to 4 tens and 2 ones.

7×5 tens $= 35$ tens. 35 tens + the 4 (changed) tens $=$ 39 tens. CHANGE 39 tens to 3 hundreds and 9 tens.

7×4 hundreds $= 28$ hundreds. 28 hundreds + 3 (changed) hundreds $= 31$ hundreds. CHANGE 31 hundreds to 3 thousands and 1 hundred. (This change is not so obvious because there is no need to combine the changed thousands with other thousands.)

If a child is not well-grounded in the rationale and the performance of changing in addition, he will have trouble with the same process in multiplication. In addition, the changed ("carried") number is used immediately as the first addend in the new column or place. In multiplication, the changed ("carried") number is put aside while the next multiplication step is done and then "picked up" again. This necessity to alternate changing, multiplying, and adding creates a much more difficult situation than is experienced in column addition. Therefore, much more maturity of understanding and better automatic recall of addition and multiplication facts are required, even though the multipliers are only one-digit numbers.

When the multipliers have two, three, or more places, the situation becomes even more cumbersome. If the type of crutch used in Forms O-1 and O-2 is used, the learner may become quite confused. See, for example, Form P in which a two-place multiplier is used. The numeral in ones place of the multiplier is the same as in Form O-2 above, necessitating the same crutches as in O-2. But when the student comes to deriving the second partial product, he must have another set of crutches. It is not difficult to see the complications that may arise as a child tries to deal with so many crutches. As the number of places in the multiplier increases, the confusion of crutches upon crutches increases. Obviously, some other form of "help" such as in Forms O-3 and O-4 must be used or else the pupil must learn to "carry in mind" the changed numerals until they are used. This requires much more command of the addition and multiplication facts. Eventually, we hope to develop such command of the process with its attendant security, but it is wishful thinking to suppose that all children can master so complex a process in equal time or to equal degrees of accuracy and facility. To attempt to push children faster than they can operate in these situations is merely to frustrate them and interfere with progress they might make under (for them) more reasonable rates of learning progress.

Apart from the "stacking up" of crutches for changing in examples with multiplace multipliers, there should be no complications when children go on to larger and larger multiplicands and multipliers. The basic principles and procedures are the same as for numbers with fewer places.

In teaching children to use two-place and larger multipliers, certain considerations not developed so far become necessary. One of these is the use

Form P

```
  5 5
  8 1
  4 5 6
× 9 7
  3 1 9 2
  4 1 0 4
  4 4 2 3 2
```

of zero in the multiplier. (See also p. 224 concerning the use of zero in the multiplicand.)

ZERO IN THE MULTIPLIER

The much discussed "zero difficulties" in multiplication probably stem almost entirely from inadequacies in the teaching of the meanings of zero and place value. If these two concepts were clearly grasped, children would not need to experience particular difficulty with the occurrence of zeros in multiplication.

The simplest case of zero in the multiplier is in multiplication by even tens, first by 1 ten, then by 2 through 9 tens. Multiplying by 1 ten is almost automatic with children who have understood place value and commutation. They already know that 3×1 ten $= 3$ tens or, stated differently, that $3 \times 10 = 30$. They also know that the multiplication factors may be reversed without changing the product; so if $3 \times 10 = 30$, then $10 \times 3 = 30$. Or: if 3 tens are 30, then 10 threes also equal 30. If children do not already have these understandings, they should be developed as the background for such paired examples as these:

Form Q		Form R		Form S		Form T	
10	5	20	4	30¢	3¢	$.50	$.06
×5	×10	×4	×20	×3	×30	×6	×50
50	50	80	80	90¢	90¢	$3.00	$3.00

A good way to review the ideas involved is to have children show how these examples would be done as addition rather than multiplication. For Q, they might write the additions as:

```
10  5+5+5+5+5+5+5+5+5+5 = 5 tens = 50
10
10
10
10
50
```

Why must the sum or the product have a zero in the ones place? Obviously, the zero is needed because there are no ones. We have only 5 tens as the sum or the product; so we must write a 0 in the ones place to make the 5 be in the tens place where it belongs.

This addition technique might also be used with other "even tens" multipliers, although as the digit in tens place increases in value, this becomes increasingly cumbersome. It is rather awkward to write 50 sixes either in a column or in horizontal addition form. The teacher may choose rather, for an example like R, to depend on the commutative principle. If a child has difficulty with 20×4, she may ask him what the product would be if he were multiplying 4×2 tens. Then she may ask, "Is 4×2 tens the same value as 2 tens $\times$ 4? Isn't 4 twenties the same value as 20 fours?"

If concrete demonstration is needed, Forms S and T might be done with play coins (dimes and pennies). Multiplying to show 3 groups of 3 dimes each is very easy. The challenge will be in showing 30 groups of 3 pennies and changing them to 9 groups of 10 pennies each (or to 9 dimes). Form T demands even more changing, first to dimes, then to dollars. If children need to know *why* they place the zeros as they do in the products, time spent in such activities may be very rewarding in prevention of future error and in carry-over to other situations involving zeros. However, the objective is to demonstrate the meanings and then rely on the commutative principle for routine later handling of the algorism.

Since multiplication by even hundreds or even thousands or any larger even place value is based on the same principles as multiplication by even tens, they will be handled in similar fashion.

Zeros occurring elsewhere in the multiplier than at the end should also be dealt with meaningfully. As with zeros at the end of the multiplier, the emphasis should not be on "multiplying

by zero," but on the idea that no multiplication is necessary. The placement of product numerals depends on keeping them in their proper places, which *may* involve writing in place-holder zeros but not necessarily. Forms U1-3 are all correct. Which should be used depends on the user and his level of understanding and skill. Many teachers like to begin with Form U1 to emphasize "no product" for the tens place of the multiplier. If that is done, the learners should be encouraged to go on to the other simpler forms, which do actually show the same relationships. We do not multiply by tens.

Form U1	Form U2	Form U3
4 2 3	4 2 3	4 2 3
× 2 0 2	× 2 0 2	× 2 0 2
8 4 6	8 4 6	8 4 6
0 0 0	8 4 6 0	8 4 6
8 4 6	8 5 4 4 6	8 5 4 4 6
8 5 4 4 6		

Therefore, we do not show any product for multiplying by tens. The tens-place zero in the second partial product (Form U2) is a place holder. No place-holder numeral is required, however, because the numerals in the first partial product (Form U3) indicate location of tens place and let us leave it unoccupied in the second partial product without "losing our place." Again, emphasis should be on meanings; the choice of a preferred form should depend on the individual and his maturity.

ONES IN THE MULTIPLIER

Earlier (chap. 9) the statement was made that there is no need for multiplication facts of the "1 times" variety as in "$1 \times 6 = 6$" except when 1's occur in multipliers of two or more digits. Even then, it is doubtful that the formal fact statement is needed as such, though it is all right for people who like that form to use it. What is really essential is the understanding that multiplying by

1 is just the same as taking any number as it is without changing its form or its value. After all, 1 of anything is just that thing; so 1 of any number is that number, whether the number being multiplied is 6 or 54 or 527.[7] See the first partial products in each of the examples below. In these examples, the only reason for writing this product (identical to the multiplicand) is that it is to be combined with another partial product to get the complete product. So much for "multiplying by 1" in the ones place of a multiplace multiplier.

6	54	527
×21	×21	×21
6	54	527
120	108	1054
126	1134	11067

When 1 occurs in the tens, hundreds, or thousands place of a multiplier, the situation is somewhat different. In such a situation it has not only its "face value" of 1 but also the place value in which it is written. The use of "1" in the tens place of the multiplier has already been discussed on pages 225-27, where the emphasis was placed not on "1×4 pennies" or "1×3 dimes" but rather on the idea of "10×4 pennies" and "10×3 dimes," or on the "10 fours" and "10 thirties." Since this has already been discussed, a multiplier with "1" in the hundreds place may be more helpful at this point.

Notice the example at the right. The numerals written in the first partial product and in the third partial product are the same. This is the result of using the *face* value "1" and merely copying the multiplicand in its original form. The very different *place* values of the two "1's" are handled entirely by place-

Form V

| 3 4 5 |
| × 1 2 1 |
| 3 4 5 |
| 6 9 0 |
| 3 4 5 |
| 4 1,7 4 5 |

ment of the partial products. Since the left-hand "1" in "121" is really "1 hundred," it is worth 100 times as much as the right-hand "1" in the multiplier. Therefore, it will have to result in a product that is 100 times as large. This is shown by writing "345" so it ends in hundreds place (third partial product in Form V).

In both Form V and Form W, the third partial product is "345 hundreds." This is the point that is some-times neglected when children deal with "1's" in the multi-plier. They are left with the idea that "1 times any number is that number" (which is true) no matter where it occurs in the multiplier (which is not always true).

Form W

| 3 4 5 |
| ÷ 1 2 1 |
| 3 4 5 |
| 6 9 0 0 |
| 3 4 5 0 0 |
| 4 1,7 4 5 |

The place-value consideration must also be developed to have the full story of the meaning of "1's" in multiplace multipliers.

As for all other place-value meanings, the point is to help children see *why* numerals are placed as they are in the algorisms and then proceed to use the algorisms without going into lengthy explanations every time one multiplies. As Banks has said, "He should know that the algorithm keeps track of its place value for him. This of course presupposes that he knows why and how the algorithm serves this purpose."[8]

Sequence of Learnings in Multiplication

To suggest a rigid sequence of detailed steps in teaching multiplication to children would be unwise. Some general recommendations may be in order, each teacher being delegated the responsibility of applying the recommendations to specific decisions about sequence of learnings:

1. The multiplication process is first introduced in problem situations that

---

[7] The meaning of 1 as the identity element for multiplication is discussed in chap. 13.

[8] Banks, *op. cit.,* p. 149.

use basic multiplication facts. By keeping the factors in the multiplication examples small, the teacher is more readily able to focus learners' attention on key ideas of the process itself such as its relation to addition and the ratio-to-one idea (in that order).

2. Multiplication with larger numbers need not be delayed until all the basic multiplication facts are mastered if teachers take care to present situations with only such larger numbers as involve the use of *known* basic facts.

3. Use of two-place multiplicands should precede introduction of two-place multipliers.

4. Three-place multiplicands can be introduced soon after two-place multiplicands since no new concepts are necessarily involved with three-place (or larger) numbers.

5. Even tens in the multiplicand are probably preferable for first use of two-place multiplicands, though some authorities disagree on this point.

6. Problems and examples *without* changing ("carrying") should precede the introduction of the same general types of problems and examples *with* changing. Again, some authorities disagree.

7. When children have a good grasp of multiplication with two-place multiplicands, two-place multipliers may be introduced, even though all basic multiplication facts may not be completely mastered. Teachers should be sure that the unknown facts are not needed in the particular situations presented to the learners. (That is, children should not need to deal with new phases of multiplication algorisms and procedures at the same time they are still unsure of the facts used.)

8. Three-place and larger multipliers introduce no new concepts other than those already encountered with two-place multipliers; therefore, they need not be delayed long after the introduction of two-place multipliers.

9. Multiplication involving "0" and "1" should be dealt with as problem situations occur that require multiplace multiplication. Then they should be treated as applications of generalizations about multiplying with and by 0 and with and by 1.

10. Place-value concepts should be taught wherever and whenever applicable, no matter what size the numbers are that are being used.

11. Meanings of the multiplicand and multiplier should be emphasized, whether these names for the terms are used or not.

12. The rules of multiplication should be developed and used throughout instruction on multiplication, being taught through use in a variety of settings. This suggestion includes the principle of commutation, the principle of distribution, the principle of association, and the rule of likeness. Distribution should be particularly emphasized in connection with the introduction of multiplace multiplication, which could not be performed meaningfully without the operation of this principle.

13. In classrooms where arithmetic instruction is closely dependent on a local course of study, a textbook series, or one of the newer experimental programs, it is usually wise to follow the general sequence suggested therein unless the teacher has some well-considered reason for deviating from it.

14. No matter what sequence of topics or phases of the process are being used, individual learners or different groups of learners should not be expected to follow that sequence at the same rate. They cannot do so; to try to insist that they do so is only to create learning problems.

15. Instruction in multiplication should not be isolated from instruction in other fundamental processes of arithmetic. It should be planned so that the relations of multiplication to addition and to division are very closely knit in the minds of the pupils.

Checking Multiplication

The value of accuracy in arithmetic is not to be disputed. Checking computations serves to assure greater accuracy. Teaching children the habit of checking their work impresses them with the importance of accuracy. This is the general rationale back of most discussions of teaching children to check their arithmetic work, and it is a defensible rationale.

Checking can serve another purpose as well. This one is not considered nearly so frequently as the accuracy purpose. It merits more attention. Checking can continue the development and support the need for practice on understandings and meanings of a process, multiplication in this case. While children are learning to check their multiplications, they should be encouraged to see new number and process relations and to apply those already encountered. Checking need not be a routine, dull, repetitive process; it should be an opportunity for learners to discover and create new and different ways of solving the same problem.

Relations to other processes are basic to some of the more common checks on multiplication. The accuracy of the multiplication in Form X may be checked by adding fifteen 32's. This gets to be cumbersome when the multiplier is large, but it works well when children are dealing with small multipliers, such as the "4" in "4 × 36." Its use with

Form X

$$
\begin{array}{r}
3\,2 \\
\times\,1\,5 \\
\hline
1\,6\,0 \\
3\,2 \\
\hline
4\,8\,0
\end{array}
$$

smaller multipliers is recommended if attention is centered on the idea that the multiplication of whole numbers is really just another way to add equal addends.

Relation of multiplication to its inverse process of division is also used as the basis for a check. The multiplication "15 × 32 = 480" may be checked by dividing the product by either the multiplier or the multiplicand. If the quotient derived by this division turns out to be the "other factor" in the multiplication, we consider our original computation to be correct. This check is not very popular, chiefly because most people consider division to be more difficult than multiplication and shy away from a check that is more difficult than the process being checked. (Its counterpart — checking division by multiplication — is very common.) Dividing to check multiplication cannot, of course, be used until children have enough facility with division forms to handle the requisite computation. At that point it is chiefly useful as an illustration of the inverse relationship, not as an "everyday" check for general use.

The *commutative principle* is the basis for what is perhaps the most commonly used multiplication check. The terms are reversed and the multiplication repeated. Since the order of the factors does not affect their product, "32 × 15" and "15 × 32" should be equal. In using this check, a person not only reverses the complete multiplier and multiplicand; he must use the reverse multiplication facts of those used in the original multiplication. The addition facts (basic facts and higher-decade facts) used are not necessarily the same. If a child is having difficulty with a certain pair of multiplication facts (e.g., 7 × 9 = 63 and 9 × 7 = 63), he may make the same error in the original multiplication and in checking it, destroying the effectiveness of the check. If he knows one of the two facts and misses the other, the check will work to point out that an error exists in one of the two multiplications.

Some checks for multiplication are based on certain features of our *decimal-place-value system*. "Casting out 9's" was formerly a popular check; it has been revived more recently along with revived interest in development of base and place-value ideas in elementary school arithmetic. "Casting out 11's" works on a similar basis but is not nearly so widely used. Casting out 9's has too often been taught merely as a tricky and perhaps amusing device for checking any of the fundamental processes. This is unfortunate since it provides such a good opportunity to stress base and place concepts. Some variations on this check are shown below:

of numerals. For example, "2435" might be marked thus: 2̸4̸3̸5̸, leaving 2 and 3 to be added. This is just another way of subtracting 9's.

When this check is used as a mechanical routine, it has little to recommend it. For checking the multiplication of relatively small numbers it may take longer than other checks. Also, it is not absolutely reliable. If the product of the reduced multiplier and multiplicand *does not* check with the reduced product, an error is indicated, and we may say the check works. If, on the other hand, the reduced products *do* agree, one cannot be certain that the original multiplication was correct. The reason is that compensating errors are not discovered by this procedure.

The chief value of this check is in the basis it provides for some interesting and fruitful discussion of relations

Original Multiplication

$$
\begin{array}{r}
2\ 4\ 3\ 5 \\
\times 3\ 6\ 1 \\
\hline
2\ 4\ 3\ 5 \\
1\ 4\ 6\ 1\ 0 \\
7\ 3\ 0\ 5 \\
\hline
8\ 7\ 9\ 0\ 3\ 5
\end{array}
$$

Form Y
Check by Adding Face
Values of Numerals

$$2+4+3+5=14 \qquad 1+4=5$$
$$3+6+1=10 \qquad 1+0=1$$

$$
\begin{array}{cccc}
2 & 4 & 3 & 5 \\
\end{array}
$$
$$
\begin{array}{ccccc}
1 & 4 & 6 & 1 & 0 \\
7 & 3 & 0 & 5 \\
\end{array}
$$
$$8+7+9+0+3+5=32 \qquad 3+2=5$$

$$1 \times 5 = 5$$

Form Z
Alternate Method
of Reducing to a
One-Digit Numeral

$$14-9=5$$
$$10-9=1$$

$$32-27=5$$
or
$$32-9-9-9=5$$

When the numerals are added, the place values are ignored. If the sum of the numerals is more than 9, it is reduced to a 1-digit number either by adding the numerals of the sum or by subtracting 9 or a multiple of 9. The latter method points up the "casting-out-9" idea. Some people cross out any "9" or sums of 9 in the original sequence

among numbers. *Why* does this check work? *Why* does adding the digits as in Form Y give the same end result as subtracting 9's or multiples of 9's as in Form Z? (The answer goes back to the same idea as applies in recognizing that subtracting 9 is equivalent to subtracting 1 ten and adding 1 one, which does not change the sum of the face values of the digits. E.g., $25 - 9 = 16$; $2 + 5 = 7$; so also $1 + 6 = 7$.)

A little-used check, which is also dependent on concepts of base and place and which offers a challenge to superior arithmetic pupils, is the translation of decimal numbers to some other base, followed by multiplication of the numbers in that other base. One of the two products should then be translated into the other base to see if they agree. A teacher will want to develop facility herself before attempting to introduce such a check as this.

Multiplication in Base Ten	Same Multiplication in Base Five	Translation to Base Ten
3 1	1 1 1	$1 \times 625 = 625$
$\times 2\ 4$	$\times\ 4\ 4$	$4 \times\ \ 25 = 100$
1 2 4	4 4 4	$3 \times\ \ \ 5 =\ \ 15$
6 2	4 4 4	$4 \times\ \ \ 1 =\ \ \ \ 4$
7 4 4	1 0 4 3 4	744

The *distributive principle* may be used in checking multiplication by distributing the multiplier or the multiplicand differently from the way it is distributed in the original algorism. This check has several advantages. It will require the use of different multiplication facts from those in the original form, making a better check. It will also emphasize the principle itself and encourage pupils to be flexible in their thinking about numbers.

Original Multiplication

```
  3 4
×1 5
1 7 0
  3 4
5 1 0
```

Form AA Check by a Different Distribution	Form BB Another Distribution
3 4 3 4 2 3 8	$15 \times 30 = 450$
$\times\ 7$ $\times\ 8$ $+2\ 7\ 2$	$15 \times\ \ 4 =\ \ 60$
2 3 8 2 7 2 5 1 0	510

Form BB of a different distribution scheme for 15×34 is not only a good

check. It is also a good example of a way of handling multiplication of 2-place (or larger) numbers without pencil and paper.

An understanding of *prime and composite numbers and of factors* underlies another form of checking.[9] Using the same multiplication example ($15 \times 34 = 510$), the check using factors might operate in either of the ways shown below:

Form CC	Form DD
3 4	1 5
$\times 5$	$\times 1\ 7$
1 7 0	1 0 5
$\times 3$	1 5
5 1 0	2 5 5
	$\times 2$
	5 1 0

Form CC is simpler, but both follow the same principle. Even more use of the same idea might be valuable, along with the principle of *association,* thus: $15 \times 34 = (3 \times 5)\,(2 \times 17) = 2 \times 3 \times (5 \times 17) = 2 \times 3 \times 85 = 2\,(255) = 510$. This method would be most appropriate for "mental checking" or for original calculation without paper and pencil. Superior pupils might gain much benefit from seeing how many such arrangements of factors they could discover. Obviously, a wide variety of multiplication facts may be used when both multiplicand and multiplier are composite numbers.

No discussion of checking should omit reference to the value of *estimating products* as a check against gross errors. Rounding off is helpful in getting quick appraisals as to reasonableness of answers. Estimation may be used either *before* the detailed multiplication to get an approximation of the product or *after* the complete multiplication process to check general accuracy. Take the

[9] Prime and composite numbers are discussed more fully in chap. 13.

multiplication example "12 × 48." One might think, "10 × 50 = 500." If one wanted an exact product, this estimate could be refined by thinking, "2 × 50 = 100; 500 + 100 = 600; that is, 12 × 50 = 600; but I was supposed to multiply 12 × 48; 48 is 2 less than 50; 12 × 2 = 24; 600 − 24 = 576." Actual multiplication in typical written form would give:

$$
\begin{array}{r}
48 \\
\times\ 12 \\
\hline
96 \\
48\ \ \\
\hline
576
\end{array}
$$

Someone who wants only the general limits within which the product should fall might think: "10 × 48 = 480; 12 × 50 = 600; the answer is between 480 and 600."

Estimating (by rounding off or some other technique) is excellent for checking and at the same time is excellent practice in dealing with approximate numbers.

Multiplication may also be checked by remultiplying, using *different algorisms* for the process.

Checking may be merely a matter of multiplying again, using the same algorism as for the original multiplication. In fact, when an error is indicated by any of the above checks, this is probably done to find the original error. As the only check, its disadvantage lies in the greater probability of repeating the same error.

If a mechanical calculating machine is available, there are real benefits in helping children learn to check their own pencil and paper calculations by using the machine. Machines vary as to their appropriateness for helping the observer see that multiplication is a matter of repeated additions and in the handling of place values. The more automatic the machine's operations, the less obvious are these relationships to the pencil and paper forms.

STUDY QUESTIONS

1. Multiply without writing: 22 × 45; 16 × 16; 13 × 64. Write out (in the language of mathematics) what you thought in doing these multiplications mentally. Did you use any shortcuts? Did you use any basic principles like the commutative, associative, or distributive laws? Could you have used them more than you did?

2. Multiply 38 × 412. Use any form to which you are accustomed in writing your work. Now explain why that form "works." The "why's" may include laws of multiplication, base and place meanings, or any other ideas you think apply.

3. See page 218 concerning the higher-decade addition facts that can occur in multiplication examples. Make a complete listing of these facts.

4. Banks has made a statement describing our present forms for multiplication as "an example of survival of the fittest." (Banks, J. Houston. *Learning and Teaching Arithmetic.* Boston: Allyn, 1959, p. 153.) What is meant by that statement?

5. Some interesting algorisms for multiplication (e.g., doubling, the lattice method, or scratch methods) are described in various books on elementary mathematics and in books on teaching arithmetic. Look up some of these methods and compare them with methods you already know as to efficiency. Try one or more of these methods with a child or a group of children. What are their reactions?

6. Describe the multiplication 4 × 37 in terms of sets.

CHAPTER 11

The Division Process
and the Basic Division Facts

THE ELEMENTARY TEACHER may as well face up to the fact that division — particularly long division — is often very unpopular with pupils. It does not have a "good name" among many of its potential and actual users. Why is this true?

Division of whole numbers is unpopular in the sense that its everyday utility is admittedly less than that of any of the other three fundamental processes in arithmetic. No later evidence has refuted this finding made by Wilson in 1926.[1]

Further, some people do not even use it when its use would be appropriate. Not only children but adults as well have been known to use rather devious means to solve division problems by much less efficient, roundabout methods in order to avoid it. They shy away from it because it seems difficult to them. Some of the difficulty may stem from their having had less practice with division than with the other processes of arithmetic, and some of the avoidance of use probably stems from feelings of inadequacy in use of division.

Perhaps the best answer to the "why" of negative reactions to division is that its users do not understand it. They have learned it (to varying levels of efficiency) as a routine process with

[1] Guy M. Wilson, *What Arithmetic Shall We Teach?*, Boston: Houghton, 1926, p. 14.

relatively little meaning. Long division is viewed by many children and adults as a complicated and dull routine of formal steps: divide, multiply, subtract, compare, bring down; divide, multiply, subtract, compare, bring down; on and on. No wonder it is dull; no wonder some of its users feel dull themselves.

Even when understood, perhaps division will not be as popular as the other processes; but surely it need not be as formidable as it sometimes has been. Well understood, it may even be fun.

What Is Division?

Like subtraction, division is an indirect process. Some writers do not even classify these two processes as "fundamental," but their use is too important in elementary school arithmetic not to treat them fully and separately at that level. The meanings of division do, however, derive from the meanings taught in developing other arithmetical processes.

DIVISION IS COUNTING BACKWARD

Addition and multiplication are extensions of counting forward; subtraction and division are extensions of counting backward.

Joe has 50¢. He wonders how many days that will last him if he spends it only for snow cones and buys one snow cone each day when the snow cone cart comes past his house. He knows that snow cones cost 10¢ each. He may very well think: "50¢, 40¢, 30¢, 20¢, 10¢, all gone." He may use his fingers for tallies to keep track as he counts backward by tens, thus:

40¢	1st finger or thumb turned down
30¢	2nd finger turned down
20¢	3rd finger turned down
10¢	4th finger turned down
All gone	5th finger turned down

On the number line, his counting backward might be indicated by arrows indicating direction of counting. The "answer" is the number of arrows. (See fig. 71.)

subgroups. Multiplication may be shown as *forward* counting; division is shown as *backward* counting. When division is not taught as a separate process, it is taught as the inverse phase of the multiplication process. Division "undoes" multiplication.

Problem M: Sue wants to buy five 4¢ stamps. How much will they cost? Sue must find the total group made up of 5 groups of 4¢ each.

Sue needs 5 groups of 4¢ each, one 4 for each stamp:

1¢1¢1¢1¢ 1¢1¢1¢1¢ 1¢1¢1¢1¢ 1¢1¢1¢1¢ 1¢1¢1¢1¢

She must combine the five 4's to make a total group:

1¢ 1¢ 1¢ 1¢ 1¢ 1¢ 1¢ 1¢ 1¢ 1¢ 1¢ 1¢ 1¢ 1¢ 1¢ 1¢ 1¢ 1¢ 1¢ 1¢

There are 20¢ in the total group; so she must pay 20¢ for 5 stamps. $5 \times 4¢ = 20¢$

Problem D: After making some purchases,

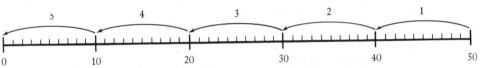

Figure 71. Division as Counting Backward.

Using reverse counting to solve a division problem necessitates some type of tallying, either during or after the process, to keep a record of the number of steps taken. Hence, while counting backward can be and is used to solve simple division problems, seeing division as counting is somewhat more complex than seeing the other processes as counting.

DIVISION IS THE INVERSE OF MULTIPLICATION

Multiplication builds up; division breaks down. Multiplication is a process of regrouping by *combining* equal-sized groups into a new total group, which then comprises all the subgroups. Division is a process of regrouping a total group by *separating* it into equal-sized

Sue has 20¢ in change. She decides to buy 4¢ stamps with it. How many can she buy? She must break down the 20¢ into groups of 4¢ each to find how many such groups she has.

Sue has a total group of 20¢:

1¢1¢1¢1¢1¢1¢1¢1¢1¢1¢1¢1¢1¢1¢1¢1¢1¢1¢1¢1¢

She must separate the 20¢ to find how many fours she has:

1¢1¢1¢1¢ 1¢1¢1¢1¢ 1¢1¢1¢1¢ 1¢1¢1¢1¢ 1¢1¢1¢1¢

She has 5 fours and can buy five 4¢ stamps. $20¢ \div 4¢ = 5$

It is obvious that the multiplication problem and the division problem are inverses. In the multiplication problem, Sue builds up five 4's to make 20. In the division problem, she breaks down 20 into five 4's. The same contrast is demonstrated if these two problems are shown on a number line. The multiplication problem is shown above the line in figure 72 and the division problem below the line. The inverse relation is shown by the opposite directions of the arrow.

The inverse relationship between multiplication and division helps children learn the division facts.

fact that this relationship is being ignored in the teaching of the long-division (or any division) process in many classrooms. Certainly any attempt at making the long-division process meaningful, so that children will know what

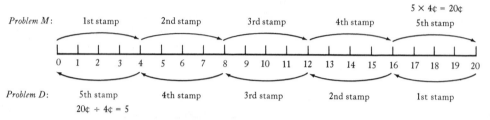

Problem M: 1st stamp 2nd stamp 3rd stamp 4th stamp $5 \times 4¢ = 20¢$ 5th stamp

Problem D: 5th stamp 4th stamp 3rd stamp 2nd stamp 1st stamp
$20¢ \div 4¢ = 5$

Figure 72. Multiplication and Division as Inverse Processes.

DIVISION IS "SPEEDED-UP" OR REPEATED SUBTRACTION

It is a special case of subtraction, applying only when the quantities to be subtracted are equal in size. One cannot subtract $12 - 7$ by division, but one can by division speed up materially the time it takes to subtract $20 - 4 - 4 - 4 - 4 - 4$ if one knows that $20 \div 4 = 5$.

Actually, this is a point that should appeal to children as a really valid reason for learning division facts to a level of automatic recall. They will thereby be saving their own precious time by learning a quick way of subtracting the same number many times. Unfortunately, many children have never noted this relationship, perhaps because their teachers and their textbooks have not stressed it.

A group of teachers in an in-service program were asked the direct question: "Why do you subtract in long division?" No one dared venture to give an oral answer. Perhaps some did not know the answer; others may have been hesitant to say anything for fear of being wrong. Why indeed? One subtracts in long division because that is what division is — subtraction. The statement is so obvious that one might hesitate to point it out were it not for the equally obvious

they are doing instead of merely "following steps," must be built on this fundamental notion of division as a form of subtraction.

The division problems cited to this point may be solved either by subtraction or by division. The latter is more efficient once one understands it and has learned the basic division facts.

How cumbersome subtraction is, relatively speaking, is readily apparent when one considers such a problem as this: How many yards are there in 5280 feet (1 mile)? Assuming one had no table of equivalent measures (in printed form or already learned), one could subtract 3's from 5280 until the full distance was "used up," but how much simpler it is when one knows how to divide 5280 by 3!

The parallel between subtraction and division is easily observable in the operation of calculating machines. Division is performed in these machines by successive subtractions.

DIVISION IS EITHER A MEASURING OR A PARTITIONING PROCESS

As division is used in real problem situations, it represents either a process of measuring or a process of sharing or partitioning. As children act out division solutions with concrete objects or with representative aids or as they draw diagrams and pictures to present problem situations and their solutions, the distinction between the two types of division situations is quite clear.

Unfortunately, as with the three types of subtraction situations, many teachers do not help children to see and use the distinction as a help to them in solving problems. This may be because of the inordinate amount of time and attention paid to drill on isolated division facts and on the "working" of countless division examples (in which the distinction is not observable) instead of solutions of true problem situations. The children pay two penalties for such neglect: (1) They cannot understand division as well as they should. (2) They do not become as proficient as they should in applying their division skills to the solution of real problems, which is surely one of the chief purposes of learning arithmetic. Further, the teacher who ignores this distinction between measurement and partition division is depriving herself of a significant aid in some rather crucial teaching situations.

The two situations may best be contrasted in relation to actual problems of the two types, as in the problems below.

Measurement Problem: Jack can ride 4 miles an hour on his bicycle. How many hours will it take him to ride to Coaling, which is 20 miles away?

Partition Problem: Jack wants to ride to Coaling (20 miles away) on his bicycle. How fast will he have to ride if he expects to get there in 4 hours?

Stated abstractly, both problems are solved by the division: $20 \div 4 = 5$. But notice that if the names are attached to the numbers (in this case, miles), a difference arises in the very statement of the simple division fact:

Measurement: 20 miles $\div$ 4 miles = 5

Partition: 20 miles $\div$ 4 = 5 miles (per hour)

In multiplication problems, the multiplicand and the product always have the same name; they represent whatever items comprise the subgroups being combined by multiplication to make a new total group (product). The multiplier, however, which represents the number of equal subgroups, is not assigned a name. It is the number of subgroups or the number of "times" the subgroup appears in the composite or total group.

Notice that both the division statements above have two "named" terms and one "unnamed" term. As with multiplication, the total group has a name (20 miles) in both problems and the subgroups have the same name (4 miles in the one problem and 5 miles in the other problem). The unnamed number in each case is the number of subgroups (5 in the measurement problem and 4 in the partition problem). The situation is more complicated in division than in multiplication because in division we sometimes know the *size* of the equal subgroups to be made from the total or composite group and sometimes know the *number* of subgroups. Whichever (size or number of subgroups) is not known is of course the answer one is trying to find by division.

Diagrams for the two problems may point up the difference. In figure 73, the total distance of 20 miles is *measured* against the 1-hour distance of 4 miles to find how many such units are possible. The 4-mile distance becomes the measuring stick against which the total distance is measured. This type of division is sometimes called "quotition division," but that term has been largely replaced by the term "measurement division" because of the obvious relation to measuring or comparing the total (dividend) with the known size of the subgroup (divisor) being used as the unit or standard of measurement. The answer is the number corresponding to the number of groups, in this case 5. Someone may say, "But 5 also has a name, 5 hours." Actually, we arrive at the concept of "5 hours" by one-to-one correspondence of the 5 subgroups to 5 hours, which is not involved in the

but a picture of the situation *after* solution, which is quite another matter.

Some books use a system of "dealing out" or "distributing" the miles and then reassembling them to show a partition-type solution, but this is too complicated in execution to be much help in teaching the idea.

Much more reasonable is the use of a flexible number line such as a string

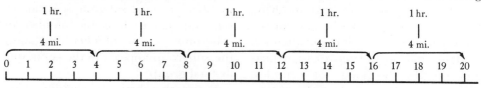

Figure 73. Measurement Division.

actual dividing. "Twenty miles divided by 4 miles" *does not equal 5 hours.* Miles ÷ miles ≠ hours. This would be ridiculous. The problem might have been: If a construction crew can pave 4 miles of road in a month, how long will it take them to pave 20 miles of road? In this case, the answer is also 5 (groups of 4 miles each), but we relate this answer by one-to-one correspondence of groups to months and conclude that it will take 5 months for the construction crew to complete the job. 12 miles ÷ 4 miles does not equal 5 hours or 5 months or 5 anything else. It simply equals 5, which then is interpreted to correspond to the problem situation at hand. The 5 is simply the number of 4-mile segments or subgroups to be found in 20 miles, and is correctly written with only the numeral, not attached to a name.

A partition problem is not at all easy to show with a rigid number line solution diagram like that used for measurement division, though one often sees it done as in figure 74. What is wrong about this? One has to know the answer before he can draw the diagram! Then the diagram is not an aid to solution

marked off in "mile units" or, even better, a tape measure with "miles" corresponding to inches. A 20-inch length (representing 20 miles) is then partitioned by folding. A child given this assignment of showing 4 equal parts of the total length will usually fold it first into two lengths and then fold it again to make four lengths, as in figure 75. He *knows* what he needs to do to solve the problem (20 "miles" to be divided to make 4 equal subgroups to correspond to the 4 hours). He finds the answer (5 miles) as a *result* of his partitioning action. That answer has a name, miles. That is what he is looking for, the number of *miles* to be traveled each of the 4 hours if the total number of miles to be traveled is 20 *miles.*

All the division problems cited in this chapter preceding the partition problem on page 243 were measurement problems. When Sue divided her 20¢ by 4¢, she was measuring the full quantity of 20¢ by another "unit," 4¢. If she had been buying 5¢ stamps, she would have measured it by 5¢ units. If "5280 feet" is divided by 3 feet to find the number of yards, then "5280 feet" is measured off against a 3-foot unit of measure. Joe was measuring his 50¢ in 10¢ units that would buy snow cones.

Partition division is a matter of sharing the total quantity among the known number of subgroups. Only the size of the total group and the number of subgroups are known, as when a quantity of books or pencils or pennies or candy bars is to be equally distributed to a

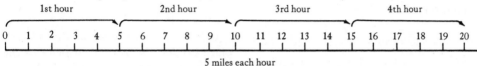

5 miles each hour

Figure 74. Partition Division.

given number of people. Partition is a "one for you, one for me, one for Sister Annie" sort of procedure. It involves dealing out the total quantity until it is completely distributed among the equal subgroups.

In summary, the two types of division situations are contrasted as to their significant features in the analysis below:

	Measurement Situations	Partition Situations
What is known?	Size of total or composite group Size of equal sub-groups	Size of total or composite group Number of sub-groups to be formed
What is unknown (to be found)?	Number of sub-groups to be formed	Size of equal subgroups
"Named" terms	Dividend and divisor	Dividend and quotient
"Unnamed" term	Quotient	Divisor

DIVISION IS A PROCESS OF

FINDING A RATIO-TO-ONE

Just as multiplication is sometimes a ratio-to-one idea, so also division involves a ratio-to-one idea. The difference is that in a multiplication ratio-to-one situation the ratio to one is known;

in division it is to be found, as would have to be true for the inverse. This is perhaps too advanced a concept for many elementary school children; it is included in the interests of complete coverage of the meanings of division.

First let us review the multiplication situation. If Frank rides 4 miles to school each day and if Wilson rides 3

times as far, how far does Wilson ride? Wilson rides 3 miles for every 1 mile Frank rides; that is a 3-to-1 ratio. Therefore, Wilson rides *3 times* 4 miles, or 12 miles. The complete statement would be: Wilson rides 3 miles to Frank's 1 mile; so he rides 12 miles to Frank's 4 miles. Figure 76 shows the situation.

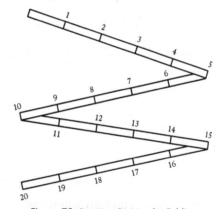

Figure 75. Partition Division by Folding.

The same number line diagram can be used to show how division *seeks* a ratio to one. If Wilson rides 12 miles to school each day and Frank rides only 4 miles each day, how many times as far does Wilson ride? Wilson's 12 miles are measured off against Frank's 4 miles as the measuring unit. The division situation is obviously of the measurement type. The dividend (12) compares with the divisor (4) as the quotient (3) compares with 1.[2]

In formal terms, the idea of division as a seeking of a ratio to one may be stated: dividend: divisor:: quotient: one. These same terms might be changed to: divisor : dividend :: one : quotient. This idea reaches into the concept of fractions, to be developed in chapter 14.

A STATEMENT OF DIVISION IS A
STATEMENT OF EQUALITY

The false notion that division is a process of decreasing a given quantity is all too prevalent. When 12 eggs are divided into 3 groups of 4 eggs each, no decrease in total quantity is involved; the same 12 eggs exist both before and after the regrouping by division. This misconception of what division really

a fraction and get an answer that is a larger number than any of the known numbers in the problem. "How can you get a bigger number for an answer when you divide?" Their bewilderment stems from having learned earlier, in division with whole numbers, a wrong idea of associating division with "getting less" for an answer.

$$12 \div 4 = n \qquad 12 \div 4 = 3$$

In the open sentence at the left the place holder "N" is used in place of the unknown numeral that will make the statement true. When "3" is written in place of "N," the statement is closed. The "=" sign then correctly states an equality between "12 ÷ 4" and "3." Later the concept of a fraction as an indicated division will be developed. Using that idea, we may state the equality as "$\frac{12}{3} = 4$."

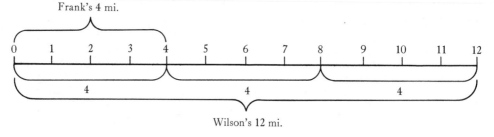

Figure 76. Division as Finding a Ratio-to-One.

means is bad enough when dealing with whole numbers; it is worse when division is done with fractions. This question will be discussed more fully in chapters 14 and 15. Suffice it merely to mention the puzzlement experienced by some children when they divide by

[2] See Buckingham. *op. cit.*, p. 75; L. Clark Lay, *Arithmetic: An Introduction to Mathematics,* New York: Macmillan. 1961. pp. 77-78; and Francis J. Mueller, *Arithmetic: Its Structures and Concepts,* Englewood Cliffs, N.J.: Prentice-Hall, Inc., 1956, pp. 145-48.

In summary, division is a form of counting backward. It is a process of regrouping, the inverse of multiplication and a special form of repeated subtraction. It always involves the separation of a total group into equal-sized subgroups. When the number of subgroups is known, partition division is used to find the size of the equal subgroups. When the size of the equal subgroups is known, measurement division is used to find the number of such subgroups.

Division Form and Terminology

Children are often taught the names of the terms in the division algorisms in terms of their position in the written forms. This procedure does not give as much emphasis to meanings as might be desired. The typical designations relate to the vertical algorism, such as those below:

```
        3 (quotient)              3          125
(divisor) 8/24 (dividend)       8/24        4/500
                                24            4
                               ───          ───
                                             10
                                              8
                                            ───
                                             20
                                             20
```

The "24" or the "500" is called the *dividend* "because it is under or inside the division sign." The "8" or the "4" is called the *divisor* "because it is in front of the division symbol." The "3" or the "125" is called the *quotient* "because it is the answer" or "because it is on top of the division sign." The positions are accurately described, but the meanings of the terms are not defined by any such "becauses." Furthermore, these terms are of little help when horizontal algorisms are used, such as:

$$24 \div 8 = 3 \qquad 500 \div 4 = 125$$

When division is presented as a condensed form of subtraction, one can draw some interesting parallels that should help establish the relationship between subtraction and division and also add meaning to the various terms used in each.

```
minuend      24¢
subtrahend  −8¢
            ────
             16¢                              3---quotient
subtrahend  −8¢          divisor---8¢ /24¢---dividend
            ────
              8¢
subtrahend  −8¢
            ────
              0¢
```

The *divisor* "8¢" corresponds to the *subtrahends* in the repeated subtraction

for the same problem situation. The *dividend* "24¢" corresponds to the *minuend* in the subtraction situation. The *quotient* "3" corresponds to the "3 times" that 8¢ is subtracted from 24¢ or contained in 24¢. A measurement division interpretation has been used because it is more readily seen as subtraction.[3]

In both subtraction and division a total or composite group is being separated into subgroups. The terms in the two processes are most meaningfully defined in relation to those groups and the separating that takes place, thus:

Meanings	Shown in Successive Subtraction by:	Shown in Measurement Division by:	Shown in Partition Division by:
Size of total group	Minuend	Dividend	Dividend
Size of equal subgroups	Subtrahends	Divisor	Quotient
Number of equal subgroups	Number of subtractions	Quotient	Divisor

These meanings for the various terms apply no matter which algorism is being used or, for that matter, whether or not any written form is being used.

The forms at the right[4] are correctly read in various ways, such as:

$$4/\overline{12} \quad \genfrac{}{}{0pt}{}{3}{}$$

$$12 \div 4 = 3$$

a. How many 4's in 12? 3.
b. Fours in 12, 3.

[3] A partition interpretation could be used, but then the successive subtractions would have to correspond to one complete "deal" or "round" in the sharing process among 8 groups. This is rather complicated to show meaningfully to young children.

[4] After fraction concepts are introduced, the same fact might be written as "$\frac{1}{4}$ of 12=3" and would be read as "one-fourth of 12 equals 3." This fraction expression should be developed in relation to the partition idea of division. Arithmetic experts are not agreed as to the appropriate point of introducing this form for expressing division facts, but it is certainly a common form of statement for everyday problems in division of whole numbers. It seems only natural to use it along with other forms for partition situations.

c. The number of 4's in 12 is 3.

d. Twelve arranged in 4's makes 3 groups.

e. There are 3 groups of 4 in 12.

f. Twelve divided to make 4 groups equals 3 things (in each group).

g. Twelve arranged in 4 groups gives 3 in each group.

h. Twelve divided into 4 equal parts gives 3 in each part.

i. Twelve divided by 4 equals 3.

Typically, expressions a through e are appropriate in connection with measurement division situations, while Expressions f through i are suited to partition division situations. The wording of the reading of a division statement should fit the problem situation in which it is used.

Expression i, which is more likely to be used in partition situations, may also be used in measurement situations. This expression merits some discussion since several objections to its use with children have been raised in books on the teaching of arithmetic. Some authorities hold that "12 *divided by* 4 = 3" conveys little meaning to children. This is somewhat like the objections to the use of the word "minus" in early subtraction. Perhaps it would be better to *build* meaning from the beginning, rather than to postpone its use until later. Certainly this is the most common expression in adult use.

The form "12 divided by 4 equals 3" simply means that "when 12 is *divided by* 4's, we can form 3 such groups." This is parallel to common usage in other situations. Children are told to "pair off by twos" or "divide by couples" or "divide the chairs by fours" at each table. These are measurement statements. Partition statements would interpret "12 *divided by* 4 equals 3" as meaning that "when 12 is divided by 4 (or into 4 equal parts), each part will

equal 3." True, the form "4's in 12, 3" is perhaps easier to read at the beginning of division instruction if one is using the vertical form for division facts. It is not easier if the horizontal form is used. Then "12 divided by 4 equals 3" fits exactly. It should be taught *along with* its appropriate meanings.

Of more importance is the need to eliminate a definitely wrong usage in reading division facts and examples. This is the "goes into" or even "guzzinta" statements: "4 goes into 12 how many times?" or "4 goes into 12 three times." This is a violation of any sound teaching of meanings in division. The divisor does *not* "go into" the dividend ever! Division is not a "going-into" process; it is a "taking-apart" or "going-out-of" process. Addition and multiplication do actually have the subgroups "going into" the total (sum or product). Subtraction and division are the inverse of that; they have the subgroups being removed from or separated out of the total (minuend or dividend). It is hard to understand how children can learn that division is a separating process if they are taught to say that the subgroups "go into" the total.

If one wants a way of reading the vertical algorism from left to right, it would be better to use some such expression as: "4 *is contained in* 12 how many times?" or "4 *is contained in* 12 three times."

Such confusions as the "goes-into" nonsense derive from routine teaching of rote facts to be learned and statements to be memorized. Stress on the real meanings of the terms in division should prevent many misunderstandings.

Some attention should also be paid to the parallel between division and its inverse, multiplication. The corresponding terms are shown diagrammatically on the following page:

Measurement Division

       3 (quotient)

(divisor) 4 $\overline{/\$12}$ (dividend)

Multiplication

  $4 (multiplicand)

  ×3 (multiplier)

  $12 (product)

Multiplication

(multiplicand) $4

(multiplier)   ×3

(product) $12

Partition Division

   $ 4 (quotient)

(divisor) 3 $\overline{/\$12}$ (dividend)

The meanings as shown in the diagram above are summarized below:

Meanings	Shown in Multiplication by:	Shown in Measurement Division by:	Shown in Partition Division by:
Size of total group	Product	Dividend	Dividend
Size of equal subgroups	Multiplicand	Divisor	Quotient
Number of equal subgroups	Multiplier	Quotient	Divisor

Since division is the inverse of multiplication, it is necessary that division always *begin* with the total group (dividend), which must be found as an end result in multiplication (product). The term that corresponds to the number of subgroups appears as the multiplier in multiplication, as the divisor in partition division, and as the quotient in measurement division.

Ignoring the distinctions between measurement and partition division and dealing with the generalized division process, one may simply say that the *factors* of the multiplication product correspond exactly to the *factors* of the dividend in division. The factors in multiplication are used to build the product. In division, the product (dividend) is broken down into a known factor and a factor to be found.

Further relationships between multiplication and division algorisms will appear in relation to the discussion of long division.

Rules of Division

The rules of division are consistent with those for multiplication and subtraction. Like multiplication, division has a principle of distribution and a rule of likeness. Like subtraction, it does not have a rule of closure for the natural numbers and must have a clearly modified rule to relate to but not coincide with the principle of commutation for multiplication and addition.

THE DISTRIBUTIVE PRINCIPLE
FOR DIVISION

Division is distributive with respect to addition. It is also distributive with respect to the inverse of addition, subtraction. The principle of distribution for division operates in analogous fashion to the distributive rule for multiplication.

Any dividend may be thought of as the sum of two or more numbers. Each of these component parts (addends) may be divided separately by a given divisor and the quotients summed. This procedure will give the same quotient as if the whole dividend had been divided by that same divisor. For example, $18 \div 3 = 6$. Consider 18 as composed of 12 and 6. Then:

$$12 \div 3 = 4 \qquad 6 \div 3 = 2 \qquad 4 + 2 = 6$$

Diagrammatically, this is shown below, on the left without applying the distributive property and on the right with the distributive principle put into play.

The distributive property of division is useful when a person wishes to make a division more manageable without benefit of pencil and paper. For example, $96 \div 6$ might be changed by the person who understands this property to $(60 + 36) \div 6 = (60 \div 6) + (36 \div 6) = 10 + 6 = 16$. Long-division algorisms rely heavily on the distributive principle, with the distribution being made in terms of place values.

The distributive property of division with respect to subtraction is used in an example such as this: 237 is to be divided by 3. One might think of 237 as being the difference $240 - 3$. Then $(240 \div 3) - (3 \div 3) = 80 - 1 = 79$. Besides its use in mental calculations, this principle applies in very useful fashion in some long-division algorisms that correct for overestimates in the quotient by applying this principle. (See chap. 12.)[5]

THE RULE OF LIKENESS

In applied problem situations, the dividend and one of the other terms (divisor or quotient) must be "like" terms. With children, this rule is usually stated in terms of "having the same name." The other term is an abstract number.

If the problem concerns the division of people into equal subgroups, the dividend and one other term must be designated as people. If the problem concerns the division of money into equal subgroups of money, the dividend

and one other term must have money names or designations.

The dividend (that is, the total group to be divided) always has some sort of name in a practical problem situation, be it people, money, elephants, bricks, or shoes. In this respect, the dividend is like the sum in addition, the minuend in subtraction, and the product in multiplication.

Which of the other two terms in division must be designated by the same name depends on whether the problem at hand involves measurement or partition.

Measurement Problem: The Girl Scouts are baking cupcakes for a cake sale. They pack 3 cakes in each package. How many packages can Jean fill with the 27 cupcakes she baked?

Partition Problem: Mother baked 27 cupcakes before she went away on a trip. She told Bill and Alice that they should not eat all the cupcakes the first day. Bill and Alice decided to divide the cupcakes so they and Daddy would have the same number to eat each day for the 3 days Mother would be away. How many should they put away for each day?

Obviously, the name "cupcakes" belongs with the items in the total group of cupcakes in both problem situations. It also belongs with the subgroup of cupcakes in each problem. It does not belong with the number of such subgroups to be formed. Thus we have the "named" terms differing in the two problem situations:

Measurement	Partition
$\dfrac{9}{3 \text{ cupcakes} / 27 \text{ cupcakes}}$	$\dfrac{9 \text{ cupcakes}}{3 / 27 \text{ cupcakes}}$

Emphasis on the rule of likeness for division of whole numbers will have much to do with the ease of teaching children to understand the long-division algorism. It will also afford a base on which to teach the common-denominator method of dividing by a fraction.

---

[5] The distributive law for division allows for handling the dividend as a sum, dividing each addend by the given divisor and then adding the quotients. It is *not* permissible to handle the divisor as a sum and divide the given dividend by the two divisors derived in this fashion.

Permissible: to change $36 \div 6$ to $(24 + 12) \div 6$, since $(24 \div 6) + (12 \div 6) = 4 + 2 = 6$.

Not permissible: to change $36 \div 6$ to $(36 \div 4) + (36 \div 2)$, because $(36 \div 4) + (36 \div 2) = 9 + 18 = 27!$

The same warning applies to subtraction as well as to addition.

It is not intended that the names must be written in every problem solution, but they should be written as long as needed to establish the understanding of the problems being solved and the meaning of the division process.

THE DIVISOR-QUOTIENT RULE

With any given dividend, the divisor and quotient may be interchanged. In an abstract statement of division, the factors of the quotient may be "commuted," as are the factors in multiplication.

$$12 \div 6 = 2; \text{ so } 12 \div 2 = 6.$$
$$\text{If } a \div b = c, \text{ then } a \div c = b.$$

Many authorities in arithmetic do not make mention of a divisor-quotient rule, perhaps for fear that it will be misinterpreted as indicating that division is commutative in the same sense that multiplication is commutative. The *known terms* in division may not be interchanged without changing the quotient. The known terms in multiplication *may* be interchanged without changing the product.

The point of similarity hinges on an understanding of the meanings of the factors of the product in multiplication and the factors of the dividend in division. When one thinks in terms of the unknown and the known factors in division (the quotient and the divisor), recognition of the divisor-quotient rule may be very helpful. If, for example, a child has learned that $54 \div 6 = 9$, he can apply this rule to help him remember that $54 \div 9$ will have to equal 6.[6]

In concrete problem situations, the meanings of $54 \div 6 = 9$ and of $54 \div 9 = 6$ are not the same. They describe different situations, but both statements are true.

[6] In later work with fractions, the rule appears and is very useful in this form: If $\frac{54}{6} = 9$, then $\frac{54}{9} = 6$.

THE RULE OF CONTINUOUS DIVISION

When a number is to be divided successively by two or more other numbers, the order in which the division is performed does not change the quotient. This is another rule that has a parallel for multiplication, but one must be careful not to give too literal a comparison with the rule of association for multiplication.

Problem: If 4 men earned $36 in 3 hours, how much was the average wage per hour?

This may be solved in two steps, as in A or B below, or it may be solved as successive divisions stated in a single algorism, as in C:

Solution A: $36 \div 4 = \$9$ (for each man)
$\$9 \div 3 = \$3$ (per hour for each man)

Solution B: $36 \div 3 = \$12$ (per hour for all the men)
$\$12 \div 4 = \$3$ (per hour for each man)

Solution C: $\$36 \div 4 \div 3 = \$4$ or $\$36 \div 3 \div 4 = \$3$

The curved lines under the successive divisions in the two algorisms for solution C demonstrate the rule of successive divisions in operation. Either order of performing the two divisions results in the same answer.

This rule applies as well to two-step algorisms like those in solutions A and B. Teachers should be careful to allow for correct alternative solutions such as these and to encourage children to seek alternative proper solutions. This rule has limited use for younger elementary school children since they seldom solve problems involving successive divisions, but when they get to a study of factors, it will prove to be very useful. If the divisor in a division is factored, the rule of successive divisions applies. Say that one wishes to divide 252 by 12.

$$252 \div 12 = (252 \div 4) \div 3 = 63 \div 3 = 21$$
$$\text{OR}$$
$$252 \div 12 = (252 \div 3) \div 4 = 84 \div 4 = 21$$

Using typical algebraic form:

$$a \div bc = (a \div b) \div c$$

OR

$$a \div bc = (a \div c) \div b$$

NO PROPERTY OF CLOSURE
FOR DIVISION OF
WHOLE NUMBERS

The property of closure does not apply to division with whole numbers. It will be discussed further in the development of rational numbers. (See chap. 14.) One *cannot* say that any natural number can be divided by any other natural number to get a quotient that is also a natural number.

This subject is related to the matter of incomplete division, which is treated in relation to the building of the remainder division facts in the next chapter.

The Basic Division Facts

BASIC DIVISION FACTS DEFINED

The basic division facts are all the numerical statements about division in which the factors (divisor and quotient) are 1-digit numbers. They are the inverse number statements that correspond to the basic multiplication facts; for both multiplication and division facts, the factors must be 1-digit numbers.[7] Since some of the basic multiplication facts have 2-digit products, the corresponding division facts must have 2-digit dividends.

All the basic division facts are shown in Table 9. They are called "basic" because they are the only necessary division facts for performing any whole-number division in our decimal-number

[7] The only exception is that there are no basic division facts in which zero is the divisor.

system. Anyone who knows the basic division facts and understands our notational system and the rules of operation of the division process can thereby perform any whole-number division. Because of their basic character, they should be learned to a level of automatic recall. This does not, of course, mean that automatic recall should be the immediate aim in learning them.

Table 9 includes 90 facts. The facts that involve the division of zero are often omitted, leaving only 81 facts. The "zero facts" are seldom needed in the early stages of learning; when they become necessary to handle the occurrence of zero in two-place or larger dividends, they can be taught through the development of a generalization that "dividing zero by any other number gives a quotient of zero." They are included in Table 9 to have a complete presentation of all basic division facts.

No "zero facts" are possible with zero as a divisor. Since division is the inverse of multiplication, every division statement must be "reversible" to form the corresponding multiplication statement. For example, $12 \div 6 = 2$ and $2 \times 6 = 12$. One can do this with 0 as a dividend, thus: $0 \div 6 = 0$ and $0 \times 6 = 0$. One *cannot* operate thus with 0 as a divisor: assume that $6 \div 0 = 6$ but $6 \times 0 \neq 6$! Zero divisors for division do not yield correct inverse multiplication facts; they are ruled out as impossible.

The foregoing type of proof is not necessary with young children, but many elementary school children can and do understand it if they really understand what is meant by inverse processes. Just on the basis of informal discussion, children will accept the impossibility of dividing by 0 after considering such questions as: If I have 8 things and divide them into groups of 0 things, how many groups can I make?

If I have 8 things and divide them into 0 groups, how large will the groups be? The answer will probably be, "You can't."

Another group of division facts is also not needed in the early stages of work with division. Obviously, if 6 or 8 or 4 things are divided into sets of 1 each, there will be 6 or 8 or 4 such sets.

When need for the "1 facts" does arise at a later point, the simple generalizations can be developed: (1) When any number is divided by 1, the quotient is that number. (2) When any number is divided by itself, the quotient is 1.

When the "0 facts" and the "1 facts" are omitted from early consideration,

TABLE 9

Basic Division Facts

0 / $1/0$	1 / $1/1$	2 / $1/2$	3 / $1/3$	4 / $1/4$	5 / $1/5$	6 / $1/6$	7 / $1/7$	8 / $1/8$	9 / $1/9$
0 / $2/0$	1 / $2/2$	2 / $2/4$	3 / $2/6$	4 / $2/8$	5 / $2/10$	6 / $2/12$	7 / $2/14$	8 / $2/16$	9 / $2/18$
0 / $3/0$	1 / $3/3$	2 / $3/6$	3 / $3/9$	4 / $3/12$	5 / $3/15$	6 / $3/18$	7 / $3/21$	8 / $3/24$	9 / $3/27$
0 / $4/0$	1 / $4/4$	2 / $4/8$	3 / $4/12$	4 / $4/16$	5 / $4/20$	6 / $4/24$	7 / $4/28$	8 / $4/32$	9 / $4/36$
0 / $5/0$	1 / $5/5$	2 / $5/10$	3 / $5/15$	4 / $5/20$	5 / $5/25$	6 / $5/30$	7 / $5/35$	8 / $5/40$	9 / $5/45$
0 / $6/0$	1 / $6/6$	2 / $6/12$	3 / $6/18$	4 / $6/24$	5 / $6/30$	6 / $6/36$	7 / $6/42$	8 / $6/48$	9 / $6/54$
0 / $7/0$	1 / $7/7$	2 / $7/14$	3 / $7/21$	4 / $7/28$	5 / $7/35$	6 / $7/42$	7 / $7/49$	8 / $7/56$	9 / $7/63$
0 / $8/0$	1 / $8/8$	2 / $8/16$	3 / $8/24$	4 / $8/32$	5 / $8/40$	6 / $8/48$	7 / $8/56$	8 / $8/64$	9 / $8/72$
0 / $9/0$	1 / $9/9$	2 / $9/18$	3 / $9/27$	4 / $9/36$	5 / $9/45$	6 / $9/54$	7 / $9/63$	8 / $9/72$	9 / $9/81$

Or if 6 or 8 or 4 things are "divided" to make 1 group, they remain as they were originally, groups of 6 or 8 or 4. Quotients of 1 are also so obvious that there is no problem; if 5 or 9 or 3 things are grouped by 5's or 9's or 3's, respectively, there will be 1 such group. Or if 5 or 9 or 3 things are divided into 5 groups or 9 groups or 3 groups, respectively, there will be 1 thing in each group. At the early stages of teaching division, to belabor the obvious is to introduce an unnecessary thought hurdle. The first use of "1 facts" for division comes in division of larger numbers. They will also occur when division is expressed as a fraction.

there are only 64 basic division facts to be taught. They may be organized for presentation in a wide variety of ways. Traditionally, they have often been presented in "tables." Any single column or row of facts in Table 9 would be a table. Written in horizontal form, the table for division by 3 would be as shown at the right. Early presentation of such tables is not recommended for a teaching program that stresses meanings. Children may well build their own tables or division charts after they have first mastered the meaning of division and have had ample

$$3 \div 3 = 1$$
$$6 \div 3 = 2$$
$$9 \div 3 = 3$$
$$12 \div 3 = 4$$
$$15 \div 3 = 5$$
$$18 \div 3 = 6$$
$$21 \div 3 = 7$$
$$24 \div 3 = 8$$
$$27 \div 3 = 9$$

experiences with division situations and uses. Pupil organization of facts into tables at a later point may be a very worthwhile experience, but students need first to have some exploratory and discovery experiences witn miscellaneous division facts.

BASIC DIVISION FACTS RELATED TO BASIC MULTIPLICATION FACTS

Most authorities recommend the presentation of basic multiplication and division facts in close relation one to the other. Since multiplication is the direct process, it is usually developed first; at least, the formal multiplication statements are presented first. Elementary school texts vary in the amount of time or pages in the book (if any) that intervene between the first formal introduction of multiplication facts and the introduction of the corresponding division facts, but teachers typically give continuous emphasis to the relationship once both have been introduced.

Actually, children in the first and second grades begin to build the relationship as they engage in activities that encourage or require them to regroup objects in a variety of groupings. As they distribute school supplies, arrange chairs around tables, or group themselves into equal groups they are practicing the idea of division. As they discuss the groupings they are making, they may not use division terminology at all.

Some second graders were putting away plastic Christmas tree ornaments in boxes partitioned to hold them securely. Each box had 8 spaces in it. Sixteen ornaments were on the table, ready to be put away. No one had asked any questions about the numerical situation; but as the ornaments were placed in the boxes, a boy was heard to say,

"Each box holds 8. We had 16 ornaments. They filled 2 boxes." As other ornaments were removed from the tree, the teacher saw to it that again 16 ornaments were placed on the table, but this time there were no boxes. She said, "Here are 16 more ornaments. I think I have some boxes in my desk that hold 4 ornaments each. George, can you tell me how many boxes like that I will need?" George said, "Wait a minute. I have to make fours out of these. Then I can tell you." Soon he announced, "I need 4 boxes."

This was no time to launch into formal statements, either oral or written, that "16 divided by 8 equals 2" and "16 divided by 4 equals 4"; but George and the other children were learning something of the basic *idea* of division preliminary to formal basic fact statements. The relationship between multiplication and division in this illustration is so close that the multiplication statements "2 eights are 16" and "4 fours are 16" would be as acceptable as the division statements "16 makes 2 eights" and "16 makes 4 fours." The action was a division action, but once accomplished, the result could be looked upon as a multiplication situation. The natural development of concepts through experiences of this type is the firmest possible foundation for later learning of the relatedness of inverse facts.

Stokes has presented an interesting interpretation of a similar situation, in which he suggests that children arrange 16 buttons in two groups of 8 each, leading to multiplication, addition, and subtraction statements ($2 \times 8 = 16$; $8 + 8 = 16$; and $16 - 8 = 8$). Then he says, "The process of *division* that led to the measurements, the groupings, is only an *idea* and will not be put into symbolic form at this level. There is no need for it. The children will get the concepts.

	Dividends									Divisors
	1	2	3	4	5	6	7	8	9	1
	2	4	6	8	10	12	14	16	19	2
	3	6	9	12	15	18	21	24	27	3
	4	8	12	16	20	24	28	32	36	4
Dividends⟶	5	10	15	20	25	30	35	40	45	5
	6	12	18	24	30	36	42	48	54	6
	7	14	21	28	35	42	49	56	63	7
	8	16	24	32	40	48	56	64	72	8
	9	18	27	36	45	54	63	72	81	9
	1	2	3	4	5	6	7	8	9	Quotients

Table 10. Division Chart.

Division is only a mental behavior at this level, when the mind is dealing with things."[8]

At the opposite extreme of the learning sequence, when children have progressed far enough in their understanding of division and in the development of division facts that they can build a division table to summarize their learnings, the relationship between multiplication and division should still be emphasized. Children who have built a division table such as the one shown in table 9 will enjoy comparing it with a multiplication table such as table 7 in chapter 9. As a matter of fact, many children see the relationship before the division chart is completed. One boy exclaimed, "Say, this is the same as the multiplication chart we made. We don't need a new chart for division. We just need to read it like division."

He was right. The multiplication and division charts (tables 7 and 10, pp. 193

and 255) are essentially the same; certain details of arrangement could be modified to make them identical in appearance. The only difference would be that the division facts would be read off the chart from the interior (dividend section) outward, whereas the multiplication facts would be read from the factors toward the interior section (products).

Any pupil activity that encourages the putting together of equal groups to arrive at a product, balanced by taking that product (dividend) apart again to find its factors, will contribute to the better understanding of both the multiplication and the division facts involved.[9]

The development and study of multiplication-division fact "families" is quite

[8] C. Newton Stokes, *Teaching the Meanings of Arithmetic*. New York: Appleton, 1951, p. 330.

[9] Some of the recently published pupil materials depend on the finding of unknowns in an equation to relate division and multiplication facts. Just as one might develop subtraction in relation to an addition statement, division may be developed in relation to a multiplication statement:

Addition Statement: $5+8=13$
Subtraction: $?+8=13$ or $5+?=13$
Multiplication Statement: $4 \times 7 = 28$
Division: $? \times 7 = 28$ or $4 \times ? = 28$

important; since the division facts seem to be harder for children to learn, the association with and stress on relatedness to corresponding multiplication facts can be most helpful. Of course the relatedness of the multiplication and division processes should be stressed whenever the opportunity affords, but when children have reached the stage at which they are learning basic facts, some extra devices are helpful.

Wooden blocks, bottle caps, corks, or counters of any kind may be arranged in patterns to show families of facts. Cards may be prepared (preferably by the children) to show families of facts. In either case, after the items are arranged, the children should be expected to supply the multiplication and division fact statements that go with the arrangement. Sometimes these statements will be given orally, sometimes in writing. The relative formality of the statements expected should fit the relative capabilities of the children making the statements. Figure 77 shows examples of such arrangements of 12, with families of facts listed for each arrangement.[10]

A simple device can be constructed by threading beads or spools on a heavy cord or wire or on a rigid rod. The rod can be left free at the ends so that different numbers of beads may be used in succession on the same rod. If ample materials are available, much time will be saved and more children accommodated at the same time by having the beads more or less "permanently" placed on rods or wires so that they cannot readily be slipped off. In that case, the teacher can prepare or have the children prepare one such rod for each "product or dividend" of a family. Two arrangements are shown in figure

78 for the 14-family rod. Notice that a single arrangement will not show the whole family of facts. Using only the measurement idea of division, the top arrangement shows "$2 \times 7 = 14$" and "$14 \div 7 = 2$." Similarly, the bottom arrangement shows "$7 \times 2 = 14$" and "$14 \div 2 = 7$." The partition description for each arrangement may be added to give two division facts for each arrangement, but two arrangements are necessary to show both multiplication facts. With a 16-rod, a single arrangement will suffice for the showing of the small family: "$4 \times 4 = 16$" and "$16 \div 4 = 4$." That same rod, when used to show the family for 2, 8, and 16, will have to be shown with two arrangements to tell the whole story of the four facts in the family.[11]

With materials readily available for their use, children will often surprise their teachers at the originality and enthusiasm with which they discuss the various arrangements, incidentally learning much about the meanings of the facts and making real progress toward mastery of the multiplication and division facts.

When a teacher feels fairly sure that children have established workable meanings for a sizable group of multiplication and division facts, she may build the fact-family idea by having them sort a miscellaneous set of cards bearing one multiplication or division fact each, the assignment being to sort the facts as quickly as possible into their respective families. (This might be a good use for the ever-present flashcards, a much better use than they are sometimes accorded.)

[10] The diagrams in fig. 77 may also be used to represent arrays for 3×4 or 4×3 and for 2×6 or 6×2.

[11] Actually, pattern arrangements such as those shown in fig. 77 are also subject to alternatives that necessitate more than one arrangement to show the full family of facts. For instance, if the 15-pattern showed 5 groups of 3's each arranged in a triangle, the pattern would have to be changed to show 3 groups of 5's, e.g., ∴ ∴ ∴ ∴ ∴ changed to ⁙ ⁙ ⁙

BASIC DIVISION FACTS RELATED TO
SUBTRACTION AND COUNTING

The relation of division facts to subtraction facts can best be demonstrated to children through measurement-type

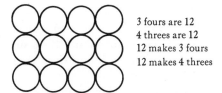

3 fours are 12
4 threes are 12
12 makes 3 fours
12 makes 4 threes

ledge to dry. At the beginning of the arithmetic lesson, Miss Albert asked, "How many papier-mâche animals do we have on the window ledge?" The answer was "15." She went on, "We decided that after the animals were

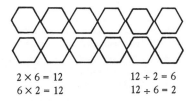

$2 \times 6 = 12$ $12 \div 2 = 6$
$6 \times 2 = 12$ $12 \div 6 = 2$

Figure 77. Multiplication-Division Fact Families for 12.

division situations, such as: finding the number of pairs in 14 (shoes, bookends, children); arranging 20 chairs in groups of 4 (e.g., around tables); finding how many 5¢ items can be purchased with 35¢; the cutting of 32 inches of ribbon to make 8-inch bookmarks.

dry, we would put them in the display cabinet on the other side of the room. This tray I have in my hand is large enough so we can put 3 animals on it at once. If a different boy or girl carries the tray full of animals each time, how many children will get a turn?"

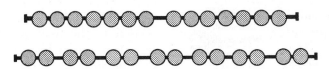

Figure 78. Product-Dividend Rods.

Assuming that the children have already had many such experiences in which they solved the problem at hand by dramatization of the situation or by use of addition, subtraction, or multiplication facts and assuming also that they are thoroughly competent in using the necessary subtractions, the teacher may well plan a presentation designed specifically to lead from subtraction to measurement division. This was Miss Albert's purpose in an arithmetic lesson she planned for her third-grade pupils.

Miss Albert's pupils had made some papier-mâché animals the previous day. They had been set along the window

Some children were sure they knew how many trips (turns, children) it would take to move 15 animals, 3 at a time. Some were not so sure. The teacher suggested that they actually move the animals in the manner proposed. At the end of each trip with a trayful of 3 animals, she stopped and asked the children what had been done. She then wrote on the chalkboard the "number story" record of what they said. (Note the sequence: action, description of action, writing of a record of action. What a change it would make in children's learning of arithmetic if more teachers would observe that sequence, instead of rushing to the written forms!)

After the first trip with 3 animals, the work proceeded thus:

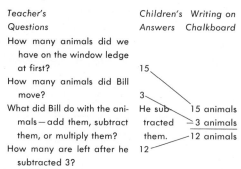

Teacher's Questions	Children's Answers	Writing on Chalkboard
How many animals did we have on the window ledge at first?	15	
How many animals did Bill move?	3	
What did Bill do with the animals—add them, subtract them, or multiply them?	He subtracted them.	15 animals −3 animals 12 animals
How many are left after he subtracted 3?	12	

After the second child had moved 3 more animals, similar questioning, answering, and written recording of the action led to an expanded written record. Other children in turn carried away 3 animals at a time until all the animals were gone from the window ledge, with oral discussion and written recording of the action after each turn. The final record of subtraction looked like Form A.

Miss Albert said, "All the papier-mâché animals have been moved from the window ledge and we have a record of all the subtractions. I wrote on the board just what you told me to write. I did this in a lazy way, without writing each fact separately as we usually do—like this:

Form A

Bill's turn
15 animals
−3 animals
12 animals

Jill's turn
−3 animals
9 animals

Phil's turn
−3 animals
6 animals

Mary's turn
−3 animals
3 animals

Sandy's turn
−3 animals
0 animals

15	12	9	6	3	
−3	−3	−3	−3	−3	(on chalkboard)
12	9	6	3	0	

"What was it we started out to find? I wonder if we have found what we started to find." A child "reminded" her that they were going to find how many children would get a turn carrying 3 animals on the tray. "Let's see now. Did we find out how many children could have a turn? Did we find how many 3's in 15?"

A lively (and very fruitful) discussion followed as the children vied with one another to tell in different ways what they had done: "The five turns are marked with the children's names." "We subtracted 3 animals 5 times." "Five trips, I counted them." "Five subtractions." "I knew all the time there were 5 threes in 15."

Miss Albert asked: "Why did we stop subtracting 3's when we did?"

She got a prompt reply: "There wasn't anything more to subtract. That's what the zero says."

This may seem like an unnecessarily long account of an unnecessarily detailed and slow-moving learning activity, but Miss Albert was more concerned with building meanings than with "saving" time by wasteful haste. Now the stage was set for showing division as a shortcut for subtraction! Now she proceeded to the writing of the division fact. Her pupils had encountered the division idea many times in their past experience, but this was their introduction to the concept of division (by name) as a "quick way" to write a "number story" for repeated subtractions of the same number. She did not bother them with designation of this division problem as "measurement division"; for the time, she was concerned only with the transition from meaningful subtraction to one type of meaningful division.

More abstract demonstrations of the subtraction-division relationship also have their place in order that children may have practice with the relationship subsequent to experiences in more concrete situations. For example, the crossing out of 2's, 3's, 4's, . . . 9's is a subtraction action that can be recorded as successive subtractions or as a simple division fact. Crossing out the "6-groups" in 30 is shown in figure 79 with various ways of writing algorisms for the action.

The "bonus" from early development of the relation between division and subtraction comes when children are being introduced to long-division algorisms, all of which are based on the subtraction idea.

for "$12 \div 4 = 3$": 1, 2, 3, 4; 1, 2, 3, 4; 1, 2, 3, 4.[12] In distributing 12 objects, one subtracts by counting out enough items to give one to each subgroup to be made, then subtracts by counting out enough items to give one more to each subgroup, and so on. In sharing 12 cookies among 4 children, 1 cookie is given to each of the 4 children ($12 - 4 = 8$); then 1 more cookie is given to each of the 4

$$30 - 6 = 24 \qquad \text{5 sixes in 30}$$
$$24 - 6 = 18 \qquad 30 \div 6 = 5$$
$$18 - 6 = 12$$
$$12 - 6 = 6 \qquad\qquad 5$$
$$6 - 6 = 0 \qquad 6\,/\,30$$

Figure 79. Measurement Division as Successive Subtractions.

In the sense that subtraction is a form of counting backward, so also division is a counting-backward process. The suggestions made for activities that develop multiplication as counting forward by regular intervals (chap. 9) are equally applicable for counting backward from the larger to the smaller numbers in equal-sized intervals.

The number line is another excellent way of showing that successive regular subtractions are shown just as is division. The division fact "$18 \div 6 = 3$" is shown in figure 80 with subtraction-type notations above the line and division-type notations below the line.

In subtraction the counting is by 6's; the direction is from larger numbers to smaller ones. In division the counting is also by 6's; the direction is also from larger to smaller numbers; and the number of 6's is also counted as 1, 2, 3 in this case.

If and when children are ready to handle the more difficult concept of partition division as subtraction, the counting idea is very helpful; but in the dealing out or sharing action, the counting may well be a repeated counting of the new *groups* being made, thus

children ($8 - 4 = 4$); and finally 1 more cookie is given to each child ($4 - 4 = 0$). The "backward" aspect of the counting is the "countdown" from 12 to 8 to 4, not the counting of the groups as the cookies are assigned to them.

It is difficult to draw a picture of partition division that is not more confusing than enlightening for divisors larger than 2. One such drawing for the divisor 2 is shown in figure 81. This drawing, to be read from right to left, preserves the backward-counting idea for the original group while using forward counting for the new group being built up by the sharing process. In any dealing or sharing action, one is quite likely to "keep track" of the distribution by thinking, "1 to that group, 1 to this group, 2 to that group, 2 to this group," etc. One advantage of this procedure is that no counting of tallies is necessary when the sharing is finished.

In handling the basic division facts with dividends as a subtraction process, or a counting backward on the hundred

[12] This paragraph and the following one, with fig. 80, represent an activity that is not difficult to do but is difficult to describe simply.

chart, the child has ample opportunity to use and to practice the higher-decade subtraction facts.

BASIC DIVISION FACTS AS REGROUPING ACCORDING TO BASE AND PLACE

So much attention has already been given to division as regrouping by sep-

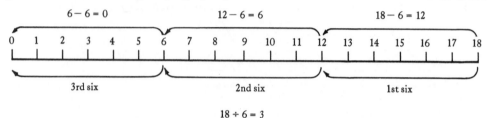

Figure 80. Measurement Division as Successive Subtractions on a Number Line.

aration that only regrouping according to the decimal-number system will now be considered. As with addition, subtraction, and multiplication, many teachers pay little or no attention to this facet of division fact meanings.

same idea for multiplication facts and will be helpful as multiplication and division facts are developed together.

The stick blocks may be used in groups of tens and ones as a starting point. Let us say the teacher shows the arrangement of 24 as 2 tens and 4 ones in figure 82A.

She tells the children she wants them to regroup the blocks to make eights. As they work from the arrangement in figure 82A, disassembling the tens and building eights instead, as shown in figure 82B, they should certainly gain a better understanding of the meaning

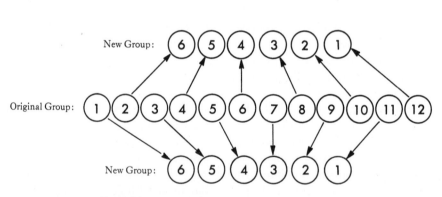

Figure 81. Partition Division as Successive Subtractions.

Children can be helped to see much more meaning in a division fact statement such as "$42 \div 7 = 6$" if their attention is called to place-value meanings by activities and assignments planned toward that end; 4 tens and 2 ones, when changed to 7's, will make 6 sevens. Pages 204-06 of chapter 9 deal with the

of the division fact: $24 \div 8 = 3$.

A practice sheet for children to use as they work alone or in pairs is helpful in giving more competent children guidance while the teacher works with others who need more direct help.

Numerous variations on this theme are possible and very much worthwhile in keeping constantly before the children the meanings of place value and the decimal base.[13]

On a more abstract level, children can use tickets and a pocket chart to work out changes from "tens and ones" in the dividend to smaller-than-ten equal-

ticed, and used in concrete situations, the names of the things being regrouped by separation into equal subgroups are important.

For most elementary school children, the distinction is spoken of as "finding the number of subgroups" or "finding

Work Sheet

Start with this:	Change to this:	Fill the blanks
2 tens and 4 ones	Groups of 4 blocks each	$24 \div 4 =$ _____
3 tens and 6 ones	Groups of 6 blocks each	$36 \div 6 =$ _____
1 ten and 8 ones	Groups of 2 blocks each	$18 \div 2 =$ _____
2 tens and 7 ones	Groups of 9 blocks each	$27 \div 9 =$ _____
2 tens and 4 ones	Make 6 groups	$24 \div 6 =$ _____
3 tens and 2 ones	Make 4 groups	$32 \div 4 =$ _____
1 ten and 5 ones	Make 5 groups	$15 \div 5 =$ _____

sized groups. Once the idea is well established as to the meanings of the base and place-value concepts used in the basic facts, children will be much better prepared for the meanings encountered when long-division forms are developed.

USING THE RULES OF DIVISION
IN LEARNING BASIC FACTS

In referring to use of the rules of division in learning basic division facts, children need not discuss by name which rule applies in each instance. Rather, the development of the facts should be accomplished in such a way that the *ideas* or *generalizations* of number relationships for division are discovered and used. What is sought at the elementary school level is not formal statements of laws, axioms, and properties, but an understanding of processes and relations among numbers involved in the process.

The rule of likeness is important in relation to the distinction between measurement and partition division. If the division facts are discovered, prac-

the size of the subgroups." If they are taught that the members of the subgroups and of the total group are the same things, there should not be too much trouble in distinguishing the like terms.

A frequent difficulty that arises is that children may want to give names to all three terms in division. This should not be permitted. Thus, $24¢ \div 8¢$ does *not* equal 4 bus tickets; the 4 is the number of "8¢'s" and should be written without any name. When 32 people are divided to ride in equal numbers in 8 cars, it is not correct to say "32 people $\div$ 8 cars = 4 people." On occasion teachers themselves have compounded the error by even insisting that every term have a name!

One should not blame teachers unduly if their own learning of arithmetic and their preparation for teaching have given them an inadequate background in the meanings of arithmetic and how they should be taught. They should, however, seek help in correcting and expanding their own concepts if they are to be truly modern in their approach to elementary school mathematics. A consultant working with a group of such teachers discovered that they them-

---

[13] Obviously, such assignments do not apply for dividends less than 10.

selves were not too clear on the teaching of division facts as found in measurement and partition situations. He sought to help them by going through a simple presentation such as they would use with children, supplemented by "tips" on their manner of presentation. Notice particularly the difficulty experienced by one teacher in devising realistic

Mrs. X: You could say you had 24 stamps and you had 5 letters to mail. How many stamps could you put on each letter?

Consultant: What about that? What is wrong with that problem?

Mrs. Y (another teacher):   You don't do it that way. It is not realistic.

Mrs. X: I thought I said 4. It should be 4.

Consultant: Mrs. X, have you ever done this? You have 4 letters. You have 24 stamps. Is that how you decide how many stamps

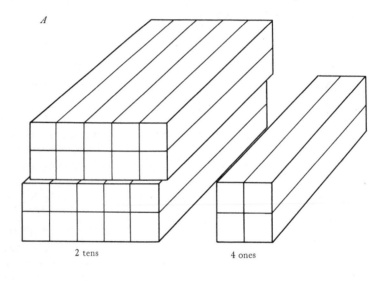

2 tens   4 ones

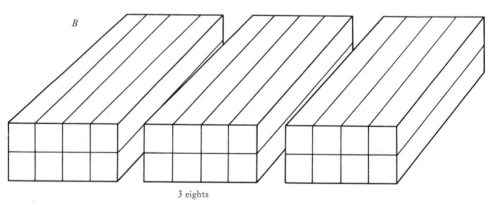

3 eights

Figure 82. Two Tens + Four Ones = Three Eights.

problem situations to use with children (an everyday necessity if teaching ventures beyond the covers of the adopted text).

Consultant: Will someone make up a problem that uses 1¢ stamps in a partition division problem?

go on each letter? Is that how you decide how much postage to use on each letter?

Mrs. X: That's a partition problem, isn't it?

Consultant: Yes, it is, but it is not a good problem because it is unrealistic. The government does not let us decide what postage to pay in that manner. If you got an answer in this way, it would be of no use to you.

Uncle Sam would still charge the standard postage rate.

Mrs. X: Could you use packages? They vary as to postage.

Consultant: Yes, they vary, but you can't decide the amount of postage that way. You can't say, "I have 4 packages and a certain number of stamps. If I divide the stamps equally, I will know how much to put on each." You just can't do that.

Mrs. X: Well, you could divide up your Christmas seals for letters that way. Say you have 4 letters to mail. You want to know how many seals to put on each letter if you divide your 24 seals equally.

Consultant: Yes, this we can do. This makes a reasonable partition problem with seals instead of stamps.

The divisor-quotient rule is very useful as children learn the basic division facts. Suggestions have already been made for activities to be used in building multiplication-division families of facts. In those activities, it should become apparent that the two division facts in each 4-fact family have the same factors but in reverse order. A child who has more trouble mastering one such fact than the other can "lean" on the one he knows for a time (not too long) until he learns the other equally well. For instance, a child who has trouble with "How many 8's in 40?" may work toward mastery of the correct answer by remembering "40 ÷ 5 = 8."

The distributive property of division with respect to addition was applied to the basic division fact "18 ÷ 3 = 6" on page 249 of this chapter. As elementary school arithmetic instruction gives more and more emphasis to pupil discovery and mental manipulation of number relationships instead of concentrating on parroting of forms and ready-made facts to be learned, there will be more and more flexibility in "figuring out" more difficult division facts by use of already known facts for smaller numbers. As that happens, the distributive rule for division with respect to both addition and subtraction will come into much wider use than has been prevalent.

One girl had been having difficulty in learning "42 ÷ 6 = 7"; she finally discovered the idea adults call the "distributive property with respect to subtraction" and was quite pleased with her discovery. Asked by her teacher to tell how she got her correct answer, 7, she said, "I thought first about what I *did* know, and that was 48 ÷ 6 = 8. Then I thought about 42 and how many 6's it had in it. Then I thought how 48 − 6 = 42. So I said to myself that if 48 ÷ 6 = 8, and if 42 has 1 less six than 48, 42 must have 7 sixes in it." One could debate whether she was applying the distributive principle or just thinking of the unanswered question as requiring "1 more 6 to be subtracted," but she no doubt did "know what she was about." It is of small consequence that she would not have reproduced what she "thought" in this formal statement:

$$(48 - 6) \div 6 = (48 \div 6) - (6 \div 6) = 8 - 1 = 7$$

INTERDEPENDENCE
OF BASIC DIVISION FACTS

Exercises such as that just described, along with others suggested for relating division facts to one another, point up the existence of numerous patterns of interdependence among basic facts. Patterns may be discovered by studying a finished division chart, like table 10 in this chapter, as well as in the building of the chart. The more stress that is placed on such patterns, the more chance there is that children will "see sense" in the division process and in the numbers themselves.

LEARNING SEQUENCE
FOR BASIC DIVISION FACTS

The suggestions that have been given for teaching the basic division facts have stressed the building of relationships and meanings of various kinds; they should be used, along with other approaches not discussed, as they seem appropriate to teaching purposes and learner development. Instead of recommending any specific order of presentation of basic division facts, some general guidelines will be provided for teachers to apply as they evaluate their own teaching-learning situations.

1. Individual children should not be expected to proceed in their learning of the basic facts for division in exactly the same order or at the same speed. To expect that they do so is unrealistic. Each should be helped to proceed at the best rate possible for him while building firm foundations of meaning for the facts.

2. Opportunities should be provided for children to "live" the division facts in a rich context of experience with situations that make sense to them before, during, and after the development of the basic facts: *before* formal fact statements are expected, *during* the development of those fact statements and used as a foundation for such development, and *afterward* as applications of the facts in meaningful ways. Division situations may not occur naturally as frequently as do those for some other processes, but a wise teacher uses those which do occur and devises enough more to supply the need, such as: distributing school supplies of various kinds, dividing into teams or work groups, arranging groups of books on shelves or pictures on a bulletin board, playing games that require "measuring" or "partitioning" the playing materials, packing objects in containers holding equal numbers of objects, and using study exercises with blocks, beads, and other manipulative materials.

3. Many teachers will want to follow the general sequence of presentation set by basic texts and courses of study. Within the bounds set by individual learner ability and progress, this is appropriate.

4. At the beginning of presentation of division facts a miscellaneous order that cuts across "the 2's," "the 3's", and so on, is recommended. The first order of business is to establish the division idea, after which grouping of facts by uniform divisors or quotients may be left to teacher choice.

5. Generally, the teacher is wise to adopt a sequence from smaller to larger division facts. The words "smaller" and "larger" may refer to the dividends or to the factors; perhaps some attention should be given to both. In any case, the teacher should feel free to deviate from this order when opportunity for experience with larger division facts is readily available.

6. When organized planning is done for presenting groups of facts, instruction should begin with problem situations (actual or contrived) in which meanings can be developed and proceed to activities that give children an opportunity to practice fact meanings and finally to practice on the abstract facts.

7. So-called "reverse" division facts will be taught together by teachers who follow the recommended use of multiplication-division "families."

8. Practice with the measurement-type situation should precede practice with the partition-type situation. Since measurement division is so easily shown in relation to repeated subtraction, the subtraction-division relationship should be emphasized early.

9. When tables of division facts or division fact charts are built, the children should build them through their own reasoning, based on past and

present experience. They may need to use manipulative materials as they analyze a total group into its separate parts, recording the successive steps as details of the table or chart. If children are not able to build their own tables and charts, they are not ready to memorize tables either.

10. The amount of disagreement concerning the order of use of various forms for talking about and writing division facts probably stems from the fact that any of the suggested forms can so easily be misused or misinterpreted both by teachers and by children. One recommendation can be emphatically stated: introduction of *any* formal algorism for division should *follow* rather extensive use and oral discussion of the idea. The present writer favors (1) earlier use of the horizontal algorism than is commonly found and (2) less

avoidance of "divided by" terminology as "meaningless" and more work on developing its meanings.

11. While learning of basic division facts should in general precede their use in "uneven" division or in division with larger numbers, it is not necessary to learn all the basic facts before proceeding to the development of these applications and extensions of division. (Both topics are discussed in chap. 12.)

12. Practice on the basic division facts is essential. The amount needed by any individual child will be different from the amount needed by other children, in general or for a specific fact. "*Enough* practice," wisely interpreted, is that amount needed to develop facts meaningfully and to a level of automatic recall and appropriate use in problem situations.

STUDY QUESTIONS

1. Take the division fact $16 \div 8 = 2$. Make up a word problem describing a situation in which that fact is needed for the solution. Draw a number line or some other diagrammatic solution for the problem. Was your problem of the measurement division or partition division type?

2. Use the same division fact. Make up another problem to illustrate the other type of division situation from that used in question 1. (If that was partition, make this measurement; if that was measurement, make this a partition problem.) Draw a number line or other diagram to represent the problem and its solution.

3. Compare the drawings you made for the two preceding exercises. How are they different? How are they alike?

4. (A) Suppose that \$125 is to be divided equally among 5 people. How much will each person get? (B) Now suppose that a sum $4 \times \$125$ is divided equally among 4×5 people. How much money will each person get? (C) Compare the answers for A and B. Why do they come out that way?

5. Compare these rules from this and other chapters: (a) the commutation rule for addition, (b) the commutation rule for multiplication, (c) the subtrahend-remainder rule for subtraction, and (d) the divisor-quotient rule for division. How are these rules alike? How are they different?

6. Why can zero not be used as a divisor?

7. Make a product-dividend rod such as that shown in figure 78. Use any suitable materials you happen to have. Work with a child and ask him to show you multiplication and division facts on the rod.

8. How is the decimal base of our numeral system used in the basic division fact $35 \div 7 = 5$? Repeat this fact with word symbols instead of numerals, stating the fact so as to emphasize our base of ten.

CHAPTER 12

Division with Larger Whole Numbers[1]

LEARNING OF THE BASIC division facts need not be completed before some of the other phases of division are introduced. Children's everyday living will have introduced them to situations involving certain of these deviations from the neatly packaged basic facts. One such deviation is *incomplete division,* often erroneously called "uneven division."

Incomplete Division

When two or more whole numbers are added, the sum is a whole number. When one whole number is multiplied by another whole number, the product is a whole number. This principle of closure does not hold for subtraction and division of whole numbers. So far as the basic division facts are concerned, the quotients are all whole numbers; but many whole numbers divided by other whole numbers yield quotients that do not fit so neat a pattern.

Very early in life, children are involved in sharing situations in which apples or candy bars or pennies or toys do not "come out even." That is, the quotient is not a whole number. "5 apples divided between 2 children" results in 2 apples for each child and

"1 left over"; "19 pennies used to buy 5¢ candy bars" buys 3 candy bars and leaves "4¢ over." In either measurement division or partition division situations, the occurrence of remainders must be faced.

To call these situations "uneven division," according to general practice, is misleading. Division is *never* uneven. By definition, division of whole numbers is the separation of a group of things into subgroups of *equal* or "even" size. If the 1 "leftover" apple is divided so each child gets half an apple, the subgroups are of *equal* size, therefore "even"; but this solution takes us out of the realm of whole numbers into fractions. If the 4 "leftover" pennies are put back in the piggy bank for future use, they have *not been divided;* so the "even division" was "15¢ ÷ 5¢ = 3," and there is *no* "uneven" division. Perhaps it is too much to assume that this well-established but inaccurate term can soon be eliminated. Teachers will be doing their pupils a big favor if they will avoid the introduction of the term "uneven division."

[1] Some of the incomplete divisions discussed in this chapter do not deal with larger numbers; the first section of this chapter is introduced here rather than in the preceding chapter because its introduction serves as background for long division.

WHAT TO DO WITH THE REMAINDER

What to do with the remainder is the important question. Resolving this question in realistic situations can be not only fairly easy but also enjoyable for children.

One third-grade teacher presented three division problems to a group of her pupils who had the requisite background of understanding of division and basic division facts. These were the problems:

Problem a: Nine candy bars are to be divided equally between 2 children. How many candy bars will each child get?

Problem b: Nine children are to be divided into work groups as equal in size as possible. How many children will be in each group?

Problem c: Nine yards of cloth are to be used in making shirts that take 2 yards of cloth each. How many shirts can be made?

The teacher suggested that the children act out or draw problem solutions that would "make sense." The children worked in pairs. For problem *a* Al and Jack cut 9 slips of paper of the same size and shape to represent candy bars. They divided them into 2 equal groups of 4 "candy bars" each and put 1 "candy bar" at the side by itself. As the teacher observed what different children were doing, she asked these two boys, "Who is going to get that candy bar?" (the 1 by itself). One boy said, "Al will get 4 and I will get 4. I don't know who gets that one. I wish Al would let me have it, 'cause I like candy." Whereupon Al spoke up, "So do I. Why don't we divide it? We can each have half." One of the boys cut the "remainder" candy bar in two equal pieces. They later explained to the group that they each got " $4\frac{1}{2}$ candy bars."

Al and Jack used a new set of 9 slips of paper to represent children for problem *b*. They separated them in "eenie, meenie, minie, mo" fashion to make two groups of 4 each. The teacher overheard Jack say, "Well, I guess we'll have to cut this one in half again." Al objected, "The teacher said, 'so it makes sense.' That doesn't make sense. You don't cut people in half." In the later group discussion with the other children, the general conclusion was, "If you were going to have 2 work groups, you wouldn't want to leave anybody out. You would probably end up with 4 children in one group and 5 in the other." This is an obviously "practical" answer. The division of 8 people into 2 groups was completed; practical considerations within the facts of the situation (not division) determined what to do with the remaining (undivided) person.

Beth and Louise worked out problem *c* by cutting a long strip of paper to represent 9 yards of cloth. They marked it off in units to represent "yards." Then they cut off 2 yards at a time. Each time they cut off a 2-yard piece, they wrote on it "1 shirt." They marked 4 such 2-yard "shirts," but they also had a 1-yard piece. In the group discussion that followed, the teacher asked Beth and Louise about their remainder.

Teacher: What do you think you would do with the remainder of 1 yard of cloth?

Louise: I guess I'd make each shirt a little longer. Each shirt could have more cloth in it.

Teacher: Would that make sense? Would you want your shirt made bigger just to use up the cloth?

Louise: No, I guess not. I guess I'd just put that cloth away. Maybe I could use it for doll dresses sometime.

Beth: Sometimes when my mother sees she has plenty of cloth, she chooses a different pattern. Maybe we could change the problem and use a pattern that takes more for each shirt. That would make sense.

Teacher: Yes, that would make sense; but, as you say, it would change the problem as I gave it to you.

The children's actions, their comments, and their diagrams (some of which are shown in fig. 83) show just how sensible children can be when they are allowed to work out simple problems in terms of what makes sense.

absurdities, they may be learning something of real importance in treatment of remainders.

With abstract division examples, one cannot tell for sure what to do with the remainders. That is why arbitrary rules

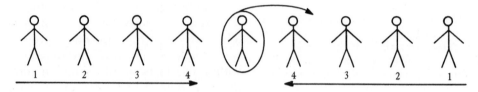

This one works with this group

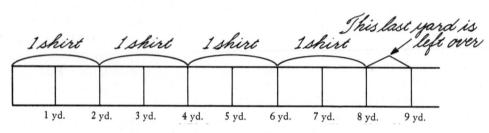

Figure 83. Drawings for Incomplete Division Problems.

The occasional teacher (rare, let us hope) who lays down a rule that the remainder must *always* be shown as a fraction or that it must *always* be written in the quotient with the letter *R* preceding it would not make such mistakes if she had given as much real thought to meanings as is shown by the children in the above account. What to do with the remainder when a division problem does not "come out even" depends on the situation in which the problem occurs. What is done with the remainder should simply be what would make sense in the particular situation.

Children seem to enjoy the absurdity of ending up with half a child (impossible) or a third of a pencil (wasteful). While given time for pointing out such

for dealing with remainders are convenient in such exercises. That is also why abstract division practice is not of any help in teaching what to do with the remainders that occur in real problem situations.

INTRODUCING THE ALGORISM
FOR INCOMPLETE DIVISION

The third-grade teacher whose teaching is described on pages 267-68 did not hurry the children on to more problems or more drill exercises. The boys and girls had time to work out their own solutions to three problems involving remainders and to discuss their actions and drawings thoroughly. Next she introduced them in deliberate fashion to some forms for recording just what they had thought and done.

For each of the three problems, the teacher developed the algorism at the chalkboard as the children reviewed what had been done in actions or drawings. Successive forms at the right indicate the growth of the "long-division" form that accompanied the oral commentary by teacher and pupils.

Teacher: Jack, what did you start out with?

Jack: Nine candy bars.　　　　9 candy bars

Teacher: What were you supposed to do with them?

Jack: Divide them between 2 boys.

Teacher: Should I write "2 boys" or just "2"?

Bill: You can't divide bars by boys. Just write "2."　　2/9 candy bars

Teacher: That's our problem record. Now what did you do to solve the problem, Al?

Al: We divided the candy bars. We made 2 groups, 4 in each.

Teacher: 4 what?　　　　4 candy bars

Al: 4 candy bars.　　　　2/9 candy bars

Teacher: How many candy bars did that use up, Jack?

Jack: Eight. Two 4's are 8.

Teacher: Watch where I　　　4 candy bars
write the "8 candy bars." Why　2/9 candy bars
did I put a minus sign in front　−8 candy bars
of the "8"?

Al: Because we took them away from the 9.

Teacher: How many were　　4 candy bars
left?　　　　　　　　　　2/9 candy bars
　　　　　　　　　　　　−8 candy bars
　　　　　　　　　　　　　1 candy bar

Al: One candy bar left.

Teacher: What did you and Jack do with the 1 bar?

Al: We split it in half. We got $4\frac{1}{2}$ bars each really.

Teacher: Then you took　　　**Form A**
away the 1 candy bar to make　$4\frac{1}{2}$ candy bars
halves, didn't you? I'll sub-　2/9 candy bars
tract it down here at the bot-　−8 candy bars
tom and write "$\frac{1}{2}$" after the　1 candy bar
"4" in the answer.　　　　　−1 candy bar

Each of the algorisms for the other two problems was developed similarly,

with comments and questions reminding all the children of what had been acted out and linking each new notation to the thought or action it served to record. The other two algorisms as finally written are shown below:

Form B	Form C
4 children	4
2/9 children	2 yards / 9 yards
−8 children	−8 yards
1 child	1 yard

Discussion emphasized that in Forms B and C the remainder should be left as one would leave any subtraction remainder, not written in the quotient. One interesting interchange with respect to Form C went like this:

Ted (new boy): In the school I went to before, the teacher wrote the remainder up in the quotient.

Teacher: Show us. (He wrote in the quotient: 4 R 1.) Is that right?

Sally: No, I don't think so.

Teacher: What is the name of the remainder?

Sally: 1 yard.

Teacher: Does the "4" in the quotient stand for "4 yards"?

Sally: No, the "1" is "1 yard," but the "4" means we can make "4 shirts." They don't belong together.

Teacher: Shall I write "shirts" in the quotient then?

John: You can't say "yards" divided by "yards" equals "shirts." Now I see why you told us not to do that before.

At this particular point, the teacher did not pursue the details of the algorism any further. She knew it was enough to let the children see the form grow out of their own thinking and action. She had intentionally included some details that would be omitted later, such as the minus sign and the rather elaborate labeling of terms; but she wanted to make sure that each essential action or meaning was reflected clearly in the earliest written forms for this type of problem.

MEANINGS OF TERMS IN THE LONG-DIVISION ALGORISM

For problems *a* and *b* above, the solution required partition division. Notice that Forms A and B indicated that the dividend and the quotient were homogeneous (had the same name). Form C shows the dividend and the divisor as the "like" terms, since problem *c* was a case of measurement division.

The long-division algorism emphasizes the division-subtraction relationship. Successive subtractions are made until the whole dividend is "used up." In the very simple cases shown thus far, only 1 or 2 subtractions were required, but the groundwork is being laid for longer examples. The carrying along of the name for the dividend at the early level of acquaintance with the algorism helps children keep in mind what it is that is being divided—candy bars, children, or yards.

The remainder is that part of the dividend that is *not* divided to make new subgroups. The reason it is not divided is that it is too small to make a new subgroup (measurement division) or to assign 1 whole member to each of the new subgroups (partition division).

Because the remainder is a part of the dividend, it should not be written as part of the quotient. It is not a part of the quotient and does not belong in the place reserved for the quotient in the algorism. In Form A above, the final quotient included "$\frac{1}{2}$," the disposition made of the remainder; but note that when each boy received $4\frac{1}{2}$ candy bars, there was no longer any remainder.[2] No candy bars (of the 9 in the dividend) remained to be divided. In Forms B and C the remainder was not disposed of by division, and it was left as the bottom notation in the algorism—a remainder of the dividend, which is its true meaning. The practical solutions of what to do with it in a real experience are separate considerations. A good idea is to have children write a sentence that gives this information. Form B might have been supplemented by the statement: "The one extra child can work with one of the groups of 4 children, making 5 children in that group." For Form C the statement might be: "You can make 4 shirts and have 1 yard of cloth left." Such statements prevent any possible confusion between the remainder of the dividend and the quotient.

Children will probably be helped by noting that the remainder in the division algorism means the same thing it means in subtraction. It is the part that is left.

THE REMAINDER FACTS IN DIVISION

Some arithmetic texts for children and many teachers present remainder division facts[3] (sometimes called "uneven division facts") to be learned as such. If it is assumed that these facts are to be "fixed" to the same level of automatic recall as required for the basic division facts, the memorization load is greatly increased, since there are 360 such remainder division facts compared with only 90 basic division facts.

Time spent practicing on rote repetition of remainder division facts seems to be time wasted, since it is wholly unnecessary. If a child understands the

---

[2] The fractional disposition of the remainder by making it a part of the quotient will be discussed in more detail in chap. 14, where the meanings of fractions are developed. When children reach the level of problems like this, they will already know a good deal about fractions.

[3] The general scheme for setting up tables of remainder facts is to use for any given divisor (e.g., 2) all the possible dividends through the number that is 1 less than $10 \times$ that divisor (e.g., $10 \times 2 = 20$; so 19 would be the largest dividend used with 2 as a divisor).

division process, really knows the basic division facts, and is competent in basic and higher-decade subtraction, he can handle any remainder division facts with adequate speed. He will not continue for long writing out the details (Forms A, B, or C); he should be encouraged to do the same computations without pencil and paper. This does not by any means require rote repetition of so-called "uneven facts."

Another argument against rote repetition of remainder facts is the difficulty of stating them correctly without cumbersome terminology. The "basic division relation" may be stated in formula form thus:

Dividend ÷ divisor = quotient

If there is any remainder other than zero, one must avoid falling into the trap of stating the relationship thus: dividend ÷ divisor = quotient + remainder, which is *not* true. This is the fundamental error involved when children are allowed—or even taught—to make such statements as: "5's in 19 are 3 and remainder 4" or "19 divided by 5 equals 3 and 4." These statements are unclear at best and wrong at worst; "19 ÷ 5" does *not* equal "3 + 4." When checking of division is discussed (pp. 290-91), this point will be elaborated. Multiplication (because it is the inverse of division) can be used to check only that part of the process for which division really took place; addition must be used to finish the checking and restore the "undivided" part of the dividend.

By using some such introduction to incomplete division as described on pages 267-69, children can learn all they need to know about simple division situations in which there is a remainder. They may use the written form as long as needed and then go on to calculations

without writing. While using the written form for simple remainder situations, they have not only learned the meanings for those simple calculations but have become familiar with the long-division form to be used later with larger numbers,[4] thus clearing two hurdles with one manageable step.

LONG AND SHORT-DIVISION FORMS

Retirement has not yet caught all the teachers or parents who were taught "short division" before they learned "long division." In fact, long division was and is sometimes defined as "division with a two-place divisor." The assumption was that any one-place divisor could be handled adequately by "short" division.

Short division in an example like the one shown below is more difficult for the beginner than is the accompanying long form, which allows for the recording of the details of computation. The short form requires that much of the work be remembered without written aids. The practice of teaching short division for all one-place divisors before introducing the long form for two-place

Short	Long
5837	5837
6/35022	6/35022
	30
	50
	48
	22
	18
	42
	42

or larger divisors has been largely discontinued, the short form being taught as what it is, a shortcut for those who have mastered the long form and are ready for the more difficult but more concise algorism.

For some years the newer dictum, "teach the long-division form before

---

[4] No matter which of the many correct algorisms a teacher wishes to present to children, it can be developed in its elementary form with simple remainder situations. The one illustrated in this section has been one that is closest to general practice in most elementary schools.

the short-division form," has led to confusion of another sort. Some people have gone so far as to teach the long form for even the basic division facts, such as:

$$4\,\overline{)\,24} \atop \quad \underline{24} \atop \quad \overset{6}{}$$

This seems wholly unnecessary.

The point at which the long form can be most sensibly introduced, it seems, is when incomplete divisions are introduced. Then there is some reason for recording the subtraction of the "divided part" of the dividend in order to learn what the remainder is. And because the long form is relatively simple at this point, children get some practice in using the form and build security in its use before having to deal with some of the other intricacies of handling large divisors and estimated quotients.

Place Value and the Distributive Principle

The concepts of place value and the distributive principle have been discussed in relation to the division of smaller numbers. Their usefulness is even more striking in the division of larger numbers. In fact, no one can fully understand the various algorisms for long division with large dividends without recognizing these two basic ideas. Children do not need to know the distributive principle by name, but they do need to understand its operation in the long-division algorism.

All the uncounted teachers who have struggled to teach Johnny and Mary where to place the quotient figures in long division will testify to the difficulty of that teaching task. True, it can be learned in a mechanical sense by rules and rote application of those rules. It cannot be understood except through

consideration of place values. The decisions as to where to write the parts of the quotient *always* rest on place-value meanings. The so-called "zero difficulties" in either the dividend or quotient can also be resolved in terms of place-value meanings. If children do not already have enough basic understanding of place value on which to build the long-division algorisms meaningfully, the only wise course is to "go back" and build it before proceeding further.

Teachers often speak of "going back" when they find a child inadequate in some basic knowledge or skill that is presently needed in order to make further progress. They may feel that teachers who previously taught the children should have built this foundation and that they should not have to take time from the development of new material to "go back and teach ideas other teachers should have taught." Sometimes it is true that other teachers could have helped the child to learn the requisite ideas at an earlier point. Sometimes, on the other hand, the child was not able or ready to grasp the ideas earlier. In either case, the responsibility of the teacher *now* is to improve the child's present readiness for new ideas. To the teacher, this may seem to be "going back"; to the child, it is the only way he can successfully "go forward" from his present state of inadequacy.

Essentially, long-division algorisms depend on taking the dividend apart (distributive principle) and dividing those parts in succession. Only thus can a very large dividend be made manageable. Place value makes this taking apart of the dividend simpler than it would otherwise be; instead of haphazard individual decisions as to how it should be taken apart, place value indicates a system for dissecting the dividend. All who use this system, then, are led to follow a consistent pattern. Note Forms D and E.

In Form D the 248 is taken apart so that 24 *tens* are first divided by 8. The first part of the quotient will have to be in the *tens* place because "24 tens ÷ 8 = 3 *tens*." Next the 8 *ones* are divided by 8, with a quotient of 1 (in the ones place).

In Form E the manner of taking the dividend apart is a little less obvious. Since 23 tens are not evenly divisible by 8, we first divide 16 *tens* by 8 to get a quotient of 2 *tens*. This leaves us 7 undivided tens and 2 undivided ones. We combine them to make 72 (ones). Applying one of the basic division facts, we have 72 ÷ 8 = 9 (ones). Stated in horizontal form the story of the two algorisms might be told thus:

Form D:
```
       Form D
         3 1
     8/ 2 4 8
        2 4
           8
           8
```

Form E:
```
       Form E
         2 9
     8/ 2 3 2
        1 6
          7 2
          7 2
```

Form D: 248 ÷ 8 = (24 tens + 8 ones) ÷ 8 =
             (24 tens ÷ 8) + (8 ones ÷ 8) =
             3 tens + 1 one = 31

Form E: 232 ÷ 8 = (23 tens + 2 ones) ÷ 8 =
             (16 tens + 7 tens + 2 ones) ÷ 8 =
             (16 tens ÷ 8) + (72 ones ÷ 8) =
             2 tens + 9 ones = 29

The "24 tens" in Form D or the "16 tens" first divided in Form E may be thought of as "240" or "160." The intent here has been to interpret the most typically used algorism of the present and recent past.

The distributive principle is the basis for the separation of the dividend into parts to be divided separately, with the separate quotients reassembled as they appear in the final quotient. Place values are the basis for the manner in which the dividend is separated and for the placement of numerals in the algorism. The "changing" concept (as when 7 tens and 2 ones are changed for considera-

tion as 72 ones) also depends on place-value ideas. Of course, the separation of the dividend into parts to be divided is also conditioned by divisibility of these parts by the particular divisor. The application of these ideas is basic as children are introduced to division with larger numbers.

Dividends of Two or More Places

The number of places in the dividend is not a reliable single index of difficulty of the division example. For example, 2/$4.26 is probably an easier example than 3/$.54 because the latter necessitates changing. The long-division algorism has more "steps" for the 3-digit dividend than for the 2-digit dividend, but each step is readily taken by the application of an easy basic division fact in each place-value position of the dividend.

DIVISION WITH TWO- AND
THREE-PLACE DIVIDENDS

A teacher might provide her pupils with play money, limiting the denominations to dollars, dimes, and pennies. This limitation is rather important if she is seeking to establish relationships between the handling of the money and the place values.

Problem: When you go to camp your father gives you $4.26 for spending money. He says it has to last you two weeks. If you spend the same amount each week, how much will that be?

Children will probably begin to act out such a problem by partitioning the "dollars" first, perhaps 2 to the left and 2 to the right. This tendency to divide the larger denominations first, proceeding downward toward the smaller coins is very helpful in helping children establish the left-to-right directional habit in using the long-division algorism. Next they will probably divide the 2 dimes, 1 to the left and 1 to the right, and finally the 6 pennies, 3 to each side.

The action is so very simple that it is a good experience setting for writing and discussing the long-division algorism. The original example and five phases of the development of an algorism for long division are shown at the right below, accompanied by comments to indicate how the written form may be developed.

Teacher Comments	Pupil Comments	
I'll write the division form on the board so we can make a record of what we did with the money.		$\overline{2\,/\,\$4.26}$
How many dollars did you put aside for each week?	2	
Where should I write the "2" in the answer to show that it means "dollars"?	Over the $4	$\dfrac{\$2.}{2\,/\,\$4.26}$
How much of your money have you put aside now? How much altogether?	4 dollars	$\begin{array}{r}\$2.\\2\,/\,\$4.26\\\underline{4.00}\\.26\end{array}$
Yes, 2 times $2 = $4. I'll write that here and subtract it to show we have used it up. How much money is still left to be divided?	26 cents	

Next you divided your dimes. How many did you put on each side? — 1 each

Yes, 2 dimes ÷ 2 = 1. One what? — 1 dime

Then where shall I write the "1" in the quotient?	In dimes place	$\begin{array}{r}\$2.1\\2\,/\,\$4.26\\\underline{4.00}\\.26\end{array}$
How much money did we divide when we divided two dimes?	20 cents	$\begin{array}{r}\$2.1\\2\,/\,\$4.26\\\underline{4.00}\\.26\\\underline{.20}\\.06\end{array}$
I must subtract that now. How much is left to be divided?	6 cents	

Now you divided the 6 pennies. How many did you save for each week? — 3

| Where shall I write that "3"? | In pennies place | *Form F* $\begin{array}{r}\$2.13\\2\,/\,\$4.26\\\underline{4.00}\\.26\\\underline{.20}\\.06\\\underline{.06}\end{array}$ |

Yes, and I'll subtract that last 6 cents that we divided.

Some readers may be disturbed by some features of this Form F. They may not like the use of the "dollars and cents" form throughout the algorism. "All those decimal points!" someone may exclaim. "My pupils haven't had decimals yet!" Children who can do such a division should certainly also be familiar with "dollars and cents" form. Using this form throughout the writing should help them see just what it is that is being divided at each step and just why each quotient figure is placed where it is placed. No discussion of "decimal points" is needed; the talk will be about dollars, dimes, and pennies.

Some may prefer the "sim-pler" Form G, but less writing does not necessarily mean it is "simpler" to understand. At early stages of developing any algorism, the more complete the record is, the more mean-ingful it probably is. Obviously, the details will be discarded as they become a burden to the child who no longer needs these crutches. Soon many children can use the simple, short Form H or no written form at all, doing all the dividing with-out benefit of pencil and paper.

Form G

$2.13
2/$4.26
  4
  ─
  2
  2
  ─
  6
  6
  ─

Form H

$2.13
2/$4.26

CHANGING OR REGROUPING
IN LONG DIVISION

The concept of changing has been fully treated with respect to addition (for which it is often called "carrying") and subtraction (for which it is often called "borrowing"). The need for changing in division is comparable to its use in subtraction. Peculiarly, chang-ing in division (e.g., in short division) is sometimes referred to as "carrying," which seems rather odd since division is an extension of subtraction rather than addition. This usage may have developed to describe the "carrying forward" of unused (undivided) parts of the dividend. The single term "chang-ing" serves for all situations in which ones, tens, hundreds, or other place values are regrouped in either direction; it merits wider use in place of the less accurate terminology that is current in many classrooms.

Sometimes the changing process is overlooked as children are instructed in division procedures. In either Form I or Form J, the most dimes that can be evenly distributed into three groups is 3 (1 to each group); so "1" is entered in the quotient.

Form I	Form J
18¢	18¢
3/54¢	3/54¢
30¢	3
24¢	24
24¢	24

Three dimes have then been distributed; so they are subtracted from the 5 dimes (or 30¢ is subtracted from 54¢). Two dimes and 4 pennies remain to be distributed. Two dimes cannot be distributed among 3 groups, so they must be *changed* and thought of as 20 pennies. The 20 pennies are com-bined with the 4 pennies to make a total of 24 pennies, which are then equally distributed among 3 groups to give 8 pennies to each of the 3 groups. Such a verbal explanation gets to be rather cumbersome, certainly so for children.

The same meanings are easily devel-oped without any cumbersome explana-tions being needed if children actually "act out" such a division with play money or counters of some kind. The form of the concrete aids used does not matter so much, just as long as children know what is being represented (dimes and pennies), and the two are readily distinguishable.

Problem: Aunt Susie had 5 dimes and 4 pennies in her coin purse. She told Eleanor, Jill, and Carol that they could have the money if they could show her how to divide it equally among them.

As children act out the division of the 54¢, the necessity for changing dimes to pennies is obvious. As soon as 3 dimes have been distributed, the children will be "stuck" unless they can change the dime for more coins of less value. Once the 2 dimes are exchanged for 20 pen-nies and combined with the other 4 pennies, distribution of 8 pennies to each child is simple. Again, if the action *precedes* the written form, the amount of explanation required of the teacher is markedly reduced. Children see what the algorism says because it tells merely what they have just *done*.

Pocket charts are often used to demonstrate the changing step in division as well as in addition and subtraction. A teacher who was working with 9 children in a subgroup of her class said to them: "Pretend you are distributing 288 tickets so each of you will get the same number. This would take a long time if you really distributed the tickets one by one. Use the pocket chart and show how you could find the answer."

First the boys and girls set up the chart as shown in figure 84*A,* showing 2 hundreds, 8 tens, and 8 ones. They saw they did not have enough hundreds to give 1 hundred (100) to each of the 9 children; so they changed each of the 2 hundred-tickets for 10 tens. Note the 20 tens that have been added to the tens section in figure 84*B.* At this point the children distributed the 28 tens as far as they would go in 9 groups. See the 9 groups of 3 tens each in figure 84*C.* One ten (28 tens − 27 tens) remained undivided. It was changed to 10 ones and added to the 8 ones already in the ones section of the chart (10 ones + 8 ones = 18 ones). See figure 84*D.* Finally, the 18 ones were distributed among the 9 new subgroups (fig. 84*E*). The algorisms accompanying *C, D,* and *E* of figure 84 show how the "division story" grew in written form to represent the actions on the pocket chart. Changing of hundreds to tens is shown between *A* and *B;* changing of tens to ones is shown between *C* and *D.* The actual division of tens is shown in *C* and the division of tens and ones in *E.*

Since changing has now been presented for all four fundamental processes, a summary of how it operates in the four processes may be of some value. Notice the similarities and differences in uses of changing in the algorisms for the different processes with whole numbers.[5] (See top of page 277.)

DIVIDENDS OF

MORE THAN THREE PLACES

No new ideas or principles are involved in the use of dividends of more than three places. If children understand the use of one-place divisors with two- and three-place dividends, it is not difficult to extend their understanding to larger dividends.

The larger the dividend, the more difficult is the arrangement of concrete representations of the actual division. Therefore, it is wise to be sure children have passed the need for such concrete aids before they are asked to do division with very large dividends.[6]

Divisors of Two or More Places

Although the longer forms for division are now being used increasingly to introduce one-digit divisors, some teachers still consider "real long division" to be that which involves two-digit divisors. The number of children (and even adults) who think of this kind of long division as difficult suggests that

[5] An interesting observation is that, whereas in subtraction one never changes more than one of the next higher place, in the three other processes one may change either from or to one or more of the higher place value (e.g., changing 80 or fewer ones to 1 to 8 tens in multiplication or changing anywhere from 1 to 8 tens to anywhere from 10 to 80 ones in division).

[6] In choosing problems for use in introducing new phases of long division the teacher will be wise to pay attention to the relative appropriateness of measurement division or partition division problems in each case. In introducing larger dividends with one-digit divisors, partition problems are more manageable. In introducing the use of two-digit divisors, usually a measurement division situation is more readily demonstrated with activities. This comment applies *only* to ease of problem-solving activities at early stages of using each type of divisor.

Processes	Direction of Changing	Occasion for Changing	Illustrations	
Addition	From lower to higher place values	When the number with the *lower* place value is in excess of 9	1 2 4 +3 8 —— 2	12 (ones) in excess of 9 (ones)
Subtraction	From higher to lower place values	When the number with the *lower* place value is too *small* for subtraction to take place	2 12 3 1 — 1 8 —— 4	2 (ones) too small to subtract 8 (ones)
Multiplication	From lower to higher place values	When the number with the *lower* place value is in *excess* of 9	3 3 5 ×7 —— 5	35 (ones) in excess of 9 (ones)
Division	From higher to lower place values	When the number with the *higher* place value is *too small* for division to take place	3$\overline{)267}$	2 (hundreds) too small to divide (2 hundreds and 6 tens considered as 26 tens)

it should be introduced only after the most careful preparation and in a very carefully planned sequence from less to more complex ideas and procedures.

The notorious difficulty of this kind of division stems from various sources. Long division cannot be accurately performed if the performer does not have mastery of the basic number facts that he must use in each particular example; this means not only basic division facts but also subtraction facts, multiplication facts, and occasionally addition facts. Further, he needs to know where these other fundamental processes fit into the picture of long division. It is sheer folly to expect children to be successful in learning long division if they cannot handle the basic facts.

Assuming that the child knows all the basic number facts and when to use them, he has a new responsibility not faced in handling any of the algorisms for addition, subtraction, or multiplication, namely, the necessity to make estimates or judgments. The making of estimates of reasonable answers as one proceeds with addition, subtrac-

tion, and multiplication problems and computations is often desirable, but the algorisms for these processes do not require such estimates to be made. Long division does require judgments as to likely quotient figures. The more steps performed in the division, the more judgments must be made.

The long-division algorism is itself rather intricate, requiring much attention to details of placement of numerals. The placement of the quotient figures has received more discussion than is usually given to the placement of figures in the various parts of the decreasing dividend, but this must be accurate if results are to be correct.

BUILDING READINESS FOR USE OF
TWO-PLACE DIVISORS

The one most important element in a sound foundation for introducing two-place divisors is a good understanding of what has preceded. This includes understanding the meaning of division itself, its rules of operation, and its relation to subtraction and to multiplication. It includes enough under-standing of and practice with solution of easier division forms that the learner has confidence in his ability to do divi-sion. It includes successful experience with numbers themselves: the decimal base, place value, rounding off and ap-proximate numbers, and practice in comparison of numbers as to relative size. The degree to which each learner possesses such knowledge and compe-tence determines to a large extent his potential success with two-place and larger divisors.

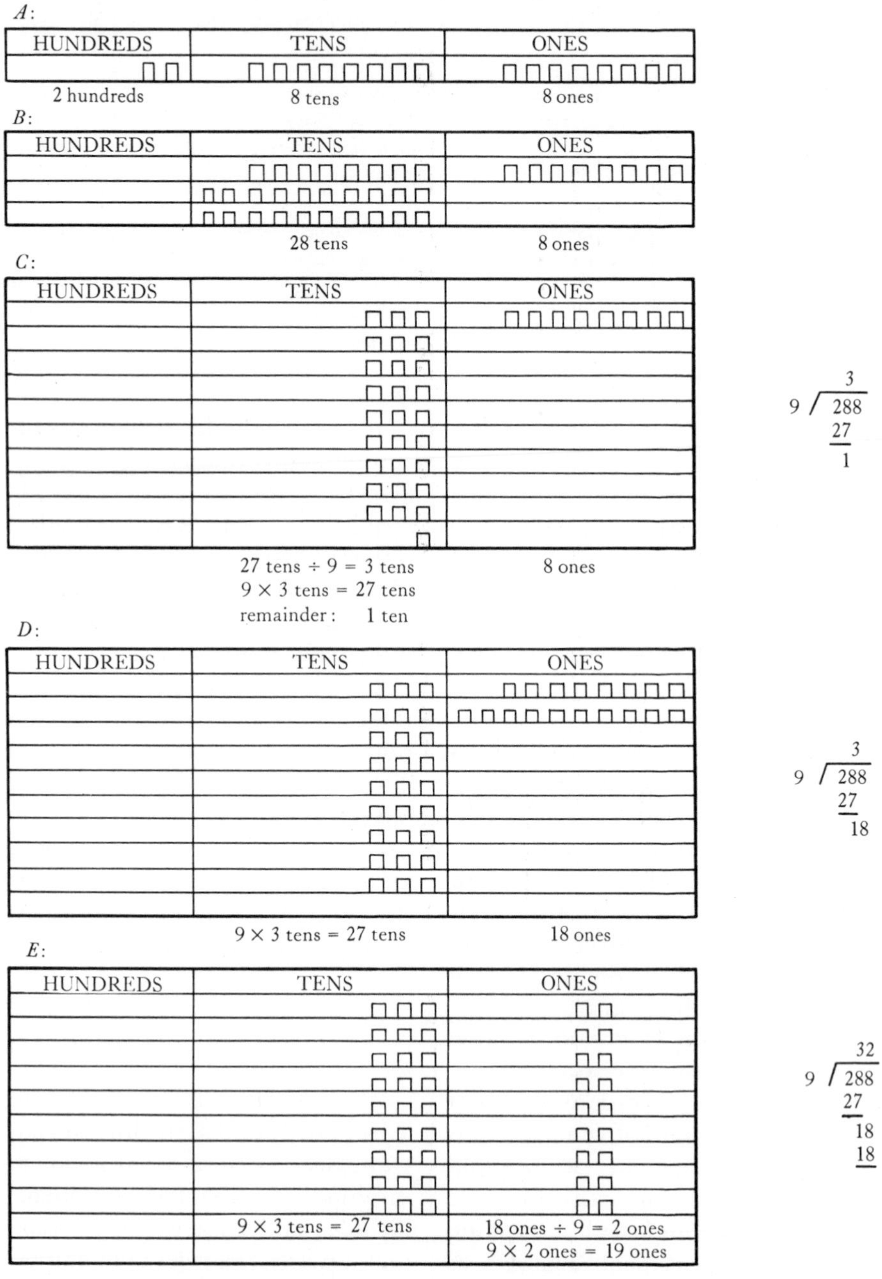

A:

HUNDREDS	TENS	ONES
2 hundreds	8 tens	8 ones

B:

HUNDREDS	TENS	ONES
	28 tens	8 ones

C:

HUNDREDS	TENS	ONES

27 tens ÷ 9 = 3 tens
9 × 3 tens = 27 tens
remainder: 1 ten   8 ones

$$9 \overline{\smash{)}\, 288} \quad \begin{array}{r} 3 \\ \hline \end{array}$$
$$\underline{27}$$
$$1$$

D:

HUNDREDS	TENS	ONES

9 × 3 tens = 27 tens   18 ones

$$9 \overline{\smash{)}\, 288} \quad \begin{array}{r} 3 \\ \hline \end{array}$$
$$\underline{27}$$
$$18$$

E:

HUNDREDS	TENS	ONES

9 × 3 tens = 27 tens

18 ones ÷ 9 = 2 ones
9 × 2 ones = 19 ones

$$9 \overline{\smash{)}\, 288} \quad \begin{array}{r} 32 \\ \hline \end{array}$$
$$\underline{27}$$
$$18$$
$$\underline{18}$$

Figure 84. Division of a Three-place Dividend on a Pocket Chart.

Assuming a modicum of all these facets of readiness, what can be done to lead the learner into dealing with a division example such as the one at the right?

$$36\,/\overline{576}$$

One way of "easing into" the use of two-place divisors is to start with even tens or even hundreds. In fact, their use can be introduced from time to time long before formal two-place divisors like "36" (in the following problem) are introduced. The sequences of forms might be from those like L and M to those like N and O. Familiarity with these forms for even tens and hundreds will be most helpful in going on to use of more difficult divisors.

Forms using one-place divisors with words to show tens or hundreds	Forms with the same meanings, but using only numerals
Form L	Form N
$\dfrac{4}{2\text{ tens }/\overline{8\text{ tens}}}$	$\dfrac{4}{20/\overline{80}}$
Form M	Form O
$\dfrac{3}{4\text{ hundreds }/\overline{12\text{ hundreds}}}$	$\dfrac{3}{400/\overline{1200}}$

Problem: A group of 576 children are to be taken to a concert at the city auditorium. If each bus holds 36 passengers, how many buses are needed?

Preliminary to the introduction of the long-division form with two-place divisors, one might dramatize the need for some such form by having the children go through the solution of one or more such division situations by a series of subtractions, as in Form P. This would also emphasize the real purpose of the long-division algorism—to short-cut the lengthy subtraction procedure. After the children have solved "576 ÷ 36" in the subtraction form by subtracting 36 sixteen times, as at the right, they can readily see the need for a better way.

Form P

$$
\begin{array}{r}
576 \\
-36 \\
\hline
540 \\
-36 \\
\hline
504 \\
-36 \\
\hline
468 \\
-36 \\
\hline
432 \\
\downarrow \\
\text{etc.} \\
\downarrow \\
72 \\
-36 \\
\hline
36 \\
-36 \\
\hline
0
\end{array}
$$

Pupils might also be challenged to see how many ways they can solve this problem by using one-place divisors. Two such solutions are shown in Forms Q and R.

Form Q:

(using successive divisions by the factors of the divisor)

$36 = 6 \times 6$ so: OR $36 = 4 \times 9$, so:

$576 \div 36 = (576 \div 6) \div 6$ $576 \div 36 = (576 \div 4) \div 9$

$$
\begin{array}{cc}
\begin{array}{r}
96 \\
6\,/\overline{576} \\
54 \\
\hline
36 \\
36 \\
\hline
\end{array}
&
\text{and}
\quad
\begin{array}{r}
16 \\
6\,/\overline{96} \\
6 \\
\hline
36 \\
36 \\
\hline
\end{array}
\end{array}
$$

$$
\begin{array}{cc}
\begin{array}{r}
144 \\
4\,/\overline{576} \\
4 \\
\hline
17 \\
16 \\
\hline
16 \\
16 \\
\hline
\end{array}
&
\text{and}
\quad
\begin{array}{r}
16 \\
9\,/\overline{144} \\
9 \\
\hline
54 \\
54 \\
\hline
\end{array}
\end{array}
$$

This procedure depends on the idea of continuous division and an understanding of factors. Chapter 13 deals rather fully with the teaching of uses of factors in elementary school arithmetic.

Another way of making this division more manageable uses the fact that this particular dividend and divisor are both divisible by the same number (that is, they have a common factor); both may be divided by that same number without affecting the quotient. Form R indicates the steps to follow.

Form R

$36 \div 6 = 6$ and $576 \div 6 = 96$

Therefore, this division: $36\,/\overline{576}$ becomes: $\dfrac{16}{6\,/\overline{96}}$

Only one-place divisors are used in Forms Q and R, thus allowing further practice at that level at the same time that the idea is being built that larger divisors *are* manageable.

AN EXPERIENCE WITH A TWO-PLACE DIVISOR IN A PROBLEM

The difficulty of using manipulative materials to develop division with larger numbers has already been mentioned. If objects are large enough to be easily handled, it becomes awkward and time-consuming to deal with them by the hundreds or thousands. If they are small enough to be easily handled in large groups, it is usually difficult to distinguish the individual items within groups and time-consuming as well. One fifth-grade teacher circumvented these objections to a large degree by using pop beads.

The pop beads had been purchased in various colors, the original chains (necklaces) disassembled, and the beads regrouped to make new chains of 100 beads each, as described earlier (p. 186). Alternating tens of beads within the 100-chains were of different colors to make the tens easy to distinguish within the closed chains of 100. The pop beads had the further advantage of being easy to separate and put back together as the regrouping proceeded.

Problem: I have 462 beads here: 4 hundreds, 6 tens, and 2 separate beads. I want to make them into bracelets that have 22 beads each. How many bracelets can I make?

Teacher: I'm going to help you get started. I have here 4 chains of 100 beads each, 6 tens in an open string, and 2 single beads. Think carefully now. Do I have enough beads to make 100 bracelets of 22 each?

(The teacher showed the beads as in fig. 85.) The pupils did not think there were enough beads to make 100 bracelets, and the teacher asked why not. (See Form S1.)

Form S1: 22 beads $\overline{)462\ \text{beads}}$

Pupil: That would be 22 hundred beads, and you don't have that many.

Teacher: That's right. I have only 4 hundred. Maybe I can make 10 bracelets, though. How many beads would I need for 10 bracelets? How many would ten 22's be?

Pupils: That would be 220.

Teacher: Do I have that many?

Pupils: Yes.

Teacher: Could I make as many as 20 bracelets? That would be twenty 22's.

Some pupils thought so; some were hesitant. The teacher gave them time to think about it and some even wrote the requisite multiplication to test the estimate. (Form S2.)

Finally, all agreed that there were enough beads to make 20 bracelets of 20 beads each.

Form S2

22 beads
×20
———
440 beads

Teacher: I will write "20" up here in the quotient to show that we are going to make 20 groups of 22's (Form S3). Next I will take 440 beads away from the 462. How can I do that?

Form S3

20
22 beads $\overline{)462\ \text{beads}}$

Pupil: Take all 4 of the hundred-chains and 4 of the tens.

Teacher: Now that is done. On the chalkboard, I must subtract 440 (4 hundreds and 4 tens) from 462. When I subtract, what is the remainder? (Form S4.)

Form S4

20
22 beads $\overline{)462\ \text{beads}}$
440
———
22

Pupils: It is 22.

Teacher: Is that the number of beads I really have left?

The children agreed that it was, and were quick to suggest that she could make one more bracelet.

Teacher: I have to show that in the quotient; so now I will write a "1" in the ones place up above the "20." What else do I need to do?

The pupils knew from past experience that she had to subtract the one 22, so that was suggested and done. (Form S5.)

Form S5

1
20
22 beads $\overline{)462\ \text{beads}}$
440
———
22
22
——

Teacher: The quotient doesn't look finished, does it? How many are 20 and 1?

It was agreed that the "20" and the "1" should be crossed out and "21" written above them, thus:

This was a very easy problem with a two-place divisor. The first one should be an easy one, allowing learners to concentrate on the meanings of the actions and the form of the algorism. Soon this same group of children were busy taking turns at "acting out" harder long-division problems with the beads. The teacher at first guided them to use divisors that would not introduce unnecessary difficulties.

Even for this simple example, it is quite obvious that more teacher guidance is necessary than with one-digit divisors. The children need to see how the long-division process proceeds and that must continue until the whole dividend is used or until what remains is less than the divisor. The questions and comments of the teacher have much to do with whether and how well children understand that process.

Space does not permit further de-

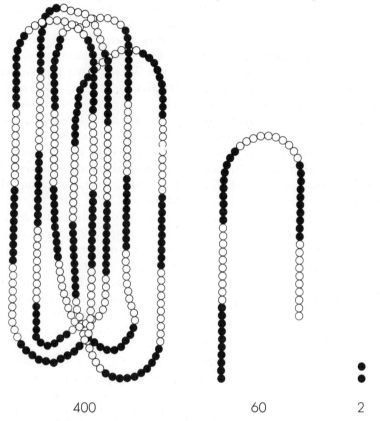

400   60   2

Figure 85. 462 Beads = 4 Hundreds + 6 Tens + 2 Ones.

why it proceeds that way. Such questions as these are in order to indicate direction: How many hundreds of the divisor can we subtract? How much of the dividend is left after that? Now how many tens of the divisor can we subtract? Now what is left of the dividend? Now how many ones (of the divisor) can we subtract? Is there a remainder? What shall we do with it?

Teachers should check carefully to see if children are getting the idea that long division is a series of subtractions tailed accounts of learning-teaching situations for long division. The procedure must vary from teacher to teacher, but all must stress what is being done and why it is being done if understanding is to result.

VARIETY OF

LONG-DIVISION ALGORISMS

Many of the algorisms for long division currently being recommended are not as "new" as one might infer from listening to some of the reactions of teachers and parents when they come upon these forms in current elementary school textbooks. Some of the opposition is surely due to unwillingness to relinquish the security of having "one right way" to rely on. Some of it is due to lack of real understanding of the former standard form itself and sincere confusion (perhaps all confusion is sincere) as to the how and why of algorisms that seem strange. As adults are challenged by "strange" and "new" forms to examine just how and why they do work, they are likely to recognize some of the meanings in long division that they have forgotten or never knew. These seemingly harsh words are not intended to lay blame on adults because their arithmetic learnings were inadequate; they have probably been "more sinned against than sinning" in their own schooling in elementary mathematics.

The relative merits of various acceptable algorisms may best be noted by comparing and contrasting some of them.

Form T1	Form T2	Form T3
238	238	238
74/17612	74/17612	74/17612
148	148	14800
281	2812	2812
222	222	2220
592	592	592
592	592	592

In terms of amount of writing required, Form T1 is most "efficient." Perhaps also as a form for general use *after* long division is well understood it is most efficient. As a complete record of the successive subtractions and the step-by-step "using up" of the dividend, Form T3 is most complete and, for the beginning learner, most efficient. In T1, T2, and T3, the first quotient figure says that two hundred 74's have been divided. Two hundred 74's are 148 *hundreds.* The numerals "148" are shown in T1, T2, and T3; but in T1 and T2 the *hundreds* are indicated only by the place value in which the last digit is written, while in T3 the complete number 14800 is written out, preventing any tendency to think only of $2 \times 74 = 148$ (as many people do) instead of the reality that $200 \times 74 = 14800$.

The oral commentary to accompany Form T1 need not go like this, but too frequently it does: "Subtract 148 from 176. Bring down 1." How lacking in meaning this is in comparison with the obvious subtraction of 14800 from 17612 in Form T3! The number 14800 has been divided to make 200 74's; so it is now subtracted from the whole dividend. That part of the dividend *remaining* to be divided is 2812, not 281. Even though "281" is written in the tens place of Form T1, this is not quite as obvious as the form in T3. Form T2 has the merit of "bringing down" *all* of the unused part of the dividend each time, but the complete subtraction is not as obvious as in T3.

The order of beginning use might well be T3, T2, T1, going from the most complete to the shorter form once the basic meanings are established (successive subtractions of divided parts of the dividend, carrying along remainders of the dividend not yet divided, and finally ending in this case with no remainder at all).

Consider now the manner of writing the quotient figures for the same example in T4, T5, and T6.

Form T4:	2	23	238
	74/17612	74/17612	74/17612
	14800	14800	14800
		2812	2812
		2220	2220
			592
			592

Form T5:

```
                    30         8⎤
        200         200       30⎬238
     74⟌17612    74⟌17612     200⎦
        14800       14800  74⟌17612
                    2812       14800
                    2220       2812
                               2220
                               592
                               592
```

Form T6 (last step):

```
        238
        200
        200
     74⟌17612
        14800
        2812
        2220
        592
        592
```

Any of these three ways of building up the quotient step by step (T4, T5, or T6) could be used with the lower parts of Forms T1, T2, or T3. The T3 form is used since it is preferable for early use by learners. Again we have a very concise, efficient form (T4), which requires a minimum of writing and is an excellent form for those who want to save time. In order to emphasize the meaning of each successively determined part of the quotient, however, either T5 or T6 is superior. In T5 the "partial quotients" are combined after the computation is otherwise completed. In T6, the notation is cumulative at each successive step. Which of these forms is to be used is dependent on the competence and understanding of the individual user.

Knowing where to write the quotient figures, particularly where to write the first one, is one of the points of frequent confusion for many children. The question of placement of quotient figures can be determined only in terms of what is meant by each part of the quotient. While the meaning of two hundred 74's *can* be indicated by writing a "2" in the hundreds place (over the hundreds place in the dividend, that is), the complete form "200" emphasizes this meaning and also gets the "2" in the hundreds place. In a sense the forms in T5 and T6 force the novice to think of the first quotient notation in its full meaning, including both place value and face value.

All the forms presented thus far place the quotient at the top of the algorism, with place values in the quotient figure lined up with similar place values in the dividend. One algorism that seems to be gaining in general acceptance places the quotient quite differently. The salient features of this form (Form U1) are best seen in contrast to another form (Form T5, the same as above).

Form T5:

```
           8⎤
          30⎬238
          200⎦
     74⟌17612
        14800
        2812
        2220
        592
        592
```

Form U1:

```
     74 ⟌17612 ⟌
        14800  ⟌ 200
        2812   ⟌
        2220   ⟌ 30
        592    ⟌
        592    ⟌ 8
               ───
               238
```

Notice that all features of these two algorisms are the same except the placement of quotient figures. The procedure indicated by Form U1 is sometimes called the "subtractive method" because of its emphasis on subtracting, e.g., 200 of the divisor, or 14800; then 30 of the divisor, or 2220; then 8 of the divisor, or 592. All the partial quotients are then added in regular column addition form and the sum shown at the bottom. The showing of the partial quotients to the right of and on the same line with the total subtracted part has merits in helping the child associate the partial quotients with the successively subtracted parts of the dividend. The old "buga-boo" of placing the first numeral in the quotient does not arise. The advantages of this form are more apparent when it is compared with Form T1 than when compared with T5, which is like it in all respects other than placement of the quotient figures.

Forms U2 and U3 illustrate another advantage of this form not shown in U1. It is not necessary to divide in exact sequence of the most possible hundreds, the most possible tens, and the most possible ones. If the learner is not yet very good at estimating quotient figures, he needs only to be sure he does not overestimate. If he does not subtract all he could have subtracted, he subtracts some more instead of changing his original partial quotient. The partial quotients need not follow the fixed demands of more conventional forms.

courage him to make better and better estimates that will shorten his work. The point is that he does not *have* to operate on that level of efficiency from the start.

Those who prefer the conventional placement of the quotient at the top of the algorism need not eschew the freedom to make "less than the best" estimates. This is shown in Form U4, in which the quotient figures are placed at the top but the same partial quotients and subtractions as in U3 are used. Of course, the "stacking" of partial quotients is hardly conventional.

The algorism to use should be chosen individually (by teachers and by learners), but the answers to the following questions should all be in the affirmative if it is a good choice: Is it correct? Does it keep the user aware of the meaning of long division as a series of successive subtractions of multiples of the divisor? Is it the most efficient form this person can use successfully at his present level of understanding? Does it leave the door open to progress toward more efficient algorisms later?

Form U2		Form U3		Form U4	
74|17612		74|17612		2	
7400	100	14800	200	6	
10212		2812		10	238
7400	100	1480	20	20	
2812		1332		200	
1480	20	740	10	74 / 17612	
1332		592		14800	
740	10	444	6	2812	
592		148		1480	
370	5	148	2	1332	
222			238	740	
222	3			592	
	238			444	
				148	
				148	

The different series of subtractions in U2 and U3 illustrate the flexibility allowed to learners in their choice of partial quotients. Certainly this does emphasize that long division is a procedure for "subtracting away" the dividend in multiples of the divisor—*any* multiples so long as they are not too large. The less accurate the computer is in his estimates, the longer his algorism becomes; this in itself should en-

ESTIMATION, TRIAL DIVISORS,
AND TRIAL QUOTIENTS

Much of the difficulty experienced in doing (and learning to do) long division hinges on the doer's skill in estimation. How many times is this particular divisor contained in this particular quotient (or part of a quotient)? All the millions of erasers worn out and all the holes worn in the paper from repeated erasures and all the "messy" arithmetic papers handed in because of "wrong guesses" for quotient figures bear witness to this difficulty.

While much of the difficulty experienced by learners must be charged to poor instruction that relied too heavily

on mechanical directives, this is not a matter to be passed over lightly by any arithmetic teacher.

In introductory lessons in long division, careful attention should be given to the two-place and larger divisors that are used. Some are much easier to use than others. One way in which to pace children's learning of the process by manageable steps of difficulty is to pay close attention to this point.

Children who have had previous experience in rounding off numbers are much better prepared for the idea of trial divisors than they would otherwise be. Such experience should be given at this point to those who have not had it. The divisor "74" is made more manageable when thought of as "70." In the immediately preceding algorisms, one uses "70" consistently in making one's estimates.

The dividend is also rounded off. Instead of thinking of the dividend "17612" in that detail, we begin by considering how many hundreds and deal with 176 hundreds (17600); we probably round off even further and think of 170 hundreds or 180 hundreds.

We think: "How many 70's in 170?" or "How many 70's in 180?" Or even, dropping off the final zeros (actually dividing both by 10), we think: "How many 7's in 17?" or "How many 7's in 18?" In this case the answer is not too puzzling; we answer ourselves with "2."

But now we must restore the parts we rounded "off" and dropped temporarily. Two what? Two hundred. We were asking really: "How many 70's in 170 (or 180) *hundreds?*" Our estimate is "2 *hundreds.*" Whether the trial quotient is written as a "2" in the *hundreds* place of the quotient or whether it is to be written as a partial quotient of *200,* this full meaning (200) must not be forgotten. (More on this later.)

Making good estimates is much easier with some numbers than with others. The numbers "74" and "176" are by no means the easiest type. In rounding 74 to 70, we lose 4 units. In rounding 176 to 170 we lose 6 units; to 180, we lose 4 units. In the second phase of the solution in Form T (1 through 6), the importance of those "lost" units becomes obvious. If we round off the divisor and the partial dividend, we ask ourselves: "How many 70's in 280 tens?" The answer is 4 tens. If we proceed to use "4" or "40" in the quotient, we soon discover that we have made an error — $4 \times 74 = 296$, and we have only 281 tens to be divided. We go back to "3" or "30" as our next trial figure in the quotient If the divisor had been 71, our estimate would have been correct the first time, because 71 is so close to 70.

The closer a two-place number comes to being an "even ten" (that is, the less the error introduced in the rounding off), the easier it is for use as a divisor. Therefore, 92 is better than 95, 39 is better than 34, for early problems and practice exercises in long division. After much detail of long division has been mastered, children can face this new difficulty with more success.

Not only the number shown in the ones place is important. The number of tens is also important in judging relative difficulty in handling trial divisors. A casual observer may be surprised to note that the smaller two-place divisors (particularly the teens numbers) are more difficult to handle. The chance of making a wrong estimate when rounding off 12 or 18 is much greater than when rounding off 72 or 88. The reason, of course, is that the ones part of the smaller numbers is a much larger proportion of the total number. Ignoring it, therefore, introduces more error. The rounded-off 10 is 16⅔ per cent smaller than 12, but the rounded-off

70 is only 2.8 per cent smaller than 72. The rounded-off 20 is 11.1 per cent larger than the original 18, but the rounded-off 90 is only 2.2 per cent larger than 88. Teachers will do well to avoid the smaller two-place numbers as divisors in introductory lessons unless they have checked carefully to note how they will work out with the particular dividends used.

Once the estimate has been made, e.g., 2 hundred 74's in 170 hundreds, the "2" becomes the trial quotient. If it "works," it is the permanent quotient figure. If it does not work, a new estimate must be made and a new quotient figure tried. The trial consists of multiplying the divisor by the trial quotient and comparing the product with the dividend. If it is too large to be subtracted from the dividend, the trial quotient must be reduced. For example, when the trial quotient 4 (tens) is multiplied times 74, the product is 296 (tens). This is too large, since there are only 281 tens in the dividend. The next trial quotient will be "3."

According to the conventional algorism, there is a possibility that the trial quotient must be changed in the opposite direction. The product of the trial quotient times the divisor, when subtracted from the dividend, may be too small to use up all the dividend available in that place value. For instance, say the dividend was 120, the divisor 17, and the trial divisor 6: $6 \times 17 = 102$ and $120 - 102 = 18$, or enough that we could have subtracted 7×17. With the conventional algorism, the pupil would have to learn to change his trial divisor "6" to "7." See the conventional Form V. With the subtractive Form W a change of this trial divisor would be unnecessary. Instead, one would just subtract another 17, thus:

Form V
(Conventional)

$$
\begin{array}{r}
6 \\
17\overline{)120} \\
102 \\
\hline
18
\end{array}
\quad \text{redone as} \quad
\begin{array}{r}
7 \\
17\overline{)120} \\
119 \\
\hline
1
\end{array}
$$

Form W
(Subtractive)

$$
\begin{array}{r|r}
17)120 & \\
102 & 6 \\
\hline
18 & \\
17 & 1 \\
\hline
1 & 7
\end{array}
$$

In either algorism, the quotient becomes 7, and there is a remainder of 1, that part of the dividend that is not used. Herein lies a real advantage for the subtractive form, particularly for children who are not very good at making the necessary estimates.[7]

Articles have been written listing as many as ten different methods for estimating the quotient figure. In practice, the number of methods in actual use would be much higher than that since it is quite common for individuals to work out their own private schemes.

Research findings concerning the effectiveness of the different methods of estimating the quotient are inconclusive; so one must evaluate them by logical analysis of their relative merits.

If the teacher feels that rules are necessary for guiding children in estimating quotients, she should choose that rule or combination of rules which seems to work best for her and for her pupils. Reliance on prescribed rules for estimating quotients is not, however, necessary! No mention of rules for estimating quotient figures has been made in any of the classroom illustrations or suggested procedures for teaching long division in prior sections of this chapter.

If children have been learning meaningfully about numbers and processes

[7] Henry Van Engen and E. Glenadine Gibb, *General Mental Functions Associated with Division,* Education Service Studios, no. 2, Cedar Falls, Iowa: Iowa State Teachers College, 1956. (This reference supplies a significant report on research with different long-division learning-teaching procedures.)

up to the point of using trial quotients, they should be able to approach the estimation challenge by applying that knowledge. The question is: What is an educated guess as to what the quotient should be? Rounding of both the divisor and that part of the dividend under consideration serve one's purpose better than any number of rules will do. In the case of the remaining dividend "2812" and the divisor "74," for example, children should be able to learn to approach the situation somewhat as follows: "280 tens divided by 70 tens; that's the same as 28 divided by 7; but that would be exactly 4. If the divisor really were exactly 70, 4 would be right; but it's really 74 so I'd better try 3 instead."

Some people argue that children become confused as to whether to increase the next trial quotient or reduce it; to say this is to admit that the process is being done mechanically. If a given trial quotient gives *too large* a product to be subtracted from the dividend, it seems fairly obvious that the only reasonable change would be to make it smaller. If the given trial quotient gives *too small* a product for algorisms requiring the "largest possible" subtraction each time, the only reasonable change would be to make the next trial quotient larger. Only if the guide numbers in the divisor and the rules themselves are used mechanically can there be any serious danger that children will not know "which way to go."

THREE-PLACE DIVISORS

Elementary school children have little need for three-place divisors in their problems of everyday living. When a problem does arise in which a three-place divisor occurs, no new ideas need

be introduced if the basic meanings of long division have been established with two-place divisors. Some three-place divisors present no special difficulties, such as in the example: $398\overline{)12338}$. Children will find no more trouble in solving this division than many with smaller numbers. If the rounding-off habit is well-established, they will immediately think of the divisor as "400" and proceed to use the same methods as if they were dealing with a smaller divisor.

Long division with three-place or larger divisors and involving advanced skill in estimation should be reserved until after the boys and girls are thoroughly competent in handling smaller divisors. Such examples are appropriate for long-division review at the junior high school level and for practice exercises to be done by upper elementary grade children who need more challenging work.

USING A TABLE OF MULTIPLES

The building and use of a table of multiples of the divisor is an interesting variation that many children enjoy. In connection with a study of the meaning of averages and their computation, one upper elementary teacher devised this practice situation. She asked the children to find the class's average height, average weight, average spelling score on a recent test, average age, and the average distance traveled by the boys and girls in coming to school. First the data had to be gathered. When all the statistics had been assembled, the averaging began. The teacher suggested that the children might like to make a table of multiples of 34, the number of children in the class, since they would be dividing by 34 for each average.

As they proceeded with their divisions in getting the averages, the children could refer to the table of multiples instead of multiplying for each step in the long-division examples. Some of those who had had some difficulty with estimating quotient figures were delighted to discover that reference to the table would help them get right quotient figures every time.

Multiples of 34	
×1	34
×2	68
×3	102
×4	136
×5	170
×6	204
×7	238
×8	272
×9	306

Even adults who are thoroughly competent in long division and multiplication find such a table useful if they have a series of lengthy divisions to make using the same divisor, as in averaging, particularly if the divisors are large. If each item will be used sparingly, preparation of the table takes more time than is saved by having it available.

As was implied in the account above, children who are having some difficulty with estimation are helped by using such a table. While building and using it, they may well build up some of the confidence they lack. Teachers might want to set up tables of multiples for easy reference while introducing the long-division algorism if they wanted to delay some of the complications of the estimation process. However, it is not wise to make children so dependent on this aid that they can not proceed effectively without it.

Some Miscellaneous Division Ideas

Some "odds and ends" about division do not relate specifically to any of the preceding major section headings, but are too important to ignore. One of these is the manner of dealing with zeros in the dividend and quotient.

Chapter 11 dealt with the impossibility of "dividing by zero" and disposed of dividing zero by another number with a simple generalization that the result of that operation is always zero. Many children, however, have difficulties with zero in division, not when it occurs by itself but when it is a part of two-place or larger numbers.

A sound basic recommendation for all such difficulties is to stress the meaning that zero is a place holder when there is no quantity in the particular place.

Zeros in two-place divisors have been treated as division by even tens (page 279). Zeros in three-place divisors may occur either in the tens place or the ones place. They do not pose any particular problem.

Zeros in dividends may cause difficulty if children have not been sufficiently impressed with the importance of the numerals in *every* place, whether held by zero or another numeral. One writer raises objection to use of the long-division form for examples like Form X1. Granted that this form makes the handling of the zero seem ridiculous, but does this not rather point up the weakness of this particular conventional algorism? Notice how sensible the handling of the same division seems when the algorism is changed (as in Forms X2 and X3). There need be no difficulty if the children are taught to think of long division as the subtraction of successive multiples of the divisor until no more can be subtracted. If they are thinking

```
          Form X1
            203
        3/ 609
            6
            0
            0
            9
            9
```

```
Form X2        Form X3
  203        3|609
   3         |600| 200
 200         |  9
3/609        |  9 |   3
 600         |    | 203
   9
   9
```

of the meanings as they do the dividend, they will know where the numerals are written because that is where they make sense: 6 hundreds ÷ 3 = 2 hundreds; 9 ones ÷ 3 = 3 ones. If a number has only hundreds and ones, it *must* have a zero in the tens place to keep the hundreds in their place.

Really, more complaint is heard about zero difficulties in the quotient, particularly the tendency to leave out essential zeros. Here, as for zeros in the dividend, the making of reasonable estimates as to the final quotient will help children see that there are enough place values. Again, the type of algorism used makes a large difference in the possibility of such an occurrence. Notice the three forms for each of two specific types of zero difficulties — zero not final in the quotient (Form Y1-3) and zero final in the quotient (Form Z1-3). Notice also the greater possibility of omitting the zeros in the quotient by the conventional algorism.

Go through the steps in each algorism. Notice the greater chance of omitting the zero in the quotient of the first form of each case (Y1 and Z1).

Placement of quotient numerals, with or without zero among them, is greatly facilitated in the forms that carry along the complete remainder of the dividend at each step and write out the full meaning of each quotient. When the complete forms of the partial quotients are summed, no problem of omitting a zero is likely to occur.

THE FORMAL DIVISION STEPS

The formal division steps reiterated in so many children's texts, on so many teachers' tongues, and on so many chalkboards might be ignored except for the prevalence of their occurrence. If a person understands the rationale of the long-division procedure, the statement of the steps does summarize that procedure; but if the procedure is well-understood, the mere statement of the steps is unnecessary.

"Divide, multiply, compare, subtract, compare again, bring down"; then again, like a broken record, "divide, multiply, compare, subtract, compare again, bring down." Why do we multiply? Why do we compare? Why do we subtract? Why do we "bring down"? If those questions can be correctly answered, the process is understood. If the words are merely parroted, perhaps the speakers understand and perhaps they do not.

The step most beclouded as to real meaning is that known as "bring down." What does it mean to bring down? Why is a numeral brought down? How many who use the terminology know that they are really subtracting? This confusion comes largely from the short-cut nature of the conventional algorism — good as a shortcut, but not good to give introductory meanings.

Zero in middle of quotient

```
Form Y1        Form Y2              Form Y3

                    7)              42|17094
      407         400) 407            12600 | 300
  42/17094    42/17094                 4494
      168        16800                 4200 | 100
      294          294                  294
      294          294                  210 | 5
                                         84
                                         84 | 2
                                            | 407
```

Zero at end of quotient

```
Form Z1        Form Z2              Form Z3

                   80)              67|25466
      380         300) 380            20100 | 300
  67/25466    67/25466                 5366
      201        20100                 5360 | 80
      536         5366                 (R)6 | 380
      536         5360
     6 (R)       6 (R)
```

Checking Division

MULTIPLICATION CHECK

Since division is the inverse of multiplication, it is usually checked by multiplication. In teaching this check the teacher has an opportunity to strengthen children's understanding of that inverse relationship: $17 \times 24 = 408$; so $408 \div 24 = 17$ (Form AA).

Form AA

The teacher need not tell children the relationships; it is enough to ask them to look for the same terms in the two algorisms. They will quickly notice that the dividend in the division example is the product in the multiplication example, that the "subtracted parts" in the division algorism are the identical partial products in the multiplication algorism, that the multiplier in the multiplication algorism is the quotient in the division, and that the multiplicand in the multiplication is the divisor in the division algorism.

Of course, the check for division may be made by multiplying "divisor × quotient" as well as "quotient × divisor." In that case, the partial products and partial dividends will not match up as in the examples above; actually, it might be a better check in that the different combinations used might avoid the repetition of the same errors in both algorisms.

Another argument in favor of this order is that the very uniformity of the terms when quotient is multiplied times the divisor may cause children to use it to force a check instead of really multiplying independently of the division already performed. (Children *have* been known to do this.)

What if the division has a remainder? Again the inverse relationship is called upon. All the subtracted terms in the long-division algorism are really added together by the multiplication process (addition the inverse of subtraction); the remainder must also be added back into the original dividend. It was found by subtraction; it must be replaced by addition.

The basic division relationship was stated on page 000: dividend = divisor × quotient + remainder. This serves as a formula for checking division. The divisor × the quotient = the part of the dividend that was divided. The remainder (undivided) must be added to make up the complete original dividend. If the remainder has been changed to a fractional part in the quotient, of course, it is handled as a part of the quotient.

CHECK BY CASTING OUT 9's

If the division is a lengthy one using large numbers, casting out 9's may be a useful division check. It operates in the same way as for multiplication. The 9's are "cast out" of the dividend, the divisor, quotient, and remainder. (See directions in chap. 10.) Then the "excesses" are substituted in the multiplication check instead of using the complete numbers. See Form BB.

Form BB

```
      296      Complete check:  296 × 47 + 45 = 13957
47 /13957
      94       Using excesses      ↓    ↓    ↓    ↙
     455       over 9's:           8  ×  2 + 0 = 7
     423
     327       Excess of 9's               16 ↘    ↓
     282       in 16 is 7; so:             7 = 7
      45
```

Anyone using the casting-out-9's check should always bear in mind that it is not an absolute check, but if a person has developed facility in casting out the 9's, it is a quicker check than multiplication of the complete numbers.

CHECKING BY REPEATING THE DIVISION

Division may, of course, be checked by going over one's original division. Better, it may be checked by dividing the same dividend by the obtained divisor. This is one good way to give pupils additional practice in the division process. If the teacher wishes to interest the children in various division algorisms, one way to get them to try them out enough to get thoroughly acquainted with different ones is to have children check their work by one algorism against another algorism. This might be a good procedure when encouraging children to move from some of the easier but lengthier algorisms to the more concise conventional algorism.

CHECKING BY ADDITION

Since division is the inverse of multiplication, it is also in a sense an inverse of addition. It can be checked by adding all the "divided parts" and the "undivided" remainder, which should equal the dividend. This is a more rapid check than the complete multiplication check and will catch the errors of subtraction but not the errors of multiplication.

Using the division on page 291, this addition check would operate as in Form CC. One merit of this check is that if the conventional algorism has been used, the child is forced to think of each "divided part" with its correct place value.

Form CC

$$
\begin{array}{r}
9400 \\
4230 \\
282 \\
45 \\
\hline
13957
\end{array}
$$

If the terminology "divided part" and "undivided part" is not understood, teachers would do well to emphasize those meanings. Many teachers who use this terminology while teaching the division algorism have found it very helpful in reminding children of what is happening as they proceed with the complete division. The names are inserted adjoining the appropriate terms in Form DD.

Form DD

$$
\begin{array}{r}
166 \\
25\,\overline{)4169} \\
\end{array}
$$

2500	divided part
1669	undivided part
1500	divided part
169	undivided part
150	divided part
19	undivided part

This terminology is also very helpful in indicating the true meaning of the remainder (if there is one) as the final undivided part.

STUDY QUESTIONS

1. The division situation in which the quotient is to be used determines how a remainder should be handled. Think of a different situation to show an appropriate setting for each of the following treatments of a division remainder: (a) Use the remainder as numerator of a fraction in the quotient. (b) Leave the remainder as a remainder, using only the whole-number answer for application in the problem situation.

2. How can you tell (without dividing) that a number is evenly divisible by 2? By 3? By 4? By 5? By 6? By 7? By 8? By 9? If you need help in suggesting tests for divisibility for some of these numbers, read about divisibility in one of these references: Banks, J. H. *Learning and Teaching Arithmetic*. Boston: Allyn, 1959. pp. 178-79; or Dutton, Wilbur H.; and Adams, L. J. *Arithmetic for Teachers*. Englewood Cliffs, N. J.: Prentice-Hall, 1961, p. 141. Can you tell why these tests work as they do?

3. Why is subtraction used in long division? Why is multiplication used in long division?

4. See page 282. Why are the shorter forms for long division recommended for later use and the longer forms for early use?

5. Read and summarize the Van Engen and Gibb research study cited on p. 286.

6. Divide 2459 by 38. Check your work by multiplication, then by casting out 9's. Compare the amount of work required for each. Which do you prefer? Why?

7. What is meant by the "bring-down" step in long division?

CHAPTER 13

Whole Numbers of Special Interest

TOO OFTEN WE ARE so engrossed in *doing* something to numbers that we do not pay enough attention to the numbers themselves and their characteristics. Surely this can be more than an interesting diversion for children and adults since recognition of number structure frequently "feeds back" very nicely to understanding of arithmetical operations and processes.

The Identity Elements

Our number system has two "identity elements," one for addition and one for multiplication. The additive identity elements is *zero;* the multiplicative identity element is *one*. When zero is added to any other number, or when any other number is added to zero, the sum is identically the same as if zero had not been combined with the other number. When any number is multiplied by one, or when one is multiplied by any number, the product is identical with the other number. We might say that adding zero does not change the other number and that multiplying by one does not change the other number.

These ideas are taught in elementary school arithmetic as generalizations enabling children to handle situations in which 0 and 1 appear. These generalizations are recommended as being superior to routine memorization of so-called "0 facts" and "1 facts." The importance of zero and one as identity elements extends far beyond the learning of a few basic number facts, however. Their further significance is more apparent in processes with numbers beyond the realm of whole numbers.

THE NUMBER "ONE"

One is the smallest counting number. We do not really need it to count "only one," but we do need it as a starting point for counting any other number of objects.

A small boy was overheard by his mother as he counted a set of pennies he had been given. He said, "Here's one. Now here's one and one; that's two. Here's another one; one and one and one, that's three. Here's another one; one and one and one and one; that's four." This child (and perhaps his mother) did not realize how fundamental his statements really were. Ones are the building blocks out of which any other counting number can be built, merely by adding one to the preceding counting number. This generalization has been discussed in some detail earlier.

The idea of ordinal number is also dependent on the significance of the number one. Four is proven to "come after" three because it can be shown to represent "three and *one*." Four is proven to "come before" five because five can be shown to represent "four and one." More succinctly, four is between three and five because it is one more than three and one less than five.

The understanding of "multiplying one" has already been discussed in chapter 9. The generalization that multiplying ones or multiplying by one will yield the other number as the product is not needed until two-place numbers are involved. The greater significance of that statement (one as the multiplicative identity element) does not appear until operations with fractions are encountered.

Frequently in processes with fractions, the need to change to another form for the same value arises. It is then that the real importance of multiplying by 1 *without changing value* becomes apparent. The changing of fractions to "lower" or "higher" terms hinges on the identity of the various forms for one, e.g., $\frac{4}{4}$, $\frac{2}{2}$, or $\frac{6}{6}$.

Because division is the inverse of multiplication, we need to examine its relation to the multiplicative identity element, one. If any number is divided by 1, the quotient is that same number. And if any number is divided by itself, the quotient is always one. But we cannot divide one itself by other counting numbers and get a counting number as the quotient. (This would take us into the realm of rational numbers.) We must conclude that the number one is not an identity element for division.

An interesting further property of one, which goes beyond the reach of elementary school arithmetic, is that one may be raised to any power and still not change in value: $1 \times 1 \times 1 \times 1 \times 1 = 1$.

THE NUMBER "ZERO"

Zero is considered as a whole number even though it is not included in the counting numbers. In a sense, we seem to count backward to zero when we go from "some" to "not any," and zero is considered as being the "count" of the number of elements in the empty set.

The sum of a counting number and zero is always the same counting number. The other number is identically the same after adding zero; so we call zero the "identity element" for addition.

When zero is subtracted from another number, the other number remains the same. When any number is subtracted from itself, the difference is zero. The natural number system is not closed with respect to subtraction, though, and we cannot subtract any counting number from zero and get another counting number.

When zero and a counting number are multiplied, the product is zero. Putting this relation in another way, if a product of two numbers is zero, one or both of the numbers must have been zero.

When zero is divided by another number, the quotient is zero. No number can be divided by zero; that is, zero cannot be a divisor. (See p. 252.)

The significance of zero as a point on the number scale is apparent when only counting numbers appear with it on the scale, but its significance is enhanced when negative numbers are introduced.[1]

[1] This text does not deal with negative numbers, since elementary school arithmetic does not usually develop them.

Factors and Multiples

Factors and multiples have been discussed in connection with multiplication and division, but most children will need further specific attention to their meanings before proceeding to work with fractions. The better they are understood within the framework of whole numbers, the more useful they will be in the realm of rational numbers.

FACTORS AND MULTIPLES

OF WHOLE NUMBERS

The factors of any whole number are the numbers that can be multiplied to "make" that number as their product. Thus 2 and 6 are factors of 12, as are 3 and 4, and as are 1 and 12. At present there is some real pressure to abandon the terms "multiplier" and "multiplicand" in favor of the single term "factor." While the use of the one term for both is certainly to be practiced, the other two terms do have some significance in discussing multiplication situations and algorisms. The term "factor" does not distinguish between the two.

If the discovery and practice experiences with multiplication and division facts have been meaningful to the learners, it is inconceivable that they should not have also learned much about integral factors.[2] The use of the term "factor" in connection with those experiences, even without any special discussion of the term, will establish a familiarity with the name of the idea that will be most valuable.

[2] Factors discussed here are limited to whole numbers. When fractions are also recognized as factors, the number of factors for any number cannot be limited, as is so easily done with whole numbers.

In discussion of multiplication and division processes that deal with larger numbers than those in the basic facts, the term "factor" provides a neat terminology for discussing such matters as the relation of multiplication and division in checking one process by the other. For example, if division is to be checked by multiplication, it does not really matter particularly whether the quotient is multiplied by the divisor or the other way around; one may simply say that division is checked by multiplying the factors (of the dividend).

Any discussion of divisibility is really a discussion of factors. For instance, a number is divisible by 2 if it ends in 2, 4, 6, 8, or 0. Or, if a number ends in 0, 2, 4, 6, or 8, one of its factors is 2. To say that a number is "divisible" by another means "evenly divisible." A mathematically more elegant way of stating this is to say that a number is divisible by another if the division process leaves a remainder of zero. (That is, there must be no remainder.)

The distinction between odd and even numbers might be stated in similar terms. Even numbers are divisible by 2; odd numbers are not divisible by 2. Or, when even numbers are divided by "2," the remainder is zero; when odd numbers are divided by "2," the remainder is one. Or, 2 is a factor of all even numbers; 2 is not a factor of odd numbers.

A multiple is the product of two or more numbers. Whereas factors correspond to the multiplier and multiplicand in multiplication and to the divisor and quotient in division, multiples correspond to the product in multiplication and the dividend in division. It is generally assumed that the term "multiple" is applied only to products that are whole numbers if no further stipulation is made.

PRIME AND COMPOSITE NUMBERS

The number 1 is handled separately as a unit. All other natural numbers are classified as *prime* or *composite*. Any natural number is a multiple of 1 and itself, or we can say that 1 and the number itself are its factors. Many numbers also have other factors; e.g., 12 has the factors 1, 2, 3, 4, 6, and 12.

A number that has no factors other than 1 and itself is called *prime*. A number that has other factors in addition to 1 and itself is called *composite*. The prime numbers are regarded as keys to the natural numbers since every composite number can be broken down into its prime factors. A prime factor, of course, is a factor that is a prime number.

To find out whether or not a number is prime, one must try out different divisors (factors) until one establishes the fact that it has no factors other than 1 and itself. Factors that are composite numbers themselves may be ignored. The prime numbers are tried as divisors in turn, beginning with the smallest prime, 2, and proceeding upward. One need not go beyond the square root of the largest square equal to or less than the number being tested. (A good thinking exercise for pupils is the explanation of this last sentence.)

The Sieve of Eratosthenes is a simple scheme for locating the primes, as useful today as it was in the third century B.C., when Eratosthenes, a Greek mathematician, devised it.

The procedure is simply this: Write all the numbers as far as one is interested in testing for primes, say to 100. Cross out 1, since it is not considered as either prime or composite. Do not cross out 2, which is prime, but cross out every number that is a multiple of 2. Do not cross out 3, but cross out every number that is a multiple of 3. The number 4 will already have been crossed out; so 5 is the next prime whose multiples are to be crossed out. Proceeding in this fashion, one soon has crossed out all the composite numbers, as in figure 86.

If a paper punch is available, children will enjoy using it to punch out the composite numbers and thus end up with a paper that looks more like a "sieve," resembling the parchment scroll of Eratosthenes with the composite numbers cut out of the scroll.

Numerous possibilities for number explorations are evident in relation to prime and composite numbers. A different way of crossing out the composite numbers might be used for each divisor (factor), e.g., a circle around all the even numbers divisible by 2, an x for each number divisible by 3, a diagonal line for each number divisible by 5, and a horizontal line for each number divisible by 7. This calls attention to the divisors as factors of particular numbers, a useful piece of knowledge for future use.

Children may make charts of prime numbers, either in 10 x 10 square forms for the first hundred numbers or in long strips. The amount of blank space between each two consecutive primes points up the existence of fewer or more composite numbers in the intervals. It also dramatizes such ideas as "twin primes," such as 11 and 13 or 17 and 19, encouraging children to seek other twin primes.

Charts may also be made of all composite numbers, all on a single chart or on separate charts for each common factor. Again this gives practice with recognition of multiples of each factor.

Some children will enjoy going beyond the first hundred numbers and will make charts of primes and composites in the second or later hundreds.

In the process they will get a good deal of practice in simple division and in the idea of factors.

PRIME FACTORS

A prime factor of a number is any factor that is a prime number. The number 4 is a factor of 36, but it is not a prime factor since it is a composite made up of 2×2. Similarly, the number

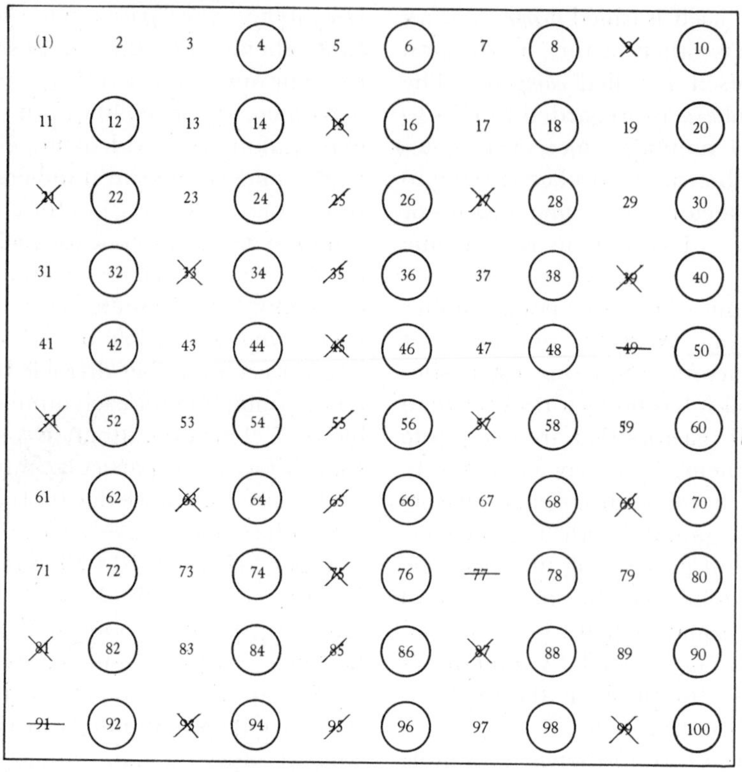

Notice that no matter which two factors are used first, the final factorization has in it the same prime factors, though they may be in a different order.

A more systematic method of complete factorization of a composite number is shown in Form A. The number is divided by the prime numbers in succession beginning with the lowest one.

Form A

$$2 \underline{)3\ 6}$$
$$2 \underline{)1\ 8}$$
$$3 \underline{)9}$$
$$3$$

Figure 86. Sieve of Eratosthenes.

9 is a factor of 36 but not a prime factor, since 9 is produced by 3×3. The factors of 36 are 1, 2, 3, 4, 6, 9, 12, 18, and 36. Expressed in terms of prime factors, $36 = 2 \times 2 \times 3 \times 3$.

The process of resolving a composite number into its prime factors is called *factoring* or *factorization*. It may be accomplished by successive divisions as shown at the top of page 207.

When any given prime divisor no longer "fits," the next higher prime divisor is used.

By either method, $36 = 2 \times 2 \times 3 \times 3$.

This leads to what is usually called the fundamental theorem of arithmetic:[3]

---

[3] This theorem is sometimes called the unique factorization theorem, a name that indicates more clearly the process with which the theorem is concerned.

$36 = 4 \times 9 =$
$(2 \times 2) \times (3 \times 3) =$
$2 \times 2 \times 3 \times 3$

$36 = 6 \times 6 =$
$(2 \times 3) \times (2 \times 3) =$
$2 \times 3 \times 2 \times 3$

$36 = 3 \times 12 =$
$3 \times (3 \times 4) =$
$3 \times (3 \times 2 \times 2) =$
$3 \times 3 \times 2 \times 2$

$36 = 2 \times 18 =$
$2 \times (2 \times 9) =$
$2 \times (2 \times 3 \times 3) =$
$2 \times 2 \times 3 \times 3$

Every composite number is the product of one particular set of primes. The order in which the primes are stated may vary, but the same prime numbers will occur. Every composite number is made up of one set of prime factors peculiar to that composite; conversely, any particular set of primes when multiplied will give only one particular composite number. Just as 36 can be factored into only the prime factors $2 \times 2 \times 3 \times 3$, so also $2 \times 2 \times 3 \times 3$ yields a unique product, 36.

Recognition of this relationship and practice in its application can remove much of the unnecessary trial-and-error behavior that often accompanies the search for common multiples and common divisors.

COMMON FACTORS

When two numbers have none of the same factors except 1, they are said to be "prime to each other." All prime numbers are prime to each other, but some composite numbers are also prime to each other. For example, 4 and 15 are prime to each other. They have none of the same factors.

When numbers are not prime to each other, they have *common factors*. That is, they have one or more of the *same* factors. The multiplication and division charts suggested on pages 193 and 255 can be used as charts of numbers with common factors.

Sometimes it is useful to know what is the *greatest common divisor* or *greatest common factor* of two or more numbers.[4]

One way to find the greatest common divisor is to list the divisors of each composite number and select the largest one that is common to both lists. The factors of 20 are 1, 2, 4, 5, 10, 20. The factors of 16 are 1, 2, 4, 8, 16. The largest factor common to both 16 and 20 is 4; so it is their greatest common divisor.

Euclid developed a procedure for finding the greatest common divisor, which is chiefly applicable when the composite numbers being tested are larger than can readily be handled by inspection. For the numbers 75 and 624, his procedure would be as follows:

Divide the larger by the smaller:

$$\begin{array}{r} 8 \\ 75\overline{)624} \\ 600 \\ \hline 24 \end{array}$$

Divide the previous divisor (75) by the remainder (24):

$$\begin{array}{r} 3 \\ 24\overline{)75} \\ 72 \\ \hline 3 \end{array}$$

Divide the previous divisor (24) by the remainder (3):

$$\begin{array}{r} 8 \\ 3\overline{)24} \\ 24 \end{array}$$

The idea is to continue dividing until there is a zero remainder, in which case the divisor (in the last step) is the greatest common divisor. Sometimes it is obvious by inspection that the remainder will be zero, and it is not necessary to perform the last step (as in the example above).

If the last divisor is 1, there is no common divisor greater than 1, and the two numbers must be prime to each other.[5]

The most efficient way of finding the highest common divisor of two numbers

---

[4] Notably in the changing of fractions to higher or lower terms.

[5] Reference to the basic division relation (dividend = divisor × quotient + remainder) establishes the rationale of this procedure.

is to perform a complete factorization of each and then find the prime factors common to both. The complete factorization of 75 and 624 is shown below:

$$75 = 3 \times 5 \times 5$$
$$624 = 2 \times 2 \times 2 \times 2 \times 3 \times 13$$

The only prime factor common to both numbers is 3; so 3 must be the greatest common divisor.

If there are two or more common factors, their product is the greatest common divisor. The factors 2 and 3 are common prime factors of 12 and 30. Consequently, their product (2×3, or 6) is the greatest common divisor of 12 and 30.

$$12 = 2 \times 2 \times 3$$
$$30 = 2 \times 3 \times 5$$

The same method may as well be applied to three or more numbers, such as 24, 60, and 96.

$$24 = 2 \times 2 \times 2 \times 3$$
$$60 = 2 \times 2 \times 3 \times 5$$
$$90 = 2 \times 3 \times 3 \times 5$$

For 24 and 60, the greatest common divisor is $2 \times 2 \times 3$, or 12.

For 24 and 90, the greatest common divisor is 2×3, or 6.

For 60 and 90, the greatest common divisor is $2 \times 3 \times 5$, or 30.

For 24, 60, and 90, the greatest common divisor is 2×3, or 6.

Notice that each prime factor must be used as many times as it appears in both (or all) the composite numbers being studied. The procedure may be summarized: (1) Factor each number. (2) Pick out the factors that appear in all the factorizations, using each as many times as it appears in all factorizations. (3) Multiply all the selected factors to secure the greatest common factor (divisor).

The development of this procedure should come after other methods have been used. Children should be led to evaluate the relative effectiveness of the various procedures so they will see the application of complete factorization as the shortcut it actually is.

COMMON MULTIPLES

Any number has an infinite number of multiples. The most obvious *common multiple* of two numbers is their product. When 5 and 12 are multiplied, the product, 60, must be a multiple of both. The product of two numbers is not necessarily the *smallest* multiple. In the case of 5 and 12, their *least common multiple* is also 60. Take 12 and 16. Their product is 192. Although 192 is a common multiple for 12 and 16, their *least* common multiple is 48. The finding of the least common multiple is important because it often allows us to use smaller numbers (as when seeking the lowest common denominator of several fractions).

Again the complete factorization of the numbers involved is a preliminary step. Let us consider 12 and 16.

$$12 = 2 \times 2 \times 3$$
$$16 = 2 \times 2 \times 2 \times 2$$
The least common multiple $= 2 \times 2 \times 2 \times 2 \times 3 = 48$

The product of *all* factors occurring in *one or the other* factorization is the least common multiple.

The same procedure applies for finding the least common multiples of more than two numbers, for example, 12, 15, and 16:

$$12 = 2 \times 2 \times 3$$
$$15 = 3 \times 5$$
$$16 = 2 \times 2 \times 2 \times 2$$
The least common multiple $= 2 \times 2 \times 2 \times 2 \times 3 \times 5 = 240$

Multiplying these numbers themselves to get a product would have given $12 \times 15 \times 16 = 2880$. As a matter of fact, the least common multiple of 15 and 16 is also 240, since 12 contains no factors not included in one or the other of the other two numbers.

For any pair of natural numbers, their least common multiple is their product divided by their greatest common factor. For example, the product of 12 and 15 is 180. Their greatest common factor is 3; $180 \div 3 = 60$, which is their least common multiple. With children, the introduction of too many procedures too close together may be confusing. Variations such as the one mentioned here may appeal to children who have already mastered the preceding one.

A most appealing and graphic derivation of the least common multiple is done with a number line. This is, of course, most appropriate with smaller numbers. In finding the least common multiple for 2 and 3, the multiples of each are shown on the number line. The least common multiple is found at the first point where the multiples of all coincide. The line in figure 87 shows two common multiples for 2 and 3 (6 and 12), but only 6 is their *least* common multiple. If multiples of 4 were indicated on the same number line, 12 would be shown to be the least common multiple of 2, 3, and 4.

The treatment of least common multiples and greatest common factors (divisors) may be and often is delayed until children need these concepts in changing common fractions to different terms. This is a mistake. If children can develop these number relations while dealing with natural numbers, the ideas can more readily be available for use with fractions. Then children do not need to learn these ideas along with the idea of changing fractions to different terms; instead, they will merely be using familiar concepts in a new setting. The general effect should be greater confidence and better continuity of learning.

Teachers often ask how to get children ready for changing fractions to lower or higher terms. They are some-times surprised when the suggestion is made that they should teach more about factors, multiples, primes, greatest common divisors, and least common multiples. Such work is a large part of the cure for pupil confusion in handling equivalent fractions—in this case, preventive medicine for a common ailment. Fortunately, this preventive can be a very pleasant experience. Children who understand these ideas about numbers enjoy discovering various number patterns and building others.

EFFECTS OF FACTORS ON PRODUCTS AND DIVIDENDS

An excellent review of multiplication and division facts may also be an excellent preview of the use of factors and multiples in later work with common fractions. If children can see that changes in the factors change the multiples (products in multiplication, dividends in division) and what the effects are, they will certainly be more competent in handling multiplication and division ideas. The following series of questions put by teachers to children indicates the line of attack in helping pupils see the existing relationships.

When you multiply one of the factors by 2, what happens to the product?

When you multiply one of the factors by 3, what happens to the product?

When you multiply one of the factors by some other number, what happens to the product?

Similar sets of questions can be worded so as to lead to all these relationships:

Action	Effect on:
Multiplying a factor	Multiple (product or dividend)
Dividing a factor	Multiple (product or dividend)
Multiplying a multiple	Effect on one or the other factor
Dividing a multiple	Effect on one or the other factor

Since "factor" may apply to a multiplicand, a multiplier, a divisor, or a quotient and since "multiple" may apply to either a product or a dividend, the list of possible relationships is rather lengthy. It would not be wise to expect children to work out all of them at the first experience. When each has been explored independently, the various

new relationships in any new number situation. In this category comes the classification of numbers according to "shapes" (e.g., square numbers, rectangular numbers, triangular numbers). Their study is a fascinating "extra" for superior students.

Square numbers may be represented as in figure 88. They are a special kind

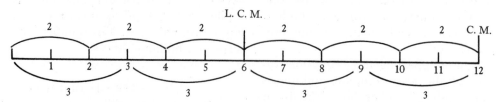

Figure 87. Finding the Least Common Multiple on a Number Line.

interrelationships may be summarized.

If children understand what factors and multiples are, they can be given statements such as a and b below and asked to decide whether or not the statements are true. Using many different numbers, they can "verify" the truth of the statements in an informal (and somewhat limited) fashion. Then they may be asked to figure out why these statements would have to be true. This can be real fun for children who have acquired a curiosity about number relations.

a. Each factor of a number is also a factor of any multiple of that number.

b. If two numbers have a common factor, that common factor is also a factor of the sum or difference of the two numbers.

SQUARE NUMBERS

Any experience in which children note interesting relationships among numbers is likely not only to add to their understanding of number structure but also to contribute to their enjoyment of arithmetic. Given such ideas, they should be stimulated to look for

of multiple, with two equal factors. Children will enjoy taking a given number of uniformly shaped objects and trying to arrange them to form a perfect square.

A more fundamental understanding

Figure 88. The Square Numbers Four and Nine.

of square numbers, perhaps, may be developed diagrammatically, relying on the distributive property. Let us say we wish to show the square of the number 12. This might be built up with counters as in the preceding suggestion, or it could be drawn on squared paper as shown in figure 89. Thus, 12×12 is shown as $(10+2)(10+2)$ rather easily. The diagram shows clearly the 10×10 section, the 2×2 section, and two sections each 2×10. Of course this is the familiar algebraic $(a+b)^2 = a^2 + 2ab + b^2$.

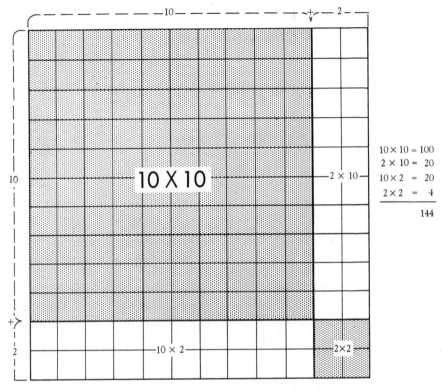

Figure 89. The Distributive Principle Shown in a Square Number.

STUDY QUESTIONS

1. What is the identity element for multiplication in our system? What is the identity element for addition in our system?

2. Make a chart of prime and composite numbers through 200. Show prime numbers in one color and composite numbers in another color. Connect twin primes by a double-headed arrow.

3. Find the prime factors of the following numbers:

a. 346   b. 105   c. 144   d. 75   e. 81

4. Group the composite numbers from question 3 that have common factors.

5. Using what you learned in questions 3 and 4, what is the least common factor for each group of numbers? The greatest common factor?

6. For each group of numbers determine their least common multiple.

7. Read these two very short references. Using ideas about rectangular, square, and triangle numbers developed in these books, plan a recreational arithmetic period with children. Adler, Irving and Adler, Ruth. *Numbers Old and New.* New York: Day, 1960. Glenn, William H.; and Johnson, Donovan A. *Number Patterns.* St. Louis: Webster, 1960.

CHAPTER 14

Meanings of Common Fractions

TALK ABOUT THE DIFFICULTY of fractions is somewhat like talk about the weather —so much talk and so little done about it. Much more is being done about the weather in this day and age than formerly, with more promised in the near future. Much should be done also about clarifying the meanings of fractions. Too much time and energy have been spent struggling with poorly understood and misunderstood mechanical *operations* with fractions. If half that amount of time were spent helping learners understand the fractions themselves, the effects might well be as revolutionary as the orbiting of weather satellites.

The prevalence of fractions in everyday affairs is so well established as to be assumed. One of them crept into the preceding paragraph all unawares.

What are Fractions?

The word "fraction" is used to refer to both numbers and numerals. Strictly speaking, the symbol "$\frac{1}{2}$" should be called a "fraction numeral," but this would become rather cumbersome in practice. Whether the fraction symbol is an expression of a number or a number relationship, the important con-

sideration is that emphasis should rest on the meaning being represented by the symbol.

Because fractions have different meanings in different situations, they are defined in a series of statements expressing the ideas that may be represented by fractions. No one of these statements gives a complete idea of fractions; some are more basic than others; some obviously overlap with others and might be applied to the same situation, depending on how one chooses to interpret the given situation. Together, they should give a more comprehensive definition of the meaning of fractions than any one statement can do.

The discussion that follows proceeds in an approximate order of occurrence in the experiences of learners, though many variations in sequence must be expected and recognized.

A FRACTION MAY EXPRESS ONE OR
MORE OF THE EQUAL PARTS
OF A WHOLE UNIT

Children experience this meaning of fractions at an early age and are quite adept in using it when they come to school. Mother tells Billy that he may have "half an apple" and he should share his candy bar with two other children so they each have "a third." He hears Mother tell Big Brother to cut the pie into "sixths" and Big Brother's reply: "Aw, be a sport. Let me cut it into fourths."

Billy knows that he gets a bigger piece of candy when it is cut in half than when it is cut in thirds. He knows that Big Brother wanted a larger serving of pie when he asked to cut the pie in fourths instead of sixths.

Thus informal experience with fraction expressions builds toward understanding, but misconceptions may also be acquired through these unplanned and incidental experiences. One is shown in the very common plaint of one child to another: "You took the big half and gave me the little half!" Or to Mother: "He's not fair! He always cuts his half bigger!"

Kindergarten and primary-grade teachers need to watch for evidences of such fallacies. Whenever and wherever children imply that halves or thirds or fourths or any other fractional parts may be "bigger" or "smaller" than other fractional parts of the same name, it is time for a lesson on the necessity that the "same-named" parts of the same thing *must be equal.*

This is one reason that the cutting of pieces of fruit and discussion of fractional parts of pieces of fruit is not a happy choice in trying to teach young children that "one-half" is "one of the two *equal* parts of a whole" or that "one-third" is "one of the three *equal* parts of a whole." Apples, bananas, peaches, and oranges are not easily cut into *equal* parts. Anyone who has conscientiously tried to cut the breakfast grapefruit into two equal parts and really observed the results knows this to be true. Some candy bars can be easily divided into equal parts, others not. Rectangular sheets of

paper or precut circles of felt are much better for this purpose. If the teacher feels she must have apples and bananas, they should be as symmetrical as possible and very carefully cut in advance. No one can casually slash either into truly *equal* parts.

The concept of fractions as expressing one or more of the equal parts of a whole thing is perhaps the best taught of all the interpretations of fractions. It may even be too well taught in the sense that it is sometimes presented as the only meaning of all fractions. Since many calculations with fractions employ other meanings, it is no wonder that learners equipped with only this limited concept are confused. This concept of a fraction as one or more equal parts of a unit should be taught early, used correctly, and recognized always as only one of the meanings of a fraction.

Teachers need also to recognize that a given item may be a part of a whole and itself a whole thing at the same time. Half a sheet of typing paper is one of the two equal parts of a whole sheet, but it is also a whole sheet of paper of a different size. One-sixth of a pie is a whole piece of pie; in the frozen-food section of the supermarket, prices are assigned to the whole pie, but in the restaurant the customer is charged by the whole piece, whether that piece be a sixth, an eighth, or even (unhappy thought!) a twelfth. A quarter has one-fourth (one quarter) the value of a dollar, but a quarter is a whole coin with a value of its own. Young children do not think of dimes as tenths of dollars or nickels as twentieths of dollars or pennies as hundredths of dollars, but those value equivalences should be developed as time passes.

The two meanings — as part of a whole thing and as a whole thing — need to be contrasted, but they are not to be thought of as in opposition one to the other. What we want eventually is for children to have a "both-and" rather than an "either-or" understanding. When a child needs to add 4 sixths of a pie and 2 sixths of a pie, we want him to recognize that he can add sixths as he adds any other whole things (sixths as units in this case) for a sum of 6 sixths; we also want him to recognize that his 6 sixths are parts of a whole pie and together equal one whole pie.

One-half, one-third, one-fourth, one-sixth, one-tenth are called *unit fractions* because only one of each fractional part is being considered. *Nonunit fractions* such as two-thirds, three-fourths, five-eighths, or six-tenths also carry a unit connotation in that they are multiples of unit fractions. They are multiples of parts that may be dealt with as wholes. The clarification of this point would do much to simplify the teaching of addition and subtraction of fractions.

A FRACTION MAY EXPRESS ONE OR MORE OF THE EQUAL PARTS OF A GROUP OF UNITS

Children have many informal experiences with this concept of fractions, as with the preceding one, but they often are not given the help some of them need to understand it well or to distinguish it from the prior concept of a fraction as one or more equal parts of a single whole.

The word "equal" has a very different connotation here. The half sheet of paper, the third of the candy bar, the tenth of a dollar has to be equal in size or value, respectively, to every other half of that size sheet, to every other third of that size candy bar, or to every other tenth of a dollar. When we speak of a fourth of a group of people, on the other hand, each person need not be and cannot be the same size, shape, or age as any other person in the group. John and Mary are two-fourths of the people seated at one table in the classroom (John, Mary, Joe, Alice). Even though Joe and Alice are older and bigger than John and Mary, they too represent two-fourths of the group. The individual children are equal in that they represent an equal *number* of people in the group (each is *one* person). This equality is not so easily represented by concrete aids as is the meaning of equality among fractional parts of the single whole thing.

Airlines struggle with this distinction continuously. They charge adult passengers the same fare, and the stewardess counts them as one unit each to check the passenger list. The 300-pound man is 1 passenger the same as the 96-pound teen-ager is 1 passenger. In a group of 20 passengers each is one-twentieth of the group on the passenger list. They are equal *because they are being considered as equal,* one person each. Weight of the load being a serious consideration to airlines, various proposals have been made to charge according to weights of passengers. If this were done, the 300-pound passenger would represent more than one-twentieth of the total *weight* and the 96-pound passenger less than one-twentieth of the total *weight.*

Sometimes the items in the group are to all intents and purposes equal. The point is that this is not a requirement. In terms of sets, each equal part of a group is equal on the basis of being one of the set.

In developing the idea of fractional parts of groups, the teacher will do well to start with groups in which the members or units are not too different, leading gradually to the unity that still exists despite diversity in other matters than group membership.

A dozen eggs serve as a useful and manageable model of a group both because 12 is divisible into halves, thirds, fourths, sixths, and twelfths and because the eggs (real ones or plastic Easter eggs or china nest eggs) are fairly uniform in appearance.

One of the obviously appropriate times for delving into the concept of a fraction as one or more of the equal parts of a group is in relation to the development of multiplication and division facts. The fact "4 × 2 = 8" is related to the fact "8 ÷ 2 = 4," which is also related to the fact that "one-half of 8 = 4." As the factors of 12 are found and discussed, the fractional parts of 12 may also be found and discussed, pointing up the fact that fractions provide different ways of talking and writing about whole numbers.

If multiplication and division are presented with arrays, the concept of a fraction as a part of a group may be related to parts of arrays, as in figure 90, where a line has been drawn around one-third of the items in the array. Obviously the array on the left is more appropriate at early stages of devel-

in themselves wholes. One-fourth of 12 eggs is 3 whole eggs. One-fourth of the 4 children at the table is 1 whole child. Five-sixths of 6 whole pies is 5 whole pies. The significance of this point is brought to light when children have been oversold on the prior concept of a fraction as a *part* of a whole thing and have difficulty expanding that idea to include parts (of groups) that are *wholes* (in themselves). As when parts of a whole unit are also thought of as wholes in themselves, the child needs to be helped to see them in relation to the situation at hand. Part of what? Whole what? The eggs are *parts of the group* of eggs, but they are *whole* eggs at the same time.

When the group under consideration is not evenly divisible, certain difficulties arise. Hence, such situations should usually be introduced after children have command of the idea with evenly divisible groups.

A FRACTION MAY EXPRESS THE SAME
EQUAL PART OF EACH UNIT
IN A GROUP

This concept overlaps the two others that have been discussed above. The distinction is apparent in relation to

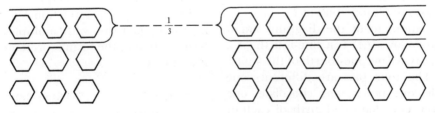

Figure 90. A Fraction as Part of a Group.

opment of the idea, the one on the right at later stages. Still, each represents *one of the three equal parts* of the array.

When only evenly divisible groups are considered, the *parts* of the *groups* are

specific situations. In figure 91 the three ideas are expressed in drawings of pies. The concept of one-fourth of one whole pie is shown by the shaded portion in *A;* the concept of one-fourth of a group of

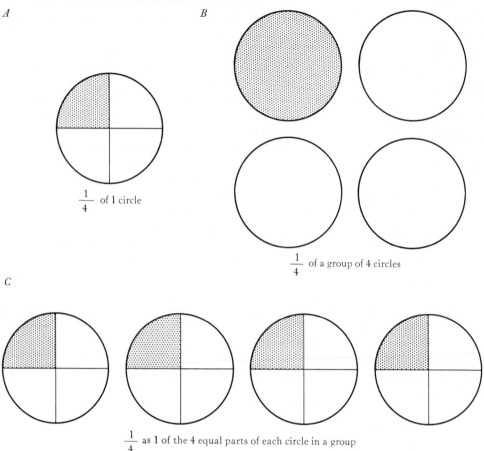

A

$\frac{1}{4}$ of 1 circle

B

$\frac{1}{4}$ of a group of 4 circles

C

$\frac{1}{4}$ as 1 of the 4 equal parts of each circle in a group

Figure 91. Three Different Meanings of the Same Fraction.

pies is shown as one shaded pie in *B;* and the concept of one-fourth of each pie in a group is shown by the shaded portions of all four pies in *C*.

Situations to fit the diagrams might be as follows: *(A)* Cut one-fourth of a pie. *(B)* Give me one-fourth of the 4 pies. *(C)* The four pies are different—one apple, one peach, one chocolate, one lemon. Give me one-fourth of each of them.

The "one-fourths" in *A* and *C* are alike in that each fourth is a part of a whole pie; the parts are equal. Situations *B* and *C* are alike in that a total group of four whole pies is involved; one-fourth of the four is the same total amount of

pie whether it is uncut as in *B* or cut as in *C*. (Equality of sizes of the different whole pies is here assumed.)

This concept of a fractional part of a group will recur with multiplication by a fraction in the form represented by *B* and by *C*.

A FRACTION MAY EXPRESS RELATIVE
COMPARISON; THAT IS, IT MAY
EXPRESS A RATIO

Before they meet this concept of a fraction, children will have had a good deal of experience with absolute comparisons and subtraction. One whole number is compared with another whole number by subtracting the smaller from the larger. The comparison is expressed by their difference. The difference represents an absolute or total or exact difference. One child is 5 feet (or 60 inches) tall, another is 4 feet (or 48 inches) tall; the taller child is 1 foot (or 12 inches) taller than the shorter. The difference is stated in the specific units of measure that apply in the situation.

Fractions represent *relative* comparisons, i.e., ratios. We can say that the taller child is "one-fourth taller" than the shorter child; we are now not stating any absolute value for the height of either child, but we are making a statement about their *relative* height. We could also say that the shorter child is "one-fifth shorter" than the other child, or that the shorter child is "four-fifths as tall" as the other child. It would also be correct to say that the taller child was "five-fourths as tall" as the shorter child, though this would not be as likely a statement. Here we have used four different fractions to describe the relative heights of the same two children.

Perhaps this is the origin of the con-

fusion in the minds of too many people in their use of ratios. Adults read that there are two-thirds as many women as men students at X college. Some of them, in attempting to repeat this bit of information, change it to the statement that two-thirds of the students at X college are women and thereby give a most inaccurate report. They repeat the same fraction but put it in an entirely different context.

For ratio to be understood, one must keep in mind *what* is being compared with *what*. Referring to figure 92*A*, the absolute difference in heights of S and T is shown as 1 foot: 5 feet − 4 feet = 1 foot. We can say that S is 1 foot shorter then T, or we can say that T is 1 foot taller than S. The difference is expressed in terms of the scale of feet.

In figures 92*B* and 92*C*, this is not the case. We are using as our standard of reference (as a basis of measurement or comparison) the height of T (fig. 92*B*) or the height of S (fig. 92*C*). Using the height of the taller person as the unit of measurement in figure 92*B*, we show T as being five-fifths, or 1 whole unit, tall. S, by the same unit of measurement,

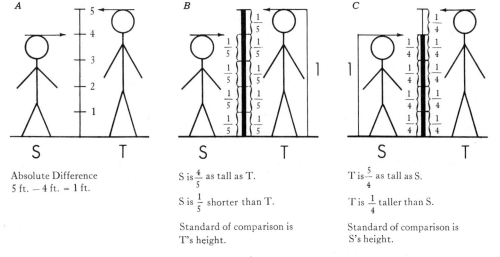

A

Absolute Difference
5 ft. − 4 ft. = 1 ft.

B

S is $\frac{4}{5}$ as tall as T.

S is $\frac{1}{5}$ shorter than T.

Standard of comparison is
T's height.

C

T is $\frac{5}{4}$ as tall as S.

T is $\frac{1}{4}$ taller than S.

Standard of comparison is
S's height.

Figure 92. Absolute and Relative Comparison — Fractions as Ratios.

is four-fifths as tall as T; or he is one-fifth shorter than T. Using the height of the shorter person as the basis of measurement and comparison in figure 92*C,* we see that S is four-fourths of that standard, whereas T is five-fourths that tall. T is one-fourth taller than the standard set by the height of S.

Stated without resort to fraction terminology, we can say that for every 4 feet of height attained by S, T has attained 1 extra foot of height; or, for every 4 feet of height attained by S, T has attained 5 feet. In reverse, for every 5 feet attained by T, S has attained only 4 feet of height, or 1 foot less for every 5 of T.

The ratio-to-one idea has been brought out in relation to the meanings of multiplication and division of whole numbers. All whole numbers have a ratio-to-one meaning. The number 4 has a four-to-one ratio to 1; the number 5 has a five-to-one ratio to 1. These ratios could be expressed as fractions but do not need to be so expressed.

$$4 = \frac{4}{1} \qquad 5 = \frac{5}{1} \qquad 1\text{-to-}5 = \frac{1}{5} \qquad 1\text{-to-}4 = \frac{1}{4}$$

When the ratio is stated in the opposite direction, e.g., one-to-four or one-to-five, a fraction form is most convenient for the expression. So also for ratios not including the number 1 in their statements; we can say "2 out of 3," but the fraction "two-thirds" states this ratio more neatly.

Schoolchildren need much practice with the simple statements of ratios in fraction form, aside from any computations that may be performed using those fractions. Classroom materials and situations suggest many opportunities for practicing the ratio concept; it is the teacher's duty to use them wisely. Some such situations are suggested below, with whole-number and fractional form

statements showing the transition that children need to make in their thinking and in their ways of speaking about ratio situations.

Ratio Situations

Expressed with whole numbers	*Expressed with fractions*
3 out of 4 children have books.	Three-fourths of the children have books.
Sue read 2 books for every 5 Jerry read.	Sue read two-fifths as many books as Jerry read.
I have worked 8 out of 10 arithmetic problems.	I have worked eight-tenths (or four-fifths) of the arithmetic problems.
I am 12 years old; my dad is 36. I have lived 1 year for each 3 years he has lived.	I have lived one-third as long as my dad.

Fraction forms are used for expressing a special kind of number called *rational numbers.* They get this name because they are *ratios.* The meaning of rational numbers will be developed more fully in the next major section.

A FRACTION MAY INDICATE
A DIVISION

Rational numbers represent the division of one number by another. In a sense, we may say that fractions express quotients.

To this point in the discussion fractions have generally been expressed in word form in the text though numerals have been used in some of the diagrams. The use of words in the text has been intentional since the numeral fraction form rests rather heavily on the meaning of fractions as expressing division. (Teachers will introduce the numeral form as early as seems desirable with a particular group of children.)

Children like an analogy between the division sign and the form for expressing fractions with numerals, as shown in figure 93. This is more easily shown on a chalkboard than in a book. First the division sign is written with or without accompanying numerals. Children may be asked to tell what it says. They will answer, "Divided by." Then numerals can be placed where the dots were, and the children will very quickly respond with "2 divided by 4" as a way to read the fraction form.[1]

The conception of a fraction as indicating a division is basic to all the other ideas that have been presented. This may be shown by reviewing each of those ideas as divisions.

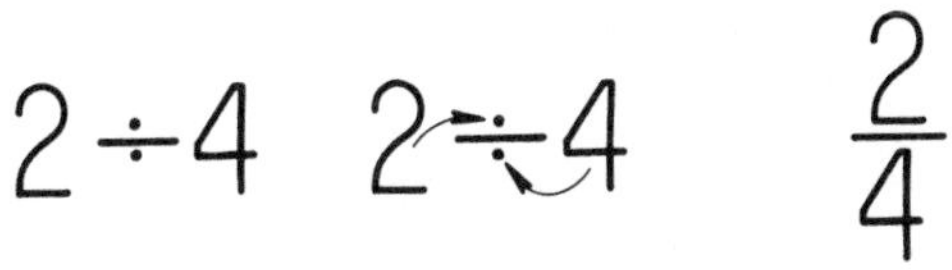

$$2 \div 4 \quad 2 \div 4 \quad \frac{2}{4}$$

Figure 93. The Fraction Symbol Related to Division.

In order to think of a fraction as showing "one or more of the equal parts of a whole unit," that whole unit must be thought of as having been *divided* to make equal parts. The fraction "$\frac{1}{2}$" means that 1 whole thing has been divided to make 2 equal parts. One-half of a dollar means 1 dollar has been divided to make 2 equal parts $(1 \div 2 = \frac{1}{2})$. One-fourth of an inch means that 1 whole inch has been divided to make 4 equal parts $(1 \div 4 = \frac{1}{4})$.

Incidentally, teachers should make sure that children understand that the equal parts into which the whole thing (unit) has been divided are not necessarily alike except as to value. Some children (and adults?) have the erroneous idea that halves or fourths or thirds of a given thing must all be the same shape. A teacher will do well to explore this idea with children, purposely pre-

senting differently shaped equal parts of a rectanglar sheet of paper or other easily manageable unit and then asking the pupils whether or not the parts are equal. (Are these real fourths?) Then the children themselves may be challenged to cut or tear a sheet of paper into fourths, for example, in as many *different* ways as possible. Figure 94 indicates some of the obvious possibilities. Alternatives *A*, *B*, and *C* are fairly obvious; *D* can be demonstrated by some matching of "parts of parts." *E* is most difficult, but may challenge some superior students.

The idea that fractions indicate division is nowhere more apparent than in so-called "uneven division." In Form A at the right, the division is only partly completed. All of 13 has not been divided. It has been separated into 12, which has been completely divided as shown by the 3 in the quotient, and a remainder of 1, which is at this point undivided. See pages 266-270 for detailed discussion.

Form A

$$
\begin{array}{r}
3 \\
4\overline{)13} \\
12 \\
\hline
1
\end{array}
$$

When thinking of a fraction as expressing "one or more of the equal parts of a group of units," we have a clear analogy to the concept of partition division (see p. 242 of chap. 11). As a dozen eggs is divided to make equal parts, we know the total number of eggs (12) and the number of equal parts into which that total is to be divided, let us say 3 such parts. We seek to know how many eggs are in each equal part. This is partition division, readily expressible in fractional form either as "$\frac{1}{3}$ of 12" or as "$\frac{12}{3}$." Dividing 12 by 3 is in this situation the same as taking $\frac{1}{3}$ of 12. The process may be recorded in any of these ways:

12 eggs $\div$ 3 = 4 eggs

$\frac{1}{3}$ of 12 eggs = 4

$$
\begin{array}{r}
4 \text{ eggs} \\
3\overline{)12 \text{ eggs}}
\end{array}
$$

$$\frac{12 \text{ eggs}}{3} = 4 \text{ eggs}$$

---

[1] The writer has not found any historical basis for suggesting this origin of the fraction form. It is presented merely as an interesting speculation for children.

Some controversy exists as to whether or not the "⅓ of 12" terminology and algorism should be introduced along with or shortly after the first use of partition division with the basic division facts. Since that manner of speaking of partition situations is so prevalent

quotient is "4," which in this particular solution may be interpreted to mean that one can purchase 4 yards of cloth. The idea is a 3-to-1 ratio. The number "12" has the same ratio to the number of yards to be purchased as "3" has to "1": $3 to buy 1 yard, $12 to buy ? yards.

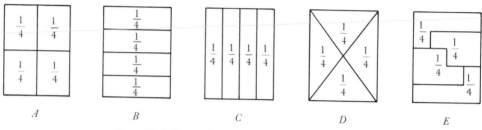

Figure 94. Different Shapes for a Single Fractional Part.

in everyday affairs, it would seem only natural to call children's attention to the "different right ways" to speak of and to record the division. On the other hand, some teachers object, saying, "When you say '⅓ of 12,' you are teaching multiplication of fractions and that comes much later." Properly handled, the introduction of this terminology at an earlier date should, rather, lay foundations for later understanding of the concepts involved in multiplication of fractions. In any event, this does show that the finding of equal parts of a group of units is basically a division process.

Since the third interpretation of fractions discussed above was merely a variation of the two earlier ones, it will not be discussed further as a form of division. The fourth interpretation, that "a fraction expresses a ratio," is clearly a division idea, though somewhat different from the ones discussed immediately above.

Ratio is a *relative comparison* of numbers. If $3 will buy 1 yard of cloth, how many yards can be bought for $12? If children are still doing all their computations with whole numbers, they think of this situation as $12 ÷ $3. The

The solution may be correctly written in any of these ways:

$$\$12 \div \$3 = 4 \qquad \frac{\$12}{\$3} = 4 \qquad \$3\overline{\smash{\big)}\$12}^{\,4}$$

The dollar signs may be omitted in any of the algorisms. They are retained to emphasize the measurement division concept.

Notice that this case is *not* analogous to the "⅓ of 12" idea that was applied earlier in a problem arising in a partition situation. This is a *measurement division* situation. The total amount of money (dividend) is known, as is the cost of 1 yard (in this case, the divisor). These two measured amounts (measured in dollars) are *compared* to show relation of the total amount available to the cost for a single yard of cloth. This relation (ratio) is 12 ÷ 3, or $\frac{12}{3}$. By performing the indicated division, the answer "4" is obtained.

The teacher who seeks to teach the meaning of fractions as expressing the concept of ratio should take heed and use measurement-type division situations for introducing the idea and for practicing it. While the mathematics of the partition and the measurement interpretations of division (and fraction) situations is the same for either, in the development of understanding of the use of the ideas in everyday affairs these distinctions should be recognized. The distinctions can be dropped when the learners no longer need them as aids to the understanding and use of mathematical concepts in problem solving.

In suggesting that fractions express division there is an implication that fractions express an operation. The question then is: Do they always express operation?

FRACTIONS SOMETIMES EXPRESS

AN OPERATION AND SOMETIMES

EXPRESS THE RESULT

OF AN OPERATION

Spencer and Brydegaard have suggested that sometimes fractions act as *verbs* and sometimes as *nouns.*[2] As numbers, fractions could hardly be considered as operators; as symbols, they may symbolize either actions or entities, hence, verbs or nouns.

Division is a mathematical operation, the inverse of the multiplication operation. If fractions express division, they express an operation. We use them to indicate operations to be performed on numbers. The expression "$\frac{1}{3}$ of" denotes the process of partitioning, whether it be the partitioning of a unit into three equal parts or the partitioning of a group of 15 things into three equal subgroups. An operation is as clearly suggested by "$\frac{1}{3}$ of" as by the expression "$\div 3$." Teachers need to be conscious of this, whether they teach it directly or not; their guidance of children's learning of fraction meanings is bound to be affected by recognition of this relationship.

[2] Peter Lincoln Spencer and Marguerite Brydegaard, *Building Mathematical Concepts in the Elementary School.* New York: Holt, 1952, p. 214.

Relative comparison of numbers is accomplished by division; since fractions are used to indicate such division, again they indicate an operation. If we know that a picture is 24 inches wide and 36 inches long, we derive a ratio (comparison) of length to width by operating on the numbers 36 and 24. In fractional notation "$\frac{36}{24}$" indicates "36 to be divided by 24." In simpler terms, it indicates "$\frac{3}{2}$" or "3 to be divided by 2." Usually the division would be expressed as yielding the result $1\frac{1}{2}$; that is, the length is $1\frac{1}{2}$ times the width. The fraction "$\frac{3}{2}$" might, of course, also be left in that form to express merely a "3-to-2" ratio of length to width.

Once the operation has been performed (or indicated as performable), the resulting fraction is often used as an entity, as a "thing" to be handled as one handles whole objects or units of measure—that is, as a "noun."

After pie has been divided to make 6 equal pieces in each whole, those "sixths" are handled as if they were whole things, whether the fraction is "$\frac{1}{6}$", "$\frac{5}{6}$," or "$\frac{7}{6}$." After the group of athletes have been divided to make 2 or 3 or 4 equal squads, halves or thirds or fourths of the total group may be thought of as entities, using fraction "names" as more precise descriptions of the "squads." One of the squads (one-third of the total group) may be sent out to practice on the field, while two squads (two-thirds of the total group) stay in the field house.

Perhaps the most frequent use of fractions for most people is in connection with measures of one kind or another. The foot has to be *divided* to get halves, fourths, eighths, and sixteenths; but once those divisions have been made, the fractions $\frac{1}{2}$, $\frac{1}{4}$, $\frac{1}{8}$, and $\frac{1}{16}$ become "names" of smaller measuring units. One-fourth of an inch is part of 1 whole inch, but it is a measuring unit in its own right. A measuring cup is certainly less useful for most purposes without the fractional markings and notations on it. The cup has been divided into equal units, usually halves, thirds, and fourths. Once the division has been made, those fractional parts are dealt with not only as parts of a whole cup but as smaller whole measuring units with their appropriate names.

This point cannot be overemphasized since the meaningful teaching of computations with fractions hinges on recognition by the teacher that sometimes the computational actions depend on the idea of fractions as *names for entities* and sometimes on the idea of fractions as indicating an *operation* (division). In the addition and subtraction of fractions, the fractions are used as entities, as units and multiples of units. In some cases of multiplication and some cases of division, the fractions are used as entities and sometimes as operators. A clear example is the dependence of the so-called "common-denominator method" of division by a fraction on the idea of fractions as units and multiples of units, whereas the "invert and multiply method" of division by a fraction relies on operational notions of fractions. The end results are the same. The two methods can be equated mathematically, but in introducing the procedures so they make sense to immature learners, an orientation to actual situations is essential. In those actual situations, the distinction does apply.[3]

FRACTIONS ARE NUMERALS FOR RATIONAL NUMBERS

Though this concept may be too advanced for typical elementary school

children, teachers should be familiar with at least the terminology. The meaning of rational numbers will be introduced as part of the expansion of our number system.[4]

From Natural to Rational Numbers

Preceding the present chapter, this book has been almost entirely devoted to whole numbers and operations with whole numbers. The whole numbers (natural numbers and zero) are sufficient for many of man's affairs, but by no means for all his needs for number. The counting numbers are called "natural" for obvious reasons. The new kind of number that was needed was, by contrast, somewhat "artificial," that is, more truly man-made.

NEED FOR NUMBERS TO EXPRESS PARTS

Man discovered a long time ago that he needed fractions. The wholes with which he dealt became broken into parts, or he divided them into parts. He had to deal with these entities that were at once parts of other wholes and wholes in themselves. The origin of the word "fraction" indicates the "broken-part" idea, coming as it does from the Latin *frangere,* "to break." At first the parts were not required to be equal, but later the concept of equality of the parts to one another was recognized, and one characteristic of our modern concept of fractions was established.

EGYPTIAN FRACTIONS

The fraction symbols of the Egyptians used the regular counting number

---

[3] The distinction will be developed with examples in the discussion of addition and subtraction of fractions (chap. 15) and multiplication and division of fractions (chaps. 15 and 16).

[4] At the secondary school level, no discussion of the meanings of fractions would be complete without reference to fractions as *ordered pairs* of integers. Since this development does not appear in most current elementary school arithmetic texts, it is omitted from this chapter.

symbols, but with a fraction-indicating symbol immediately above the number. This mark was ⬤. This notation scheme worked out fairly well for the Egyptians, since they used only unit fractions, except for two-thirds, which had its own special symbol. They did not need anything to indicate a numerator because it was always *one*. "Half" had its own symbol, which was [, and "two-thirds" was shown as ⬧. Since three tally marks in the Egyptian notation scheme meant three, those same three tally marks with the fraction symbol above them meant one-third, thus: ⬧. The counting number twelve was shown by a ten-symbol and two tally marks, thus: ⋔⋔; so the fraction one-twelfth was shown thus: ⬧.

This was a very efficient way of showing the denomination of each fractional part, but the limitation to unit fractions created some very awkward situations. Nonunit fractions such as five-sixths, which we show so easily as $\frac{5}{6}$, had to be shown as the sum of one-half and one-third. This does not seem too bad, but the difficulty is more striking when a fraction like $\frac{2}{43}$ is shown as the Egyptian numeral equivalent of our $\frac{1}{42}+\frac{1}{86}+\frac{1}{129}+\frac{1}{301}$.[5]

The Egyptians' scheme for handling fractions seems awkward to us, but it did fit into their additive system with its dependence on multiplication and division by doubling and summing.

Mueller has pointed out that we use a similar scheme of dependence on unit fractions in making change with our modern money denominations.[6]

[5] This is one of the examples that appears in the classic Egyptian source the *Rhind Papyrus* (c. 1650 B.C.), which includes a table for expressing all fractions of the form $\frac{2}{n}$ for all odd n from 5 to 101. Only one decomposition was given for each fraction. One might well wonder—as many people have—why $\frac{2}{43}$ was not expressed as $\frac{1}{43}+\frac{1}{43}$.

[6] Francis J. Mueller, *Arithmetic: Its Structure and Concepts.* Englewood Cliffs, N. J.: *Prentice-Hall,* 1956, p. 152.

Most of us like to receive as few coins as possible in receiving change; a cashier usually tries to oblige. In making change for "9¢ out of dollar," he may give you 1 half-dollar, 1 quarter, 1 dime, 1 nickel, and 1 penny. That is, you would receive $\frac{1}{2}+\frac{1}{4}+\frac{1}{10}+\frac{1}{20}+\frac{1}{100}$ (all parts of 1 dollar) instead of the "neater" $\frac{91}{100}$. We say we get "91¢" in change, but it is doled out to us in unit fraction form.

Children's books sometimes have exercises in which they are asked to tell how to make the same sum of money with the fewest possible coins or with other special stipulations. These could be modified to fit with the idea of Egyptian fractions as suggested above as a special activity for those who are interested in the history of numeration.

In summary, the Egyptian system provided for the expression of any size part but was restricted to showing one of each of those parts.

BABYLONIAN, GREEK, AND ROMAN FRACTIONS

Since the Babylonians used a base of sixty for their whole numbers, it is not surprising that they should use sixtieths and sixty-times-sixtieths as fractions. They extended their place-value system to represent sexagesimal fractions much as we do in expressing decimal fractions by place-value notation. Our continued use of sixtieths and of three-hundred-sixtieths in telling time and in parts of a circle goes back to these early Babylonian fractions.

Greek astronomers who extended the ideas of the Babylonians continued to use their fractions. Finally, through the translation of Greek works into Arabic and of Arabic works into Latin, these fractions received names that are very close to our everyday usage. The sixtieths of the Babylonians became the *pars minuta prima* (first small parts), which we call *minutes*. The sixtieths-of-sixtieths of the Babylonians became the *pars minuta secunda* (second small parts), which we call *seconds*.

The key idea here, in contrast to the idea of the Egyptians, was the restriction of certain sizes of fractional parts (sixtieths and powers thereof) rather than restriction of the number of parts (one of each part) placed by the Egyptians on their fraction system.

The Romans carried further this standardization of the size of the parts, but the astronomers' sixtieths and sixtieths-of-sixtieths were smaller and more precise measures of parts than were needed for everyday commerce and practical affairs. The Romans set up their own "submultiples," called *uncials*. An uncial was one-twelfth of the whole. This was a very practical choice since twelve is evenly divisible by two, three, four, and six. Our words "inch" (one-twelfth of a foot) and "ounce" (then a twelfth of a pound) come from the name of the Roman uncial. The uncials are referred to as "submultiples" because they were used as smaller units and handled as if they were units, just as we still do with inches, ounces, pennies, or other subunits of common measures.

In a sense, our modern use of percentages is similar to the Roman use of uncials. To the extent that we transfer other fraction forms into the "hundredths" of the per cent terminology, we are making the hundredth a standard fraction size.

The Roman notation for uncials was a system of combining a straight horizontal line, which meant 1 uncial, with an s-shaped symbol, which meant 6 uncials (from the Latin word for half, *semis*).

Actually, the Romans were avoiding fractions as we think of them today, just as we avoid computing with fractions now by using "3 cups" instead of "$\frac{3}{4}$ quart" or "4 tablespoons" instead of "$\frac{4}{16}$ cups," or "$\frac{1}{4}$ cup."

HINDU-ARABIC FRACTION NOTATION

The Egyptian fractions were flexible as to size of part but rigid because of being limited to "one of each." The Roman fractions were flexible as to specifying the number of parts being used but rigid as to size of parts. Finally, the Hindu-Arabic fraction system reached Europe and displaced the less efficient systems. The Hindus invented the system, which came to us through the Arabs. It allowed for keeping units and subunits as before but set up a scheme so the parts could be dealt with as parts and as subunits simultaneously.

They allowed for infinite variation both in the size of the parts and in the number of parts. By placing the digits in a vertical positional relation to each other, they made it possible to use any natural number as the number of parts and any natural number for the size of the part (by telling the number of equal parts in one whole). The top number was assigned the meaning "number of parts"; the bottom number was assigned the meaning "size of part." The Arabs are said to have added the horizontal line to separate the two numerals in the fraction. While its use is standard today, there have been fluctuations in this usage, chiefly because of difficulties in printing when the art was not fully developed.

Sometimes a question arises about whether or not children should be allowed to write fractions with the dividing line slanted, thus: 3/4. This form was common until printing improvements standardized horizontal line form. However, it is interesting to notice that the use of the typewriter (with only "$\frac{1}{2}$" and "$\frac{1}{4}$" usually available on a single key) has again encouraged the use of the slanted form. In handwritten usage in elementary schools, the horizontal form has definite advantages and should be in general use.

FURTHER NEED FOR A NEW KIND
OF NUMBER

We have reviewed some of the history of man's development of fractions to express ideas of parts of units. He learned to apply these fraction-numerals to parts of whole things and to parts of groups of things, but he still needed fraction-numerals for another reason.

In our whole-number system as we use it today, addition is always possible and multiplication is always possible. We say the number system is "closed" with respect to these two operations, meaning that when any whole number is added to (or multiplied by) any other whole number, the sum (or product) is another whole number. This closure, however, does not apply to the inverse operations, subtraction and division. It is, for example, impossible to subtract 9 from 4 and stay within the whole-number system. Therefore, negative numbers and the concept of positive and negative integers were developed.[7]

A new number was clearly needed to make division always possible. Some whole numbers are divisible by other whole numbers; e.g., 12 is divisible by 2 or 3 or 4 or 6. It is not divisible by 5 or 9 or 7. The study of factors and multiples in chapter 13 emphasized the patterns by which natural numbers are "made up of" other natural numbers but also indicated that for any whole

---

[7] These ideas are not developed in this text because they are not used to any appreciable extent in the elementary school.

number there are a limited number of factors of which it can be "made."

Division is defined as the inverse of multiplication: $3 \times 4 = 12$; so $12 \div 4 = 3$; $2 \times 3 = 6$; so $6 \div 3 = 2$. Division undoes multiplication. In more general terms, if $4 \times n = 24$, then $24 \div n = 4$.

We have also said that one meaning of fractions is that they express division. The fraction $\frac{2}{3}$ means $2 \div 3$; the fraction $\frac{12}{6} = 12 \div 6$. Now $12 \div 6$ can be divided to get a whole-number quotient, 2. But 2 cannot be divided by 3 to get a whole-number quotient. We need fractions to express quotients that cannot be expressed by whole numbers! In the case of $\frac{2}{3}$, it does mean $2 \div 3$, but the very statement of the fraction as $\frac{2}{3}$ has already given the answer, the fraction itself.

Much more sophisticated development of this idea would be required by mathematicians, but children are satisfied to see this idea of fractions in simple situations. Two such will be given.

First, let us suppose that 3 mothers have brought pies to school for a special entertainment. Each mother brought several pies; each mother brought the same number (the exact number brought does not matter). When the "cleaning up" is completed, 2 whole pies remain. All the rest of the pie has been used up. One of the women says, "Let's divide the two pies equally since we each brought the same amount. It will be good to have some ready-made dessert to take home for the family's supper."

This is a sample situation in which division is not closed for whole numbers. Two cannot be divided by 3 to get a whole number answer. Two pies *to be divided* equally among 3 women! Perhaps one of the women says, "That's too complicated. Why don't you two each take one pie and I won't take any. I never was good at arithmetic."

She has given up too easily. The very statement of the problem is its solution. The number 2 (pies) to be divided by the number 3; $2 \div 3$; $\frac{2}{3}$! Two $\div$ three $=$ two-thirds.

Two-thirds is an example of a *rational number,* an indicated division, the expression of a ratio. This idea gives rise to the idea of the system of *rational numbers,* not a matter for concern in the elementary school; but elementary school teachers should know that the fractions express rational numbers.

Another helpful setting for the development of this idea is the use of the number-line. This type of problem may be set up: A board fence needs to be painted. Three boys agree to take the job, each boy to paint an equal length of the fence. The fence is 11 yards long. How long a piece of the fence should each boy paint?

The solution may be shown on a rigid number line drawn on the chalkboard or on paper, but the use of a flexible line would be better. Figure 95 indicates

be, with reference to the figure: Where are the two thirds (of the $3\frac{2}{3}$)? In this particular illustration, the $\frac{2}{3}$ is shown for the first section as $\frac{2}{3}$ of the fourth yard; for the second section, as $\frac{1}{3}$ of the fourth yard and the first $\frac{1}{3}$ of the eighth yard; and for the third section as the latter $\frac{2}{3}$ of the eighth yard.

The complete quotient may be expressed as $\frac{11}{3}$ ($11 \div 3$) or, in more conventional form, as the whole number 3 plus the fraction $\frac{2}{3}$.

Accepting rational numbers such as the quotients in the preceding illustrations as belonging to an expanded number system, the operation of division *is* possible when any whole number is divided by any natural number.[8] The quotient may turn out to be a whole number, a fraction, or a combination of a whole number and a fraction.

Any whole number may, of course, be expressed in the form of a fraction. Whole numbers are included in the realm of rational numbers. Four may be expressed in whole-number form as "4" or in fraction (rational number) form as "$\frac{4}{1}$" or as "$\frac{8}{2}$," since all these ex-

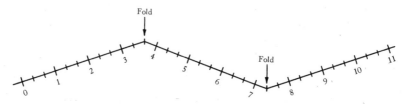

Figure 95. Partition Division with a Fraction in the Quotient.

the dividing of 11 (yards) by 3. The first time such a demonstration is attempted, the teacher might use a paper strip marked into units and also into thirds of units; so the quotient ($3\frac{2}{3}$ yards) is readily seen as soon as the dividing is done. Later, part of the work to be done by the learners is the "figuring out" of the fractional part that is shown. A good question to ask the children would

pressions (and many more) have the same value.

Without fractions, there would be no way to specify numbers for each of the points of division in the line in figure 95, because the whole-number system sup-

[8] Since zero is not acceptable as a divisor (see pp. 252-53), the divisors must be limited to natural numbers. Zero is permissible in the position of dividend.

plies no numbers to coincide with those "in-between" points. The rational number system supplies numbers that fill this need.[9]

Numerators and Denominators

Perhaps the introduction of a discussion of numerators and denominators of fractions has been too long delayed. At any rate, to wait so long is surely to avoid the common teaching error of placing much reliance on defining the numerator and the denominator and then assuming that fractions are understood.

The names of the terms of a fraction arise from their early meanings in the framework of the idea that a fraction may express one or more of the equal parts of a whole thing. The numeral written above the horizontal bar was called the *numer*ator because it was the *number*er; it told *how many* parts were being considered. The numeral below the horizontal bar was called the *denomin*ator because it was the *namer* of the fractional part. It told into how many equal parts a whole had been divided and so indicated size of the part.

Definitions can be most misleading, especially with literal-minded children. This has been particularly true for definitions of the denominator of a fraction. Take the fraction $\frac{3}{4}$. The "old reliable" definition was: The denominator is the number of parts into which the whole has been divided. This may not be so reliable; it may be true if you have just cut a pie into fourths and are considering 3 of those 4 equal pieces. Sometimes it is not a true definition.

[9] Further discussion of the use of rational numbers in demonstrating that for every multiplication there is a corresponding division inverse will be delayed until the idea of reciprocals has been introduced (p. 379).

The division may not have been completed; maybe it is just indicated. At an adult level, there is the legal terminology "an undivided $\frac{3}{4}$ interest in the property." But the teacher says, "Let them learn it this way for now. They can learn the exceptions later." This is not a safe procedure.

Some authorities suggest that children should be taught to think of the denominator as the *size* of the fractional part. This suggestion has some merit if children also clearly understand that the larger the denominator (that is, the more parts there are), the smaller will be the part. If this definition is used, one other limitation must be placed on it. The denominator does indicate the *size relative to that particular whole* of which it is a part. The teacher does well to make sure that children do not fall into the trap of thinking that every $\frac{1}{3}$ equals every other $\frac{1}{3}$ or that every $\frac{3}{4}$ is the same size as every other $\frac{3}{4}$. This can be easily shown with sheets of paper of different sizes, with flannel "pies" of different sizes, or even with the same fractional names of different-sized total groups.

The safest beginning definition of the denominator may well be the simplest one, the *name* or *namer* of the fraction. This is true for all situations in which the fraction does refer to parts of wholes or groups; it is very useful later in using the measurement concept for some phases of computation with fractions. This is not a full meaning; children should be taught that this is one simple meaning to which others will be added.

The last sentence is really the clue to proper instruction concerning these two terms, numerator and denominator. As with other concepts, the teacher must continually build on old foundations while laying new foundations for later expansion and addition of concepts. No matter what terminology a teacher uses in introducing children to the terms, she should not define them in *finished* and *restricting* statements that may interfere with later learning.

When children get to the point that they learn that a fraction expresses a division, they are ready for a clear expansion of their meanings for numerator and denominator. Now the numerator becomes the dividend, and the denominator becomes the divisor. Anything that they have correctly learned about dividends and divisors will now apply to numerators and denominators of fractions.

$$\frac{\text{Numerator}}{\text{Denominator}} = \frac{\text{dividend}}{\text{divisor}}$$

$$\text{(divisor) } 3\overline{\smash{\big)}6} \text{ (dividend)}^{\!\!2\ \text{(quotient)}} \qquad \frac{6 \text{ (dividend)}}{3 \text{ (divisor)}} = 2 \text{ (quotient)}$$

In the examples shown here, a whole-number quotient is available to simplify the situation. How would the quotient be shown in a division-indicating fraction such as $\frac{5}{6}$? The "5" is the numerator, hence the dividend. The "6" is the denominator, hence the divisor. The fraction "$\frac{5}{6}$" is the quotient. Remember, a fraction, when it expresses a division, is the quotient of two numbers—in this case, 5 and 6.

When a fraction has a ratio meaning, the significance of the numerator and denominator is important with special reference to which comes first, which last. This is another way of saying that with ratio situations, either number may be the numerator or the denominator; but once that position has been given, the interpretation and use of the fraction from then on *must* respect the relative position of the numbers. If there are 5 girls for every 6 boys in a class, we may use the fraction $\frac{5}{6}$ and interpret it to mean that $\frac{5}{6}$ tells how many

girls in relation to how many boys; we may not keep that fraction written that way and say it tells how many boys in relation to how many girls.[10]

Forms of Fractions

The basic meanings of fractions, emphasized to this point, occur even though the forms of the fractions vary widely. Certain less important features of fractions have sometimes been emphasized more than the meanings; one such feature is the classification of fractions according to certain standard forms. These should not be ignored, but the similarities among all fraction forms should be emphasized even while the distinctions are being taught.

UNIT VS. NONUNIT FRACTIONS

Unit fractions have already been mentioned in connection with Egyptian fractions. Any fraction that has a numerator of 1 is a unit fraction. These are all unit fractions: $\frac{1}{1}, \frac{1}{2}, \frac{1}{5}, \frac{1}{10}, \frac{1}{63}, \frac{1}{100}$.

Nonunit fractions must, of course, be fractions with numerators other than one. They may have any of the fraction meanings already discussed. These are examples of nonunit fractions: $\frac{2}{3}, \frac{4}{5}, \frac{8}{8}, \frac{16}{10}, \frac{67}{120}$.

PROPER VS. IMPROPER FRACTIONS

As long as fractions were thought of only or primarily as the broken parts of whole things, it was reasonable to think of those which expressed less than one whole thing as being "proper" and those which expressed more than that as "improper." As fraction meanings expanded, the latter group of fractions

[10]This point has already been discussed earlier (pp. 306-08), but it is so often misunderstood that repetition of the caution may be needed.

were seen as no less "proper" than the former; but the terminology has persisted.

Examples of proper fractions are: $\frac{1}{3}$, $\frac{4}{5}$, $\frac{6}{9}$, $\frac{10}{15}$, $\frac{36}{72}$. Examples of improper fractions are: $\frac{2}{1}$, $\frac{5}{4}$, $\frac{8}{6}$, $\frac{10}{7}$, $\frac{120}{100}$.

MIXED NUMBERS

In elementary school arithmetic, improper fractions are usually changed to mixed-number form when they appear as answers to problems. A mixed number is the sum of a whole number and a proper fraction.[11] The improper fraction $\frac{9}{2}$ may be changed to its equivalent value and be shown as the whole number 4 + the proper fraction $\frac{1}{2}$, or $4\frac{1}{2}$. The logic is simple. If 2 halves equal 1, then 8 halves equal 4 ($\frac{2}{2}=1$; so $\frac{8}{2}$ must equal 4). One half remains, so the final result is $4+\frac{1}{2}$, or $4\frac{1}{2}$.

WHOLE NUMBERS AS FRACTIONS

Those improper fractions which have equal numerators and denominators all equal the whole number 1. For example, $\frac{2}{2}$, $\frac{4}{4}$, $\frac{6}{6}$, and $\frac{18}{18}$ all equal 1. Those improper fractions which have numerators that are multiples of their denominators are equal to whole numbers; for example, $\frac{4}{1}$, $\frac{6}{2}$, $\frac{15}{5}$, $\frac{24}{4}$, and $\frac{100}{25}$ are equal respectively to: 4, 3, 3, 6, and 4. Any rational number may be shown in fraction form. These particular ratios are of a special kind, but still ratios. These fractions express division just as truly as do proper fractions. A number divided by itself equals 1. A number divided by one of its factors equals some whole number.

In figure 96 a number line is shown with various forms of fractions plotted

[11] A mixed number is a sum in the same sense that the whole number 125 is the sum of 1 hundred, 2 tens, and 5 ones ($100+20+5$).

on it. Notice particularly the different forms in relation to one another.

Look at the whole-number designations just below the line. Then look at the "halves" designations above and the "fourths" designations below the whole numbers. The same points on the line are shown by 1, $\frac{2}{2}$, and $\frac{4}{4}$; by 2, $\frac{4}{2}$, and $\frac{8}{4}$; and by 3, $\frac{6}{2}$, and $\frac{12}{4}$. Of course the whole numbers might also have been written as $\frac{1}{1}$, $\frac{2}{1}$, and $\frac{3}{1}$.

Notice the point at which the proper fractions give way to improper fractions —at $\frac{2}{2}$ or $\frac{4}{4}$ or 1. Clearly, any fraction between 0 and 1 on the number line is a proper fraction.

Where are the mixed numbers? Clearly, to the right of 1 on the number line. Children can be encouraged through an informal discussion of the number line to "define" proper fractions, improper fractions, and mixed numbers in terms of relations to the whole numbers, with which they are already familiar. The meanings of both fractions and whole numbers will be enhanced.

An interesting consideration that might be developed with superior learners is the idea of *density* of fractions on the number line. For example, the question might be asked as to how close a proper fraction might come on the left side of 1 or how many fractions might be inserted on the line between 1 and 2 (or any other two points). The answer is an infinite number, leading to the descriptive term *dense*.

LIKE FRACTIONS VS. UNLIKE FRACTIONS

When two or more fractions have the same denominator, they are called *like fractions*. We might say they have the *same name*. Later, we say they have *common denominators*, which is just another term for *same name.* Unlike fractions have different denominators.

Basically, like fractions are those which are stated in the same subunits. One-half and one-fourth are unlike fractions; in that form they cannot be added; but one-half can be changed in form to its equivalent, two-fourths. One-

fractions. Decimal fractions are treated in chapters 17 and 18. Actually, everything that has been said about the meanings of common fractions in this chapter applies as well to the meanings of decimal fractions. The differences that exist relate to form, not meaning.

Common fractions are written as two

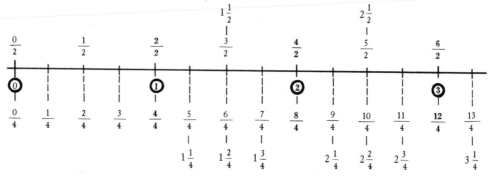

Figure 96. Whole Numbers as Fractions on the Number Line.

fourth and two-fourths are said to be *like fractions* because they are expressed in terms of the same fractional part, the same unit of measure, the same subunit. Any two common fractions *can be expressed* in like subunits. The process by which they are so changed will be developed in the next section.

Understanding of the meaning of *likeness* in describing fractions is extremely important. Much of what children need to learn about computation with fractions depends on understanding what is meant by like fractions.[12]

COMMON VS. DECIMAL FRACTIONS

In keeping with the usual practice of distinguishing between common and decimal fractions and teaching them separately, the discussion in chapters 14 through 16 centers around common

[12] Likeness actually means "likeness with respect to some specified condition." Just as the number of a set of boys and the number of a set of girls may be added when we want to consider each as a set of children, so unlike fractions can be added if they can correctly be changed to meet a similar specification such as having the same size, same unit of measure, or same "name."

numbers in vertical position with respect to each other, separated by a horizontal bar. They were used by "the common people" and acquired the designation "common" in contrast to the astronomers' sexagesimal fractions.

Decimal fractions *may be* common fractions. The form "$\frac{1}{10}$" and the form ".1" are both decimal fractions, as are "$\frac{2}{100}$" and ".02" or "$\frac{35}{1000}$" and ".035." All refer to fractions based on ten. If any of the numerals in this paragraph were to be read aloud, the hearer could not tell which of the forms was intended by the reader. Each listed pair is a pair of written forms for the *same* fraction.

In everyday usage, however, the term "decimal fractions" is usually applied to the forms in which the denominator (the name) of the fraction is indicated by place-value position, not by a numeral written under a horizontal bar. The numerators are written the same way for common and decimal fractions except when zeros must be included to establish proper place values.

EQUIVALENT FRACTIONS

Changing Fractions to Other Terms

Equivalent fractions are fractions that have the same numerical value. Just as the whole-number values may be shown in many forms, so also with fractions. Some examples of expressions of the whole number 4 are $2+2$, $1+3$, $8 \div 2$, 2×2, $7-3$, and $\frac{8}{2}$. These expressions are equal in value though different in form.

All these fractions are equivalent: $\frac{1}{2}$, $\frac{2}{4}$, $\frac{3}{6}$, $\frac{5}{10}$, $\frac{25}{50}$, $\frac{256}{512}$. They all belong to a "family" or set of fractions having the same value.

Another way of defining equivalent fractions is to say that fractions are equivalent if they express the same ratio. Each of them represents the same rational number. Typically, if we were to name the family of fractions, we would designate it by the form that uses the smallest numerals, but this is not a requirement. The fractions listed in the paragraph above could then be designated as "the set of fractions that are equivalent to $\frac{1}{2}$."

Any two fractions that belong to the set of fractions for the same rational number meet this test: the numerator of each fraction times the denominator of the other yields the same product. For example, $\frac{3}{4}=\frac{6}{8}$ because $3 \times 8 = 4 \times 6$. This property of equivalent fractions is very useful in testing equivalence and in other ways. (It is, of course, parallel to the familiar statement about the equality of the products of the means and the product of the extremes in a proportion.)

When the manner of expressing a fraction is changed without changing its value, we say we change it to other terms. That is, the numerator and denominator (the terms of the fraction) are changed, but the value of the complete expression remains the same.

Children should be provided with many experiences in which they can compare fraction values and build up assurance in recognizing the equivalent fractions that are most common in their everyday affairs. These experiences should begin in the first grade and continue through the point of introducing the more efficient mathematical operations by which one fraction is changed to another with the same value. No doubt, thousands upon thousands of children would have less trouble computing with fractions if they had been helped to understand and derive equivalent fractions before getting involved with the details of adding, subtracting, multiplying, and dividing fractions. To omit this preparation is most wasteful in terms of pupils' and teachers' time, energy, and mental health.

EXPERIENCES WITH EQUIVALENCE
OF FRACTIONAL PARTS

The easiest demonstration of equivalence is with concrete objects or representations of objects that have been divided into parts. Even before the child comes to school he may have been asked by his mother to get one-half pound of butter from the refrigerator. If he has trouble with the idea, she will probably tell him to bring two sticks or two quarters. He does not hear anything or see anything about numerators and denominators, but he is beginning to experience equivalence of different ways of talking about the same fractional part of a pound of butter. Then there are, of course, the ubiquitous pies at home and in early elementary school arithmetic. If they are real, it will be a matter of real concern that one-half of the whole pie will make three-sixths; if not, one of three pie lovers may be left without his share.

A group of fourth graders had been asked to measure their arithmetic books as accurately as possible preliminary to cutting paper covers to protect them. The children did not all have the same kinds of rulers. Though she had not planned this development in advance, the teacher made good use of it when children came up with different (but equal) answers as to the length and width of the book covers. Each of these reports was given for the cover's length by one or more pupils: $7\frac{3}{4}$ inches, $7\frac{6}{8}$ inches, and $7\frac{12}{16}$ inches, plus some less exact reports that had to be discarded. The teacher had the different reported lengths of the book cover written on the chalkboard as a basis for discussion. Some children quickly recognized that all the measurements were equal; some "had to be shown." Finally, all were convinced. (Incidentally, the teacher also used this experience as the basis for pointing out the greater precision of the measurements with the smaller fractional units.)

Many manipulative materials that are readily available feature equivalence of fractional parts. Among these, some of the most useful are interlocking paper circles, circles and rectangles of flannel for the flannel board, fractional parts with magnets attached for use on a steel board, fraction boards, and fraction number lines.

The interlocking paper circles are very helpful for use with children who are soon to receive instruction in addition and subtraction of fractions. The circles may be cut by the pupils, but precut circles are available from school supply houses. Devices for accurately marking the circles into various fractional parts are also available. The pupils should do the marking into equal parts if possible, as this in itself is a good learning experience. Carelessness will result in unequal parts, which will not "work out" and thus dramatize the need for accuracy. Figure 97 shows how some of the circles might be marked. Preferably, each circle should be a different color. Each circle should be cut along only one of the demarcation lines (radii of the circle). By interlocking any two circles along these slits, the circles can be revolved and thirds matched against sixths, halves matched against sixths or fourths, and so on. The first activities may be purely exploratory, with children trying to see how many "matches" they can make and writing the equivalent fractions they can demonstrate with the circles. Beginning with two interlocked circles, they may go on to interlock three and more as they develop facility.

The flannel and magnetic parts are useful for demonstrations for a group of children, with various fractions being shown and compared as to equivalence. Again, tables of equivalent fractions can be built. The children who are most proficient will make longer tables and will explore more difficult comparisons, which is as it should be.

The fraction board, in one form or another, is excellent for exploring equivalent fractions. In figure 98, for example, even a young child can follow the indication of the "string" that is stretched vertically across the board to show that $\frac{1}{2}=\frac{2}{4}=\frac{3}{6}=\frac{6}{12}$.

EXPERIENCES WITH
EQUIVALENT RATIOS

More mature pupils may be able to handle explorations into the equivalence of ratios while some of the less mature arithmetic pupils are still becoming acquainted with the equivalent fractional parts of objects or diagrams.

A teacher presented this problem to some of her "faster" arithmetic learners. She said, "It has rained on 2 of the last 3 days. If we have rain $\frac{2}{3}$ of the days during the rest of the month, I wonder if you can tell me how many days will be rainy for each number of days I have written in the last column." Then she put up the chart shown in figure 99, with directions for the children to work cooperatively in filling in the blank

situation, the children may discover it for themselves. Whether or not this activity leads to that next very important step depends on the circumstances, of which the teacher is the best judge.

MEANING OF CHANGING

OR REDUCTION OF FRACTIONS

For a long time (perhaps too long a time) the changing of fractions to equivalent fractions with other terms has been called "reducing" or "reduction."

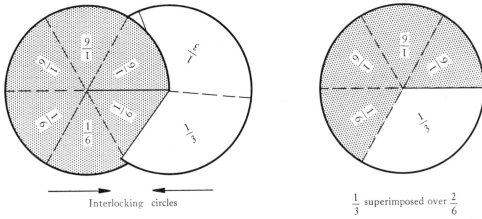

Interlocking circles

$\frac{1}{3}$ superimposed over $\frac{2}{6}$

Figure 97. Interlocking Fraction Circles.

spaces in the chart. When the chart was finished, the teacher asked which fractions on the chart were equal. The discussion brought out the equivalence of all these fractions.

Figures 100 and 101 show different work sheet solutions of the chart problem, the former using a sheet from a calendar and the other using a cumulative totals procedure. Notice that once the "solver" got the sequential idea in mind, he went through the sequence whether all the steps in the sequence were requested or not.

From such a situation as this, the teacher may well proceed to the formulation of the rule for changing fractions to different terms. In fact, in such a

Because "reduce" means to "make smaller" when applied to speed, prices, weight, size, and other everyday considerations and because children have heard the word largely or entirely in such settings, it is a most unfortunate word to describe the process of changing numerator and denominator while *keeping the same value.*

The word "reduce" comes from the Latin *reducere,* meaning "to bring back, restore, or replace." Its use in specialized fields such as mathematics and surgery still carries that meaning, but common parlance makes it a synonym for "diminish" or "decrease." For this reason, another term is recommended for use with children in their early

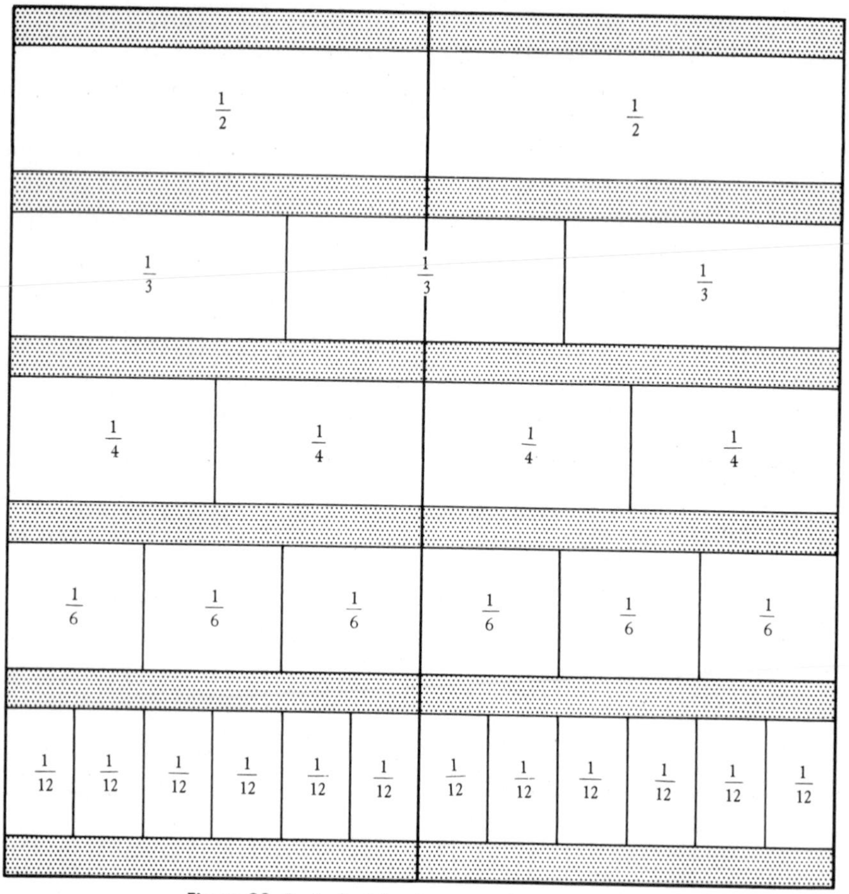

Figure 98. Equivalent Fractions on a Fraction Board.

experiences. The terms "transform" and "transformation" have been suggested and are used in some references. The term that will be used in this book is "change" and "changing." This is consistent with the use of that term in algorisms for whole numbers.

THE "GOLDEN RULE OF FRACTIONS"

The idea of compensation is often used in doing mathematical processes. With whole numbers this takes these forms: (a) If a given number n is added to one addend and subtracted from another addend, the sum is not changed. That is, the one action compensates for the other action. (b) In subtraction, if the same number is added (or subtracted) from the minuend and subtrahend, the remainder is not changed. (c) If one factor is multiplied by a given n and the other factor is divided by that same n, the product does not change. One action compensates for the other. (d) In division, the quotient is not changed if the dividend and divisor are either multiplied or divided by the same number.

Since a fraction is an indicated division and since the fraction may actually be considered the quotient of such a division, this same idea of compensation in division (d above) may be applied to fractions by merely changing a few words. When applied to fractions, this

If it rains $\frac{2}{3}$ of the days, how many days will be rainy?

2	out of	3	or	$\frac{2}{3}$
4	out of	6	or	$\frac{4}{6}$
8	out of	12	or	$\frac{8}{12}$
12	out of	18	or	$\frac{12}{18}$
6	out of	9	or	$\frac{6}{9}$
14	out of	21	or	$\frac{14}{21}$

Figure 99. Fractions on a Ratio Chart.

rule is often called in children's books the "golden rule of fractions" because of its importance in dealing with fractions. To emphasize the similarity of the two ideas — actually their identity — they are given below in parallel arrangement.

Compensation Rule for·Division	Golden Rule of Fractions
The *quotient of a division* is not changed if both the *dividend* and *divisor* are either multiplied or divided by the same number.	A *fraction's value* is not changed if both the *numerator* and *denominator* are either multiplied or divided by the same number.

Example: $12 \div 4 = 3$
$(2 \times 12) \div (2 \times 4) =$
$\qquad 24 \div 8 = 3$

$(12 \div 2) \div (4 \div 2) =$
$\qquad 6 \div 2 = 3$

Example: the fraction $\frac{4}{12}$

$\frac{4}{12} = \frac{2 \times 4}{2 \times 12} = \frac{8}{24}$

$\frac{4}{12} = \frac{4 \div 2}{12 \div 2} = \frac{2}{6}$

Of course, in the fraction situation, obviously the multiplication or division of the numerator and denominator by the same number constitutes multiplying or dividing the whole fraction by the identity element 1, since $\frac{2}{2}$ is just another form for 1. (See p. 330.)

COMMON DENOMINATORS

The expression "common denominators" means literally "same names." This is a very useful alternate terminology to use with children *provided* that they are also taught to recognize the underlying ideas for which the names stand.

Experiences that children should have with equivalence of fractional parts and with equivalence of ratios have been suggested. These give the

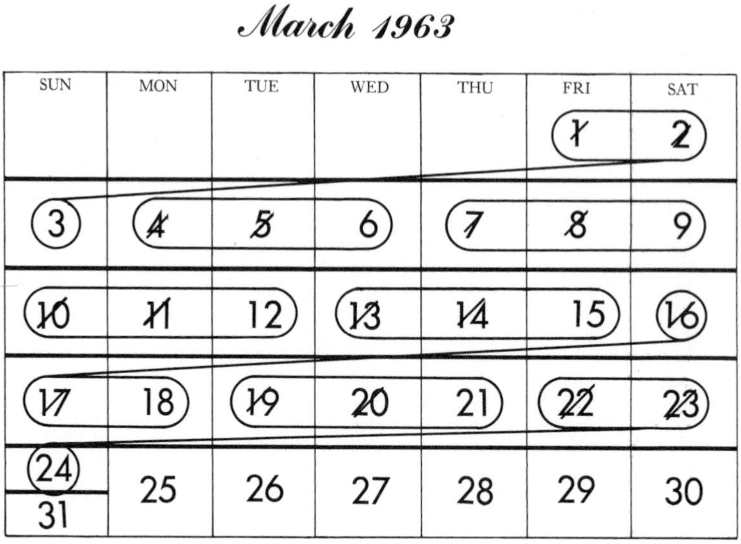

March 1963

SUN	MON	TUE	WED	THU	FRI	SAT
					1	2
3	4	5	6	7	8	9
10	11	12	13	14	15	16
17	18	19	20	21	22	23
24 31	25	26	27	28	29	30

Figure 100. A Calendar Solution for a Ratio Problem.

RAINY DAYS		ALL DAYS	FRACTIONS
2	RRC	3	$\dfrac{2}{3}$
4	RRC	6	$\dfrac{4}{6}$
6	RRC	9	$\dfrac{6}{9}$
8	RRC	12	$\dfrac{8}{12}$
10	RRC	15	$\dfrac{10}{15}$
12	RRC	18	$\dfrac{12}{18}$
14	RRC	21	$\dfrac{14}{21}$
16	RRC	24	$\dfrac{16}{24}$

R = rainy day   C = clear day

Figure 101. A Tabular Solution for a Ratio Problem.

children a background of familiarity with some of the common equivalent fractions and with the idea that any one fraction has many equivalent forms with the same value.

The new idea at this point is to take two "unlike" fractions and find ways of changing one or both so that they will be "like" fractions. First, it is important to recognize that this is *always possible* with common fractions. Second, children's experience with this concept should be limited to those fractions whose common denominators are not difficult to find, saving the more difficult situations until the general procedure is well-established. Fractions whose common denominators are very large and seldom used may be ignored for most children, but they do serve as an interesting challenge for some children.

NEED FOR COMMON DENOMINATORS

The need for finding common denominators arises typically in situations where fractional parts of units or of groups are to be added or subtracted.[13] Accordingly, that is the point at which the process is usually developed.

Problem: In the refrigerator are parts of two pies, $\frac{1}{2}$ of an apple pie and $\frac{1}{3}$ of a cherry pie. How much pie is there in all?

Paper plates cut into various fractional parts are very useful for this sort of situation, as are flannel fractional parts for the flannel board. Children may first solve the problem by manipulating various fractional parts, finding that 1 half = 3 sixths and that 1 third = 2 sixths. Now, of course, it is easy to show that $\frac{1}{2}+\frac{1}{3}=\frac{3}{6}+\frac{2}{6}=\frac{5}{6}$. See figure 102 and further discussion of addition of fractions in chapter 15.

[13] It does not apply to the addition of fractions that are ratios.

A variety of such problem situations, solved by means of manipulation of concrete materials of one kind or another, will show quite soon that it is all well and good to try out one equivalent fraction after another to see which "size of piece" will fit both of the fractions to be combined but that this trial-and-error procedure is very slow if we do not already have these equivalences at the tips of our fingers (or minds).

As individual learners and groups of learners within a whole class come to see this point, they will be ready for some carefully planned instruction in finding common denominators. Such planning falls naturally into two parts: (1) developing the "golden rule for fractions" and (2) using common factors and common multiples in finding common denominators. In actual practice, these two phases of the instruction need not be kept separate; discussing them separately may emphasize the contribution of each.

DEVELOPING THE "GOLDEN RULE FOR FRACTIONS"

This rule, already stated, need not be dictated to children. They can be helped to discover it inductively. Once discovered and carefully formulated (in the children's own words, but correctly and as concisely as possible), it should be applied through deductive reasoning from the generalization to the particular cases it fits.

Though horizontal number lines are used more than vertical ones, this is a situation in which there is some special merit in using the less common vertical line, as in figure 103. It allows the writing of equivalent fractions in horizontally arranged statements of equality. Such a number line can be developed at the chalkboard by teacher and pupils working together. The teacher might prefer to use only the section between 0 and 1 at first, but using the fractions between 1 and 2 expands the possibilities within which children can notice existing relations between equivalent fractions. Teachers will want to use similar number lines showing halves, thirds, sixths, and twelfths or showing

When agreement is reached that multiplying numerator and denominator by 2 does not change the value of the fraction, similar discussion may continue with the fractions for which both numerator and denominator are multiplied by 4 (e.g., $\frac{3}{2}$ and $\frac{12}{8}$). Other lines featuring other equivalent frac-

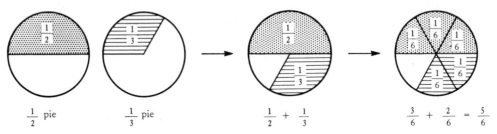

$\frac{1}{2}$ pie $\frac{1}{3}$ pie $\frac{1}{2} + \frac{1}{3}$ $\frac{3}{6} + \frac{2}{6} = \frac{5}{6}$

Figure 102. Development of the Common Denominator Idea.

halves, fifths, and tenths; but each may be handled in somewhat the fashion indicated by the questions and answers below:

Question: Now we have built our number line, and we have shown the fractions that have the same values. Let's look at one set of equivalent fractions like $\frac{1}{2}$, $\frac{2}{4}$, and $\frac{4}{8}$. How are they alike?

Answer: They all have the same value.

Question: Now let's look at their numerators. All the numerators are different. How much bigger is this numerator than this one (pointing to the 2 of $\frac{2}{4}$ and the 4 of $\frac{4}{8}$)?

Answer: The 4 is twice as big as the 2.

Question: Now let's look at the denominators. How much bigger is this one than this one (pointing to the denominator 4 in $\frac{2}{4}$ and the denominator 8 in $\frac{4}{8}$)?

Answer: The 8 is twice as big as the 4.

This same procedure may be applied to various pairs of equivalent fractions until the generalization "dawns" on some child or until the teacher asks the direct question.

Question: When the numerator is twice as big and the denominator is twice as big, what happens to the value of the fraction? (Or, when you multiply both the numerator and denominator by 2, does it change the value of the fraction?)

tions may be used. Sooner or later, the teacher will guide the children to formulate in their own words the generalization that multiplying the numerator and denominator of any fraction by the same number yields an equivalent fraction (does not change the value of the fraction).

While considering the *multiplication* of numerator and denominator by the same number, children may themselves notice that *dividing* the numerator and denominator by the same number also does not change the value of the fraction. If they do not, the teacher should call attention to features of equivalent fractions that will lead to the appropriate generalization. Finally, the effects of multiplying and dividing both terms of the fraction should be brought together in a single statement.

The task of understanding is not finished when the children reach the procedure for changing any fraction to other terms. It is also important that they see some of the rationale behind the generalization. Seeing that it *does work* that way is not the same as seeing *why* it works that way.

This point may be pursued with the aid of number line fractional parts, with the fraction board, with folded sheets of paper, or with parts of groups such as parts of a dozen blocks or a package of 10 items. The use of concrete objects or graphic representations is almost essential since the relationships are apparent in that form but very difficult to state in child-level language apart from specific cases.

If the *parts* are *half as big*, it takes *twice as many parts* to equal the original amount. This can be easily demonstrated. Now the task is to translate that into the numerator-denominator changes. When *parts are half as big*, we use *twice as big a denominator*. When we need *twice as many parts*, we use *twice as big a numerator*.

Stated differently, we may say that multiplying the numerator by 2 gives us twice as many parts, while multiplying the denominator by 2 gives us parts that are half as big. One change undoes the other.

If coins are thought of as representing fractional parts of a dollar, children know that 4 dimes are worth the same as 8 nickels. This is because each nickel is worth half as much as a dime and it takes twice as many of them to equal the same value. Each dime is $\frac{1}{10}$ of a dollar (in value); each nickel is $\frac{1}{20}$ of a dollar (in value): $\frac{4}{10}=\frac{8}{20}$. The second numerator is twice as large as the first. The second denominator is twice as large as the first. The two fractions are equal, because the second one shows twice as many parts, but each part is half as valuable.

The use of a group, such as a dozen artificial eggs in a carton, is often helpful because it establishes a relation to whole numbers that helps build the concept of relative quantities. For example, 8 eggs may be shown to be equal

to $\frac{2}{3}$ of a dozen and to $\frac{4}{6}$ of a dozen. The fact that both fractional parts of a dozen are shown as 8 eggs establishes their equality. Changing thirds of a dozen to sixths of a dozen is a matter of making *twice as many parts* (multiplying the denominator by 2). These parts are

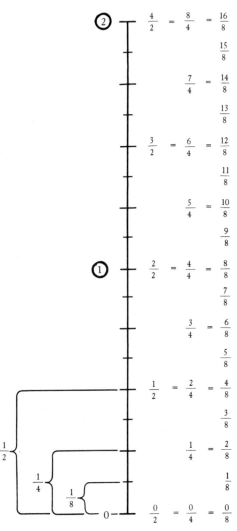

Figure 103. Equivalent Fractions on a Vertical Number Line.

only half as big; so we must use twice as many of those parts (multiplying the numerator by 2).

All the comments above relate to multiplying numerator and denominator by 2, but the same reasoning would apply to multiplying and dividing both terms by some other number.

The general rule for changing fractions to other terms may be expressed thus:

$$\frac{\text{Numerator}}{\text{Denominator}} = \frac{n \times \text{numerator}}{n \times \text{denominator}} = \frac{\text{numerator} \div n}{\text{denominator} \div n}$$

Substituting 4 for n in that formula, specific cases would be written as shown by examples:

$$\frac{1}{2} = \frac{4 \times 1}{4 \times 2} = \frac{4}{8} \quad \text{OR} \quad \frac{8}{12} = \frac{8 \div 4}{12 \div 4} = \frac{2}{3}$$

This form may seem complicated to some elementary teachers who have not used it with their pupils, but experience with it may lead to its adoption for early stages of changing fractions to other terms. It helps children recognize what is really being done.

One more reason for introducing this form (with numerator and denominator showing the multiplication or division by the same number) is that it leads very nicely into the form to be used in using factoring in finding common denominators.

Further, it provides an easy step to showing that when numerator and denominator are multiplied (or divided) by the same number, the fraction is really being multiplied (or divided) by 1.[14] Multiplying (or dividing) by the identity element 1 does not change value.

$$\frac{1}{2} = \frac{4}{4} \times \frac{1}{2} = \frac{4}{8} \qquad \frac{8}{12} = \frac{8}{12} \div \frac{4}{4} = \frac{2}{3}$$

FINDING COMMON DENOMINATORS
WITHOUT FACTORING

The various situations in which a common denominator must be found will be considered in the next chapter

[14] This idea should probably not be introduced until multiplication and division of fractions are studied.

(pp. 341ff.). Here we shall concentrate on the situation in which neither of the given denominators can serve as a common denominator. This is the case with which children need most help.

Too often children have so little help in finding common denominators that they do much more trial-and-error fumbling than is necessary. Some trial and error may be acceptable at first—if nothing else, to dramatize the real help it is to have a technique that makes random trials unnecessary. That period should, however, be brief.

Let us say that the fractions to be added are $\frac{5}{6}$ and $\frac{3}{8}$. Obviously neither denominator can serve as a common one. The product of 6 and 8 is 48, but that is a rather large number. If such a large denominator is to be avoided (and children will be happy to avoid it), a scheme for finding a smaller one is worth seeking.

Here we are face to face with the need for the *least common denominator* (the "least common multiple" in a new guise). If fraction charts have been prepared that include both 24ths and 48ths, they might be used for reference. When the denominators get as large as this, fraction charts that include them tend to get rather large and unwieldy except for display on large wall areas.

Another possibility is for the teacher to have the children prepare (prior to this need) tables of equivalents such as the one shown on page 331. Incidentally, the preparation of these tables is in itself a good learning exercise.

One table may be prepared for each combination of denominators that occur frequently together, with extensions in either direction (to the right to take in higher denominators for each and vertically to include more denominators).

If such charts have been prepared and there is a need to find a common denominator for sixths and eighths,

Equivalent Fractions for Denominators 2, 3, 4, 6, 8

$$\frac{1}{2} = \frac{2}{4} = \frac{3}{6} = \frac{4}{8} = \frac{5}{10} = \frac{6}{12} = \frac{7}{14} = \frac{8}{16} = \frac{9}{18} = \frac{10}{20} \quad \text{etc.}$$

$$\frac{1}{3} = \frac{2}{6} = \frac{3}{9} = \frac{4}{12} = \frac{5}{15} = \frac{6}{18} = \frac{7}{21} = \frac{8}{24} = \frac{9}{27} = \frac{10}{30} \quad \text{etc.}$$

$$\frac{1}{4} = \frac{2}{8} = \frac{3}{12} = \frac{4}{16} = \frac{5}{20} = \frac{6}{24} = \frac{7}{28} = \frac{8}{32} = \frac{9}{36} = \frac{10}{40} \quad \text{etc.}$$

$$\frac{1}{6} = \frac{2}{12} = \frac{3}{18} = \frac{4}{24} = \frac{5}{30} = \frac{6}{36} = \frac{7}{42} = \frac{8}{48} = \frac{9}{54} = \frac{10}{60} \quad \text{etc.}$$

$$\frac{1}{8} = \frac{2}{16} = \frac{3}{24} = \frac{4}{32} = \frac{5}{40} = \frac{6}{48} = \frac{7}{56} = \frac{8}{64} = \frac{9}{72} = \frac{10}{80} \quad \text{etc.}$$

the children learn quickly to spot the common denominators in the sixths row and the eighths row. Both rows have twenty-fourths and forty-eighths; the obvious choice is twenty-fourths. (A table of multiples could be used in the same way.)

One objection to the use of such a chart is that some children may become so dependent on the chart that they are later hampered by reliance on it. If they have prepared it themselves, however, this chance is lessened; they will then probably quickly learn the least common denominators for various frequently used fractions. If a child does tend to become dependent on the chart, the teacher should certainly wean him away from it.

Many teachers train their pupils to follow this procedure: first, try the larger of the two denominators to see if it can be a common denominator; if not, try successive multiples of the larger denominator. With sixths and eighths, this would work out this way: 8 is not a common denominator; $2 \times 8 = 16$; 16 is *not* evenly divisible by 6; $3 \times 8 = 24$; 24 is evenly divisible by 6. This is perhaps the most common procedure among adults, and it is a fairly efficient one.

More attention should be given to another approach to finding the least common denominator. It depends on previous learnings concerning primes,

factors, and multiples. This is the factoring method.

FINDING COMMON DENOMINATORS BY FACTORING

If guidance has already been given in finding the least common multiple of whole numbers (chapter 13), the transfer of that skill to finding least common denominators is easy. Though the finding of common denominators is used most in connection with getting fractions into like terms preliminary to computations, we shall take a different situation in which to suggest use of factoring to arrive at a least common denominator.

Problem: A lemon pie has been cut into sixths and four of them remain uneaten. A chocolate pie (of the same original size) has been cut into eighths with five pieces left. Is there more lemon pie or more chocolate pie left? Which is the larger fraction, $\frac{4}{6}$ or $\frac{5}{8}$?

If there were 4 pieces in each pie plate, we would know that 4 sixths would have to be larger than 4 eighths because sixths are larger than eighths; or if there were 5 pieces in each, the same relationship would hold. What we need to do is to "transform" them into equal-size pieces in order to make the comparison easy. One way would be to cut the pie into smaller and smaller pieces until we had cut both sixths and eighths into similar smaller parts. (But the pie would be badly mutilated!)

This is a good situation for factoring the two denominators just as whole numbers have been factored previously. We need to find which factors the two numbers have in common and which factors are unique to each. (In this case, there is no need to factor the numerators.)

$$\frac{4}{6} = \frac{4}{2 \times 3} \qquad \frac{5}{8} = \frac{5}{2 \times 2 \times 2}$$

Using the rule for finding the least common multiple, we know that we must use all factors occurring in one or the other factorization. In this case this will mean: $2 \times 2 \times 2 \times 3 = 24$. The least common multiple of 6 and 8 is 24. The least common denominator is 24.

$$\frac{4}{6} = \frac{16}{24} \qquad \frac{5}{8} = \frac{15}{24}$$

Once the two fractions are changed to have the same denominator, there is no longer any question as to which is larger. Obviously $\frac{16}{24}$ is more than $\frac{15}{24}$. There is therefore more lemon than chocolate pie.

Finding the least common denominator by factoring is particularly useful with larger denominators or those seldom used. A greater benefit to children, however, is the preparation they receive for factoring in later work in mathematics.

CHANGING TO HIGHER AND LOWER TERMS BY USE OF FACTORS

Emphasis has been placed in the discussion thus far on changing fractions to higher terms, that is, to equivalent fractions with larger numerators and denominators. This requires multiplication of the numerator and denominator by the same number and is used when unlike fractions need to be added, subtracted, or divided.

Changing fractions to lower terms is used to bring them to the form in which they have smaller numerators and denominators and, in a sense, the simplest form. Whereas there is no such thing as bringing fractions to their *highest* terms, changing in the other direction is usually a matter of changing not only to *lower* but to *lowest* terms — to the smallest numerator and denominator that will express the equivalent value. The most common situation in which this is done is that in which the result of an operation with fractions is not expressed in its lowest terms. Some teachers make almost a fetish of having children change all fraction results to lowest terms. While often appropriate, this is not always necessary or even desirable.

Take, for example, a problem in which money values have been handled as fractional parts of a dollar. The answer may be $\frac{4}{10}$ (of a dollar). This could be changed to lowest terms and stated as $\frac{2}{5}$ (of a dollar), but our coinage system is such that tenths are more suitable than fifths. We have dimes to represent tenths of a dollar but no coins to represent fifths of a dollar. Another answer might be $\frac{3}{12}$ (of a foot); whether or not this should be changed to lowest terms and stated as $\frac{1}{4}$ (of a foot) would depend on whether the answer could better be used in that form or simply translated to "3 inches."

In changing fractions to lowest terms, the factoring of both terms is very useful. Some fractions are stated below, followed by their factorizations:

A: $\frac{21}{35} = \frac{3 \times 7}{5 \times 7}$ B: $\frac{12}{15} = \frac{2 \times 2 \times 3}{3 \times 5}$ C: $\frac{18}{30} = \frac{2 \times 3 \times 3}{2 \times 3 \times 5}$

Once the prime factors have been stated, it is a simple matter to select the factors that are common to both numerator and denominator. In example A, the common factor is 7; in B, it is 3; and in C, 2 and 3 are both common factors. Dividing numerator and denominator by their common factors reduces the fraction to lowest terms. This may be accomplished in various ways. The factors may be regrouped to show that the common factors in numerator and denominator form the equivalent of the rational number 1. Whether the omission of the common factors in the last step is considered as the result of "dividing by 1" or "omission of the prime factor 1" does not matter.

A: $\dfrac{21}{35} = \dfrac{3 \times 7}{5 \times 7} = \dfrac{3}{5} \times \dfrac{7}{7} = \dfrac{3}{5}$

B: $\dfrac{12}{15} = \dfrac{2 \times 2 \times 3}{3 \times 5} = \dfrac{2 \times 2}{5} \times \dfrac{3}{3} = \dfrac{4}{5}$

C: $\dfrac{18}{30} = \dfrac{2 \times 3 \times 3}{2 \times 3 \times 5} = \dfrac{6}{6} \times \dfrac{3}{5} = \dfrac{3}{5}$

The same final result may be secured by that old standby of formal arithmetic, cancellation. Because of the fact that it is so often done mechanically, with no understanding of the underlying rationale, and because it often leads to careless habits that lead to error, it is not recommended for use as a basic method.[15] It will be discussed further in connection with multiplication of fractions.

[15] Many modern writers on mathematics warn that cancellation should not be considered a mathematical operation but rather a processing of numerals.

All the written methods presented above are rather "extended" as to form. Many teachers will be anxious to "get on" to quicker methods of changing fractions to lowest terms. If they consider the loss in understanding that may result from too hasty adoption of more "efficient" methods, they may be more willing to see that children have the time to work enough with "longer" methods to get clearly in mind just what is being accomplished.

FOCUS ON MEANINGS OF FRACTIONS

This chapter may seem unduly long merely as an introduction to addition, subtraction, multiplication, and division of fractions. This plan has been followed with definite intent to focus attention on the meanings of fractions, their uses, and their forms before getting involved in computations with them. Many of the serious difficulties experienced by some children (and perpetuated in their adult lives) arise from being taught "what to do with fractions" without really understanding what fractions were or why those procedures would lead to problem solutions. The teacher should not conclude that everything presented in this chapter must be taught to the children before they do any computing with fractions, but teachers should know the meanings well and bear them in mind as they introduce children to fractions and their uses in everyday affairs.

STUDY QUESTIONS

1. Review the various answers to the question: What are fractions? (pp. 302-12.) Think of a recent experience you have had in which you used each of those meanings of a fraction.

2. Give an example of each kind of fraction: unit fraction, nonunit fraction, improper fraction, mixed number, common fraction, decimal fraction. Give a pair of fractions for each of these kinds: like fractions, unlike fractions, equivalent fractions.

3. How is the work with changing fractions to other terms made easier by a knowledge of factors and multiples?

4. Perform the mirror experiment suggested in Reiss, Anita P. *So These Are Fractions!* Englewood Cliffs, N. J.: Prentice-Hall, 1962, pp. 89-93. If possible, try it out with children. Do you consider it to be effective in developing the ratio idea of fractions?

5. Draw separate pictures to show each of these meanings of the fraction: (a) $\frac{2}{3}$ of a whole thing; (b) $\frac{2}{3}$ of a group of things; (c) a ratio of one group to another group of things. How are your pictures alike? How are they different? Why?

6. Copy ten common fractions with their context from a daily newspaper. Try to have each represent a different area of use. Tell which are ratios and which refer to parts of units or groups.

CHAPTER 15

Addition, Subtraction, and Division
of Common Fractions

TEACHERS OFTEN SEEK to arouse pupils' interest in a new topic or process by saying in a spirited, pleasant manner, "Today we are going to take up something *new!*" They may even say *"entirely* new" by way of emphasizing just how different the new material is. Newness is supposed to challenge the learners to anticipate something pleasant, as it may indeed do in certain situations. On the other hand, teachers might well consider the possibility that newness may imply strangeness, which in turn may arouse some fear of what is coming next.

The introduction of the arithmetical processes with fractions might better emphasize the close relationship between the processes with whole numbers and with fractions. It is safe to say that much past teaching of addition and subtraction of fractions has erred in pointing up the differences between adding and subtracting whole numbers and adding and subtracting fractions instead of pointing up the similarities.

Background for Addition and Subtraction of Fractions

The psychological benefits of "easing into" the learning of computations with common fractions are very much worth the seeking. Improving children's readiness for this work depends on making sure that they have certain background understandings and abilities. These include: (1) clear, correct concepts of the addition and subtraction processes when applied to whole numbers; (2) understanding of basic principles such as the commutative and associative laws and the rule of likeness; and (3) understanding of the meanings of the types of fractions to be used.

ADDITION AND SUBTRACTION CONCEPTS

The meaning of addition as a process of combining holds for addition of common fractions as for addition of whole numbers. Statements concerning the addition of fraction numbers are statements of equality, as for addition of whole numbers. The combination of two or more fractions by adding does not represent a "getting-more" process but indicates a regrouping of the addends to form a total or sum.

The meaning of subtraction as a process of separating or taking apart applies to subtraction of fractions as well as to subtraction of whole numbers. The situations in which subtraction of fractions occurs are of the same three different types already discussed for subtraction of whole numbers: decomposition or "taking away," comparison or matching, and additive subtraction.

335

The subtraction of fractions is a process of taking apart a known total group to form a known subgroup and to find an unknown subgroup.

The same basic process meanings for addition and subtraction hold for proper fractions, improper fractions, mixed numbers, and whole numbers. Children just learning to add and subtract fractions should be reminded of these similarities continuously as an aid to the new learning and for the assurance it gives to know that the new learning is "just a little bit different" from that already accomplished.

BASIC PRINCIPLES OF ADDITION AND SUBTRACTION

The commutative and associative laws for addition operate for addition of fractions. The order in which fractions are added does not affect their sum. When more than two fractions are added, they may be associated or grouped in any way.

The basic principles discussed in chapter 7 for subtraction of whole numbers apply in exactly the same fashion for subtraction of fractions. The same qualifications and restrictions mentioned in that earlier discussion also apply to subtraction of fractions.

A fundamental idea that is of particular importance in helping children to move smoothly and with understanding from addition and subtraction of whole numbers to addition and subtraction of fractions is the principle or rule of likeness. Just as addition and subtraction are limited to *like* terms, so also addition and subtraction of fractions are limited to *like* terms. Just as people are added to people or boxes to boxes, just as tens are added to tens and hundreds to hundreds, so fourths are added to other fourths and sixths to other sixths. Just as children are subtracted from children and houses from houses, just as ones are subtracted from ones and hundreds from hundreds, so thirds are subtracted from thirds and eighths from eighths.

When whole-number terms are unlike, the first step is to change their form to equivalent like terms, so that addition or subtraction can proceed. Number of boys and number of girls are correctly added when both are considered as numbers of children; tens and ones may be correctly added or subtracted when either is changed to fit the form of the other term. So it is with addition and subtraction of fractions. If terms are unlike, one or more of the terms are changed so that all have the same designations (denominators) before the addition or subtraction may be performed.

Finding common denominators (same names) and changing numerators (numberers) accordingly is not a new concept for addition and subtraction of fractions; it is rather an extension of a concept already in use with whole numbers.

MEANINGS OF FRACTIONS

Various meanings have been discussed for fractions. Addition and subtraction of fractions do not apply to all fraction meanings. They apply to those fraction meanings which refer to parts of wholes or parts of groups. They do not apply when fractions express ratios.[1] In using and in devising situations in

---

[1] Children sometimes make the error of adding both numerators and denominators. If ratio-type fractions were added, such a procedure would actually give a correct answer. For example, if a dart thrower hit the target 2 out of 3 times on one occasion and 4 out of 5 times on a second occasion, it would be true that he hit the target 6 out of 8 times in all ($\frac{2}{3}+\frac{4}{5}=\frac{6}{8}$).

which to develop the addition and subtraction of fractions, the teacher should be sure that the meanings used are the "part" meanings.

Correct meanings of numerators and denominators are also essential if children are to understand what actually happens when fractions are added and subtracted. The concept of the denominator as the *name* of the fractional part is basic to application of the rule of likeness. The concept of the denominator as indicating the *size* of the part is also helpful, provided that size is seen as relative to size of a particular whole.

Addition and Subtraction of Like Fractions

ADDITION OF LIKE FRACTIONS

One teacher had 4 blocks of wood, which were the same size as the sticks of butter or oleomargarine that weigh one-fourth of a pound each; the sticks were painted yellow to look like butter. She placed these sticks in a butter carton and used them in presenting addition of fractions to her pupils. She wanted to use a problem situation that was so easy that her pupils would surely handle it correctly, thus giving her an opportunity to lead into addition of fractions with a minimum of "newness" and a maximum of understanding.

Miss Smith: I have here some sticks that look like butter or oleomargarine sticks. How much would this carton of butter weigh if it were real butter?
Pupils: One pound.
Miss Smith: How much would each stick weigh?
John: One-fourth of a pound.
Alice: My mother always calls it a quarter-pound, but that's the same as a fourth.
Miss Smith: Yes, we can call each of them a stick or a quarter-pound or a fourth-pound. Since we all know it is part of a pound, we may also say simply "quarter" or "fourth."

Let's suppose now that your mother is reading a recipe in her cookbook that calls for butter. She wants to know how much butter she has in the house so she will know whether she has enough for this recipe. She knows she has two sticks of butter in the refrigerator and there is one full stick of butter on the butter plate. This is a very easy problem. How many sticks of butter does she have?

Children: Three sticks. (They seemed to be amused at such a simple "problem." One boy suggested that any first grader could do that.)
Miss Smith: I know that seems awfully simple to you, but I want to start with something very simple and lead up to something else. Let's write what we have done on the chalkboard. (She writes the first sentence shown in the picture of the chalkboard, figure 104.)
Miss Smith: Now we said these sticks of butter could be called by other names. Peter, will you please go to the chalkboard and write the same sentence, using different names. (Peter wrote the second sentence shown in fig. 104.)
Miss Smith: Who can write the sentence again using still another name for the sticks of butter? All right, Sharon. (Sharon wrote the third sentence.)
Miss Smith: All of these sentences say the same thing. Now I am going to write it still another way. Watch while I write it a shorter way. We might say this is a shorthand way to write what we do when we add fractional parts of something. (She wrote the fourth statement in fig. 104.) We have been adding fractions, and this is one way we write the addition of fractions.

Whereas the children a few minutes earlier had been amused at being asked to "solve" such an easy whole-number "problem," they were now impressed with themselves for having added fractions and pleased to see how easy it could be. Some of their older brothers, sisters, and friends may have told them addition of fractions was going to be hard. Here it was—not hard at all as yet.

Miss Smith was stressing the easy transition from adding whole numbers to adding like fractions. Her method was entirely correct yet simple because of basing the unknown upon the known. Her pupils had already been introduced to fraction numerals; so the only new feature was the use of those numerals in making the addition statement.

If the teacher will think of fractions as a new kind of unit, she can introduce addition of fractions in close harmony with addition of whole numbers. The denominator of the fraction then is seen as the *name* of the fraction-unit. The numerators tell the number of such units being added and the number of such units in the sum. A reminder is in order (and essential) that the reason we merely add the numerators is that they refer to the same fraction-units. Just as we add sticks to sticks, we add fourths to fourths.

Measures provide many parallel situations to the one described above. Some of the possibilities for capitalizing on whole-number additions for development of analogous fraction additions are suggested by the groups of statements below.

4 inches + 5 inches = 9 inches
4 twelfths + 5 twelfths = 9 twelfths (of a foot)

$$\frac{4}{12} + \frac{5}{12} = \frac{9}{12}$$

4 days + 2 days = 6 days
4 sevenths + 2 sevenths = 6 sevenths (of a week)

$$\frac{4}{7} + \frac{2}{7} = \frac{6}{7}$$

In each of the three cases above (quarter-pounds, inches, days), the first statement is in terms of whole numbers, with the "name" being the designation of the objects or measures being added. The second statement uses identically the same numerals, but the "names" designate fraction-units that relate to some larger whole or unit (pound of butter, foot, or week). The third statement in each case would sound exactly the same as the second statement if read aloud; the difference is only in the written form for it. In each

case the third statement uses the "fraction shorthand" mentioned by Miss Smith, the *denominator* of the fraction form designating exactly the same meaning as the *fraction-unit word* in the second statement of each series. The teacher should use as many situations and series of such statements as seem to be needed for pupils to grasp the transition from whole-number statements to fraction statements. Of course, the amount of reliance that needs to be placed on the presence of concrete aids to understanding and the number of transitional experiences of situations and of statement making will vary widely from pupil to pupil and from group to group.

SUBTRACTION OF LIKE FRACTIONS

The procedure for introducing subtraction of like fractions follows the same pattern as for addition of like fractions. In fact, many teachers will choose to present them together or in immediate succession during the same lesson. For example, Miss Smith might well have gone directly to a subtraction "problem."

Problem: If I have 3 sticks of butter and use 1 stick for spreading sandwiches for our picnic, how many sticks of butter will be left?

The sequence of actions for this and other situations may be shown by transitionary statements such as:

3 sticks − 1 stick = 2 sticks
3 fourths − 1 fourth = 2 fourths (of a pound)

$$\frac{3}{4} - \frac{1}{4} = \frac{2}{4}$$

5 squares − 2 squares = 3 squares (of candy)
5 sixths − 2 sixths = 3 sixths (of a candy bar)

$$\frac{5}{6} - \frac{2}{6} = \frac{3}{6}$$

8 eggs − 5 eggs = 3 eggs
8 twelfths − 5 twelfths = 3 twelfths (of a dozen)

$$\frac{8}{12} - \frac{5}{12} = \frac{3}{12}$$

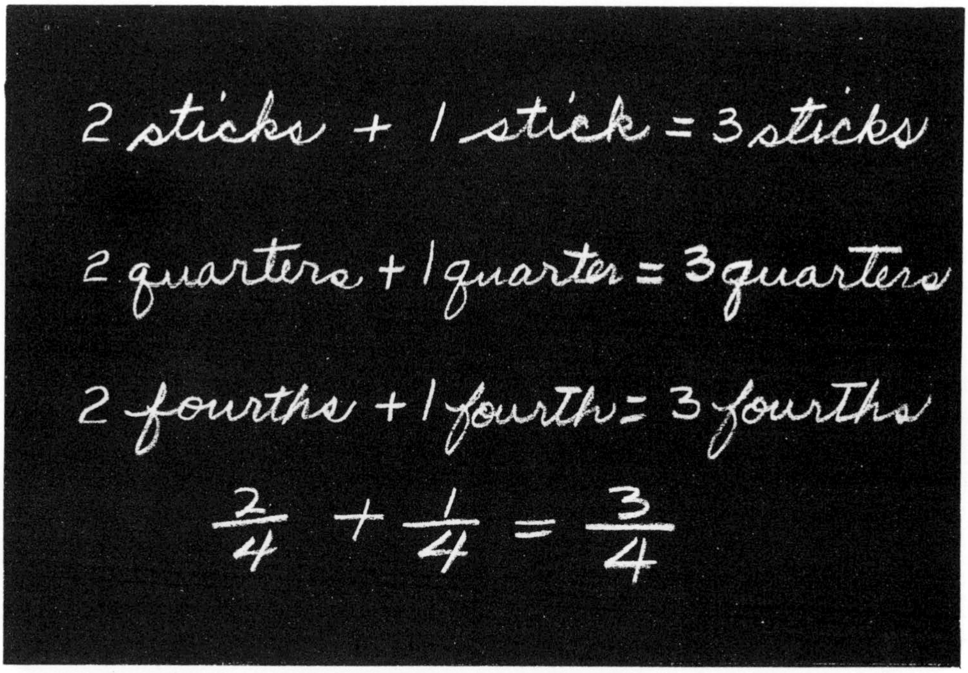

Figure 104. Simple Addition of Fractions.

As with addition of like fractions, there is nothing new about subtraction of fractions except the terminology and the use of names and notation. One must assume, of course, that before such activities are presented, the children will have had sufficient experiences with the meanings of the fractional parts themselves in many concrete and semiconcrete situations.

In all the examples given for addition and subtraction of like fractions, the reader should note that fractions are being used as measures—measuring units for whole groups and measuring units for whole things. In this sense, each fraction designation is also a fraction-unit designation.

FRACTIONS AS MULTIPLES OF UNITS

Overemphasis on fractions as representing parts of single whole things has obscured for many children (and perhaps for many teachers) the concept of fractions as representing units or multiples of units. Children need to see that whether a given item is to be considered as a unit or a part depends on our way of viewing it; also, it may serve both functions at the same time if that is what we want it to do. A dime may be thought of as a single coin, *1 dime.* It may be thought of as having the value of *10 pennies,* that is, as a multiple of a smaller unit value. It may be thought of as having the value of $\frac{1}{10}$ *of a dollar,* that is, as a fractional part of a larger unit value. Three dimes would have the value of 3 tenths of a dollar, that is, a multiple of the fraction-unit *tenth of a dollar.*

In the children's book, *So These Are Fractions!*[2] Anita Riess brings out these meanings by reference to symmetrical forms in nature and art and by use of supplementary manipulative aids that are provided. In the Teacher's Edition this comment appears:

[2] Anita P. Riess, *So These Are Fractions!,* Englewood Cliffs, N. J.: Prentice-Hall, 1962, 123 pp.

"Both whole numbers and fractions are treated as multiples of units. The whole numbers are presented as multiples of the unit one, or of units larger than one; the fractions, of units smaller than one. . . . The basic operations are the same for whole numbers and fractions; they are performed on the number that counts the units, no matter what kind of unit is involved."[3]

Nonunit fractions might be called *multiple fractions* in that they represent multiples of unit fractions. The numerators tell how many of each unit fraction are being considered. Thus $\frac{2}{3}$ represents

the various forms used. Typically, the horizontal forms for computation with fractions are used in algebra, with more use being made of the vertical forms in arithmetic, particularly with mixed numbers. The present tendency to introduce more use of horizontal forms in the elementary school work with fractions seems to be worthwhile. Certainly both styles of writing should be taught.

One of the addition sequences and one of the subtraction sequences previously introduced are supplied here in vertical form for comparison.

Addition		Subtraction	
4 inches	$\frac{4}{12}$	8 eggs	$\frac{8}{12}$
+5 inches		−5 eggs	
9 inches	$+\frac{5}{12}$	3 eggs	$-\frac{5}{12}$
4 twelfths (of a foot)	$\frac{9}{12}$	8 twelfths (of a dozen)	$\frac{3}{12}$
+5 twelfths (of a foot)		−5 twelfths (of a dozen)	
9 twelfths (of a foot)		3 twelfths (of a dozen)	

2 of the unit fraction $\frac{1}{3}$; $\frac{3}{2}$ represents 3 of the unit fraction $\frac{1}{2}$.

This concept of common fractions as multiples of units is extremely important to the understanding of addition and subtraction of fractions and to the understanding of division of fractions by the common-denominator method. It also applies in some multiplication situations, but not when the multiplier is a fraction (i.e., multiplying *by* a fraction).

VERTICAL AND HORIZONTAL ALGORISMS

Only horizontal forms have been used thus far in presenting addition and subtraction of fractions. This has been done to emphasize the statement idea and to dramatize the parallel nature of

There are no differences in meaning or interpretation of the processes or the fractions themselves as presented by either form, vertical or horizontal.

ALGEBRAIC DEFINITION OF ADDITION
AND SUBTRACTION
OF LIKE FRACTIONS

Using words to define addition and subtraction of like fractions, we might say that these processes are performed as for whole numbers when the numerals refer to *like* items. First, we check to see that the names (denominators) for each term are the same, and then we add (or subtract) the numbers (numerators).

We might use words in a more mathematically familiar form, thus:

$$\frac{\text{Numerator}_1}{\text{Denominator}} + \frac{\text{numerator}_2}{\text{denominator}} = \frac{\text{numerator}_1 + \text{numerator}_2}{\text{denominator}}$$

$$\frac{\text{Numerator}_1}{\text{Denominator}} - \frac{\text{numerator}_2}{\text{denominator}} = \frac{\text{Numerator}_1 - \text{numerator}_2}{\text{denominator}}$$

[3] Anita P. Riess and Grace A. Packer, *Teacher's Edition, So These Are Fractions!*, Englewood Cliffs, N. J.: Prentice-Hall, 1962, 46 pp., p. Ti.

In simpler algebraic form, the different numerators might be designated by n and m and the same denominator by d, thus:

$$\frac{n}{d} + \frac{m}{d} = \frac{n+m}{d}$$

$$\frac{n}{d} - \frac{m}{d} = \frac{n-m}{d}$$

Addition and Subtraction of Unlike Fractions

When *unlike* fractions are to be added or subtracted, a preliminary step is necessary. This preliminary step is really not a part of the addition or subtraction; it is rather a preparation for those processes, a procedure that makes them possible.

Since only like terms may be added or subtracted, unlike terms must be changed to like terms *before* the adding or subtracting can take place. With common fractions, this change takes the form of changing unlike denominators to like denominators. Since a change in denominators implies a change in the fraction-units being used to state the given quantities, changes must also occur in the numerators to preserve the original values for each fraction.

This is not an entirely new idea for common fractions, though it is particularly pertinent to unlike fractions. Let us trace the same idea as already used with addition and subtraction of whole numbers.

CHANGES IN DESIGNATIONS
OF WHOLE NUMBERS

If they have been well taught, children will already have had many experiences in which they have changed the designations (names) as well as the values of those designations in order to make addition and subtraction possible.

Changes in name only. Sometimes the changes of designation or name are only changes in name, and correctly so. We teach children that when they add apples and oranges, the sum cannot be called either "apples" or "oranges"; they must define both apples and oranges in some more inclusive way such as "pieces of fruit": 3 apples + 4 oranges = 7 pieces of fruit. If boys and girls are added, we speak of the process thus: 4 children + 4 children = 8 children. We may even add sticks, stones, and bones, but the sum is not correctly designated except by some term that includes each and every addend.[4] Thus: 4 sticks + 5 stones + 3 bones do *not* equal 12 sticks or 12 stones or 12 bones; 4 sticks + 5 stones + 3 bones = 12 things, a general-enough term to include all.

Such changes in name are quite common in primary-grade arithmetic situations. No changes in the numbers involved are needed, but the teacher must nevertheless emphasize the basis on which it is correct to change all the different names to one common name.

Name changes that change value. The next step with whole numbers relative to name changes includes changes in value of the numbers. Miss Allen's class of third graders found themselves involved in a discussion on this point. Chris had said, "You can't add nickels and dimes and quarters." Since some argument of the "'tis-and-'taint" variety seemed to be building up, Miss Allen referred the children to the lunch money, the counting of which had precipitated the argument.

[4] Sets are defined either by listing the members of the set or by defining the set in terms of some common property or properties on the basis of which the members belong to the set and non-members are excluded from the set. This idea is being used in the accompanying discussion.

Under her guidance, the children listed some true statements and some false statements concerning this situation. These served to clarify the situation and bear repeating here.

You can't add nickels and dimes and quarters. (False)

You can add nickels and dimes and quarters *if* you are just talking about them as *coins:* 3 nickels and 4 dimes and 1 quarter are 8 coins. (True)

Nickels and dimes and quarters are all money, so you add their numbers to find how much money. (False)

You can't add the numbers of nickels and dimes and quarters *if* you want to find out what all are worth: 3 nickels and 4 dimes and 1 quarter do *not* equal 8 cents. (True)

Nickels and dimes and quarters all have *different values;* so you should *change* them to the *same value* before you add the numbers to get the total value: 3 nickels and 4 dimes and 1 quarter = 15 cents + 40 cents + 25 cents = 80 cents; 15¢ + 40¢ + 25¢ = 80¢. (True)

Miss Allen had helped the children to understand that the *numbers* represented by the numerals could not be added when each of them referred to a different *value,* but that the numbers could be changed along with the names so as to keep the values unchanged. Finally, the children saw that these changed numbers *could* be added to get a correct sum after they had the same value designation, *cents.*

This is the type of change that occurs when denominators need to be changed in order to have common denominators (same names) for common fractions that are to be added, subtracted, or divided. The forms of the fractions must be changed so that they have the same denominators (names), but the numerators must also be changed so as to keep the *value* of each fraction unchanged.

The changing step preceding adding and subtracting of fractions varies in difficulty depending on the type of change necessary. Usually the various

types of change in finding the common denominator are classified as: (1) those in which one of the denominators is the common denominator, (2) those in which the product of the denominators is used as the common denominator, and (3) those in which some other number is the least common denominator.

As suggested earlier, children should be introduced to common multiples and common denominators before they have occasion to find common denominators in order to add and subtract fractions. They should also have had experience with equivalent fractions. If these ideas are well in hand, they can be used rather than introduced at this point.

A GIVEN DENOMINATOR

AS THE COMMON DENOMINATOR

The easiest type of addition or subtraction of unlike fractions is that in which one of the given denominators is also the common denominator. The use of a ruler can be very helpful.

Consideration of this situation might be started with a very easy problem in order that full attention may be concentrated on the manner in which unlike denominators are handled. For instance, the same problem described on pages 337-38 might be used with only slight variation.

Problem: If Mother has $\frac{1}{4}$ of a pound of butter outside the refrigerator and $\frac{1}{2}$ pound of butter in the refrigerator, how much butter does she have in all?

If the teacher wished, she might choose to start the addition statement, using words for the denominators and numerals for the numerators, thus: 1 fourth + 1 half = ?

Discussion should center on the fact that these two terms have different denominators (names) and the reminder that unlike terms may not be added until they are changed to like terms. If the children have had sufficient experiences with equivalent fractions, they should have no trouble in recognizing that they must change the half to fourths. If they do not, the teacher can lead them to this decision by questions such as these: Can we add halves and fourths just as they are? (No.) What do we have to do before we can add them? (Change them so they have the same name.) Shall we change the fourth to halves or the half to fourths? (The half can be changed to fourths.) How many fourths are equal to 1 half? (One half equals 2 fourths.)

Wooden sticks or other representations such as Miss Smith used (p. 337) may be used to dramatize the changing of 1 half to 2 fourths. When the change has been made, the written record of the thinking may be expanded:

1 fourth + 1 half = 1 fourth + 2 fourths = 3 fourths

Then it may be written in "fraction shorthand":

$$\frac{1}{4}+\frac{1}{2}=\frac{1}{4}+\frac{2}{4}=\frac{3}{4}$$

A variety of problems should be solved, the first ones all being based on concrete situations in which the reasoning can be firmly grounded in reality. Abstract practice may follow, once the basic procedure is understood.

A good subtraction situation might be one like that used by Miss Tilton. She used flannel "pieces of pie" on a flannel board. She had worked with halves, thirds, fourths, sixths, and eighths of "pies" on the flannel board: so the children had already had a good deal of experience in comparing fractional parts and finding equivalent fractions.

Miss Tilton: Here is one-third of a pie. Joe, I am going to call this your piece. It is yellow; so we will call it lemon pie. Here is one-sixth of a pie. Tommy, you may have

this piece of cherry pie shown by the red one-sixth. Now I want you two boys to come up here and show us how much more pie Joe has than Tommy.

The boys came to the flannel board and pondered the situation briefly.

Joe: Let's put your piece on top of mine. Then we can see the difference.

Tommy (pointing to the exposed part of the "lemon pie"): That's the difference.

Miss Tilton: What fractional part of a whole pie is it?

Tommy: It looks as if it is just as big as my one-sixth.

Miss Tilton: How can you prove whether it is or not?

Joe: Let's take another sixth and put it on top to see if it fits.

Finding that it did "fit" over the difference, the boys decided that Joe had one-sixth of a pie more than Tommy.

Miss Tilton: It looks to me as if the one-third pie that Joe had is all covered up now. What have you put in place of the one-third?

Boys: Two-sixths.

Miss Tilton: Yes, you changed one-third to two-sixths. Really you ended up comparing two-sixths with one-sixth, didn't you? Who can write on the chalkboard the complete record of what Joe and Tommy did?

Nell volunteered to do so, writing:

1 third − 1 sixth = 2 sixths − 1 sixth = 1 sixth

Bill said he knew another way to write the record:

$$\frac{1}{3}-\frac{1}{6}=\frac{2}{6}-\frac{1}{6}=\frac{1}{6}$$

Miss Tilton: Can anyone write it still another way?

Brock: When my dad helped me with adding fractions, he wrote one under the other. I think you can do that with this.

Miss Tilton: Show us.

Brock wrote, with some assistance from Miss Tilton:

$$\frac{1}{3}=\frac{2}{6}$$
$$-\frac{1}{6}=\frac{1}{6}$$
$$\overline{\quad\frac{1}{6}}$$

The discussion that followed indicated that all the ways of writing the subtraction record were correct. Some children liked one way; some preferred another.

Miss Tilton told each child to write his subtractions the way that made best sense to him.

The addition and subtraction problems that have been given above are very simple. As the teacher sees that children understand the meanings and the procedures, she will encourage them to do more difficult additions and subtractions in which one denominator is the common denominator. As the boys and girls work with examples like those below, they may use whatever aids they need. A fraction board, a table of equivalent fractions, concrete aids such as the flannel fractional parts, and original drawings are all useful.

$$\frac{2}{3}+\frac{1}{6}=? \qquad \frac{2}{5}+\frac{3}{10}=? \qquad \frac{5}{6}+\frac{1}{2}=? \qquad \frac{7}{8}+\frac{3}{4}=?$$

Eventually, of course, the teacher seeks to bring the pupils to the level of confidence and competence at which they can operate freely and correctly without any such aids. The development of the procedure for changing fractions to higher and lower terms has already been discussed in chapter 14.

Children who are progressing faster than the others will enjoy adding more than two fractions. They should benefit from practice with examples such as these:

$$\frac{1}{2}+\frac{1}{4}+\frac{1}{8}=? \qquad \frac{1}{6}+\frac{1}{3}+\frac{1}{2}=? \qquad \frac{1}{10}+\frac{2}{5}+\frac{1}{2}=?$$

The difficulty of these exercises can be extended considerably by working out examples with sums beyond 1.

THE PRODUCT OF DENOMINATORS
AS A COMMON DENOMINATOR

The next step is that of using the product of the denominators as the common denominator. This product is always a correct common denominator,

but it is not always the *least* common denominator.

Examples of appropriate problems for introducing the addition and subtraction of fractions with the product of denominators as the common denominator might be:

Addition Problem: Mary had a yard of cloth. She used $\frac{1}{2}$ yard for a scarf for herself and she used $\frac{1}{3}$ yard to make a book cover. How much cloth did she use?

Subtraction Problem: Jeff's father started to paint a board fence and had to stop to do some other work. Two-thirds of the fence still had to be painted. Jeff's father told Jeff to paint as much as he could on the unpainted part. Jeff painted $\frac{1}{4}$ of the whole fence. How much of the whole fence remained to be painted?

Any number of aids may be used to solve such problems and to demonstrate the meanings involved. Number lines would adapt readily to both of these problems, as would informal drawings representing the situations. Children who did not need such devices might proceed directly to use of the product of denominators and application of the "golden rule of fractions."

Any of the solutions below should be counted as correct; but comparison and discussion should lead the children to select the most efficient forms (viewed as an individual matter, since the most efficient procedure for one might not be readily understood by another). The drawings in figure 105 suggest sample solutions in graphic form.

Addition Problem Solutions:

1 half + 1 third = 3 sixths + 2 sixths = 5 sixths

$$\frac{1}{2}+\frac{1}{3}=\frac{3}{6}+\frac{2}{6}=\frac{5}{6}$$

$\frac{1}{2}$ yard is $\frac{3}{6}$ yard

$\frac{1}{3}$ yard is $\frac{2}{6}$ yard

$\frac{3}{6}$ yard + $\frac{2}{6}$ yard = $\frac{5}{6}$ yard

$$\begin{array}{r}\frac{1}{2}=\frac{3}{6}\\+\frac{1}{3}=\frac{2}{6}\\\hline \frac{5}{6}\end{array}$$

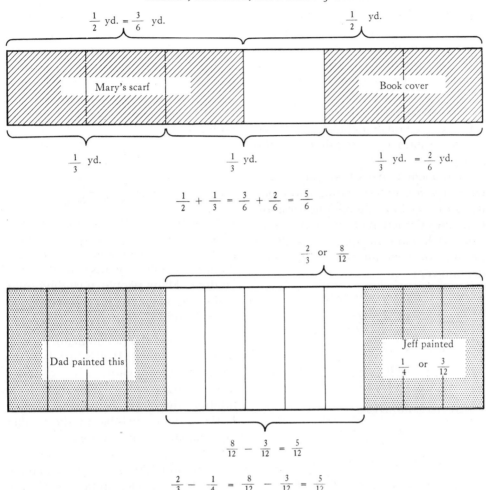

Figure 105. The Product of Denominators as a Common Denominator.

Subtraction Problem Solutions:

2 thirds − 1 fourth = 8 twelfths − 3 twelfths = 5 twelfths

$$\frac{2}{3} - \frac{1}{4} = \frac{8}{12} - \frac{3}{12} = \frac{5}{12}$$

$\frac{2}{3}$ is the same as $\frac{8}{12}$

$\frac{1}{4}$ is the same as $\frac{3}{12}$

$\frac{8}{12} - \frac{3}{12} = \frac{5}{12}$

$\frac{2}{3} = \frac{8}{12}$

$-\frac{1}{4} = \frac{3}{12}$

——————

$\frac{5}{12}$

A good deal of practice should be given with different problem situations at first, followed by practice examples stressing the computation phases of the work. To practice the computational aspects extensively before children have experienced the requisite meanings in problems is not a good use of children's time for learning.

In order that enough problem situations may be available for those children who do not "get the idea" quickly, teachers should make collections of realistic word problems from various texts and other sources, keep samples of real problems that occur in classroom living, urge pupils to bring in problems requiring addition and subtraction of fractions, and invent problems of their own — preferably of types that may be developed with a variety of demonstration techniques.

Of course, children who have progressed to a high level of understanding will not need drawings or other outside aids. They will probably know by simple inspection what common denominator is appropriate and proceed to change each fraction to the equivalent fraction with the common denominator and then add or subtract as required by the problem.

Some elementary school pupils who have superior understanding may enjoy using the algebraic definitions for addition and subtraction of unlike fractions. These definitions depend on use of the product of denominators as the new denominator.

Addition of Unlike Fractions

$$\frac{a}{b} + \frac{c}{d} = \frac{ad + bc}{bd}$$

Let $a = 2$, $b = 5$, $c = 1$, and $d = 3$. Then:

$$\frac{2}{5} + \frac{1}{3} = \frac{(2 \times 3) + (5 \times 1)}{(5 \times 3)} = \frac{6 + 5}{15} = \frac{11}{15}$$

Subtraction of Unlike Fractions:

$$\frac{a}{b} - \frac{c}{d} = \frac{ad - bc}{bd}$$

Again, let $a = 2$, $b = 5$, $c = 1$, and $d = 3$. Then:

$$\frac{2}{5} - \frac{1}{3} = \frac{(2 \times 3) - (5 \times 1)}{(5 \times 3)} = \frac{6 - 5}{15} = \frac{1}{15}$$

LEAST COMMON DENOMINATORS

The two problems used in the preceding section used for their solution common denominators that were the products of the denominators occurring in the problems. It so happened that these products were also the *least* common denominators. This might not have been the case, as when common denominators are needed for fourths and sixths and eighths. The following examples are correct but unnecessarily cumbersome.

$$\frac{3}{4} + \frac{1}{6} = \frac{18}{24} + \frac{4}{24} = \frac{22}{24}$$

$$\frac{5}{6} - \frac{3}{8} = \frac{40}{48} - \frac{18}{48} = \frac{22}{48}$$

Not only is it harder to compute with the large denominators in these two examples, but they also yield answers that must be changed to lower terms if they are to be in their simplest form. The use of a *least* common denominator in each example would be better on both counts.

$$\frac{3}{4} + \frac{1}{6} = \frac{9}{12} + \frac{2}{12} = \frac{11}{12}$$

$$\frac{5}{6} - \frac{3}{8} = \frac{20}{24} - \frac{9}{24} = \frac{11}{24}$$

Since the only new feature of such situations is the finding of the smallest possible common denominator, the only point to be developed is how that may be done. Many people, including some authorities in the teaching of arithmetic, recommend this procedure:

1. Is one of the denominators a multiple of the other? If it is, use it as the common denominator.

2. If suggestion 1 does not work, multiply the larger denominator by 2. Is the product divisible by the smaller denominator? If it is, use it.

3. If suggestion 2 does not work, continue to multiply the larger denominator by 3, 4, etc., until a product is secured that is a multiple of the smaller denominator. Use the smallest such product.

This may be a good preliminary procedure; but certainly many children will enjoy and profit from other ways of finding the least common denominator, such as the number line procedure and the factorization method (see chap. 14).

One interesting activity, which can be quite fascinating, is the use of a common denominator strip.

The Common Denominator Strip

1. Take a strip of paper (preferably a foot or more in length).

2. Fold it into a given number of equal parts. Crease the folds sharply.

Open out and draw lines to indicate the location of the folds.

3. Fold the length of paper again into a *different* number of equal parts. Crease, fold, and draw lines on new folds.

4. The full length will now be divided into parts of unequal sizes. Locate the smallest-size part.

5. Using this smallest part as a unit of measure, fold the whole length of paper into units of that size. (Draw lines on these new folds if you wish.)

6. What part of the whole strip is each small part? What is the name of this fractional part? Is it the least common denominator for the two kinds of fractional parts into which the whole strip was divided by folding?

7. Try doing the same thing for more than two fractions with unrelated denominators. Does it work?

Addition and Subtraction Including Whole and Mixed Numbers

Restriction of the preceding discussion to proper fractions has been intentional in order to separate more clearly two classes of fraction form changes: (1) the changing of proper fractions to other equivalent fraction froms and (2) the changing of whole and mixed numbers to fraction forms. This separation is not intended to suggest that work with whole and mixed numbers be postponed until all variations with proper fractions have been introduced. The teacher should feel free to follow the particular sequence used in the basic text or her preference from among the various texts in use. She may experiment with different sequences to see which seems to work out best with her pupils. Further, in using real problem situations connected with everyday classroom problems or those brought in by the children, whole numbers and mixed

numbers are likely to appear along with proper fractions; in that case, the sensible thing to do is to go ahead and use them.

CHANGING WHOLE NUMBERS

TO FRACTION FORM

Meaningful introduction of fractional parts in relation to wholes is the foundation for changing whole-number notation to fraction notation. Most elementary school teachers have done a good job of instruction in helping children to see that 1 whole equals 4 equal parts of that whole, 5 equal parts of that whole, or 12 equal parts of that whole thing. Some teachers have perhaps not given sufficient attention to the idea of whole numbers in general as fraction-type numbers, i.e., as rational numbers. Children should learn that when we think of 2 pies as $\frac{12}{6}$, we are dealing with a fraction just as truly as when we think of $\frac{4}{6}$ of a pie.

As soon as children can change 1 whole thing or group into any designated number of equal parts, they should be given experiences in which they change more than 1 whole thing or group into designated fractional parts. They should learn to answer such questions as: How many half-sheets in 3 whole sheets of notebook paper? How many halves of a pair in 4 pairs of socks? How many thirds of a foot in 4 feet? How many twelfths of a dozen in 3 dozen? How many sixths of a candy bar in 7 candy bars?

They should also learn to write in fraction notation:

$$3 = \frac{6}{2} \qquad 4 = \frac{8}{2} \qquad 4 = \frac{12}{3} \qquad 3 = \frac{36}{12} \qquad 7 = \frac{42}{6}$$

The early experiences basic to answering such questions should relate to manipulation of real things and to "reading and writing" drawings or using other representative aids. As soon as the idea is clear, however, children should be encouraged to formulate a more efficient procedure for changing whole numbers to fractions. Most children are capable of formulating in their own words the "rule" for doing this. Preferably, the rule should first be stated in some such form as statement A rather than statement B:

Statement A: To change a whole number to a fraction, multiply the whole number by the number of equal parts in 1.

Statement B: To change a whole number to a fraction, multiply the whole number by the given denominator.

The former type of wording emphasizes the meaning of the denominator rather than routine manipulation of numerals. Any correct pupil wording of the idea should be accepted. Having him memorize a teacher-dictated statement may keep both the pupil and the teacher in the dark. The pupil may be in the dark as to the meanings involved, and the teacher is in the dark concerning the pupil's lack of understanding. If the pupil makes his own statement, the teacher can detect whether or not he really knows whereof he speaks.

CHANGING MIXED NUMBERS
TO FRACTION FORM

Assuming that children have learned the meaning of whole numbers as fractions and the meaning of proper fractions, the key to understanding the changing of mixed numbers to fraction form hinges on their understanding that a mixed number is the statement of a *sum* — the sum of a whole number and a proper fraction.

$$1\frac{3}{4} = 1 + \frac{3}{4} \qquad 4\frac{3}{8} = 4 + \frac{3}{8}$$

Then it is an easy step forward to change whole number and proper fraction to the *same* form. The 1 in $1\frac{3}{4}$ is changed to $\frac{4}{4}$; then the $\frac{4}{4}$ and the $\frac{3}{4}$ are added to give a sum of $\frac{7}{4}$. $1\frac{3}{4} = \frac{4}{4} + \frac{3}{4} = \frac{7}{4}$ Similarly, $4\frac{3}{8} = \frac{32}{8} + \frac{3}{8} = \frac{35}{8}$.

A considerable number of adults who have no difficulty writing "$4\frac{3}{8} = \frac{35}{8}$" are surprised to learn the meanings in terms of sums as expressed above. Why? Because they learned a rule that they applied mechanically: "Multiply the denominator times the whole number; add the numerator; write the answer over the denominator." Even some teachers, introduced to what may seem a most obvious idea, say: "Is *that* what it means? I never thought about it much."

Again, aids of various kinds should be used to help children as they change mixed numbers to improper fractions with understanding, the aids being abandoned as soon as meanings are adequate.

CHANGING IMPROPER FRACTIONS
TO WHOLE OR MIXED NUMBERS

Changing improper fractions to whole or mixed numbers is the other side of the coin. Since the inverse of changing whole numbers to fraction form is changing a fraction to a whole-number form, an inverse process is needed to get the job done. Whereas multiplication is used to change a whole number to a fraction, division is used to change an improper fraction to a whole number. Development of the idea might begin with study of a ruler and such questions as: How many whole inches are the same as 8 half-inches? How many whole inches are the same as 16 fourth-inches? What is a simpler way to say that I have $\frac{4}{2}$ inches?

Discussion of these and similar questions relating to the ruler or other aids should lead to a generalized procedure and pupil statement of a rule of operation, such as: Divide the number of parts by the number of those parts in one whole. Finally, this will resolve itself to: Divide the numerator by the denominator.

Changing an improper fraction to a mixed number follows the same procedure and is based on the same fundamental concepts. In fact, a child may not know when he starts out whether he is going to end up with a whole number or a mixed number. The only difference is that the division process turns out to be a case of incomplete division (division with a remainder), and one must know what to do with the remainder. This too can readily be resolved by reference to a ruler, fractional parts on a flannel board, or other aids. It is important to have enough discussion of what is done with the "leftover parts" to ensure pupil understanding. The change of improper fractions to whole or mixed numbers occurs chiefly with respect to the final form of answers to computations.

Some writers of professional books go into considerable detail as to the various situations in which whole and mixed numbers occur in addition and subtraction problems. Writers of children's texts use much care so as to introduce the variants gradually, and teachers will often benefit from careful study of teachers' guides for use of the texts. The basic ideas underlying all these variations are the same. Only examples of some of the more troublesome variants will be developed here. Of particular importance are the types of changing frequently referred to as "carrying" or "borrowing."

CHANGING OR REGROUPING

OF PARTIAL SUMS

Two problems using the same numbers will serve to point up some similari-

ties and some contrasts in dealing with the changing or regrouping of partial sums.

Problem 1: Jenny used $2\frac{2}{3}$ cups of flour in baking one cake and $1\frac{2}{3}$ cups of flour for another cake. How much flour did she use for both cakes?

Problem 2: Ned used $2\frac{2}{3}$ yards of twine to tie up one package for mailing and $1\frac{2}{3}$ yards to tie up another package. How much twine did he use in all?

The solutions might be dramatized in many ways, but drawings will be used here to illustrate two approaches. Figure 106 fits problem 1, and figure 107 fits problem 2.

Any of the algorisms below fit rather well with problem 1 and figure 106. In Forms A and B the proper fractions are added first, the resulting $\frac{4}{3}$ is changed to $1\frac{1}{3}$, and then the whole number 1 is added to the other whole numbers. In Form B the whole number 1 is "carried" to the top of the whole-number column, as typically done in column addition, whereas in Form A the new mixed-number sum is moved under the sum of the whole numbers and added there.

In Form C the proper fractions are added, the whole numbers are added, and then the regrouping is done to change $3\frac{4}{3}$ to $4\frac{1}{3}$. Each algorism is correct. In Form A the vertical line separating whole numbers from fractions is essential. Without it the line under the long horizontal line would read $3\frac{4}{3} = 1\frac{1}{3}$, which is definitely wrong.

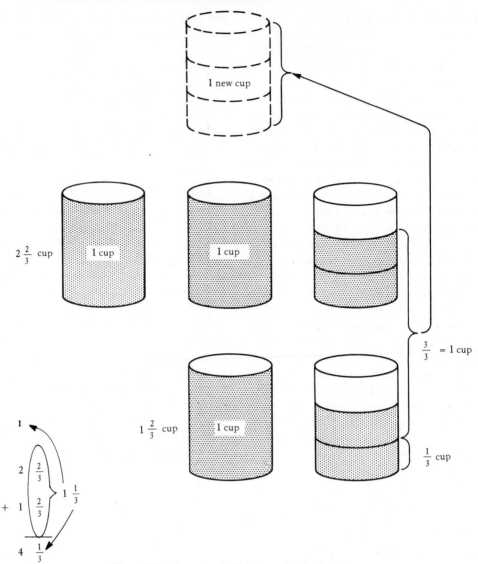

Figure 106. Regrouping Partial Sums—Thirds of a Cup.

Forms D and E correspond to figure 107. These solutions of problem 2 are not widely used in elementary schools, but their introduction serves at least two good purposes. First, these solutions familiarize children with algebraic form and smoother transition to later work in mathematics. Second, they fit the drawing in figure 107 much better than do the algorisms associated with figure 106, though the numbers are the same.

Form D: $\quad 2\dfrac{2}{3} + 1\dfrac{2}{3} = \dfrac{8}{3} + \dfrac{5}{3} = \dfrac{13}{3} = 4\dfrac{1}{3}$

Form E: $\quad 2\dfrac{2}{3} + 1\dfrac{2}{3} = \dfrac{8+5}{3} = \dfrac{13}{3} = 4\dfrac{1}{3}$

A number line is very useful in teaching addition of fractions; but when mixed numbers are used, complications sometimes arise. The reader can better interpret this statement by drawing a number line and marking off $2\frac{2}{3}$ units.

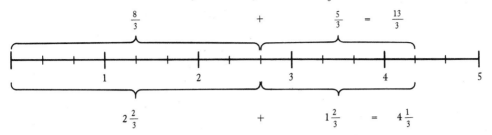

Figure 107. Number Line Solution with Improper Fractions.

The question immediately arises as to how to proceed from there. Whether one marks off the "1" first or the "$\frac{2}{3}$" first, at one time or another a whole number has to "bridge" from the "interior" of one whole unit into the "interior" of another. For children this is often confusing and difficult. By using the type of thinking represented by Forms D and E, this difficulty and source of confusion are removed. All the whole-units on the number line are first marked off in thirds (or other pertinent fractional units). Each number is changed to those common fractional units, and then the numbers of fractional units are added: 8 thirds + 5 thirds = 13 thirds. Finally the $\frac{13}{3}$ must be changed to mixed-number form.

CHANGING OR REGROUPING MINUENDS

Changing minuends in this case might be called "regrouping to make subtraction possible." When the fraction part of a mixed number is smaller than the fraction to be subtracted from it, the minuend must be changed to a new form in which subtraction of the fraction is possible. When the minuend is a whole number and the subtrahend includes a fraction, the same situation prevails.

Problem: Scout camp is 4 miles from Henry's home. Henry gets a ride toward home for $1\frac{3}{4}$ miles and walks the rest of the

way home. How far does he have to walk to get home?

Figure 108 shows the problem situation and solution.

Form F	Form G	Form H
$3\frac{4}{4}$	$4 = 3\frac{4}{4}$	4
$-1\frac{3}{4}$	$-1\frac{3}{4} = 1\frac{3}{4}$	$-1\frac{3}{4}$
$2\frac{1}{4}$	$2\frac{1}{4}$	$2\frac{1}{4}$

Form I
$$4 - 1\frac{3}{4} = \frac{16}{4} - \frac{7}{4} = \frac{9}{4} = 2\frac{1}{4}$$

Form J
$$4 - 1\frac{3}{4} = \frac{16-7}{4} = \frac{9}{4} = 2\frac{1}{4}$$

The 4-mile distance in the diagram or in the minuend of the algorisms is stated in whole miles. In order to subtract fourths, at least 1 mile of the distance must be changed to the form $\frac{4}{4}$, leaving only 3 whole miles not so changed (Forms F, G, and H). The procedure is based on exactly the same ideas as in subtraction of whole numbers when 1 ten is changed to 10 ones so as to make subtraction of ones possible. This relation to a familiar changing situation should be used in introducing this modification to children.

The changing of the whole minuend to fraction form as in Forms I and J fits very nicely the drawing in figure 108. Here the whole distance is changed from whole-mile form to fourth-of-a-mile form. Children may enjoy trying to draw a different number line picture that fits more closely with Forms F, G, and H.

Form H is the most advanced form and for most children should be postponed until they have acquired firm meanings through use of less abbreviated forms.

tablishes the common denominator first and then changes the mixed numbers to fraction form. If figure 109 were to be changed to fit the two horizontal algorisms, all the "bars" would have to be marked off in sixths.

The particular algorism or illustration used does not matter so much (provided

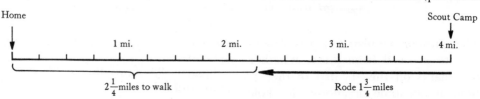

Home   Scout Camp

1 mi.   2 mi.   3 mi.   4 mi.

$2\frac{1}{4}$ miles to walk   Rode $1\frac{3}{4}$ miles

Figure 108. Regrouping the Minuend — Number Line Solution.

Two types of form changes are involved in the solution of the next problem. Here the "solver" must handle both (1) a change designed to achieve a common denominator and (2) a change of the regrouping or "borrowing" type.

Problem: Buster had $3\frac{1}{2}$ candy bars on Monday morning. He ate $1\frac{2}{3}$ bars during the week. How much candy did he have left at the end of the week?

The change to a common denominator (sixths) is usually made first, followed by the changing of 1 whole (bar) to sixths in order to have enough sixths from which to subtract the 4 sixths. This is the sequence of procedures in Forms K through M below. Differences among those forms are really only differences in recording those two essential steps. Figure 109 shows the same two steps in graphic form. Both the one-half bar and one whole bar are changed to sixths in step A. In step B, 1 whole and 4 sixths are crossed out to represent subtraction, leaving 1 whole bar and $\frac{5}{6}$ of another bar.

Forms N and O, using the horizontal form, differ in that N changes both mixed numbers to improper fractions first and then changes them to have common denominators, whereas O es-

each is correct), but it does matter a great deal whether or not each child understands the background meanings of the one or the ones he uses. Only thus can he reason well in the solution of this or similar problems.

Form K

$$3\frac{1}{2} = 3\frac{3}{6} = 2\frac{9}{6}$$
$$-1\frac{2}{3} = 1\frac{4}{6} = 1\frac{4}{6}$$
$$1\frac{5}{6}$$

Form L

$$3\frac{1}{2} = 3\overset{9}{\underset{2}{\cancel{3}}}\frac{}{6}$$
$$-1\frac{2}{3} = 1\frac{4}{6}$$
$$1\frac{5}{6}$$

Form M

$$3\frac{1}{2} = 3\frac{3}{6}$$
$$1\frac{2}{3} = 1\frac{4}{6}$$
$$1\frac{5}{6}$$

Form N

$$3\frac{1}{2} - 1\frac{2}{3} = \frac{7}{2} - \frac{5}{3} = \frac{21}{6} - \frac{10}{6} = \frac{11}{6} = 1\frac{5}{6}$$

Form O

$$3\frac{1}{2} - 1\frac{2}{3} = 3\frac{3}{6} - 1\frac{4}{6} = \frac{21-10}{6} = \frac{11}{6} = 1\frac{5}{6}$$

Although everyday usage of addition and subtraction of fractions is not very extensive in comparison with the usage of addition and subtraction of whole numbers, it may be extremely important to perform these operations correctly when they apply. The most frequent uses are in situations involving standard measures of one kind or another — in cooking; in buying, selling, and using materials such as cloth or rugs or lum-

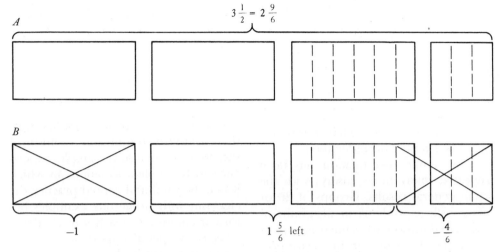

Figure 109. Regrouping the Minuend—Solution with Rectangles.

ber; in nursing; and, of course, in various industrial and business applications.

Common Denominators and Division of Fractions

Typically division of fractions is introduced after multiplication of fractions, which in turn is typically introduced after addition and subtraction of fractions. The present text deviates from common practice by introducing division of fractions immediately after addition and subtraction of fractions and preceding multiplication of fractions.

REASON FOR INTRODUCTION OF DIVISION OF FRACTIONS HERE

If, as has been recommended in earlier pages, the meanings of common multiples, the meanings of fractions, and the finding of equivalent fractions have been introduced prior to computation with fractions, addition and subtraction of fractions can be introduced meaningfully without the double burden of "newness," which is present when the concept of common denominators is introduced along with the teaching of the addition and subtraction processes with fractions. Further, once the common-denominator concept has been practiced in adding and subtracting like and unlike fractions, the introduction of division of fractions by the "common-denominator method" seems logical.

Further, those problem situations which lend themselves readily to solution by the common-denominator method are *measurement* situations such as are used in addition and subtraction of fractions. The transition from adding and subtracting fractions to dividing fractions by the common-denominator method is a comparatively easy transition for children. (For their teachers and parents it may seem difficult because they are so thoroughly grounded in the "invert and multiply method" that they can not readily put it aside while considering the common-denominator method the first time.)

The "invert and multiply" method of dividing by fractions will not be neglected. It will be introduced after multiplication of fractions in the next chapter. There it can be introduced in terms of meanings that are appropriate at that point.

COMMON USES OF

DIVISION OF FRACTIONS

Division of and by fractions is not used by most people with anything like the frequency that other processes with fractions are used. This may be one of the reasons that the division process with fractions is so widely misunderstood or simply not understood.

This simple investigation has been repeated many times, always with the same general results. Groups of 20 or more college students in programs of teacher education and similar groups of experienced teachers in in-service programs have been given an example of division by fractions like $\frac{2}{3} \div \frac{1}{6}$ with the request that they devise a verbally stated problem situation in which the suggested computation would be used for the solution. Invariably, a large proportion of each group have either not come up with any problem or have given a problem in which the division of fractions is not appropriate. This is probably partly due to unfamiliarity because of lack of use of division with fractions, as suggested above; but perhaps this state of incompetence is more closely related to the fact that far too many people have learned only the form of such computations and never did understand the meanings involved. This sad state of affairs needs to be drastically improved.[5]

One early step toward better understanding of division by fractions is concentration on the meanings involved in the common-denominator method. The meanings of particular importance here are: (1) the relationship with measurement division of whole numbers and (2)

[5] The most frequent error the writer has found in her numerous repetitions of this informal experiment is that people give problems in which multiplication rather than division of fractions is the appropriate process.

the concept of fractions as measures, as used in addition and subtraction of fractions.

DIVIDING A WHOLE NUMBER

BY A PROPER FRACTION

Teachers who are not familiar with the common-denominator method should give themselves ample experience with problem situations in which it may be used and should practice the algorism with numerous examples before attempting to teach it to children. This is of special importance for this particular method because many teachers have difficulty in adapting their thought patterns to a method so different from the "invert-and-multiply" form that they have practiced so long. They will do well to focus their attention on the meanings of the problems and let the form evolve from the problem and process meanings, rather than focusing rigidly on the form alone.

As with any new step in learning, the children also need numerous and varied opportunities to practice problem solving as well as routine calculation. Use of any form of manipulative materials that emphasize fraction meanings is in order. Drawings are also of particular benefit in keeping the learner's attention focused on the problem and its reasonable solution. The following problem and the accompanying drawing (fig. 110) show the necessity for changing the whole number 4 to the fractional form $\frac{12}{3}$.

Problem: The children in a school club bought ribbon and tied it into decorative bows to put on gift packages. Then they sold the ready-tied bows to raise money for their club. Each bow took $\frac{2}{3}$ of a yard of ribbon. If Betty had 4 yards of ribbon, how many bows could she make?

Figure 110 represents four stages in the solution of this problem. Only one

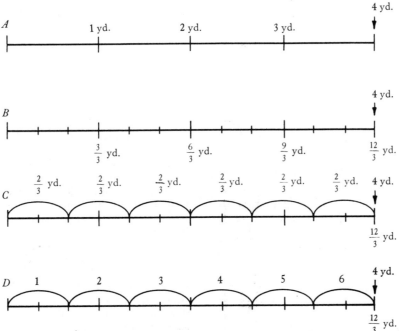

Figure 110. Dividing a Whole Number by a Proper Fraction.

such drawing would need to be made in the actual solution-by-drawing; the separate stages are shown merely to indicate the successive steps in reasoning.

Some typical questions and answers that might accompany the use of the drawing are suggested:

Question: How could I draw something to help us solve our problem?

Answer: Draw a number line to show the 4 yards of ribbon. (Stage A.)

Question: Now Betty is going to use $\frac{2}{3}$ of a yard each time. If I am going to measure off $\frac{2}{3}$ of a yard for each bow, what should I do to the number line first to make that easier?

Answer: Mark off thirds in every yard. (See stage B.)

Question: How many thirds will there be in 4 yards?

Answer: Twelve ($\frac{12}{3}$ written as equal to 4).

Question: How can I show how many two-thirds in twelve-thirds?

Answer: Mark off thirds two at a time. (See stage C.)

Question: Well, then, how many $\frac{2}{3}$'s are there in $\frac{12}{3}$?

Answer: Six. (See stage D.)

The writing of the common-denominator algorism is now merely a matter of *writing* what has already been *done* in the drawing.

$$4 \text{ wholes} \div 2 \text{ thirds} = 12 \text{ thirds} \div 2 \text{ thirds} = 6$$

$$4 \div \frac{2}{3} = \frac{12}{3} \div \frac{2}{3} = 6$$

Such a solution by drawing depicts the meaning of the process, clearly showing the need for changing the whole number 4 into 12 thirds before marking off the 2 thirds for each bow. There is a clear need for changing the 4 to a fraction form with the same denominator as the divisor, $\frac{2}{3}$.

DIVIDING A PROPER FRACTION
BY A PROPER FRACTION

The same relationships hold when one proper fraction is divided by another proper fraction, as in this problem.

Problem: Mrs. Wilson usually cuts her pies into sixths. If she has ⅔ of the pie left in the pie tin, how many usual-size pieces can she get from it?

Figure 111-*A* shows the ⅔ pie before Mrs. Wilson cut the sixths. Figure 111-*B* shows the same ⅔ pie after she cut the sixths. (The white areas are included to show the missing parts of a whole pie.) Here again one can readily see the need for changing the dividend (⅔) to the same denominator as the divisor (⅙). The problem situation demands that this be done since it describes ⅔ as being divided to make sixths. The problem requires finding how many ⅙'s there are in ⅔. The answer is clearly 4.

2 thirds ÷ 1 sixth = 4 sixths ÷ 1 sixth = 4

$$\frac{2}{3} \div \frac{1}{6} = \frac{4}{6} \div \frac{1}{6} = 4$$

DIVIDING A MIXED NUMBER
BY A PROPER FRACTION

One teacher working with a group of children who had a good grasp of adding and subtracting proper fractions and mixed numbers gave the following introduction to division with fractions. She used a mixed number divided by a proper fraction. The teacher carefully worded the problem so as to leave the plan of solution open for pupil exploration.

Teacher: We have spent quite a long time on adding and subtracting fractions, and you are pretty good at that. Today let's do something different. I think you will enjoy acting out a solution to the problem I am going to give you.

Here are some small sheets of paper. Please pretend that they represent cakes. I want each of you to have 2½ cakes. (Paper passed out to children.) Each two people may share one sheet so each of you has a half cake to go with your two whole cakes.

Now let's say that you have 2½ cakes and that you are going to serve the cake to your family. You cut the cakes so each serving is ⅛ of a whole cake. If there are 5 people in your family, how many times can you have this cake for dessert? Please do not write anything. Just go ahead and use the paper. Cut or tear it as you would cut the cake. Then act out how you would serve it to your family.

Jack: How many pieces does everybody get each time?

Teacher: Each person gets 1 piece each time you serve cake. (The teacher observed what children were doing, asking questions of individuals who did not proceed as well as others. When all had worked out the solution in one way or another, she continued.)

Teacher: Virginia, how did you work out the servings?

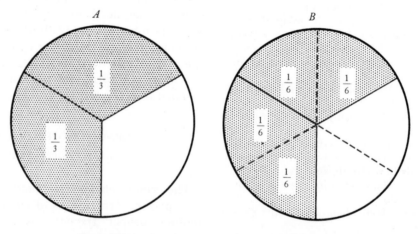

Figure 111. Dividing a Proper Fraction by a Proper Fraction.

Virginia: I divided each cake into 6 equal pieces, or sixths. Two cakes made 12 pieces and the half cake made 3 pieces. That was 15 pieces in all. Then I gave one serving to each member of the family like this. (She dealt out 5 paper sixths as she spoke.) That was enough dessert for one meal. Then I did it again. That is the dessert for the second meal. Then there was enough for a third serving each.

Teacher: What was your answer? How many times can you serve cake to 5 people?

Virginia: Three times.

Teacher: If you were going to write a record of what you just did, how would you write it? (Various records were written on the chalkboard by different children. Forms P through R are samples of these records.)

Form P

1 cake makes 6 pieces	15 pieces
1 cake makes 6 pieces	−5 pieces
$\frac{1}{2}$ cake makes 3 pieces	10 pieces
	−5 pieces ←3 servings
$2\frac{1}{2}$ cakes make 15 pieces	5 pieces
	−5 pieces
	0 pieces

Form Q

1 cake = 6 sixths
1 cake = 6 sixths
$\frac{1}{2}$ cake = $\frac{3 \text{ sixths}}{15 \text{ sixths}}$

$$5 \text{ sixths} \overline{\smash{)}15 \text{ sixths}}^{\,3}$$

Form R

$2\frac{1}{2} = \frac{5}{2} = \frac{15}{6}$; so there were 15 pieces of cake ($\frac{1}{6}$ each)

$\frac{15}{6} - \frac{5}{6} = \frac{10}{6}$ dessert the first time

$\frac{10}{6} - \frac{5}{6} = \frac{5}{6}$ dessert the second time

$\frac{5}{6} - \frac{5}{6} = \frac{0}{6} = 0$ dessert the third time

Notice that Forms P and R use a series of successive subtractions, fitting very well the successive steps of "serving the dessert." P, however, uses only whole-number terminology, whereas R uses fraction notation.

Both Q and R use the name "sixths" for the equal parts, but Q uses words whereas R uses numerals to record what was being done with those sixths. Q might be said to have a more mature or

concise solution in that division is used instead of successive subtractions, but R definitely shows a more mature level of calculation in changing $2\frac{1}{2}$ to $\frac{15}{6}$.

When the children had had a chance to compare and discuss the various algorisms and had agreed that all were correct, the teacher led them on to the notation for division of fractions. By that time, the problem and its solution were well in hand, and the children could attend to the new algorism as just another way of writing out something they already understood.

First, the teacher called their attention to the division algorism in Form Q. Then she asked if they could write a simple division like that another way. They readily suggested the horizontal form:

$$15 \text{ sixths} \div 5 \text{ sixths} = 3$$

Teacher: This is most interesting. We have performed a division. We have divided a fraction (sixths) by a fraction (sixths). This is something new that you have done today.

From this point on the teacher led the children from the series of algorisms they had used to a single concise algorism:

$$2\frac{1}{2} \div \frac{5}{6} = \frac{15}{6} \div \frac{5}{6} = 3$$

In doing so, she used questions, suggestions, and general discussion to bring out the meanings of division of fractions, with each meaning based on prior learnings about division, about whole numbers, and about fractions.

The teacher who is to be successful in guiding children to understand the common-denominator method of division of fractions must herself be clear on such ideas as these:

1. The denominator of a fraction is considered here as the *name* of the fractional part and does not enter into the division computation.

2. The common-denominator method of division of fractions depends on having the dividend and the divisor designated by the *same name*, after which the numerators are simply divided as whole numbers are divided.

3. In measurement division problems with whole numbers, the dividend and divisor always are like terms (have the same name). In common-denominator division of fractions also, the dividend and divisor have to be *like terms* (have the same name).

4. In measurement division with whole numbers, the quotient is not designated by reference to any name. In common-denominator division of fractions, the quotient does not have a name; it is an unnamed number designating the number of subgroups in the dividend.

5. In the common-denominator method of division of fractions the divisor is used as a unit of measure. In the preceding problem situation, the divisor was $\frac{5}{6}$ of a cake. The total amount of cake ($2\frac{1}{2}$ cakes) was measured by $\frac{5}{6}$ cake. That is, the question was: "How many $\frac{5}{6}$'s are there in $2\frac{1}{2}$?"

6. This use of the divisor as a measuring unit is analogous to the use of fractions as units of measure in addition and subtraction of fractions. This is the basis of the requirement that terms must be changed to the same kind of measure (common denominator) before the calculations can proceed.

Since the children will already have learned about common denominators and how to achieve them while adding and subtracting fractions, this phase of the common-denominator method of dividing fractions will not be new. It will merely provide a new application for skills already developed.

All the divisors used in the illustrative problems above have been proper frac-

tions. Whole numbers or mixed numbers might also have been used as divisors, provided such use was appropriate to the measurement division situation in which they were used.

The rationale would be the same as that already developed. Following the rationale is more difficult, however, when the divisor is larger than the dividend or when there is a division remainder that is expressed as a fraction in the answer—that is, when the answer is not a whole number.

FRACTIONS IN THE QUOTIENT

A problem situation involving linear measure is particularly appropriate for developing the meaning of a fractional answer for a computation like:

$$3\frac{1}{2} \div 1\frac{1}{2} = \frac{7}{2} \div \frac{3}{2} = \frac{7}{3} = 2\frac{1}{3}$$

What is the meaning of the $\frac{1}{3}$ in the answer?

Problem: Joe has a board that is $3\frac{1}{2}$ feet long. He is going to use it for making shelves for a bookcase. Each shelf has to be $1\frac{1}{2}$ feet in length. How many shelves can he cut from the $3\frac{1}{2}$-foot board?

A number line is helpful in showing the meaning of the fraction part of the mixed-number answer. Figure 112-*A* shows the length of the board, $3\frac{1}{2}$ feet. Figure 112-*B* shows the changing of $3\frac{1}{2}$ feet to $\frac{7}{2}$ feet. Figure 112-*C* shows $1\frac{1}{2}$ feet, or $\frac{3}{2}$ feet, measured off against the full length of the board. It is clear that Joe can cut two $1\frac{1}{2}$-foot shelves from the board. Actually the real-life answer to the problem question is a whole number: Joe can get 2 shelves from his board.

But what is the meaning of the remainder marked with the question mark in figure 112-*C*? It is $\frac{1}{2}$ foot. But the fraction that occurs with the whole number 2 in the answer is $\frac{1}{3}$. How can $\frac{1}{2}$ of a whole thing (foot) be $\frac{1}{3}$?

Figure 112-*D* answers that question. The last $\frac{1}{2}$ *foot* of the board is equal to $\frac{1}{3}$ *shelf*. The $\frac{1}{2}$ foot that is left is $\frac{1}{3}$ of what would be needed to make another shelf. Joe has enough material to make 2 whole shelves and $\frac{1}{3}$ enough to make another shelf.

A group of teachers working with a consultant discussed a problem similar to this one. One of them said, "That is rather a difficult idea. I don't remember ever having had this difficulty before of figuring out the meaning of the fractional part of a mixed-number answer to such a division problem. I guess I was just satisfied to get a right answer and didn't try to think it through." She was probably right; she had been computing according to a prescribed procedure (probably the invert-and-multiply procedure) and had not been much concerned about the meanings.

A mixed-number answer to this type of situation is easier to interpret than a proper-fraction answer. The 2 whole shelves in the answer to the last problem are a helpful point of reference in recognizing the $\frac{1}{2}$ foot as $\frac{1}{3}$ of another such whole shelf. The lack of a whole number in the answer to the next problem makes it somewhat harder for the learner to interpret.

Problem: Some boys at camp had set themselves a goal of rowing a boat $\frac{1}{2}$ mile. The swimming instructor told them that the distance from the dock to a certain marker was $\frac{1}{8}$ mile. The boys rowed from the dock to the marker. How far had they rowed in terms of what they said they would do?

One must remember the measurement idea. How many half-miles have they rowed when they have rowed $\frac{1}{8}$ mile? How many $\frac{1}{2}$'s in $\frac{1}{8}$? Obviously, the answer cannot be a whole number.

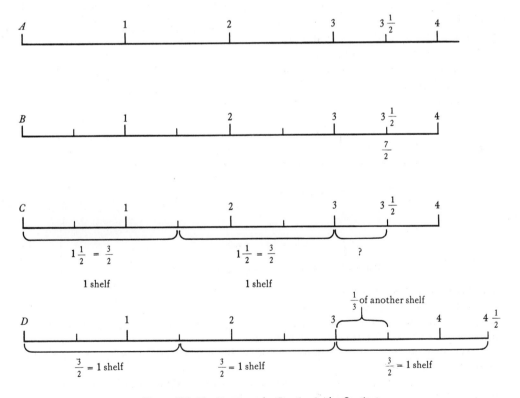

Figure 112. The Meaning of a Fraction in the Quotient.

Figure 113 shows graphically what this computation says with numerals:

$$\frac{1}{8} \div \frac{1}{2} = \frac{1}{8} \div \frac{4}{8} = \frac{1}{4}.$$

The full distance is $\frac{1}{2}$ mile. When the boys have rowed $\frac{1}{8}$ mile, they have gone $\frac{1}{4}$ of the full distance. The answer "$\frac{1}{4}$" is not $\frac{1}{4}$ mile but $\frac{1}{4}$ of the full distance. How many $\frac{1}{2}$ miles are in $\frac{1}{8}$ mile? Only $\frac{1}{4}$.

There may be some children for whom this line of reasoning is too difficult. Some will enjoy it very much. The teacher should use her own good judgment in deciding how far to pursue it for different children.

Problems like the last one do not occur frequently in the everyday affairs of elementary school children or even of many adults. No doubt, many people who have learned to do such computations correctly would be hard put to it to rationalize what they had done. The common-denominator algorism or form should be of help in making the computations meaningful to a majority.[6]

The present chapter might appropriately have been named "Working with Common Denominators." The addition of fractions, subtraction of fractions, and measurement-type division of fractions all depend on the concept of common denominators. The concept of like terms is ever-present in these processes. The first step in all three processes is to check on the presence of common denominators. If they are not present, common denominators must be achieved by changing one or more terms. The changing is always a matter of form without change in value. We might say that the numerals change but the numbers do not. Finally, the computations are done using the *like* forms.

[6] Sometimes when the common-denominator method of dividing common fractions is introduced, the learners ask this type of question: In adding and subtracting fractions, the common denominator is found in the answer. Why does the common denominator not appear in the division answer? The questioner should be referred to the occurrence of like terms (same names) in addition, subtraction, and division of whole numbers. The common names appear in all terms in addition and subtraction, but they occur in only two terms in division. Since the common-denominator method of dividing fractions is a measurement division process, the like terms are the dividend and divisor with the quotient being an unnamed number as with other measurement division situations.

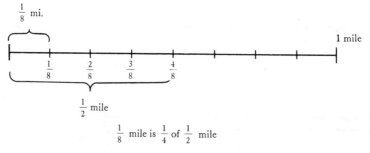

$$\frac{1}{8} \text{ mile is } \frac{1}{4} \text{ of } \frac{1}{2} \text{ mile}$$

Figure 113. A Proper Fraction as the Whole Quotient.

STUDY QUESTIONS

1. Follow the directions for using the common-denominator strip (pp. 346-47). Use any two denominators you wish. Describe what you did at each step in terms of numerals and mathematical symbols for processes performed.

2. You may not be used to the introduction of division of fractions before multiplication of fractions, as in this chapter. What are some arguments pro and con for this sequence?

3. Make a word problem for which each of the following divisions would be used in the solution (three problems): (a) $1\frac{1}{2} \div \frac{3}{4}$; (b) $\frac{5}{6} \div \frac{1}{3}$; (c) $2\frac{1}{3} \div \frac{5}{6}$.

4. Two of the divisions in question 3 have mixed numbers for quotients. Draw number line or other graphic solutions that show the meanings of those quotients clearly.

5. Read George H. McMeen's article in the March, 1962, issue of *The Arithmetic Teacher* called "Division by a Fraction—A New Method," pp. 122-26. Construct the materials described and try out the method. Evaluate it.

6. Compare "changing" as practiced in subtraction of whole numbers with "changing" as practiced in subtraction of mixed numbers.

CHAPTER 16

Multiplication and Division
of Common Fractions

MULTIPLICATION PROBLEMS in which common fractions occur may be classified in various ways, one of which is as follows: (1) a whole number times a proper fraction, such as $4 \times \frac{2}{3}$; (2) a proper fraction times a whole number, such as $\frac{1}{2} \times 6$; and (3) a proper fraction times a fraction, such as $\frac{2}{3} \times \frac{1}{4}$. If similar variations are considered for improper fractions and mixed numbers, the list gets much longer. In this chapter the three listed types will be considered in some detail, followed by some attention to use of mixed numbers and improper fractions. Finally, a generalized procedure for all such types will be presented.

MULTIPLICATION OF A
WHOLE NUMBER TIMES A
PROPER FRACTION

Addition of common fractions depends on the concept of fractions as describing fraction-units, a measurement idea. Since one of the basic concepts of multiplication is that of repeated additions, our first problem in multiplication of proper fractions grows easily out of already developed ideas.

Problem: Jean practices her piano lesson $\frac{2}{3}$ of an hour every day except Sunday. How many hours does she practice each week?

A "time line" may be quickly constructed using long, narrow wooden blocks of uniform size. Let each block equal $\frac{1}{3}$ of an hour. Then the problem can readily be solved by addition—laying two blocks on the table, end to end, for each $\frac{2}{3}$ hour. Six sets of 2 thirds each will look like figure 114. The action is easily recorded by use of the familiar algorism for adding common fractions. If the children have understood multiplication as a quick way of adding several addends of equal size, they should not have difficulty in moving on to the multiplication algorism. Adding "2 thirds" 6 times is obviously the same as multiplying 6×2 thirds. The progression of steps in this transition is shown in the series of statements below:

2 thirds + 2 thirds + 2 thirds + 2 thirds
+ 2 thirds + 2 thirds = 12 thirds

$$\frac{2}{3} + \frac{2}{3} + \frac{2}{3} + \frac{2}{3} + \frac{2}{3} + \frac{2}{3} = \frac{12}{3}$$

6×2 thirds = 12 thirds

$$6 \times \frac{2}{3} = \frac{12}{3}$$

All the statements tell the same story, but in progressively more efficient form.

Including the first and third statements in this sequence may not seem necessary. Perhaps it is not necessary for all pupils, but it serves to emphasize an important reminder—that the denominator "3" in this problem tells the "name" of the parts being combined. The multiplication does not involve this name; the multiplication is that of the whole number times the numerator. (If any confusion develops on this point, the teacher needs only to remind children of the multiplication of whole numbers in problem situations. The multiplier is always an abstract "number of times" that the repeated addend (multiplicand) occurs; the multiplicand and the product have whatever "same name" fits the facts of the concrete problem situation.)

as the numerator of the fraction part of a mixed-number answer (e.g., $4 \times \frac{2}{3} = \frac{8}{3} = 2\frac{2}{3}$).

Additional problems should use other concrete and semiconcrete representations (pies, flannel board fractional parts, ruler fractions) until the children understand (preferably develop as their own) the generalization that when a whole number is multiplied times a proper fraction, *the whole number is multiplied times the numerator of the fraction, and, if necessary, the product is divided by the denominator of the fraction.*

Further practice will be more meaningful and more effective if the teacher

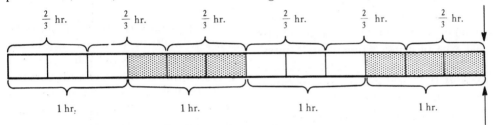

Figure 114. Multiplication of a Whole Number Times a Fraction.

The changing of $\frac{12}{3}$ to whole-number form will be obvious in the block demonstration if the teacher uses different colors of blocks for each successive "3 thirds," or each new "hour." This arrangement is suggested by the shaded and unshaded sections of figure 114. As that final step is taken, each of the algorisms above will be extended to show that the $\frac{12}{3}$ equal 4.

This last step, the changing of the improper fraction to a whole number (in some problems it would be a mixed number), should serve as a reminder of another meaning of a common fraction. A common fraction is an implied division; the changing of the improper fraction to whole-number or mixed-number form requires that this implied division be performed: $12 \div 3 = 4$. If the division had not "come out even," the remainder would have been retained

checks frequently on pupils' grasp of the important meanings used in this type of problem, namely: (1) multiplication as repeated additions, (2) fractions as measuring units, (3) the denominator as the name of those measuring units, (4) the multiplicand and product as like terms with the same name, (5) the multiplier as an abstract "number of times" the same addend is used, and (6) a fraction as an implied division. The length of this list indicates the way in which earlier meanings accumulate to bolster the development of new phases or applications of any process.

MULTIPLICATION OF A PROPER FRACTION TIMES A WHOLE NUMBER

Some teachers introduce the multiplication of a proper fraction times a whole number simply by invoking the commutative law for multiplication.

$$6 \times \frac{2}{3} = 12; \text{ therefore, } \frac{2}{3} \times 6 = 12$$

While this is true, it is by no means an adequate treatment of this second type of fraction multiplication. The basic meanings of the two situations are quite different in certain respects.

New uses of old ideas. The use of a fraction as a multiplier is new. In none of the computations to this point has the multiplier been anything but a whole number. It is a simple matter to spend a given amount of money or use a given part of a pie "2 times" or "4 times" or "9 times"; it is not so simple to spend that amount of money or use that part of a pie "$\frac{2}{3}$ times" or "$\frac{1}{2}$ times" or "$\frac{3}{8}$ times." Something must be done to expand the meaning of multiplication and of the multiplier to include proper fractions as multipliers. In the addition, subtraction, and division of fractions and in the one type of multiplication of fractions developed to this point, fractions have not been interpreted as *operators*. Now that must be done.

Another hurdle to negotiate is the reconciliation of the terminology "$\frac{1}{2}$ of" or "$\frac{3}{4}$ of" with the meaning "$\frac{1}{2}$ times" or "$\frac{3}{4}$ times." The loose and incorrect practice of equating "of" with "times" is so common that one must conclude that teaching has been inadequate to develop the true relationship.

Whereas the multiplication of a whole number times a proper fraction has been developed as the multiplication of a fraction-form measuring unit, the multiplication of a fraction times a whole number involves a partitioning idea. Obviously, this requires clarification if learners are to see the process in correct light.

The ratio idea as expressed in fractions and the ratio-to-one idea of mul-

tiplication by whole numbers can be neatly related when a fraction is used as a multiplier. This again is a new application at this point of a previously developed concept.

All in all, there is too much that is new in the multiplication of a fraction times a whole number to pass it off by simply applying the commutative law to the multiplication of a whole number times a fraction.

Multiplying by a unit fraction. Beginning with a unit fraction as the multiplier allows the learner to focus on the already established relationship between two forms for stating partition division.

Unit fractions referring to parts of groups should be reviewed, beginning with such questions as: What is $\frac{1}{4}$ of a dozen? Children who are ready to study multiplication of a fraction times a whole number will certainly know that the answer to the question is "3." When asked, "How do you know?" various correct answers might be given, such as:

If you divided a dozen eggs into 4 equal parts, there would be 3 eggs in each part of the dozen.
Twelve divided by $4 = 3$.
One-fourth of $12 = 3$.

Other total groups and fractional parts may be used. Teacher and pupils may develop an organized summary of which the following statements (to be read from left to right) are a sample:

What is $\frac{1}{2}$ of 14?	$14 \div 2 = 7$	$\frac{1}{2}$ of $14 = 7$
What is $\frac{1}{2}$ of 16?	$16 \div 2 = 8$	$\frac{1}{2}$ of $16 = 8$
What is $\frac{1}{2}$ of 18?	$18 \div 2 = 9$	$\frac{1}{2}$ of $18 = 9$
What is $\frac{1}{3}$ of 12?	$12 \div 3 = 4$	$\frac{1}{3}$ of $12 = 4$
What is $\frac{1}{3}$ of 15?	$15 \div 3 = 5$	$\frac{1}{3}$ of $15 = 5$
What is $\frac{1}{3}$ of 18?	$18 \div 3 = 6$	$\frac{1}{3}$ of $18 = 6$

At the same time, or later if the teacher prefers, such a summary might be extended to include mixed-number quotients, thus:

What is $\frac{1}{2}$ of 14?	$14 \div 2 = 7$	$\frac{1}{2}$ of $14 = 7$
What is $\frac{1}{2}$ of 15?	$15 \div 2 = 7\frac{1}{2}$	$\frac{1}{2}$ of $15 = 7\frac{1}{2}$
What is $\frac{1}{2}$ of 16?	$16 \div 2 = 8$	$\frac{1}{2}$ of $16 = 8$
What is $\frac{1}{2}$ of 17?	$17 \div 2 = 8\frac{1}{2}$	$\frac{1}{2}$ of $17 = 8\frac{1}{2}$

From such thinking and emphasis on situations in which these statements are true, the key idea may be readily demonstrated that:

$\frac{1}{2}$ of	means the same as	$\div 2$
$\frac{1}{3}$ of	means the same as	$\div 3$
$\frac{1}{4}$ of	means the same as	$\div 4$

In adult language, we might say that multiplication by a unit fraction has the same effect as division by the whole number that is the denominator of that same fraction. For children the type of statement given above in terms of examples of the relationship should suffice.

Note that this is a *partition* idea. The action being shown is finding a part of a group or finding the size of one of the equal subgroups into which the total group has been divided (the partition meaning of division of whole numbers). The fraction here suggests an operation —division. The fraction tells what is to be done to the whole number. It tells us to divide the whole number. In the expression "$4 \times \frac{1}{2}$" the direction is to do something to the fraction (multiply it by 4). In the expression "$\frac{1}{2}$ of 4" the direction is to do something to the whole number (divide it by 2). This is an entirely different use of the fraction from that in which a whole number is multiplied times a fraction.

So much for equating "$\frac{1}{2}$ of" with "$\div 2$" or "$\frac{1}{3}$ of" with "$\div 3$". But we must go one step further. We want also to equate "$\frac{1}{2}$ of" with "$\frac{1}{2}$ times," or "$\frac{1}{2} \times$," and to equate "$\frac{1}{3}$ of" with "$\frac{1}{3}$ times," or "$\frac{1}{3} \times$."

One good way to do this is suggested frequently in teaching guides. This is a series of multiplications that begins with multiplication statements in which all terms are whole numbers. The multiplicand stays the same all through the series, but the multiplier is progressively reduced according to some consistent pattern. The products must accordingly be reduced in the same consistent pattern. The series at the left below shows multipliers being divided by 2 successively; that on the right shows multipliers being divided successively by 3.

$4 \times 8 = 32$	$6 \times 15 = 90$
$2 \times 8 = 16$	$3 \times 15 = 45$
$1 \times 8 = 8$	$1 \times 15 = 15$
$\frac{1}{2} \times 8 = 4$	$\frac{1}{3} \times 15 = 5$

As such series (and longer ones) are built, the teacher should question the children as to what is happening—to the multipliers and to the products—in each sequence. After noting that "$\frac{1}{2} \times 8$" is the same as the more familiar "$\frac{1}{2}$ of 8," children will be ready to accept the equivalence of the "$\frac{1}{2}$ of" and "$\frac{1}{2}$ times" terminology.[1]

Once the idea has been established that "$\frac{1}{2}$ of" may be correctly changed to "$\frac{1}{2} \times$," appeal can be made to the logic of "things equal to the same thing are equal to each other."

Multiplying by a nonunit fraction. The next problem uses the same numbers as those in the preceding problem (p. 362), making it possible to draw

---

[1] The equivalence of "$\frac{1}{2}$ of" and "$\frac{1}{2}$ times" terminology should not be confused with the erroneous statement sometimes made (and even put into print) that "'of' means 'times.'" This latter statement is not true. The equality of meanings applies only to *a fractional part of* and *a fraction times* some other number.

more easily some comparisons and contrasts.

Problem: Joe's teacher told him to practice his trumpet lesson 6 hours a week. His mother said that Joe practiced only $\frac{2}{3}$ as long as he should have. How long did Joe practice?

A number line for this problem would first have to show 6 units for the 6 hours Joe was supposed to practice. (See fig. 115*A*.) Now what must be done to solve the problem? How much is $\frac{2}{3}$ of 6 hours? Clearly, one must first determine what is $\frac{1}{3}$ of 6 hours; i.e., we must divide the number line into 3 equal parts. (See fig. 115*B*.) It is clear that $\frac{1}{3}$ of 6 hours = 2 hours: 6 hours ÷ 3 = 2 hours. But Joe practiced *two*-thirds of 6 hours; so we must take *2 times* 2 hours, which is 4 hours (Fig. 115*C*): 2×2 hours = 4 hours.

Actually, that is exactly what was done with the number line solution.

Think back now to the earlier problem (p. 362) in which the multiplier was the whole number 6. Compare it with this problem, in which the multiplier is a fraction, $\frac{2}{3}$. In the first problem, one first multiplies "times 2" and then divides by 3. In the second problem, one first divides by 3 and then multiplies "2 times." In both cases, the operations were the same, but in reverse order. In both cases, the denominator of the fraction was used as a divisor; but in the first problem, that division came only as part of the changing of the quotient to lower terms.

Look at figure 116, in which the number line solutions of the two problems are contrasted. Notice that the "6" in the first problem was an abstract

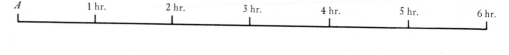

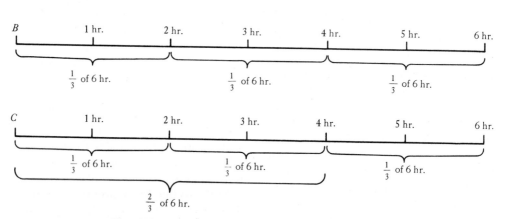

Figure 115. Multiplication of a Fraction Times a Whole Number.

Such a number line solution can be completed by children who are operating with whole numbers. They use two steps to solve the problem:

(1) $6 \div 3 = 2$
(2) $2 \times 2 = 4$

"6 times," whereas in the second problem "6" was the number of hours Joe was supposed to practice. The "$\frac{2}{3}$" in problem 1 told how much time Jean practiced each day, $\frac{2}{3}$ hours; it referred to 2 of the 3 equal parts of 1 hour. In problem 2, "$\frac{2}{3}$" referred to 2 of the 3 equal parts of 6 hours.

This comparison shows that the two quite different problem situations yield the same result. This is analogous to the demonstration with multiplication of whole numbers that 3 groups of 4 balls each are not the same as 4 groups of 3 balls each, but that both "3×4 balls" and "4×3 balls" represent the same product, or 12 balls. The commutative principle for multiplication operates in similar fashion with whole-number and fraction factors, so that "$6 \times \frac{2}{3}$ hours" and "$\frac{2}{3}$ of 6 hours" (or "$\frac{2}{3} \times 6$ hours") both emerge as 4 hours.

Such informal demonstrations of commutativity are adequate for elementary school children. More sophisticated proofs are left for later experiences in mathematics.

The basic similarity within different situations may be summarized for these problems as follows:

What is $6 \times \dfrac{2}{3}$?	What is $\dfrac{2}{3}$ of 6?
a. 6×2 thirds $= 12$ thirds or	e. $\dfrac{1}{3}$ of 6 means $6 \div 3$
b. $6 \times \dfrac{2}{3} = \dfrac{6 \times 2}{3} = \dfrac{12}{3}$	f. $6 \div 3$ may be written as $\dfrac{6}{3}$
c. $\dfrac{12}{3} = 12 \div 3$	g. If $\dfrac{1}{3}$ of $6 = \dfrac{6}{3}$,
d. $12 \div 3 = 4$	h. then $\dfrac{2}{3}$ of $6 = 2 \times \dfrac{6}{3}$
	i. $2 \times \dfrac{6}{3} = \dfrac{2 \times 6}{3} = \dfrac{12}{3} = 4$

These two contrasting lists of statements for solving contrasted problems serve two purposes: (1) the commutative principle is clearly demonstrated, and (2) the expression "$\frac{2}{3}$ of 6" is logically converted to $\frac{2 \times 6}{3}$, which may readily be changed to $\frac{2}{3} \times 6$, thereby demonstrating the logic of changing "$\frac{2}{3}$ of" to "$\frac{2}{3} \times$."

The equivalent ratios concept. The idea of a common fraction as the ex-

pression of a ratio has been discussed earlier (chap. 14). In this sense, "$\frac{2}{3}$" means "2 out of 3" or "2 to 3." Suggestions were made for helping children develop equivalent ratios as equivalent fractions (pp. 322ff). If a teacher has been successful in building this concept, it can be of help in establishing a ratio interpretation for the multiplication of a fraction and a whole number.

In the problem about Joe's practice on the trumpet, his mother stated that he had practiced $\frac{2}{3}$ as much as he was supposed to do. His teacher had told him to practice 6 hours. The question was: How many hours did he practice?

Stated in ratio language, Joe practiced 2 hours for each 3 hours he was supposed to practice; the time spent practicing bore a 2-to-3 ratio to the time he was supposed to spend. How can this ratio idea help in solving the problem? Figure 117 is a number line very similar to that in figure 115, but it emphasizes the ratio concept. The notations above the line indicate a scale of hours of practice time. The whole line is "6 hours long"; it therefore represents the whole time suggested by Joe's teacher. Below the line the notations fit the idea of the *total* recommended practice time; it is 1 unit long, the unit being the whole job of practicing. Notations are entered to show $\frac{1}{3}$ of the whole recommended time and $\frac{2}{3}$ of the recommended practice time.

The bracketed section of the line shows 2 of the 3 equal parts of the total recommended practice time; the ratio is 2 to 3. Immediately above the "$\frac{2}{3}$" notation is the notation "4 hr.," which is the answer to the problem question. What number of hours has the same ratio to 6 hours that 2 had to 3? That number is 4; 2 is to 3 as 4 is to 6; 2:3::4:6.

In order to help children understand this relationship, the teacher might

Problem 1:

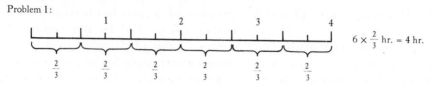

$6 \times \frac{2}{3}$ hr. = 4 hr.

Problem 2:

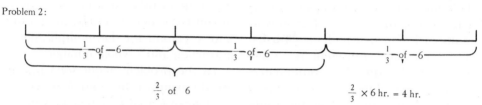

$\frac{2}{3}$ of 6 $\qquad$ $\frac{2}{3} \times 6$ hr. = 4 hr.

Figure 116. Contrasted Multiplications: $6 \times \frac{2}{3}$ and $\frac{2}{3} \times 6$.

draw (or have the children draw) on a strip of paper the number line as shown, but without the notations below the line in figure 117. Then the suggestion could be made to fold the line to show thirds and to mark the place corresponding to $\frac{2}{3}$ of the whole line (whole practice period). The fold at "4" would establish the relation between $\frac{2}{3}$ (of the total time) and "4 hours" as "$\frac{2}{3}$ of 6 hours."

Another approach to this same idea would be the use of the same form used when changing a common fraction to higher or lower terms: $\frac{2}{3} = \frac{?}{6}$. If thirds are to be changed to sixths, 6 must be *divided by 3*: $6 \div 3 = 2$. To keep the fractions equivalent, and since the denominator "6" is *2 times* the denominator "3," the numerator "2" in the first fraction must be multiplied by 2 to get the unknown numerator: $2 \times 2 = 4$, so the numerator of the equivalent fraction (equivalent ratio) is 4.

$$\frac{2}{3} = \frac{?}{6}$$

$$\frac{2}{3} = \frac{2 \times 3}{2 \times 3} = \frac{4}{6}$$

Notice that the computations performed in using this ratio solution are the familiar ones already referred to so frequently in the preceding discussion: divide by 3; multiply by 2. In more general terms: divide by the denominator; multiply by the numerator.

The ratio-to-one idea has been discussed in interpreting the meaning of multiplication of whole numbers and division of whole numbers. The same idea is operating here. In figure 117, the ratio of 6 to 1 is known (6 hours to 1 whole task done). The unknown is the number that has the same ratio to 6 (hours) that $\frac{2}{3}$ (of the task) has to $\frac{2}{3}$ or 1 (whole task).

Expanding the meaning of multiplication. Perhaps the typical elementary school child does not need to think of multiplication in the manner suggested here, but the teacher will do a better piece of teaching if she has clearly in mind just what multiplication means. In multiplication by a whole number, the additive interpretation of multiplication serves very well in most situations. In multiplication by a fraction, it does not. At this point, the interpretation of multiplication needs to be extended; it needs to be defined so as to include the additive interpretation of the same addend being taken so many times and also to include the interpretation of taking a fractional part of another number. When the multiplier is a whole number, it tells *how many times* the other factor is to be used. When the multiplier is a fraction, it tells what fractional part of the other factor is to be used. In *both cases,* multiplication is the process of finding the number that has the same ratio to the multiplicand as the multiplier has to one. Stated as a proportion:

Multiplier : 1 :: unknown number : multiplicand

In the problems with which we have been dealing in this chapter, this means that: (1) in the problem requiring the computation "$6 \times \frac{2}{3}$," the substitution in the given proportion would give $6 : 1 :: 4 : \frac{2}{3}$; (2) in the problem requiring the computation "$\frac{2}{3} \times 6$," the substitution in the given proportion would give $\frac{2}{3} : 1 :: 4 : 6$.

In the multiplication of a whole number times a fraction, the product always has the same denominator as the given fraction (provided there is no cancellation). In the multiplication of a fraction times a whole number, the product likewise has the same denominator as the fraction (again if there is no cancellation).

An area problem situation is particularly helpful in developing the meaning of multiplication of a fraction times a fraction. One teacher set the stage for some real problem solving with her pupils by giving them directions for

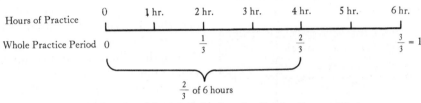

Figure 117. Ratio Idea in Multiplication of a Fraction Times a Whole Number.

MULTIPLICATION OF
TWO PROPER FRACTIONS

Since the major distinction in types of multiplication situations with fractions is the type of multiplier being used (whole number or fraction), there is nothing basically different in the meaning of multiplication of two fractions from the multiplication of a fraction times a whole number. A difference in the processing of the multiplication algorism does appear in that the children must learn how to handle the two given denominators and come out with a third denominator in the product.[2]

[2] If the whole numbers in the two preceding types of situations have been written in fraction form with a denominator of "1," the procedure for dealing with the denominators in those situations is similar to that used when both factors are proper fractions. In that case, the multiplications would have been written thus:

$$\frac{6}{1} \times \frac{2}{3} = \frac{12}{3} = 4 \qquad \frac{2}{3} \times \frac{6}{1} = \frac{12}{3} = 4$$

folding paper in a certain specified way. After the folding was completed, she posed the problem on which she based the development of the procedure for multiplying a fraction times a fraction.

The directions for handling the paper are given here in abbreviated fashion. (The reader may benefit from following the directions as he reads.) The teacher actually took time after each direction to be sure all the children understood and were doing it correctly.

1. Take any rectangular sheet of paper.

2. Fold the paper lengthwise so as to make *thirds*.

3. Open up the paper and draw heavy lines where your folds are.

4. Color 2 of the thirds of your paper with a yellow crayon.

5. Now fold the whole sheet of paper in the other direction to make fourths.

6. Open up the paper and draw heavy lines where the new folds are.

7. Do not pay any attention to the yellow part. Look at the whole sheet of paper and find 3 of the fourths you just made by folding the paper. Color 3 of the fourths with a blue crayon. Color blue over yellow if you have to.

8. Now I have a problem question for you to answer. *What part of the whole sheet of paper is green?*

Figure 118 shows the appearance of a sheet of paper after these directions have been followed. (Horizontal lines have been used to show the yellow $\frac{2}{3}$; vertical lines have been used to show the blue $\frac{3}{4}$; the resulting cross-hatching shows the green part of the sheet.)

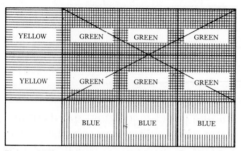

Figure 118. Folding and Coloring Exercise: $\frac{2}{3} \times \frac{3}{4} = \frac{6}{12} = \frac{1}{2}$.

Notice that no mention was made by the teacher of multiplication. The children merely followed the directions for folding and coloring.

Some of the key questions from the "solution" discussion will indicate the teacher's approach in guiding children toward multiplication of a fraction times a fraction.

Question: Your heavy pencil lines mark the sheet into parts. Are these parts equal in size? How do you know?

(One child suggested folding the whole sheet down to the size of the individual parts.)

Question: What is the name of these small equal parts? (Twelfths.) How do you know? (I counted them.) ($3 \times 4 = 12$.)

Question: How many of those parts are green? (Six.) How do you know? (Count.) ($2 \times 3 = 6$.)

Question: Now what part of the whole sheet is colored green? ($\frac{6}{12}$.)

Question: Can you change $\frac{6}{12}$ to a simpler fraction? (The discussion of $\frac{6}{12}$ as being equal to $\frac{1}{2}$ gave a chance to emphasize that the green $\frac{1}{2}$ and the not-green $\frac{1}{2}$ were different shapes but equal because each was made up of 6 twelfths.)

Any good teacher of children knows that this account has been cut to minimum essentials. It is important that time be allowed for ample discussion and for "thinking through" the problem and the situation. The essentials for the multiplication process are all contained, however, in the shortened account.

Contrary to so much classroom practice, the algorism for this multiplication was developed *after* the situation was thoroughly discussed and seemed to be well understood by the pupils. Teachers who are not in the habit of doing this should try it and see how beautifully the algorism unfolds as an outgrowth of "what we did." Notice how the form develops naturally from the preceding actions and thinking:

Question: Now let's write out what we did as we found the area of the green part of the sheet. How have we found areas before?

Answer: Multiply.

Question: What did we multiply to ge. this area?

Answer: We multiplied $\frac{2}{3} \times \frac{3}{4}$.[3] (This after some further discussion and labeling of the diagram. Written on board: $\frac{2}{3} \times \frac{3}{4} =$).

Question: This is the multiplication of a fraction times a fraction. We have not done this before; so we must be careful to do it right. What did we do to find *how many parts* were green?

Answer: We multiplied: $2 \times 3 = 6$.

Question: Where do you see "2×3" on the board?

Answer: The numerators. Multiply the numerators.

Question: Where should I write the "6"?

[3] This could with equal accuracy have been shown as $\frac{3}{4} \times \frac{2}{3}$.

Answer: It's the numerator of the answer.

Question: That tells how many parts are green. Now how did we find *the size or name of the equal parts?*

Answer: We multiplied: $3 \times 4 = 12$.

Question: Where is that on the board? Be careful now.

Answer: It must be the denominators. That would be 3×4.

Question: Where do you suppose I write the "12"?

Answer: It tells the name or size of the parts; so it would be the denominator of the answer.

One such group experience, involving individual participation and group discussion and sharing of ideas, is of immeasurably greater value than dozens of routine prescription-type "examples worked." Practice with other problem situations will be required, plus a good deal of practice with the computation exercises; but the importance of taking plenty of time with one good learning situation cannot be overestimated. No drill exercise can ever do what can be done with a good, sound learning situation such as that described briefly above.

How far one should go in attempting to rationalize the multiplication algorism must be left to the teacher's good judgment. It may be appropriate to seek an explanation of "what happened" in one such experience with multiplication of fractions as the area problem, or it may be better to wait until children have had other experiences as well in which they use other settings for the idea. Two illustrations (figs. 119 and 120) show other ways of attacking the question: What is $\frac{2}{3}$ of $\frac{3}{4}$?

Problem: Mary had $\frac{1}{4}$ of a dozen candy Easter eggs. She divided them equally with two friends, so that each of the three girls had the same number. What part of a dozen eggs did she give away?

In figure 119, the first action was to show $\frac{3}{4}$ of a dozen, which required divi-

ding the whole dozen into 4 equal parts and designating 3 of these parts as Mary's. The next step was to show *thirds of the $\frac{3}{4}$* (not thirds of a dozen). Because Mary already had 3 parts (fourths) of a dozen, it is easy to take 2 of those three parts ($\frac{2}{3}$). The problem with a dozen eggs is a good opportunity to develop the relation of each numeral in this algorism to the drawing because the $\frac{6}{12}$ are shown as 6 of 12 eggs.

$$\frac{2}{3} \times \frac{3}{4} = \frac{6}{12} = \frac{1}{2}$$

Problem: It is $\frac{3}{4}$ mile from Fred's home to the swimming pool. He ran $\frac{2}{3}$ of that distance. How far did he run?

The drawing made to solve this problem (fig. 120) is perhaps self-explanatory. A crucial point for the teacher to watch is that the children take careful note of what the *whole* is in each case: $\frac{3}{4}$ of what? $\frac{2}{3}$ of what? $\frac{1}{2}$ of what?

The distance to the pool is $\frac{3}{4}$ of *1 whole mile.* The distance he ran is $\frac{2}{3}$ of *1 whole distance to the pool* ($\frac{3}{4}$ mile). The product is $\frac{1}{2}$ of *1 whole mile.* The ratio concept is obviously operating here. *Two-thirds* has the same ratio to *one* as *one-half* has to *three-fourths.* Such a statement may not be of much help to the typical child who has to solve such a problem, but the picture will be a real help.

Understanding the multiplication of denominators. The only really new consideration in the multiplication of a proper fraction by a proper fraction is the multiplication of the denominators of the two fractions to secure the denominator of their product.[4] Just what does this mean? That question should be answered adequately enough that the procedure "makes sense" to

---

[4] This statement assumes that multiplication of a whole number times a proper fraction and of a proper fraction times a whole number has preceded.

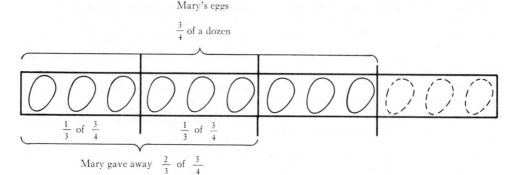

Figure 119. Finding Two-thirds of Three-fourths of a Dozen Eggs.

the users of the procedure. Understanding of this operation is also involved in answering the question: Why is the product of two proper fractions always a smaller number than either of the fractions used in the multiplication?

Actually, reasoning through any multiplication problem begins with attention to the multiplicand. That is, what is to be multiplied? Figure 121 will be discussed as a diagrammatic presentation of:[5]

$$\frac{2}{5} \times \frac{3}{4} = \frac{6}{20}$$

Each step in drawing the diagram will be stated separately. The multiplication algorism will be developed alongside, step by step.

Steps in Drawing the Diagram (Fig. 121)	*Step-by-Step Algorisms*

1. Draw the outer rectangle to represent the meaning: 1 whole field.
2. Draw horizontal lines to cut the field into **4** equal parts, or fourths. $\overline{4}$
3. Shade **3** of the fourths. $\frac{3}{4}$
4. Draw vertical lines to cut the shaded area (and, incidentally, the whole area) into **5** equal parts. $\overline{5} \times \frac{3}{4}$

[5] Or: $\frac{3}{4} \times \frac{2}{5}$.

5. Mark **2** of the fifths (of the $\frac{3}{4}$) with cross-hatching. $\frac{2}{5} \times \frac{3}{4}$
6. Multiply **5 × 4** to see how many small equal parts the field has been divided into. **5 × 4 = 20**. This also gives the name of the small equal parts. $\frac{2}{5} \times \frac{3}{4} = \frac{}{20}$
7. Multiply **2 × 3** to find how many twentieths are in $\frac{2}{3}$ of $\frac{4}{5}$ of the field. **2 × 3 = 6** $\frac{2}{5} \times \frac{3}{4} = \frac{6}{20}$

Step 7 might precede step 6. As written, step 6 is the one with which we are particularly concerned. Why are the denominators multiplied to get the denominator of the product?

The denominator "4" tells how many equal parts were made in the first division of the field. When the field was divided into 5 equal parts in the other direction, *5 times as many* fractional parts were created; 5 times 4 parts equals 20 parts. The 20 equal parts are indicated by the "20" shown as the denominator of the product. Or, when a thing is divided into 20 equal parts, each part is called a *twentieth,* shown by the denominator "20" in the product.

All the denominators here are divisors, telling into how many parts the whole field has been divided. First 4 was the partition divisor; then 5 was the partition divisor; finally, 20 was the partition divisor, which showed 5×4 parts created by the partitioning.

In multiplication by a proper fraction, in a sense one is multiplying by an indicated division.

Why is the product $\frac{6}{20}$ (or the simpler form $\frac{3}{10}$) smaller then either $\frac{3}{4}$ or $\frac{2}{5}$? It is a smaller amount because it is the result of dividing into smaller pieces and taking only part of those pieces.

In more abstract form, the same idea can be presented by series of multiplications, with the multiplicand a constant fraction and the multiplier being divided by the same number repeatedly. For each successive division of the multiplier by 2 (or 3), the denominator gets to be 2 (or 3) times as big; the effect on the product is the same.

$$4 \times \frac{1}{2} = 2 \qquad 9 \times \frac{1}{3} = 3$$

$$2 \times \frac{1}{2} = 1 \qquad 3 \times \frac{1}{3} = 1$$

$$1 \times \frac{1}{2} = \frac{1}{2} \qquad 1 \times \frac{1}{3} = \frac{1}{3}$$

$$\frac{1}{2} \times \frac{1}{2} = \frac{1}{4} \qquad \frac{1}{3} \times \frac{1}{3} = \frac{1}{9}$$

$$\frac{1}{4} \times \frac{1}{2} = \frac{1}{8} \qquad \frac{1}{9} \times \frac{1}{3} = \frac{1}{27}$$

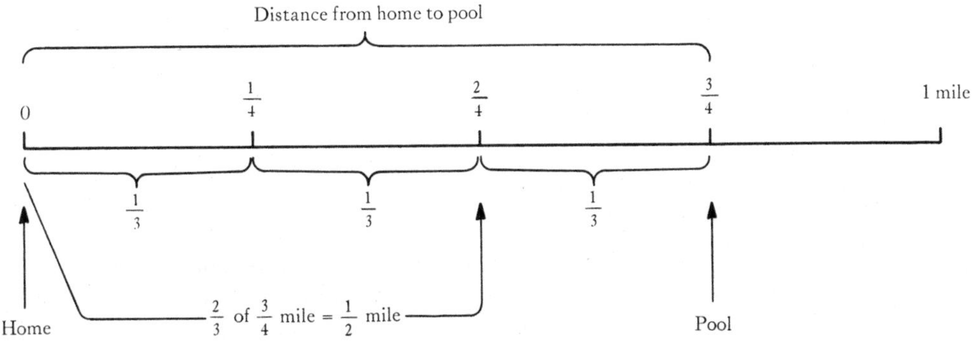

$$\frac{\text{Numerator}_1}{\text{Denominator}_1} \times \frac{\text{numerator}_2}{\text{denominator}_2}$$

$$= \frac{\text{numerator}_1 \quad \times \quad \text{numerator}_2}{\text{denominator}_1 \times \text{denominator}_2}$$

The algebraic form for making the same statement is much more compact. It is usually stated as:

$$\frac{a}{b} \times \frac{c}{d} = \frac{ac}{bd}$$

Pupils who are able should be encouraged to learn how to make such statements, provided the form is introduced as a summarizing of experiences that provide the requisite meanings.

When one recognizes that any whole number is a rational number and can be shown in fraction form, this statement of multiplication of rational numbers applies equally well to whole numbers and proper fractions. The transition is indicated for the examples below:

$$2 \times \frac{3}{4} = \frac{6}{4} = 1\frac{1}{2} \text{ becomes: } \frac{2}{1} \times \frac{3}{4} = \frac{2 \times 3}{1 \times 4} = \frac{6}{4} = 1\frac{1}{2}$$

$$\frac{3}{4} \times 8 = \frac{24}{4} = 6 \text{ becomes: } \frac{3}{4} \times \frac{8}{1} = \frac{3 \times 8}{4 \times 1} = \frac{24}{4} = 6$$

Figure 120. Finding Two-thirds of Three-fourths of a Mile.

Bigger and bigger denominators! Smaller and smaller parts!

Algebraic definition of multiplication of fractions. A generalized definition of multiplication of fractions might be stated as:

The time for introducing the fraction form for writing the whole numbers in multiplications such as these varies with the preference of the teacher (and the series of texts in use). No matter when it is introduced, the generalized statement of multiplication of fractions should certainly be stressed as a pulling together of various procedures when all the different forms have been introduced.

Mixed numbers fit the generalized form equally well, once they have been changed to improper fractions. The horizontal statement type of algorism is not, however, as popular when mixed numbers are part of a multiplication problem. Therefore some different algorisms merit discussion.

MULTIPLICATION OF MIXED NUMBERS

Since a mixed number represents the sum of a whole number and a proper fraction, it is sometimes convenient to rely on the distributive principle when mixed numbers occur as multipliers, multiplicands, or both.

A mixed number occurs as the multiplier in solving this problem:

Problem: What is the cost of $2\frac{1}{2}$ yards of ribbon at 24¢ per yard?

Computing mentally, most people would think:

$$2 \times 24¢ = 48¢$$
$$\frac{1}{2} \text{ of } 24¢ = 12¢$$
$$48¢ + 12¢ = 60¢$$

The same computations might be written in such a way as to perform separately the multiplication by 2 and the multiplication by $\frac{1}{2}$, thus:

$$
\begin{array}{ll}
2\,4\ ¢ & 2\,4\ ¢ \\
\times\, 2\frac{1}{2} & \times\, 2\frac{1}{2} \\
\hline
1\,2\ \left(\frac{1}{2} \times 24\right) & 4\,8\ (2 \times 24) \\
4\,8\ (2 \times 24) & 1\,2\ \left(\frac{1}{2} \times 24\right) \\
\hline
6\,0\ ¢ & 6\,0\ ¢
\end{array}
$$

Similarly, when the multiplicand is a mixed number, the calculations may be recorded separately for the whole-

number and fraction parts of the number.

Problem: If ribbon is sold at $12\frac{1}{2}$¢ per yard, how much would 5 yards cost?

The computations for solving this problem might be recorded in these or other forms:

$$5 \times 12\frac{1}{2}¢ = (5 \times 12¢) + \left(5 \times \frac{1}{2}¢\right) = 60¢ + 2\frac{1}{2}¢ \times 62\frac{1}{2}¢$$

$$\text{(or 63¢)}$$

$$
\begin{array}{l}
1\,2\frac{1}{2}\ ¢ \\
\times\, 5 \\
\hline
2\frac{1}{2}\ ¢ \\
6\,0 \\
\hline
6\,2\frac{1}{2}\ ¢
\end{array}
\qquad
\begin{array}{l}
2 \times 12\frac{1}{2}¢ = \$.25 \\
2 \times 12\frac{1}{2}¢ = \ .25 \\
1 \times 12\frac{1}{2}¢ = \ .12\frac{1}{2} \\
\hline
\$.62\frac{1}{2}
\end{array}
$$

When both terms are mixed numbers, these algorisms can become rather cumbersome. Suppose the ribbon cost $12\frac{1}{2}$¢ per yard and someone bought $6\frac{1}{2}$ yards. Then the distributive principle would allow us to use such algorisms as:

$$
\begin{array}{ll}
1\,2\frac{1}{2}\ ¢ & 6\frac{1}{2} \times 12\frac{1}{2}¢ = \\
\times\, 6\frac{1}{2} & (6 \times 12) + \left(\frac{1}{2} \times 12\right) + \\
\hline
\frac{1}{4}\ \left(\frac{1}{2} \times \frac{1}{2}\right) & \left(6 \times \frac{1}{2}\right) + \left(\frac{1}{2} \times \frac{1}{2}\right) = \\
6\ \left(\frac{1}{2} \times 12\right) & 72 + 6 + 3 + \frac{1}{4} = 81\frac{1}{4} \\
3\ \left(6 \times \frac{1}{2}\right) & \\
\hline
7\,2\ (6 \times 12) & \\
\hline
8\,1\frac{1}{4}\ ¢ &
\end{array}
$$

Obviously, while correct, such procedures can become unnecessarily complicated and also subject to numerous possibilities for error. When both terms are mixed numbers (and often when only one term is a mixed number), the most efficient procedure is to change the mixed numbers to improper fractions and multiply as for proper fractions. The three problems already cited might then be solved by such procedures as this:

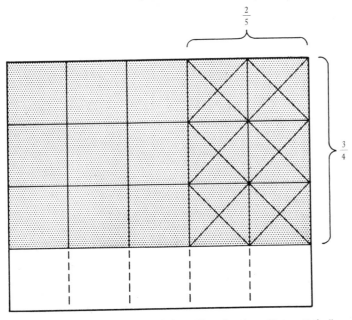

Figure 121. Diagram of "Two-fifths × Three-fourths = Six-twentieths."

$$2\frac{1}{2} \times 24 = \frac{5}{2} \times 24 = \frac{120}{2} = 60$$

$$5 \times 12\frac{1}{2} = 5 \times \frac{25}{2} = \frac{125}{2} = 62\frac{1}{2}$$

$$6\frac{1}{2} \times 12\frac{1}{2} = \frac{13}{2} \times \frac{25}{2} = \frac{325}{4} = 81\frac{1}{4}$$

After being exposed to both the vertical and horizontal forms, pupils should be allowed some personal preference in choosing the form to use, provided they handle the preferred form well (that is, accurately and with reasonable speed).

Cancellation can be used to limit computations to smaller numbers.

CANCELLATION

In several of the multiplication examples that have been introduced in this chapter cancellation would have been possible, even desirable. Discussion of cancellation has intentionally been delayed in order that it might be discussed apart from the multiplication process with fractions. Since cancellation in arithmetic is so often taught only in connection with multiplication of fractions, children sometimes infer that cancellation is an essential part of the multiplication of fractions, which is, of course, not true. If pupils are taught to understand and perform the four operations with fractions before cancellation is introduced, they will not get this erroneous impression.

Cancellation is not a mysterious "trick" or "stunt"; it can be understood without much difficulty. Nor is it one of the fundamental mathematical operations. It is a procedure for simplifying mathematical expressions, short-cutting some of the work to be done in processing the numerals.

Lay refers to cancellation as "the removal from an expression of two inverse operators."[6] He states further that: "The two operators that cancel must be in succession, that is, one must follow the other immediately, or it must be possible to arrange them in this manner by using the commutative and associative properties of the operators."[6]

[6] Lay, *op. cit.*, p. 176.

Take an example that occurs earlier in this chapter:

$$\frac{2}{3} \times \frac{3}{4} = \frac{2 \times 3}{3 \times 4} = \frac{6}{12} = \frac{1}{2}$$

The "3" in the denominator of the first fraction goes with the meaning "÷3"; the "3" in the numerator of the second fraction goes with the meaning "×3." Since "divided by 3" and "multiplied by 3" have inverse effects, they cancel each other.

$$\frac{2}{\cancel{3}^{1}} \times \frac{\cancel{3}^{1}}{4} = \frac{2 \times 1}{1 \times 4} = \frac{2}{4} = \frac{1}{2}$$

If the denominator "4" in the second fraction is factored, we find that we have another pair of inverses: "2 ×" in the first numerator and "÷ 2" in the second denominator:

$$\frac{\cancel{2}^{1}}{\cancel{3}^{1}} \times \frac{\cancel{3}^{1}}{\cancel{2}^{1} \times 2} = \frac{1 \times 1}{1 \times 2} = \frac{1}{2}$$

When both pairs of inverses are canceled out, there is no need to change the product to lower terms. The changing to lower terms has already been accomplished through cancellation. We see that the use of cancellation serves the purpose of changing to lower terms *before* the multiplication of numerators and multiplication of denominators. Thereby it reduces the size of the numbers that are to be multiplied. In the example given, this is no great advantage; but it would be a real advantage in such an example as: $\frac{9}{10} \times \frac{25}{36}$.

Particularly in the early stages of learning to cancel correctly, children should write out the factors in numerator and denominator. This focuses their attention on the fact that it is the factors that are being canceled. It also promotes accuracy by making it easier to follow what the pupil is doing. The cancellation that was done above in two stages would be taken care of at once:

$$\frac{2}{3} \times \frac{3}{4} = \frac{\cancel{2}^{1} \times \cancel{3}^{1}}{\cancel{3}^{1} \times \cancel{2}^{1} \times 2} = \frac{1}{2}$$

Since cancellation serves the purpose of changing to lower terms *before* the multiplication of numerators and denominators, pupils who have understood what happens in changing to lower terms should not have much difficulty in seeing that the same thing is happening here. Since changing to lower terms turns out to be "division by 1" and since division by 1 does not change value, therein lies the reason that cancellation does not change values. The discussion of the "golden rule of fractions" and changing to lower terms in chapter 14 (particularly p. 330) develops this point in detail. In the preceding example, division of both numerator and denominator by 2 was division by $\frac{2}{2}$, or 1. In the same example, the division of both numerator and denominator by 3 was division by $\frac{3}{3}$, or 1.

Although it may seem cumbersome and time-consuming to do so, the writing of the "1's" above or below the canceled numerals, as the case may be, should not be neglected. Children should learn to think, for example, $3 \div 3 = 1$; $2 \div 2 = 1$. When the "1's" are omitted, children may become confused as to just what remains in the numerator and/or denominator. In the preceding example, if the "1's" are not written, some child may get the impression that the numerators have been removed or that the numerator in the product should be "0."

Cancellation, then, is a useful technique; but if it is to be taught at all, it should be taught meaningfully. It should be thought of as changing to lower terms early so as to have smaller numerals to work with instead of waiting to change the product to lower terms. It should not be taught as an essential part of the multiplication process with fractions.

Division of Fractions by Inversion

The common-denominator method of dividing by a fraction concentrated on the concept of the divisor as a measuring unit, measured off against the dividend. Once the denominators were the same (that is, once the dividend and divisor were the same kind of measuring units), the numerators could be divided just as whole numbers are divided. This is a very useful procedure and one that is fairly easy to teach so that children see sense in what is done.

Some problems in the division of fractions lend themselves more readily to another line of reasoning that is more closely related to the classic "invert-and-multiply" procedure. Since this requires knowledge of multiplication of fractions, it must follow the development of understanding and skill in use of multiplication of fractions.

Many intelligent adults are baffled when faced with the question: Why do you invert and multiply to divide by a fraction? Some have never considered the question; they merely do what some teacher once told them to do: "turn the fraction upside down and then multiply." Some may have wondered why that "worked" but have not answered their own wondering. Certainly all intelligent adults *can* make sense of this procedure, properly taught. Most sixth-grade children *can* see much more sense in it than would be considered possible

by the doubters who say: "Teach them how to do it and get the right answer. Don't worry about why it works."

This procedure rests on such concepts as these:

1. Division is the inverse of multiplication.
2. A fraction is an expression of an indicated division.
3. Division may be a measuring process, or it may be a partitioning process.
4. Multiplying the numerator and the denominator of a fraction by the same number does not change the value of the fraction. (Only the form is changed.)

Some other meanings that are helpful may need further elaboration sooner or later in seeking to rationalize the "invert-and-multiply" procedure. One group of such meanings is the set of relationships that exist among the magnitudes of numerators and denominators. Another is the meaning of the term "reciprocal."

RELATIVE MAGNITUDES OF

NUMERATORS AND DENOMINATORS

The effect of size of either factor on their product and the effect of size of dividend or divisor on their quotient were discussed in some detail earlier. (See chap. 13.) Since a fraction is a quotient, these relationships are very important in interpretation of some of the uses of fractions.

The relationships for fraction-type quotients may be learned or taught as indicated by the following exercise. (The original $\frac{4}{6}$ is shaded in all the drawings.)

1. Draw a picture of $\frac{4}{6}$ of a pie.
2. Multiply the numerator by 2.

$$\frac{2 \times 4}{6} = \frac{8}{6}, \text{ or } 1\frac{2}{6}, \text{ or } 1\frac{1}{3}$$

3. Change the picture (a) to show what happened.

$$\frac{8}{6} = 1\frac{1}{3}$$

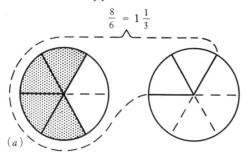

(a)

4. Start again with $\frac{4}{6}$ of a pie. Multiply the denominator by 2.

$$\frac{4}{2 \times 6} = \frac{4}{12}, \text{ or } \frac{1}{3}$$

5. Change the picture (b) to show what happened.

$$\frac{4}{12} = \frac{1}{3}$$

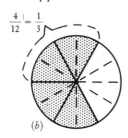

(b)

6. Start again with $\frac{4}{6}$ of a pie. Divide the numerator by 2.

$$\frac{4 \div 2}{6} = \frac{2}{6} = \frac{1}{3}$$

7. Change the picture (c) to show what happened.

$$\frac{2}{6} = \frac{1}{3}$$

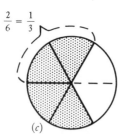

(c)

8. Start again with $\frac{4}{6}$ pie. Divide the denominator by 2.

$$\frac{4}{6 \div 2} = \frac{4}{3}, \text{ or } 1\frac{1}{3}$$

9. Change the picture (d) to show what happened.

$$\frac{4}{3} = 1\frac{1}{3}$$

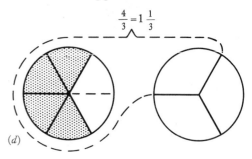

(d)

10. What happened to the amount of pie when you:
    a. Multiplied the numerator by 2?
    b. Divided the denominator by 2?
    c. Multiplied the denominator by 2?
    d. Divided the numerator by 2?
11. Which two actions (operations) resulted in *twice* as much pie?
12. Which two actions (operations) resulted in *half* as much pie?

This exercise may be repeated with other fractions and with other whole numbers used as multiplier or divisor. Inductively, such "experimentation" will help children come to enough understanding of relationships to be able to draw such generalizations as these:

1. Dividing the numerator by a whole number divides the fraction by that number.

2. Multiplying the numerator by a whole number multiplies the fraction by that number.

3. Dividing the denominator by a whole number multiplies the fraction by that number.

4. Multiplying the denominator by a whole number divides the fraction by that number.

Of course, all these generalizations assume that the term that is not mentioned remains the same.

MEANING OF RECIPROCALS

The reciprocal of a number is defined in various ways, all describing the same entity. One may say that the reciprocal of a number is "1 divided by that number" or "unity divided by the number"; or "two numbers are reciprocals if their product is 1." Examples follow:

Reciprocal of a Whole Number:

The reciprocal of 4 is $\frac{1}{4}$; that is, $1 \div 4 = \frac{1}{4}$

And: $\frac{1}{4} \times 4 = \frac{4}{4} = 1$

Reciprocal of a Unit Fraction:

The reciprocal of $\frac{1}{4}$ is 4; that is, $1 \div \frac{1}{4} = \frac{4}{4} \div \frac{1}{4} = 4$[7]

And: $4 \times \frac{1}{4} = \frac{4}{4} = 1$

Reciprocal of a Nonunit Fraction:

The reciprocal of $\frac{2}{3}$ is $\frac{3}{2}$; that is, $1 \div \frac{2}{3} = \frac{3}{3} \div \frac{2}{3} = \frac{3}{2}$[7]

And: $\frac{3}{2} \times \frac{2}{3} = \frac{6}{6} = 1$

The timing of such discussions depends on the teacher's best judgment of her pupils' individual and collective readiness for the ideas. The teacher, though, must have such ideas well in mind if she is to do a good job of helping children rationalize the process of dividing by inverting and multiplying.

It is obvious from the definition of a reciprocal that it is an inverse idea, closely associated with the inverse relation between multiplication and division. Another name for the reciprocal is the "multiplicative inverse." That is, multiplying a number by its reciprocal "undoes" the effect of that number as a multiplier; it is reduced to the factor "1." When 1 appears as a factor, the product is unchanged.

[7] The common-denominator method is used in these divisions.

DIVISION OF A FRACTION
BY A WHOLE NUMBER

Division by a proper fraction, improper fraction, or mixed number usually occurs in measurement-type division problems such as those which were used in developing the common-denominator procedure for dividing by any kind of fraction. Fractions (other than those which can be changed to whole numbers) are not usually divisors in partition division situations. In partition problem situations, the divisor tells into how many parts something (the dividend) is to be divided. The idea that something is to be divided, for example, into $\frac{3}{4}$ parts is awkward, to say the least. Whole-number divisors should be used in introducing partition division with fraction-form dividends.[8]

Dividing by any whole number has the same effect as multiplying by its reciprocal. This is not difficult to demonstrate.

Problem: Four-fifths of a city lot is covered with grass. John and Bill agree that they will mow it. If each of the 2 boys does an equal share, how much of the whole lot does each boy have to mow?

Figure 122*A* shows the $\frac{4}{5}$ lot to be mowed. Figure 122*B* or *C* shows the $\frac{4}{5}$ lot divided into 2 equal parts (partition division). Figure 122*B* or *C* also shows $\frac{1}{2}$ of $\frac{4}{5}$, another way of saying $\frac{4}{5} \div 2$. Commuting the $\frac{1}{2} \times \frac{4}{5}$ gives $\frac{4}{5} \times \frac{1}{2}$. Clearly, $\frac{4}{5} \div 2 = \frac{4}{5} \times \frac{1}{2} = \frac{4}{10}$, or $\frac{2}{5}$.[9]

Using ideas already developed, what happens here may be described in various correct ways. The teacher should

[8] It is incorrect to say that fractions *never* serve as divisors in partition situations. For example, to find "miles per gallon" one divides number of miles traveled by number of gallons used, which is often a mixed number readily expressed as an improper fraction.

[9] Fig. 122*B* shows $\frac{4}{10}$ more clearly; fig. 122*C* shows $\frac{2}{5}$ more clearly.

be alert to the various possibilities since different pupils will probably have different ways of describing the solution:

a. 4 fifths ÷ 2 = 2 fifths   dividing by a whole number

b. $\dfrac{4}{5} \div 2 = \dfrac{2}{5}$ dividing by a whole number

c. $\dfrac{1}{2}$ of $\dfrac{4}{5} = \dfrac{4}{10} = \dfrac{2}{5}$ multiplying by a fraction

d. $\dfrac{1}{2} \times \dfrac{4}{5} = \dfrac{4}{10}$ or $\dfrac{2}{5}$ multiplying by a fraction

e. $\dfrac{1}{\cancel{2}} \times \dfrac{\cancel{4}^{2}}{5} = \dfrac{2}{5}$ multiplying by a fraction (with cancellation)

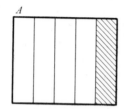 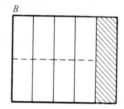 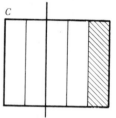

Figure 122. "$\frac{4}{5} \div 2$" or "$\frac{4}{5} \times \frac{1}{2}$" Shown as Equivalents.

Dividing the fraction $\left(\dfrac{4}{5}\right)$ by a whole number (2) gets the same result as multiplying by its reciprocal $\left(\dfrac{1}{2}\right)$.

Dividing the numerator of the fraction $\left(\dfrac{4}{5}\right)$ by a whole number (2) has the same effect as multiplying the denominator (5) by that same whole number (2).

Best of all is the recognition by as many learners as possible that all these statements fit the simple problem solution. Together they show "sense" in the "invert-and-multiply" procedure when the divisor is a whole number.

DIVISION OF A WHOLE NUMBER
BY A FRACTION

The process of dividing a whole number by a fraction has already been thoroughly discussed on pages 354ff. This fits well in a measurement rather than a partition situation. The common-denominator method and explanation of the computation was recommended

for children's introduction to division by a fraction because of the ease with which it could be developed rationally and because of the easy transition that was possible from use of common denominators for addition and subtraction of common fractions.

The same computation used there may be used to lead from the common-denominator method to the inversion method of dividing a whole number by a proper fraction. The problem was to find how many bows using $\frac{2}{3}$ yard each could be made from 4 yards of ribbon. The solution involved measuring 4 yards by $\frac{2}{3}$-yard measuring units. The logic of the solution is indicated by these statements:

4 wholes ÷ 2 thirds = 12 thirds ÷ 2 thirds = 6

$$\text{OR: } 4 \div \frac{2}{3} = \frac{12}{3} \div \frac{2}{3} = 6$$

A review of the computations that were made shows that in order to change 4 whole yards to thirds of a yard, 4 was multiplied "times 3," since there are 3 thirds in 1 yard. Then the 12 thirds were divided by (measured against) the 2 thirds for each bow. The computations were:

$$4 \times 3 = 12$$
$$12 \div 2 = 6$$

If the invert-and-multiply method were to be applied to the solution of this same problem, this is how it would be written:

$$4 \div \frac{2}{3} = 4 \times \frac{3}{2} = \frac{12}{2} = 6$$

What computations would have to be done? Exactly the same computations that are done in the common-denominator method: $4 \times 3 = 12$ and $12 \div 2 = 6$! For teachers who think some or all of their pupils are ready to go on to the inversion method, this transitional development should prove helpful. It at least shows that both algorisms require the same operations by the same numbers; consequently, they get the same results.

DIVISION OF A FRACTION
BY A FRACTION

On the television show called "Candid Camera" much confusion for the unwitting subjects and much merriment for the observers resulted from asking people to perform this multiplication: $\frac{7}{8} \div \frac{2}{3}$. Not only did the victims have great difficulty; at least one of them was sure it could not be done! The need for understanding division of and by fractions was only too obvious. The person who concluded that it could not be done will probably never read this book, but that example will serve the purpose as well as any other in seeking to show how and why fractions *can* be divided by other fractions.

Problem: The distance around a racetrack is $\frac{2}{3}$ miles. If a horse runs $\frac{7}{8}$ mile, how many times has he gone around the track?

As must so often be done in developmental teaching, one does well here to "go back in order to go forward." Let us go back to the common-denominator method (which fits this measurement division problem better) in order to lead up to the interpretation of the inversion method as applied to the solution of this particular problem.

The common denominator method would use this algorism:

$$\frac{7}{8} \div \frac{2}{3} = \frac{21}{24} \div \frac{16}{24} = \frac{21}{16} = 1\frac{5}{16}$$

See figure 123. The oval track has been "stretched out" in a straight line. The distance $\frac{7}{8}$ mile is shown above the line. The distance $\frac{2}{3}$ mile is shown twice under the line. The eighths shown above the line and the thirds below the line have been further subdivided into twenty-fourths, which are marked but not numbered. One can see easily that $\frac{7}{8}$ mile does equal $\frac{21}{24}$ mile and that $\frac{2}{3}$ mile does equal $\frac{16}{24}$ mile, as stated in the common-denominator algorism. Each $\frac{1}{24}$ of a *mile* is $\frac{1}{16}$ of a *lap around the track.* If the horse runs $\frac{21}{24}$ of a *mile,* he runs $\frac{21}{16}$ of the *distance around the track,* or $1\frac{5}{16}$ of that distance. The answer to the problem question is: The horse runs 1 time around the track and $\frac{5}{16}$ of another time around the track or $1\frac{5}{16}$ in all.

As when a whole number is divided by a fraction, it is most interesting to compare the common-denominator algorism and the inversion algorism for the same problem. In the statements below, notice that the same computations are performed (and really for the same reasons, though the logic is not so clear for the inversion algorism).

The computations are:

$$3 \times 7 = 21;$$
$$8 \times 2 = 16;$$
$$21 \div 16 = 1\frac{5}{16}.$$

Common-Denominator Method:

$$\frac{7}{8} \div \frac{2}{3} = \frac{21}{24} \div \frac{16}{24} = \frac{21}{16} = 1\frac{5}{16}$$

$$3 \times 7 = \boxed{21} \qquad 8 \times 2 = \boxed{16} \qquad 21 \div 16 = \boxed{1\frac{5}{16}}$$

Invert-and-Multiply Method:

$$\frac{7}{8} \div \frac{2}{3} = \frac{7}{8} \times \frac{3}{2} = \frac{21}{16} = 1\frac{5}{16}$$

$$7 \times 3 = \boxed{21} \qquad 8 \times 2 = \boxed{16} \qquad 21 \div 16 = \boxed{1\frac{5}{16}}$$

Some people prefer a rationalization of the inversion method that relies on the fact that the numerator and denominator of a fraction may be multiplied by the same number without changing the value of the fraction.

Applying that rule, one can defend both the common denominator and the inversion algorisms by applying this principle:

$$\text{C.D.} \quad \frac{7}{8} \div \frac{2}{3} = \frac{21}{24} \div \frac{16}{24} = \frac{21}{16} = 1\frac{5}{16}$$

Instead of changing both terms to the common denominator 24, multiply both terms by 24:

$$\frac{7}{8} \div \frac{2}{3} = \left(\overset{3}{\cancel{24}} \times \frac{7}{\cancel{8}}\right) \div \left(\overset{8}{\cancel{24}} \times \frac{2}{\cancel{3}}\right) = (3 \times 7) \div (8 \times 2) =$$

$$21 \div 16 = 1\frac{5}{16}$$

$$\frac{7}{8} = \frac{21}{24}$$

the dividend-fraction and the denominator of the divisor-fraction to get the numerator of the quotient-fraction; then multiply the denominator of the dividend-fraction and the numerator of the divisor-fraction to get the denominator of the quotient-fraction. This wording should not by any stretch of the pedagogical imagination be dictated to children for them to memorize. It is a summary statement for teachers, which states in more formal fashion just what is done in either the common-denominator or the inversion method of dividing fractions.

Incidentally, this summary statement is also the basis of the technique called

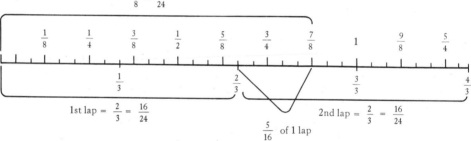

Figure 123. Division of a Fraction by a Fraction.

Now begin again, but multiply both terms by $\frac{3}{2}$, the reciprocal of $\frac{2}{3}$:

$$\underbrace{\frac{7}{8} \div \frac{2}{3}}_{A} = \underbrace{\left(\frac{3}{2} \times \frac{7}{8}\right)}_{B} \div \underbrace{\left(\frac{\cancel{2}}{\cancel{2}} \times \frac{\cancel{3}}{\cancel{8}}\right)}_{C} = \underbrace{\frac{3}{2} \times \frac{7}{8}}_{D} = \frac{7}{8} \times \frac{3}{2} = \frac{21}{16} = 1\frac{5}{16}$$

The term marked B reduces to 1; the preceding term ÷ 1 = that same term. Term C is commuted to become term D. Terms A and D are equal; by themselves, with intervening steps omitted, they represent the typical invert-and-multiply algorism.

Both division algorisms for fractions may thus be reduced to this common procedure: Multiply the numerator of

"division by cross multiplication." It is not a good method to teach to children except as an interesting short-cut for those who have thoroughly mastered the meanings involved in the other two methods. For the latter purpose, it may be an interesting procedure. Better yet, it might be presented to superior arithmetic students with a challenge to defend it.

Cross-Multiplication Method:

$$\frac{7}{8} \times \frac{2}{3} = \frac{21}{16} = 1\frac{5}{16} \quad \text{(Follow the arrows.)}$$

Separate discussion of division with mixed numbers seems unnecessary, since they are merely changed to improper fractions and processed in exactly the same manner and according to the same rationale as proper fractions.

RELATIVE MERITS OF
COMMON-DENOMINATOR
AND INVERSION METHODS

Though the common-denominator and the invert-and-multiply methods for division of fractions have been shown to accomplish the same task, teachers should weigh carefully whether to teach one or the other or both methods, and to whom.

The common denominator method has these advantages:

a. It is easier to "see why" this method leads to correct results, particularly for children.

b. The rationale of this method fits better than the inversion method with the typical real problem in which division of fractions must be used. That is, it fits the measurement-type division situation in which fraction-divisors occur much more frequently.

c. If the meanings of common denominators and the appropriate use of like terms have been well taught, there is little new to teach in presenting this method.

The inversion method has these advantages:

a. It allows for shortening the calculations when cancellation is possible and large numerators and denominators are used.

b. Parents (and many teachers) are more likely to be familiar with this method; so presentation of the common-denominator method may be unpopular. Also, if adults are resistant to it, they may cause confusion for the children by putting them into the awkward position of trying to learn two methods without understanding either one.

c. The inversion method fits with algebraic procedures to follow.

The recommendations that seem most sensible at the present time are these:

a. Teach the common-denominator method first. Go on to the inversion method when and if children have grasped the common-denominator method well. Avoid confusing children by introducing a second method when the first is not well in hand.

b. Teach either method in terms of what it *means* as well as how it is *done*.

c. Stress problem situations, concrete aids, and pictorial descriptions of solutions until they are no longer needed.

STUDY QUESTIONS

1. Make a word problem you consider appropriate as a setting for *introducing* children to each of these: (a) multiplication of a whole number times a proper fraction, (b) multiplication of a proper fraction times a whole number, (c) multiplication of two proper fractions, and (d) multiplication of a proper fraction by a mixed number.

2. Suggest ways in which each of the problem situations you have suggested (question 1) might be developed meaningfully with children who are just learning the process.

3. Plan a procedure by which you could introduce children to the ideas presented in this statement: $\frac{1}{3}$ of $12 = \frac{1}{3} \times 12 = 12 \div 3 = 4$.

4. Draw a picture that depicts the meaning of this multiplication: $1\frac{2}{3} \times \frac{4}{5} = 1\frac{1}{3}$. Be sure the meaning of the fraction part of the answer is clear.

5. Write a brief explanation of the rationale behind the inversion method of dividing by a fraction. Be able to tell how you would develop the idea with children.

6. What is the reciprocal of: (a) $\frac{1}{5}$? (b) $\frac{5}{8}$? (c) $1\frac{1}{2}$? (d) 32?

7. Defend or reject: (a) use of cancellation in early work with multiplication of fractions and (b) teaching the cross-multiplication algorism.

CHAPTER 17

Decimal Fractions

STRICTLY SPEAKING, decimal fractions may be expressed in common fraction form. If tenths, hundredths, and other fractions based on ten are written in the form of common fractions, they are also decimal fractions, e.g., $\frac{2}{10}$ or $\frac{25}{100}$; they are *decimal common* fractions. In keeping with general usage, however, this chapter uses the term "decimal fractions" to refer to fractions that use the same notational scheme as whole numbers in our decimal-place-value system, e.g., .5 or .25.

Understanding Decimal Fractions

DECIMAL WHOLE NUMBERS, FRACTIONS, AND MIXED NUMBERS

Since our place-value system has a base of ten, we have decimal whole numbers (e.g., 245), decimal fractions (e.g., .245), and decimal mixed numbers (e.g., 2.45). If we used (or when we use) a place-value system with a base of two, we would have (do have) binary whole numbers, binary fractions, and binary mixed numbers. Children of the present elementary school generation are fortunate in that they are having much better opportunities than did

their parents to learn about place value and number base before they take up study of decimal fractions. When the concepts of base and place are under control in connection with computation using whole numbers, the place-value meanings of decimal fractions and mixed numbers are merely extensions of already familiar ideas.

The practice of calling decimal *fractions* and decimal *mixed numbers* simply "decimals" is unfortunate.[1] The shortening of the terminology is convenient; but it also tends to encourage neglect of the decimal character of *whole numbers,* which existed in common use long before decimal notation for fractions was used. Teachers would do well to speak of "decimal fractions" and "decimal whole numbers" and "decimal mixed numbers," particularly during the earlier phases of developing decimal-fraction notational patterns.

Decimal fractions are taken for granted in modern usage. Many people are very much surprised to learn that their form and use were introduced in a book published in 1585. Actually, the author of that work, Simon Stevin, did not use our modern decimal-fraction

[1] A worse misuse of the word "decimal" is to call the "decimal point" the "decimal." There is no excuse whatsoever for this usage.

notation, which came even later; he did present the decimal-fraction *idea* less than four hundred years ago.[2]

What a far-reaching idea this was! By its application, the decimal-place-value notation was extended to the right of the ones place as far as anyone would have need to extend it. Fractions could be recorded as whole numbers were recorded, with absolute value (face value) shown by numerals and with powers of the base shown by position (place value).

Decimal fractions are, then, fraction *forms* that use numerals to designate the numerators and place value to designate the denominators. The numerators of decimal fractions are used just as are numerals designating whole numbers. We do not have a whole new set of rules for dealing with the decimal-fraction numerals, since the rules are the same as for whole-number notation. Any "newness" in computation with decimal fractions and decimal mixed numbers relates to the management of the denominators as shown by place value, not to the numerators.

IMPORTANCE OF THE ONES PLACE

When children are introduced to place value in the notation for whole numbers, they must learn first about ones, then tens, then hundreds, and so on. They must learn that tens place represents a value *ten times* that of ones place; that hundreds place represents a value *ten times* that of tens place; that thousands place represents *ten times* the value of hundreds place; so on and on. Understanding of all place values hinges on the importance of *ones,* which are

[2] Actually, an earlier work by Christoff Rudolff presented the idea of decimal fractions in 1530, but his work did not have the effect of Stevin's in encouraging the use of decimal-fraction notation. See D. E. Smith, *History of Mathematics.* New York: Dover, 1958, Vol. II, p. 240.

regrouped into larger and larger values as shown in other places.

The same importance should be attached to ones place in developing understanding of decimal fractions. Tenths place must be seen as having *one-tenth* the value of ones place; hundredths place, as having *one-tenth* the value of tenths place; and so on. *Units* or *ones* place is the key reference place for all other place values.

Take the number 1111.111 shown diagrammatically below:

The same sort of pattern might have been extended to include larger place values to the left and smaller ones to the right; but this number has enough places to illustrate the major consideration, that the focal point of attention is *ones* place. Tens place is for tens. Tens of what? Tens of *ones.* Tenths place is for tenths. Tenths of what? Tenths of *one.* Hundreds place is for hundreds of *ones.* Hundredths place is for hundredths of *one.* Thousands place is for thousands of *ones.* Thousandths place is for thousandths of *one.*

A beginning teacher of an older generation told of her struggles to teach children to call the decimal fractions by their correct names. This is her account:

I had so many pupils who would read decimal fractions wrong. If they were supposed to read a two-place decimal fraction, they wanted to call it tenths; if they had a three-place decimal fraction, they would call it hundredths. The book said that if a numeral was 1 place to the right of the decimal point, it was tenths; 2 places to the right of the decimal point was hundredths; and so on.

We practiced and practiced reading decimal numbers. I thought I was very patient with them and I think they really tried, but it was a real struggle. One boy said: "Well, I don't see why that hundredths place isn't tenths. Tens is 2 places to the left of the decimal point; why isn't tenths 2 places to the right of the decimal point? And hundreds is 3 places to the left of the point; why isn't hundredths 3 places to the right of the point? Why doesn't it match up on both sides of the decimal point?"

I saw what his trouble was, but I couldn't help him. I said, "It does seem as if the place names ought to match up as you say. It seems peculiar, but that is not the way it is. I guess you will just have to get used to the idea that the names *don't* balance around the decimal point."

I wish I could have those children back in front of me now. I could answer that boy's question better than I did then. In fact, I know my present pupils do not have so much trouble, because their teacher knows now that the place names *do* match up around a central point, *ones* place.

The book led us astray with all that reference to the decimal point—so many places this way or that way from the point. If only they had talked about the number of places away from the ones place we would have understood so much better!

That boy wanted the pattern to make sense, but I didn't have the sense to help him see that the pattern he was looking for was there all the time.

This teacher is not an isolated case by any means. Many a teacher has failed to help children on this very same point. Elementary school texts are better now and teachers have had better instruction themselves; so children can benefit from instruction such as this account from Miss Harper's classroom. Miss Harper led her pupils in a discussion of the money number: $3421.685. As each place value was discussed and named, lines were drawn as shown in the diagram (as a following through of

$$\$ \; 3 \; 4 \; 2 \; 1 \; . \; 6 \; 8 \; 5$$

questions and answers like these):

Question: What does the 6 refer to? 6 what?
Answer: Dimes.

Question: Yes, dimes. What else can we call it? What would we call it if this were not a money number?
Answer: Tenths.
Question: Tenths of what?
Answer: Tenths of a dollar.
Question: Which numeral shows a dollar?
Answer: The "1." Six tenths of 1 dollar.
(Teacher drew arrow from "6" to "1.")
Question: Where are the tens?
Answer: The "2" is in tens place.
Question: Tens of what?
Answer: Dollars. Twenty dollars.
Question: Shall I draw a line here, then, to show that the 2 means 2 tens times 1 dollar? (Drew line from "2" to "1.")
Question: Who can come up here and show two other numerals that balance around the ones place? (A child drew arrows from the "8" and "4," pointing to the ones place.)
Answer: The "8" is 8 pennies; that's 8 hundredths of a dollar. The "4" is for 4 hundreds. They match up.

This teacher was leading her pupils to see the balanced naming of place values around the ones place. Her questions directed them toward the relationship that so clearly exists.

The rewards of correct teaching on this matter are great. The whole task of teaching meanings of decimal fractions and mixed numbers is lightened and shortened. The arrows focus attention where it belongs. Some teachers dramatize the "matching" place names by using the same color of chalk for tens place and tenths place, another color for hundreds place and hundredths place, another for thousands and thousandths place. Such "crutches" should be used only to help make the point clear, but they can be very helpful as introductory aids.

THE DECIMAL POINT

The story told by the older teacher made the decimal point the "villain of the piece." The decimal point has had entirely too much emphasis placed on it. Books, teachers, and parents have drummed into children's ears constant references to the decimal point as if it were the key to the whole matter of decimal fractions and mixed numbers. Boys and girls have heard too much talk about a numeral's being so many places this or that way from the decimal point. They have had to memorize rules for placing the decimal point. These rules, if properly applied, will locate it correctly; but the rules are not absolutely necessary to one who really understands place value of whole and fractional numbers.

In fact, the decimal point itself is *not* an essential element in the notation for decimal fractions any more than it is an essential element in the notation for whole numbers. It is convenient, but it is not necessary. To rest the whole explanation of decimal-fraction notation on it is very unwise.

In figure 124*A* is a check, correctly written. It shows $24.50 written as "Twenty-four and $\frac{45}{100}$ ----Dollars" and as 24^{\underline{45}}$, neither of which includes a decimal point. In figure 124*B* is a set of columns from a bookkeeping ledger. It shows $347.62, but no decimal point is employed. Figure 124*C* shows a part of a federal income tax form; again no decimal point is used in showing dollars and cents. Prices are often written without the decimal point as in figure 124*D* ($6.50). Odometers on automobiles typically show tenths of miles in a different color; no decimal point is needed. (See figure 124*E*.)

The decimal point has at times become a stumbling block instead of the help it should be. This has happened because it has been overemphasized and because many people have passed on to others their own wrong ideas of what the decimal point really is.

The decimal point is not the pivot on which the whole-number place values and fraction place values balance. It is not the proper reference point for place values on either side of it. The decimal point has no place value of its own. It has no number value whatsoever. It occupies no place in the sense that numerals or digits occupy a place.

What is it? It is a punctuation mark. That is all it is. It is a punctuation mark serving a function like that of a comma. (On the European continent, a comma may be used as we use a decimal point, e.g., 5,23 instead of our 5.23.) We use a comma to separate thousands from hundreds or to separate millions from hundred thousands in 3,425,376. We use a decimal point to separate ones and tenths in 4.5 miles. We use a decimal point sometimes in writing a whole-number notation such as $25. The decimal point is like a period indicating: "This is the end of the whole number." We use a decimal point before a fraction notation such as .375 inch. It is like a capital letter indicating: "This is the beginning; this is where a decimal fraction begins."

The decimal point is a notational punctuation mark. It tells where the decimal whole number ends, where the decimal fraction begins; it separates the whole number from the fraction in a decimal mixed number. (It is sometimes called a "separatrix.") It is not an essential; some other symbol can be and is sometimes used instead. When we speak of "placing" the decimal point, we are not giving it place value. It is a signal used *with* numerals, but it cannot signify what numerals signify. A numeral is a symbol of an absolute (face) value; a decimal point has no number value. The space occupied by a numeral has positional or place value; the space occupied by a decimal point alone does not have positional or place value.

The proper place for the decimal point is with the numeral in *ones* place. There it indicates, "this is *ones* place." Once the decimal point is "put in its proper place," it becomes a punctuation mark, and its service to the notation of decimal fractions and mixed numbers properly begins. This is an important service.

NUMERATORS AND DENOMINATORS

OF DECIMAL FRACTIONS

The definitions of "numerator" and "denominator" as terms of common fractions (chap. 14, pp. 317-18) bear repeating in considering the meanings of those same terms when applied to decimal-fraction notation.

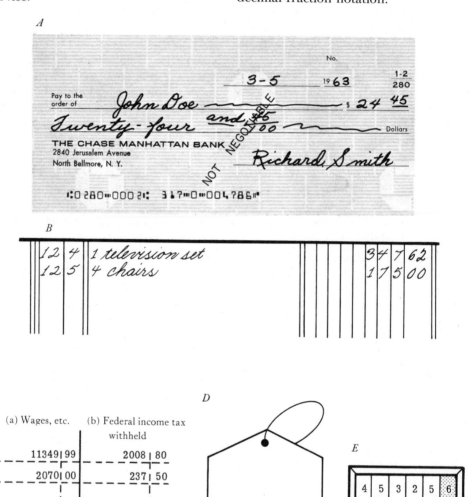

Figure 124. Decimal Fraction Notations without the Decimal Point.

When a common fraction expresses one or more of the equal parts of a whole thing or of a group of things, the numerator is the "numberer"; it tells the *number* of parts; it tells *how many* of each kind of part. When a decimal fraction refers to one or more equal parts of a whole thing or of a group of things, the numerator is also a "numberer"; or it tells the *number* of parts; or it tells *how many* of each kind of part. For example, in the expression ".45," the numerator is "45," which tells how many hundredths are being used or recorded. It might be 45 hundredths of 1 single mile, or it might be 45 hundredths of a group of people. It tells the number of hundredths.

In common fractions such as "$\frac{45}{100}$," the denominator was defined as the "namer" or the "name" of the fractional part. In $\frac{45}{100}$ of a mile or of a group of people, the "100" below the bar tells the name of the parts of the mile or parts of a group, "hundredths." The decimal fraction ".45" also has a denominator, though it is not written with numerals. The place value of the last numeral in the numerator tells the name of the fractional parts being considered; hence, place value indicates the de*nominat*or, the "namer." In this case, the place value two places to the right of ones place is "hundredths"; so the name of the parts of a mile or parts of a group of people is "hundredths."

This is how we use place values of whole numbers, though we do not usually apply the term "denominator." The names "hundreds" and "tens" and "ones" are not shown by numerals; they are shown by position, by place value. Similarly, the names of the parts in a decimal fraction are shown by place value.

When a common fraction expresses an *indicated division,* the numerator is the dividend, and the denominator is the divisor. Thus when "$\frac{8}{10}$" expresses a division, the "8" is the dividend, which is to be divided by the denominator "10" ($8 \div 10$). With decimal notation, the parallel situation prevails. The fraction ".8" may mean "8 divided by 10." (For example, we often indicate a division by 10 by simply changing "8" to ".8.") In this case the numerator "8" is the dividend, while the place value serves as the indicated divisor telling us to divide by ten.

When a common fraction has a *ratio* meaning, the fraction tells the relation of the numerator to the denominator. Thus, "$\frac{5}{10}$" would mean "5 out of 10," or "5 to 10." So also with the decimal fraction ".25," which expresses the relation of the numerator "25" to the place-value denominator "100." The fraction ".25" means, then, "25 out of 100," or "25 to 100." This meaning will be more fully developed in connection with per cent, certainly the most common application of this meaning.

CLASSIFICATION OF

DECIMAL FRACTIONS

Pure decimal and mixed decimal fractions. Just as common fractions are classified as proper and improper, so also decimal fractions are classified as pure and mixed. A common fraction with a value less than one is called a *proper* fraction; the corresponding decimal fraction form is called a *pure decimal* fraction. Examples are: .5; .24; and .0268.

Common fractions that have larger numerators than denominators have a value of one or more; they are called *improper*. The corresponding decimal-fraction form becomes either a *whole-number* decimal or a *mixed decimal* number. Examples of mixed decimal numbers are: 1.3; 25.83; and 456.098.

Complex and simple decimal fractions. *Complex decimal* fractions are those which include a common fraction, such as $.27\frac{1}{2}$ or $.12\frac{1}{4}$. The contrasted *simple decimal* fractions would be .275 or .1275. The common-fraction part of a complex decimal fraction is read as belonging to the same place value as the digit preceding it. The common fraction does not qualify to hold a place as do the regular whole-number digits. The two complex decimal fractions above are read as: "twenty-seven and one-half hundredths" and "twelve and one-fourth hundredths." "One-half tenth" would be written as $.0\frac{1}{2}$. There is no such notation as $.\frac{1}{2}$ because this would mean "one-half one," which would be written simply as "$\frac{1}{2}$." Children in the elementary school have little use for complex decimal fractions except as they occur in aliquot parts of a hundred and in per cents.

Similar and equivalent decimal fractions. In common-fraction terminology, fractions having the same denominators (same names) are usually called *like* fractions; decimal fractions having the same denominators as shown by place value are usually called *similar*. This is an important idea, whether or not the term "similar" is applied, because similarity of denomination is the basic criterion for much of the computation with decimal fractions and mixed numbers. The fractions .35 and .92 are similar; .6 and .25 can be made similar by annexing a zero to .6 to make it .60.[3]

Equivalent decimal fractions are like equivalent common fractions in that

[3] Care should be exercised in making such changes of form as this. The matter of precision of measurement indicated by annexing zeros at the end of such a number notation will be discussed in chap. 19.

they have the same *value*. For example, .275 and $.27\frac{1}{2}$ are equivalent fractions; their forms are different, but their values are the same. Common fractions and decimal fractions may be equivalent, such as: $\frac{1}{4}$ and .25; .24 and $\frac{24}{100}$.

DIVERSITY OF NOTATIONAL FORMS

Since most elementary school children make the acquaintance of common fractions before decimal fractions (except for money notation), they and their teachers usually rely on the relationship between common-fraction notation and decimal notation to give meaning to the latter. This practice serves to show that only the notational form is different, not the basic number values or meanings. It is important that children understand that the *same number* is symbolized by the different forms. Whole-number meanings as well as fraction meanings may be related as in table 11.

The simplicity and efficiency of the decimal-place-value notation scheme for both whole and fractional numbers is obvious when one compares the bottom numeral "1,111,111.111111" with the cumbersome task of writing the same values by using words or the common-fraction denominators. This table can be limited to fewer place values at first and built up (at both ends) as children become more familiar with the scheme and have need for reading, writing, and using larger whole numbers and smaller decimal fractions.

The contrasted meanings of place values with related names (such as hundreds and hundredths) can be highlighted by such comparisons as this in which the "numerator" is consistently "3" but the denominator changes with

1 million	1 hundred-thousand	1 ten-thousand	1 thousand	1 hundred	1 ten	1 one	1 ten*th*	1 hundred*th*	1 thousand*th*	1 ten-thousand*th*	1 hundred-thousand*th*	1 million*th*
1,000,000	100,000	10,000	1,000	100	10	1	$\frac{1}{10}$	$\frac{1}{100}$	$\frac{1}{1,000}$	$\frac{1}{10,000}$	$\frac{1}{100,000}$	$\frac{1}{1,000,000}$
1	1	1	1	1	1	1.	1	1	1	1	1	1

Table 11. Chart of Decimal Place Values.

the value of the place in which that "3" is written:

$$
\begin{aligned}
3,0\ 0\ 0. \quad &= 3 \times 10 \times 10 \times 10 \\
3\ 0\ 0. \quad &= 3 \times 10 \times 10 \\
3\ 0. \quad &= 3 \times 10 \\
3. \quad &= 3 \times 1 \\
0.3 \quad &= 3 \times \frac{1}{10} = \frac{3}{10} \\
0.0\ 3 \quad &= 3 \times \frac{1}{10} \times \frac{1}{10} = \frac{3}{10 \times 10} \\
0.0\ 0\ 3 \quad &= 3 \times \frac{1}{10} \times \frac{1}{10} \times \frac{1}{10} = \frac{3}{10 \times 10 \times 10}
\end{aligned}
$$
$$ 3,3\ 3\ 3.3\ 3\ 3 $$

"Thousands" can be seen here as using "10" as a factor three times, while "thousandths" uses "$\frac{1}{10}$" as a factor three times. Similarly, "hundreds" place is worth the product of two "10's," while "hundredths" place is worth the product of two "$\frac{1}{10}$'s." The "10's" that appear as whole-number multiples for the whole-number places appear as multiples in the common-fraction denominators for the fractional value places. Another way of drawing the contrast is to say that whereas the "3" in "3,000" was *multiplied* by "$10 \times 10 \times 10$," the "3" in ".003" was *divided* by "$10 \times 10 \times 10$." The sum "3,333.333" combines all the separate values.

ALGEBRAIC EXPONENTS
TO SHOW DECIMAL FRACTIONS

Algebraic exponents are useful to indicate place values for multiplace whole numbers. They are also useful in providing a more concise notation for multiplace decimal fractions. The way in which exponents are used in notation for decimal fractions shows clearly the likenesses and the differences in notation for decimal fractions and for decimal whole numbers. The pattern fits well with the preceding discussion of the place values of "3" in "3,333.333," with its emphasis on places to the left of ones place as having values of ten and powers of ten, while the places to the right of ones place have values indicating division by ten and powers of ten. Negative exponents are used to show the powers of the decimal *fraction* place values just as positive exponents are used to show the powers of the decimal *whole-number* place values.

At the elementary school level the work with exponents is not developed with all children. When it is taught, the scheme shown in the following summary is perhaps adequate to establish the pattern of their use.

Exponent Form	Meaning	Usual Form	Number of Zeros (Including Ones Place)
10^3	$= 10 \times 10 \times 10$	$= 1{,}000.$	3
10^2	$= 10 \times 10$	$= 100.$	2
10^1	$= 10 \times 1$	$= 10.$	1
10^0	$= 1$	$= 1.$	0
10^{-1}	$= 1 \div 10$	$= 0.1$	1
10^{-2}	$= 1 \div 10 \div 10$	$= 0.01$	2
10^{-3}	$= 1 \div 10 \div 10 \div 10$	$= 0.001$	3

SIMILARITIES OF MEANINGS SHOWN BY DIFFERENT FORMS

For the common-fraction forms and the decimal-notation forms, certain important meanings must be developed

millions	hundred-thousands	ten-thousands	thousands	hundreds	tens	ones	tenths	hundredths	thousandths	ten-thousandths	hundred-thousandths	millionths
10^6	10^5	10^4	10^3	10^2	10^1	10^0	10^{-1}	10^{-2}	10^{-3}	10^{-4}	10^{-5}	10^{-6}
b^6	b^5	b^4	b^3	b^2	b^1	b^0	b^{-1}	b^{-2}	b^{-3}	b^{-4}	b^{-5}	b^{-6}

Table 12. Exponential Chart of Decimal Place Values.

The word names in table 12 fit a decimal system, but the notations in the two bottom rows might be used with any base, not necessarily our ten. Those pupils who can achieve an understanding of the generalized forms above will have an excellent idea of our notational system. They may write either very large or very small numbers by use of decimal notation. Comparisons of what a given numeral (written in a base other than ten) would mean if translated into our base of ten would be interesting as well as rewarding. Some such "translations" are given as examples:

	Translation to Our Typical Notation
Base Four Notation	
10.	$= 1 \times 4 = 4$
1.1	$= 1 + \frac{1}{4} = 1\frac{1}{4}$
1.11	$= 1 + \frac{1}{4} + \left(\frac{1}{4} \times \frac{1}{4}\right) = 1 + \frac{1}{4} + \frac{1}{16} = 1\frac{5}{16}$
1111.	$= (1 \times 4^3) + (1 \times 4^2) + (1 \times 4) + 1$
	$= 64 + 16 + 4 + 1 = 85$

if the forms are to be understood. Some minimum concepts are:

1. Our numbers are shown as made up of superunits and subunits.[4]

2. With ones place as the starting point, the places to the left are multiples of ones, and the places to the right are parts of ones. (The multiples are the "superunits," the parts the "subunits.")

3. When the same numeral is written one place to the left (beginning anywhere), its place value is ten times as large. (It is multiplied by ten.)

4. When the same numeral is written one place to the right (starting anywhere), its place value is ten times as small. (It is divided by ten.)

Generalizing for any base, these same relationships may be developed for

[4] Anita P. Riess, *So These Are Fractions!* Dr. Riess uses the terms "super-units" and "sub-units" very effectively throughout her discussion of decimal and common fractions.

some learners with points 3 and 4 stated as:

3. When the same numeral is written one place to the left (beginning in any place), its place value is multiplied by the base.

4. When the same numeral is written one place to the right (beginning in any place), its place value is divided by the base.

Introducing Decimal Fractions to Children

DECIMAL FRACTIONS IN EVERYDAY EXPERIENCES OF CHILDREN

The everyday experiences that children have with fractions are by no means as likely to deal with tenths as with halves, thirds, fourths, sixths, or even eighths; but use of decimal fractions is definitely on the increase in science, business, engineering, medicine, and research in all fields. As these adult applications in various occupations become more common, no doubt decimal fractions will become more common in so-called "everyday affairs," including those of children. For some time to come, however, elementary school teachers are going to need to provide much school experience to give background for instruction concerning the meanings, uses, and procedures for using decimal fractions.

The widest general use that is made of decimal fractions relates to money. Cents and dollars-and-cents are items of great interest and concern to children from a very early age. Much to be desired though they are, children's early ideas of them and their uses have little bearing on decimal-fraction notation. Even when children in the primary grades learn to read and write money numbers, even indeed after they learn to add, subtract, multiply, and divide money numbers, these activities are no guarantee that cents have been recognized as "hundredths" of dollars or dimes as "tenths" of dollars. Early instruction (appropriately enough) deals with "hundredths" of dollars as "cents," and children think of them as "pennies," whole coins they can spend or get in change. Dimes to them are not "tenths" or parts of dollars, but rather coins that are worth ten pennies.

Money numbers and problems using money numbers are used extensively in teaching computations that involve changing or regrouping ("carrying" and "borrowing"), since it is helpful to have something readily available that fits our decimal-number system. When 10 pennies are changed for 1 dime or 10 dimes for 1 dollar, the notations might as well be with whole numbers, the presence of the decimal point notwithstanding. The decimal point at this stage of children's arithmetic learning is just a mark to separate the dollars and cents.

Teachers from the United States of America who teach in schools for American dependents abroad are often much concerned about the fact that children's textbooks in arithmetic "from home" make so much use of money problems. If the money of the foreign country (e.g., England or Venezuela) is not based on a decimal system, the assumed familiarity of children with dollars and cents is not present to those particular children. On the other hand, the country (e.g., Venezuela) may use a metric system of linear measure, which would be most useful in building decimal-number concepts; but the American texts do not use such measures! The general adoption of metric measures would be a 'great boon to both the teachers and the pupils in our country for instructional purposes as well as for their general usefulness to the citizenry.

Whether or not money numbers referring to sums less than 1 dollar have been thought of as decimal fractions, teachers do well to draw that connection when they teach decimal fractions in the intermediate grades. Beginning with the familiar coin values, they can build up the idea of a cent as having 1 tenth of the value of a dime, 1 dime as having 1 tenth of the value of 1 dollar, and 1 cent as having 1 hundredth of the value of a dollar.

Tenths are usually a better starting point for introducing decimal-fraction concepts than are hundredths. For that reason, any everyday use of tenths is probably better than money in earliest problem applications. The most common in everyday experience is probably tenths of a mile. Fortunately odometers on automobiles or mileage indicators on other vehicles are quite generally familiar to children. There will not be a decimal point, but that is not the essential thing; there *will* be some way of separating the tenths from the whole miles, by color or style of numeral.

Sometimes children buy a foot-ruler with no intention of being able to use it to measure with any units except feet or inches or common-fraction parts of inches, such as halves, fourths, and eighths. Perhaps they do not notice until after the purchase that the ruler has two different scales—inches and parts of inches on one edge and centimeters and millimeters on the other edge. When the teacher is questioned about "those other marks" on the ruler or when she initiates attention to them, a good opportunity is present for developing an application of decimal fractions. Not only should the metric measures on the ruler be explained; children should be encouraged to do some of their measuring with that side of the ruler.

A good "homework" assignment is discussion with parents of their uses of decimal fractions. Many fathers and mothers will be delighted to have their children show interest in such matters and will be most helpful, not only in helping their children make a list but in demonstrating uses of containers, simple tools, or even precision instruments that employ decimal fractions.

CLASSROOM AIDS TO UNDERSTANDING OF DECIMAL FRACTIONS

Many of the best aids to understanding of decimal fractions are the same as those used in helping children understand decimal whole numbers. Some of these have to be modified slightly. Others can be used in exactly the same form they were used in developing whole-number concepts; the difference is only in the way they are used.

Ten-by-ten squares of various types are readily adaptable to use in demonstrating meanings of decimal fractions. A blackboard hundred chart may be modified with numerals omitted. The individual small squares that formerly represented "ones" may now be used to represent "hundredths" of the big square. Whereas a row of ten small squares or a column of ten squares was formerly used to show "one ten," it may now be used to show "one tenth" or "ten hundredths" of the whole large square. The large square will mean "one whole thing."

Squared paper, already ruled, may have been used for individual pupils' hundred charts. It may now be used to show tenths and hundredths and to show the changing of hundredths and tenths. Some teachers stitch the lines for such squared paper on the sewing machine (without threading the needle) and have ample supplies of perforated squares.

Sheets of 1¢ postage stamps have been mentioned earlier as useful aids in teaching relative values of ones, tens, and hundreds. They may now be used to represent decimal fractions and wholes.

A chain of beads or spools, previously used as a "hundred line" may be adapted to become a "hundredths line." Incidentally, such a chain of 100 items is excellent for teaching per cent, as are several of the other items mentioned in this section. One bead or spool is considered as .01 of the chain; ten spools are .10 or .1 of the chain.

Place-value pocket charts may be used just as they are, with names of the "places" changed to fit the fractional place values to be discussed; or they may be extended toward the right so that the fraction decimal places will be "new" places following those formerly used. This might suggest a neat analogy to the idea of extending the number system to include decimal fractions.

The fraction board used for developing concepts of common fractions serves very well for decimal-notation "tenths" and even for "hundredths" if the length of each unit on the fraction board is adequate. If decimal-fraction sections are not available, making them is a good activity for the children. The tenths may be marked into hundredths instead of trying to have 100 separate pieces, each of which would probably be too small for efficient handling.

The abacus is obviously readily adaptable to use with decimal fractions. A decimal point may be attached to the base at the appropriate point to mark ones place, or the name ONES may be attached to that place in some obvious manner.

Commercially available number lines (free or inexpensive) are easily secured, as well as tape measures and meter sticks. One teacher brought back from a trip to South America a tape measure marked in centimeters and found it most useful in teaching decimal- fraction meanings. It was more useful than the meter stick because she could manipulate it so much more easily (for example, bend it in showing division).

Containers marked in metric system units may be borrowed from the chemistry laboratory or purchased for regular use. Play money, readily available at the "five-and-ten," is also very useful.

Marks, Purdy, and Kinney[5] show a mock-up of an odometer that could easily be made by children who are studying decimal fractions. It would be an excellent aid in problems involving tenths.

School supply houses have numerous other manipulative aids that are specifically prepared for teaching decimal-fraction meanings or can be easily adapted to that use.

READING AND WRITING
DECIMAL FRACTIONS

The sequence of experiences in getting acquainted with decimal fractions should be the same as that for getting acquainted with whole numbers or common fractions, that is, acquaintance with situations in which the decimal-fraction *meanings* can be experienced and discussed orally; acquaintance with the written symbols and learning to read them correctly; and finally, experience in writing them.

One matter that often leads to some confusion is more difficult to remedy than is would have been to prevent its occurrence. This is the pronunciation

[5] John L. Marks, C. Richard Purdy, and Lucien B. Kinney, *Teaching Arithmetic for Understanding.* New York: McGraw, 1958, p. 232.

of the names of the decimal-fraction places. On the diagrams of the place values on pages 385 and 391 the "th" at the end of each of the fraction place names was printed in italic type. This was done to emphasize the need for articulating the final sound in those words. If "hundred*th*" is carelessly pronounced by either the teacher or the pupils, it will sound so much like "hundred" that children may very easily become confused as to just what is being discussed. Some erroneous ideas may result from hearing "hundreds" when the speaker meant to say "hundredths."

The correct use of the word "and" in reading decimal fractions and mixed numbers needs special attention. To tell children to say "and" for the decimal point is not correct; it is not a name for the decimal point. Preferably children should learn to recognize that "and" is used in the reading of *decimal* mixed numbers exactly as "and" is used in the reading of mixed numbers that include a *common* fraction. The complete numeral of the mixed number $2\frac{1}{2}$ is read "two *and* one-half." The "and" is like a plus. It is a conjunction joining the whole number and the fraction that make up the mixed number. That is exactly the function of the "and" in the reading of a mixed number composed of a whole number and a decimal fraction.

Much practice to the contrary, the joining of a whole number and a common or decimal fraction to produce a mixed number is the *only* correct use of the word "and" in reading numerals. Its indiscriminate use in the reading of whole numbers or in reading the numerators or denominators of fractions can be most misleading. Witness, for example, the difference in meaning of 100.042 and .142. Of course, only the former number is correctly read, "One hundred and forty-two thousandths." If people get into the habit of reading the whole number "142" as "one hundred *and* forty-two," they will read .142 as "one hundred and forty-two thousandths," which is *not* correct.

This is one of the reasons that decimal fractions and mixed numbers are often read thus, "One, zero, zero, point, zero, four, two," or "One, oh, oh, point, oh, four, two." Children should be taught the complete form, naming the place value of the last fraction decimal place as the denominator of the fraction. When much dictating of numbers is needed in statistical records or calculations, the other form has more merit.

ZERO IN DECIMAL FRACTIONS

Pupils have less trouble with the zeros in decimal fractions if they have understood the role of zero in whole numbers and if time is taken to compare and contrast the use of zeros in fractions with that in whole numbers.

Zero may serve a place-holding function in decimal fractions just as it does in whole numbers. If there is no quantity to be expressed for any given place value, zero occupies the space so that other place holders that do express quantity can stay in their proper places. Thus:

304 boxes $3.04   30.4 miles   .304 inch

The zero in "304 boxes" holds the tens place so that the "3" in the hundreds place will stay there. In $3.04, a decimal number applied to money, the zero holds the dimes (or tenths) place so that the "4" in the pennies (or hundredths) place will stay where it belongs. The zero in "30.4 miles" keeps the "3" in the tens place where it belongs. The zero in ".304 inch" keeps the "4" in the thousandths place, since there are no hundredths in this number.

Consider some numbers in which zero is not between two other number symbols:

250   2500   .025   .0025

Here it is clear that the more zeros we have, the farther the other digits are pushed away from the ones place. The zeros at the *end* of a whole number push the other numerals away from ones place into the places to the *left,* to the bigger place values. The zeros at the *beginning* of the decimal fraction push the other numerals away from ones place and into the places to the *right,* to the smaller place values. As children would probably say it, the zeros "that matter" come (1) between other numerals or (2) at the end of the whole numbers or (3) at the beginning of the fraction numbers. We could have any number of zeros *before* the other whole-number numerals without making any difference in value. We could have any number of zeros *after* the other numerals in the fraction without making any difference in value.

The pocket chart helps to show this relationship with slips of paper in the appropriate pockets and with empty pockets where the zeros belong. As various numbers with "empty places" are shown in the pocket charts, children may practice writing the correct notation for each. The empty pockets are then obviously seen as holding a place, showing the need for some symbol to do the same thing in the written form.

On a somewhat more abstract level, the abacus can serve the same purpose. With a decimal point or other marker in the ones place to indicate its location, the abacus may then be used to represent whole and fractional decimal numbers written with zeros in them. The opposite direction of activity is also useful, from the number shown on the abacus to the written notation. One type of commercially produced abacus can be simply disassembled or reassembled. Sticks or rods with counters on them may be added as needed. With such an abacus, a number such as 75 could be shown on two rods. With the children watching, the teacher might take those two rods apart and insert an empty rod, asking the children to tell what the new number is. The same sort of exercise might then be performed with the ones place clearly marked by the decimal point in a number such as 7.5. As the children recognized that the decimal point went with the ones place, they would see that the new "empty" place would have to be in the fraction part of the number to push the "5" into the hundredths place.

When an abacus is used for showing pure (proper) decimal fractions, the presence of the ones place is desirable. True, a decimal point may be entered preceding the tenths place without the ones place being shown, but this tends to contribute to the emphasis on counting from the point rather than from the ones place.

This interpretation is also to be considered in deciding whether decimal numerals less than one should be written with a zero in the ones place, thus: 0.6; 0.275; 0.34. Engineers use the zero rather consistently, as do research workers in a great many other fields. Though this is not common practice in elementary school classrooms, it is a good practice that would start children on a procedure they may use later and would also support orientation toward ones place, even when there is no quantity indicated in that place.

MEANINGS OF DECIMAL FRACTIONS
AND COMPUTATION

Children's acquaintance with decimal-fraction meanings should be developed in use, with or without relation to computation. Meanings need to be developed prior to computational applications and should be continually expanded as the computational uses are expanded. In fact, the ways in which decimal fractions are used in adding, subtracting, multiplying, and dividing should add meanings not otherwise observed.

Addition and Subtraction of Decimal Fractions

Some authorities recommend that the teaching of decimal fractions and the processes with decimal fractions should precede the comparable work with common fractions. Certainly there is much merit in that suggestion since decimal fractions and the computations using decimal fractions are so similar to the meanings and processes for whole numbers. Since the commercial and scientific uses of decimal fractions are steadily expanding, a change in this sequence for elementary schools may well occur within the not-too-distant future.

Mention has already been made of the early and continuous use of money numbers in and out of school. Discussion of addition, subtraction, multiplication, and division of money numbers has been included with study of the four fundamental arithmetic processes with whole numbers. This inclusion is appropriate on the basis of extensive pupil experience with money numbers and the fact that the money problems have been oriented toward *cents* as *ones,*

with *dimes* considered as *tens* of ones and *dollars* as *hundreds* of ones.

As the teacher moves into the teaching of processes with decimal fractions, the same money problems that have been solved in that orientation can be reviewed from a new orientation, with attention focused on *dollars* as *ones,* with *dimes* becoming *tenths* of a dollar and *cents* becoming *hundredths* of a dollar.[6] This review should not be used, however, as the introductory material for addition and subtraction of decimal fractions. It is better to "start new" with something that does not have this "double" interpretation. Since tenths of miles are among the more familiar applications of decimal fractions already known to most children, problems concerning distances are particularly appropriate.

INTRODUCING ADDITION AND
SUBTRACTION WITHOUT CHANGING

One teacher started with a pair of problems, first presenting problem 1, then going on to problem 2.

Problem 1: From our school it is 14 miles to New Town. Centerville is 23 miles from our school in the opposite direction. How far is it from New Town to Centerville?

Problem 2: Jack lives 1.4 miles from our school. Mac lives 2.3 miles from school in the opposite direction. How far apart do Jack and Mac live?

Of course, problem 1 was very easy for the children, and they were able not only to give the numerical answer, but they cooperated in giving the teacher directions as to how she could show the solution on a number line. (Fig. 125*A* is a copy of that line.)

---

[6] This shifting of the numeral to be considered as *ones* is entirely defensible. This is a common practice in scientific work and is increasingly used in business and newspaper writing.

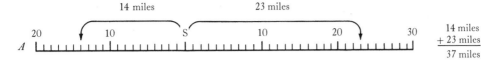

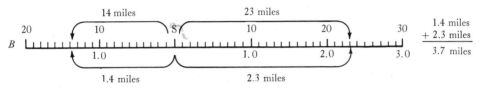

Figure 125. Addition of Whole Numbers and Decimal Fractions Compared.

The teacher introduced the second problem with a comment that the numerals were the same but that decimal fractions were present. She suggested that they work out what they thought would be a correct computational procedure and also draw a number line solution.

None of the pupils in this class had any trouble in getting a correct answer for the addition, but some of them did not seem to know how to proceed with the number line assignment. When asked if they were sure the correct sum was 3.7 miles, most of the children said they were. When asked to tell why they were sure, again some had difficulty. This is typical. In fact, one of the pitfalls of addition and subtraction of decimal fractions is that the algorisms are so very similar to those with whole numbers that children often can get right answers without really understanding very well just what they are doing or why.

After some discussion, it was brought out that the 4 tenths and 3 tenths could be added since they both referred to *tenths* and that 1 and 2 were added because they both referred to *whole miles.* These children had recently learned that the numerals showing the decimal

fractions were the *numerators* and that place value (tenths in this case) told the name or denominator. One child suggested that "it's just like adding the other fractions." The teacher asked her to write what she meant on the chalkboard. She wrote:

$$1\tfrac{4}{10} + 2\tfrac{3}{10} = 3\tfrac{7}{10}.$$

Some children drew new number lines, but they all liked best the idea of one boy that they could use the same line as for problem 1. He changed the original line (fig. 125A) so that it looked like figure 125B.

The teacher asked: "How can the same line represent such different distances? If it shows 14 miles + 23 miles, how can the same line show 1.4 miles + 2.3 miles?" The boy who had made the changes to the original drawing said: "Well, it isn't *really* miles, and it isn't *really* tenths of miles. It's like the scale of miles in our geography book. On top of our line is the scale that shows miles, and below the line is the scale that shows miles and tenths of miles."

The teacher was pleased with this explanation, but even more pleased when another child volunteered: "Above the line it shows 14 + 23 = 37 and all those numbers are miles, and below the line it shows the same thing, $14+23 = 37$, but then those numbers are tenths of miles."

In the time taken for the complete discussion of two simple problems, the same children could have added a large number of "examples" in which all they would have had to do was to follow a routine pattern. But this group of children were having time to think through the two problems and the relation between them. When the lesson was over, the teacher felt that most of them really understood the procedure and were ready for further practice.

Subtraction of decimal fractions can be introduced simultaneously with or immediately after addition of decimal fractions. No illustration of procedure will be given since there is really nothing new or different involved. The teacher should make sure that the easy first problems in adding and subtracting decimal fractions are taught so that these points are fully developed: (1) the fractions to be added or subtracted must be similar fractions (have the same denominators or "same names"); (2) the numerals (really, the numerators) are added or subtracted just as whole numbers are added or subtracted; (3) the sum or the difference must be a similar fraction to those added or subtracted (have the same denominator or "same name").

ADDITION AND SUBTRACTION
OF DECIMAL FRACTIONS
WITH CHANGING

Soon after the introduction of addition and subtraction of decimal fractions that do not require changing, the idea of changing (regrouping according to place value)—already supposedly well-established in addition and subtraction

of whole numbers and common fractions—should be considered.

A problem like the last one might be modified so that changing is necessary, e.g., 1.4 miles + 2.9 miles. Then obviously, the .4 and .9 must be regrouped to be considered as 1.3 miles. In the common algorism, the 1 whole mile will be added with the other whole numbers and the sum will come out as 4.3 miles.

$$\begin{array}{r} 1 \\ 1.4 \text{ mi.} \\ 2.9 \text{ mi.} \\ \hline 4.3 \text{ mi.} \end{array}$$

Money numbers might come back into the picture here. The regrouping formerly discussed in terms of pennies, dimes, and dollars might now be reinterpreted as dealing with hundredths, tenths, and whole dollars. Form A might be discussed first in terms of changing 10 of the 13 *pennies* for 1 *dime* and 10 of the 14 *dimes* for 1 *dollar*. Next it should be discussed as changing 10 of the 13 *hundredths* for 1 *tenth*, and 10 of the 14 *tenths* for 1 *one* (whole dollar). The crutches are included here, but they are not necessary if children can keep their thinking straight without them.

Form A	Form B
1 1	5 14
$ 2. 6 5	$ 5. ̸6 ̸4
+ 1. 7 8	− 3. 3 8
$ 4. 4 3	$ 2. 2 6

Similarly, Form B could be interpreted first as requiring the changing of a *dime* for 10 *pennies,* later as the changing of 1 *tenth* (of 1 dollar) for 10 *hundredths* (of 1 dollar).

Changing decimal fractions from one denomination to another is also basic in those addition and subtraction examples in which "ragged decimals" appear. In Form C the decimal fractions to be added do not form a neat margin on the right. Before children are confronted with such an example, they will no

Form C

$$\begin{array}{r} 2.435 \\ 315.24 \\ 27.6 \\ 1.785 \\ \hline \end{array}$$

doubt have met the dictum, "Keep the decimal points in a line." If not from the teacher or other children at school, they will probably hear it from parents, brothers, or sisters at home. The decimal points *should* be written in a straight column, of course, as an aid to keeping the numerals of the fraction and of the whole number in their proper places. It is unfortunate that so much stress is placed on the points with no mention of the reason for such concern.

If it is advisable to insert nonessential zeros to manage the addition of the thousandths and hundredths in Form C, why is it not also advisable to insert nonessential zeros to manage the addition of the tens and the hundreds along the ragged *left*-hand margin?

If the zeros are inserted, this is a form of changing. If 315.24 is changed to 315.240, then *24 hundredths* have been changed to *240 thousandths*, since the last decimal-fraction place used gives the decimal fraction its name. If 27.6 is changed to 27.600, the change is the same as if the common mixed number $27\frac{6}{10}$ is changed to $27\frac{600}{1000}$.

Whether or not it is correct to make these changes depends on the relative accuracy or precision of the numbers involved. In the case of money, for example, .6 of a dollar and .60 of a dollar are exactly equal. If .6 refers to a relatively coarse measurement to the nearest tenth of an inch and the .60 refers to a more refined measurement to the nearest hundredth of an inch, they may not be equal.

As a matter of fact, it is a good thing that children's texts now include little or no work with ragged decimals since children have very few uses for them (except in those standardized tests whose writers have not kept in step with the modern curriculum in arithmetic).

When problems do occur in which numbers to be added or subtracted do not "line up" on the right-hand margin of the algorism, the situation can be handled with relative ease in terms of the meanings involved for each number in that specific problem.

Suppose children have been working with sheets of stamps, surplus Christmas seals, or perforated hundred-sheets of blank paper. Children may devise their own problems for purposes of practice with the concepts involved. Say that one child has 60 "stamps" from an original sheet of 100, and he gives away 38 stamps. A primary consideration before going any further is to establish what the parts of the whole sheet are to be called. This is essential for understanding of the decimal fractions. The agreement as to assigned meanings might be:

$$100 \text{ stamps} = 1 \text{ whole sheet}$$
$$1 \text{ stamp} = \frac{1}{100} \text{ of a whole sheet, or } .01 \text{ sheet}$$
$$10 \text{ stamps} = \frac{1}{10} \text{ of a whole sheet, or } .1 \text{ sheet}$$

According to that agreement, the child who has 60 stamps has .6 of a whole sheet of stamps. (See fig. 126*A*, in which the rest of the whole sheet is shown by dotted lines to indicate the whole of which .6 is being considered.)

Now suppose this child is asked to give .38 of a whole sheet to another child. He will probably tear off the 38 hundredths somewhat as shown in figure 126*B*, leaving 22 hundredths. Actually the .6 of a sheet was changed to .60 of a sheet. In algorism form:

$$\begin{array}{cc} .6 & \text{becomes:} \quad .60 \\ \underline{-.38} & \underline{-.38} \end{array}$$

This is entirely right and proper since .6 sheet and .60 sheet are truly equivalent fractions.

To subtract .08, one of the 6 tenths must be thought of as 10 hundredths, so that 8 hundredths may be subtracted from it. This shows clearly in the diagram (fig. 126*B*) where 1 tenth of the sheet is broken into 8 hundredths and the remaining 2 hundredths. Form D shows the complete algorism, including crutches, to tell the whole story.

Here tenths are changed to hundredths *for a reason,* and the "ragged-decimal" notation of the original algorism is modified accordingly. Such treatment as this should help children see the sense of the action better than any prescription to "fill the empty spaces with zeros."

Form D

$$\begin{array}{r} \overset{5\ \ 10}{\cancel{6}\,\cancel{0}} \\ -.3\ 8 \\ \hline .2\ 2 \end{array}$$

Because of the necessary stress on addition and subtraction of numerators that go with *like* place-value denominators, the principle of likeness has been stressed.

Multiplication of Decimal Fractions

Multiplication and division of decimal fractions might be discussed together as inverse processes much as the inverse processes addition and subtraction have been discussed. They will be treated separately, however, because these processes with decimal fractions require more detailed treatment than do addition and subtraction.

Conventional instruction in multiplication with decimal fractions and mixed numbers has relied on some such prescription as this: Multiply the same way you usually do. Then count the number of places to the right of the decimal point in both the multiplier and the multiplicand. Point off that many places in the product.

Uncounted millions of children have followed such a procedure and have learned to "point off" correctly in the product. Their teachers have been satisfied because the answers have been correct. The children have been satisfied because their teachers have been pleased with their performance. The parents of the children have been satisfied if their children learned that procedure because it is true to the way *they* learned it a generation earlier.

But that is not good teaching! The learning is not adequate! The children have learned only to memorize a directive and follow it blindly. They have not learned to think about the meanings involved or even to follow the reasoning of someone else as to why that neat prescription works so well.

Later when those same children apply their routine learning in a real problem situation, the answer may not look right to them. Working with hypothetical examples and problems, they have not realized what a big change takes place in the product just by "pointing off."

THE MEANING OF "POINTING OFF"

Rules for pointing off in products (later, in quotients) have their rightful use as short-cut procedures. Most people can understand the logic back of those rules and use them more intelligently if the rules are developed *after* appropriate experiences that lead inductively to the rules themselves.

Actually, it is not the decimal point that moves or is moved when we multiply. It is rather the numerals that move. Because it is easier to move the point than to rewrite the numerals, moving the point becomes a timesaving device. When the decimal point is moved, it serves to redefine or relocate the *ones place.*

This goes back to multiplication of whole numbers by 10 or 100 or 1000 and so on. When a whole number (e.g., 4) is multiplied by 10, the product is that number of tens (4 tens); so a zero is written as a place holder in the ones place. The number of ones (4) becomes the number of tens; so it belongs in the tens place.

$$10 \times 4 = 4 \times 10 = 40$$

If the multiplier had been 100 instead of 10, two zeros would have been needed to move the original numeral two places so it would be in the hundreds place.

$$100 \times 4 = 4 \times 100 = 400$$

In each of these cases, suppose the original numeral had been written with a decimal point in the ones place. Then:

$$10 \times 4. = 40.$$
$$100 \times 4. = 400.$$

order to indicate that the numbers have changed their place values and that we have to show which numeral is now in the ones place. Moving the decimal point is only a quick notational scheme.

The following problem will serve as a basis for the discussion, though it is not perhaps the type of problem with which a teacher would begin the development with children.

Problem: Tom agrees to pay $29.80 for a used bicycle. He agrees to pay for it in 10 equal payments. After he has made 7 payments, how much has he paid?

The question to be answered is: What is 7 tenths of $29.80? The "7 tenths" may be written as "$\frac{7}{10}$" or as ".7." Since the development with multiplication by common fractions has been completed,

A

.6 = .60

.1

B

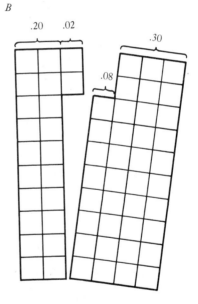

.20   .02

.30

.08

Figure 126. Changing or Regrouping in Subtraction of Decimal Fractions.

Did the decimal point move? Did the ones place and the tens place and the hundreds place move? No. The 4 moved from the ones place to the tens or to the hundreds place.

The decimal point always stays in the ones place. If we move the point, we do it in

let us first solve the problem with a common-fraction multiplier.

$$\frac{7}{10} \times \$29.80 = \frac{7 \times \$29.80}{10} = \frac{\$208.60}{10} = \$20.86$$

Actually, the solution involves two steps: $7 \times \$29.80$, then $\$208.60 \div 10$.

The same answer would have been obtained by first dividing $29.80 by 10, then multiplying by 7. The logic would be: 1 payment is $\frac{1}{10}$ of $29.80, or $2.98. Seven payments would be $7 \times 2.98, or $20.86.

We *must* remember that multiplying by a fraction always has two facets: multiplying by the numerator and dividing by the denominator. Now let us turn to solving the same problem using a conventional decimal-fraction algorism (Form E).

Completing this algorism requires exactly the same steps as in the first solution with common fractions. The first step is to multiply by 7. The second step, division by 10, is performed by the placing of the decimal point to indicate where ones place is (where the dollars end). If the multiplier had been the whole number 7, the product would have been $208.60, but it is .7; so one more decimal place is needed in the fraction part of the decimal mixed number, yielding $20.86 as the product.

Another way of describing the processes involved would be: multiply by 7; divide by 10. Still another way would be: multiply by 7; multiply by .1. It all boils down to the fact that dividing by 10 is the same as multiplying by .1, or $\frac{1}{10}$.

Figure 127 shows a device called a place finder by its originator. The base, made of either wood, cardboard, or any substantial material, has the place values named with words. A prominent decimal point is shown *in* ones place (not after ones place). The notched top edge of the base fits with an upper section that has space for writing whatever numerals are needed in a given situation. The base remains stationary; the top section bearing the numerals is moved to either the left or right as the problem demands.

Form E

$29.80
$\times\ .7$
$20.860

The numerals in figure 127 correspond to those in the last problem. The result of multiplying $7 \times 29.80 was entered on the top section of the place finder (fig. 127A). Figure 127B indicates the movement of the numerals to the right to show that the number is being divided by 10 (multiplied by .1). Figure 127C shows the final result. The decimal point "stayed put"; the numerals moved.

The place finder can be used in many situations with whole numbers and with fractions, to show the changes in place value that occur in either multiplication or division by powers of ten.

MULTIPLICATION OF DECIMAL
FRACTIONS BY WHOLE NUMBERS

Children should begin with easier problems, preferably with situations fitting the idea of multiplying as a form of adding and with a whole number as multiplier. A good choice is one in which the multiplier is clearly the whole "number of times" an equal addend is used. The *name* of the product is the same as the *name* of the multiplicand, since the product includes the same items as a total group that are included in the separate subgroups represented by the multiplicand. If the multiplicand is feet, the product is feet; if the multiplicand is money, the product is money.

The names of the place values in the product correspond similarly to those in the multiplicand when the multiplier is a 1-digit whole number, as in the examples on page 405.

Easy though it is to get such examples right without reasoning very much, the teacher should help children make sure that each numeral in the product is written where it is written because that is where it *belongs;* e.g., its name is tenths, so it is written in tenths place.

The understanding developed in multiplying common fractions by whole numbers can also be used to draw the obvious parallels and to strengthen the importance of keeping place values in mind. Ignoring place values in work with decimal fractions is just as serious

The common-fraction algorisms beside each decimal-fraction algorism below are good examples of the similarity of meanings in the contrasted forms. The obvious need to multiply 2×333 in all the examples emphasizes the similarity of the computation so far

```
      3 3 3
      × 2
      ─────
      6 6 6
```

2 × 3 ones = 6 ones

2 × 3 tens = 6 tens
2 × 3 hundreds = 6 hundreds

```
     3.3 3
     × 2
     ──────
     6.6 6
```

2 × 3 hundredths = 6 hundredths

2 × 3 tenths = 6 tenths
2 × 3 ones = 6 ones

```
     .3 3 3
     × 2
     ──────
     .6 6 6
```

2 × 3 thousandths = 6 thousandths

2 × 3 hundredths = 6 hundredths
2 × 3 tenths = 6 tenths

as ignoring the relative sizes of denominators in work with common fractions.

The three examples above could be written with common fractions, as:

$$2 \times \frac{333}{1} = \frac{666}{1} = 666$$

$$2 \times 3\frac{33}{100} = 2 \times \frac{333}{100} = \frac{666}{100} = 6\frac{66}{100}$$

$$2 \times \frac{333}{1000} = \frac{2 \times 333}{1000} = \frac{666}{1000}$$

Children may learn a good deal from discussing the relative merits of the decimal- and common-fraction forms and from suggesting other ways in which the computations could have been written.

MULTIPLICATION OF WHOLE NUMBERS BY DECIMAL FRACTIONS

The next step, in relative difficulty, is to multiply whole numbers by decimal fractions. This *must* be recognized by the teacher as a quite different situation from the preceding one so far as the meaning of the multiplication process is concerned. This is the two-way process of multiplying by the numerator (the numeral or numerals of the decimal fraction) and dividing by the denominator (represented by the place value of the decimal fraction).

as the *numerals* are concerned. The differences are in the place values or denominators.

```
    3 3 3
    ×.2
    ─────
   6 6.6
```
$$\frac{2}{10} \times 333 = \frac{2 \times 333}{10} = \frac{666}{10} = 66\frac{6}{10}$$

```
    3 3 3
    .0 2
    ─────
   6.6 6
```
$$\frac{2}{100} \times 333 = \frac{2 \times 333}{100} = \frac{666}{100} = 6\frac{66}{100}$$

```
    3 3 3
    .0 0 2
    ──────
   .6 6 6
```
$$\frac{2}{1000} \times 333 = \frac{2 \times 333}{1000} = \frac{666}{1000}$$

The procedure may be summarized as follows:

For Multiplication of a Whole Number by a Common Fraction:

1. Multiply the whole number by the numerator of the common fraction.
2. Divide the product by the denominator of the common fraction.

For Multiplication of a Whole Number by a Decimal Fraction:

1. Multiply the whole number by the numerator of the decimal fraction.
2. Place the decimal point in the product so it will show the right denominator. (One decimal fraction place means tenths; two, hundreds; three, thousandths; etc.)

This is one of the situations in which a comparison of the number of zeros in the common fraction and the number of fraction decimal places is helpful.

A

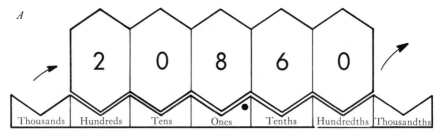

| Thousands | Hundreds | Tens | Ones | Tenths | Hundredths | Thousandths |

B

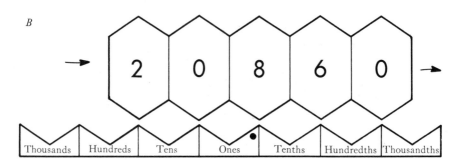

| Thousands | Hundreds | Tens | Ones | Tenths | Hundredths | Thousandths |

C

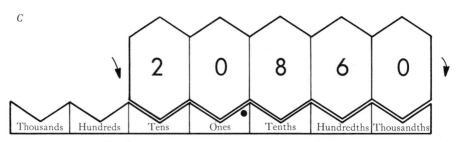

| Thousands | Hundreds | Tens | Ones | Tenths | Hundredths | Thousandths |

Figure 127. Multiplying by .1 or Dividing by 10 with a Place Finder.

This is true, of course, because $\frac{1}{10}$ is expressed with one decimal-fraction place; $\frac{1}{100}$ with two decimal-fraction places; and so on—always as many zeros in the denominator of the common-fraction form as there are places in the decimal-fraction notation that indicates that same denominator.

MULTIPLICATION OF DECIMAL
FRACTIONS BY DECIMAL FRACTIONS

As with multiplication of whole numbers and multiplication of common fractions, an area representation is helpful in representing multiplication of one decimal fraction by another.

Figure 70 in chapter 9 represents an area 22 feet wide and 33 feet long. That same drawing would serve very well as a representation of an area 2.2 feet wide by 3.3 feet long, just by changing the labeling of the parts. The relative size and position and distribution of the parts of that area would be the same. That same picture might also represent an area .22 feet wide by .33 feet long, again with different notations as to the meaning of each part in the diagram.

In the original diagram (fig. 70) each unit of square measure was 1 square foot. If the dimensions were 2.2×3.3, each square unit would be much smaller, .01 square foot, or 1 hundredth of a square foot ($\frac{1}{10} \times \frac{1}{10} = \frac{1}{100}$). If the dimensions were $.22 \times .33$, each square unit would be very, very small; it would be .0001 square foot, or 1 ten-thousandth of a square foot ($\frac{1}{100} \times \frac{1}{100} = \frac{1}{10000}$). It would be a very good learning situation for children to construct such an area, contrasting and comparing its meanings with different whole-number and fraction-number interpretations.[7]

The distributive principle is very helpful in the situation presented by the example below. The multiplying is not done all at once. Each digit in one term is multiplied by each digit in the other term and then all the products are added. If either digit is in a fraction place value, one must also divide by the appropriate denominator for that place. If both digits have a fraction place value, a person must divide by each separately or else divide by their product, as is done with common fractions.[8]

$$\begin{array}{r} 3.3 \\ \times 2.2 \\ \hline 6\ 6 \\ 6\ 6 \\ \hline 7.2\ 6 \end{array}$$

$\dfrac{2}{10} \times \dfrac{3}{10} = \dfrac{2 \times 3}{10 \times 10} = \dfrac{6}{100} = .06 \longrightarrow .06$

$\dfrac{2}{10} \times \dfrac{3}{1} = \dfrac{2 \times 3}{10 \times 1} = \dfrac{6}{10} = .6 \longrightarrow .6$

$\dfrac{2}{1} \times \dfrac{3}{10} = \dfrac{2 \times 3}{1 \times 10} = \dfrac{6}{10} = .6 \longrightarrow .6$

$2 \times 3 = \dfrac{6.}{7.26} \nearrow \begin{array}{l} 6. \\ 7.26 \end{array}$

[7] Caution: be sure that the various units involved are really comparable in relative size; one could not, for example, use that diagram to represent an area 2.2 feet by .33 feet. "Why not?" is a good question for learners.

[8] In the conventional algorism the partial products do not include decimal points. The partial products as shown are really only the numerators; the denominators are shown only by placement with reference to the total product. While this works all right, the longer algorisms at the right in each case make clear what the denominators are in the partial products as well as in the final product.

The procedure for multiplying a decimal fraction by another decimal fraction may be summarized thus:

1. Multiply the numerators.
2. Place the decimal point in the product so that it has the right denominator. The number of fraction places should be the sum of the fraction places in the multiplier and multiplicand.

This summary may sound very much like the prescribed procedure that was earlier described as inadequate. It *is* inadequate when such a statement and the application of that statement constitute the total instruction on multiplication of decimal fractions. After time has been taken to work through the meanings suggested above, the summary statement becomes a concise representation of those meanings.

Division of Decimal Fractions

The division of decimal fractions has tended to be relatively difficult for children (and some adults). The two chief reasons probably are (1) the long-division process with whole numbers may not have been mastered before the children became involved in the extension of that process to its use with decimal fractions, and (2) the "pointing-off" process has been taught rather mechanically and with a minimum of attention to the why's and wherefore's. In the discussion that follows, it is assumed that adequate attention has already been given to the long-division process with whole numbers, to the meanings of decimal fractions, and to the common-denominator method of dividing common fractions.

DIVISION OF DECIMAL FRACTIONS

BY WHOLE NUMBERS

Partition division situations are preferable for introducing the division of decimal fractions (including mixed numbers) by whole numbers. The teacher may wish to begin with a whole number divided by a whole number and then proceed to the use of decimal fractions (pure and mixed) in the dividend. Such a progression makes clear to the pupils that the division of the numerals (numerators) proceeds exactly the same for whole numbers and for decimal fractions. The differences are all in determining the correct denominator for the quotient.

Problem: Farmer Jones said: "It's wonderful what modern machinery will do. You know, my neighbor with his modern equipment harvested 216 acres of wheat in 8 hours!" How many acres were harvested per hour?

This partition problem should be easily solved by pupils who are beginning work on division of decimal fractions. As a quick review, the teacher might want to have the boys and girls demonstrate the meaning of the division algorism by demonstrating with some concrete aid just what is meant by the algorism. A pocket chart would serve the purpose. Beginning with 2 markers in the hundreds pocket, 1 in the tens pocket, and 6 in the ones pocket, the explanation would proceed somewhat as follows: The 2 hundreds will have to be changed for 20 tens and put with the 1 ten in the tens pocket; 21 tens ÷ 8 = 2 tens and some left over; so we put 2 tens in each of 8 groups, and we write "2" in the tens place of the quotient. That uses up 16 tens; so we subtract 16 tens from 21 tens, leaving 5 tens. Then we have to change the 5 tens for 50 ones and put them with the 6 ones in the ones pocket; 56 ones ÷ 8 = 7 ones; so we put 7 ones in each of the 8 groups, and we write "7" in the ones place of the quotient. We have 27

Form F

```
        2 7 acres
8 / 2 1 6 acres
      1 6
        5 6
        5 6
```

in each of the 8 groups. That means that 27 acres of wheat were harvested every hour. The computation is shown in Form F.

Going directly to the next problem, the analogy is fairly direct.

Problem: It took a truck farmer 8 hours to prepare his 21.6 acres of land for planting the new crop. How many acres did he prepare per hour?

Since the numerals are the same, the children should find this problem very easy to solve after the preceding one. The main point is to see that they recognize the difference in the designations of the place values. This time they must start with 2 *tens*, 1 *one*, and 6 *tenths*. Perhaps the action with the pocket chart should be completed before writing anything. If necessary, the teacher should ask appropriate questions and challenge incorrect procedures; if not, the children may proceed on their own. Many will be able to reason out the solution directly from the preceding one: The 2 tens have to be changed to 20 ones and put with the 1 one; 21 ones ÷ 8 = 2 ones and a remainder; so we put 2 ones (acres) in each of 8 groups. That uses up 16 ones (acres); so we have 5 ones (acres) left. We change them to tenths; that would be 50 tenths. We have 6 tenths already; so that is 56 tenths; 56 tenths ÷ 8 = 7 tenths. Now we divide out 56 tenths, 7 to each of the 8 equal groups.

From some such discussion, it is easy to move to Form G. The question of where to put the decimal point in the quotient is readily answered on the basis of the preceding action. If not, it can be settled by answering these questions: How many whole acres were in each of the 8 equal groups? (2.) How many tenths were in each of the equal groups? (7.) Or, you

Form G

```
        2 . 7 acres
8 / 2 1 . 6 acres
      1 6
        5 6
        5 6
```

put 2 of something in each of 8 equal groups. What were they? (Ones or whole acres.) You put 7 of something in each of the 8 equal groups. What were they? (Tenths of acres.) Then what do you suppose we must do to the quotient to show the right answer? How can you show which is ones place? (Put the decimal point in ones place right after the "2.")

Reference may also be made to solution of the problem using proper fractions. In fact, such solutions might precede the decimal-fraction solution.

$$21\frac{6}{10} \div 8 = \frac{\overset{27}{\cancel{216}}}{10} \times \frac{1}{\underset{1}{\cancel{8}}} = \frac{27}{10} = 2\frac{7}{10}$$

OR

$$\frac{1}{8} \text{ of } 21\frac{6}{10} = \frac{1}{\underset{1}{\cancel{8}}} \times \frac{\overset{27}{\cancel{216}}}{10} = \frac{27}{10} = 2\frac{7}{10}$$

If cancellation is used, the computations are the same as in the long-division algorism with decimal-fraction notation; but the method of recording the computations is different. In the common-fraction forms, 216 (tenths) is divided by 8 as part of the cancellation procedure; in the decimal notation, the 216 (tenths) is divided by 8 in regular long-division form. In common-fraction form, 27 is divided by 10 as the reduction of $\frac{27}{10}$ to $2\frac{7}{10}$; in the decimal notation, 27 is divided by 10 by the placement of the decimal point to show that "2" is in the ones place.

If further discussion is needed, the divisions may be written out as in Forms H and I:

Form H	Form I
7 tenths	2 7 tenths
8/5 6 tenths	8/2 1 6 tenths
	1 6
	5 6
	5 6

Problem: Mr. Smith has a big garden. It covers 2.16 acres. If it takes him 8 hours to hoe and weed his whole garden, how much does he hoe and weed per hour?

Again, the computation is the same so far as the numerators are concerned. The only differences relate to the names (place-value denominators) to which those numerals apply. This time, since 216 *hundredths* are being divided by the abstract number 8, the quotient will have to be 27 *hundredths*. All the steps taken in each of the preceding solutions will apply *except* as to the place-value designations for each of the numerals.

Such a series of problems should serve to highlight both the similarities and the differences between the algorisms for decimal whole numbers and for decimal fractions in the dividends.

Another series of problems might relate to money numbers. For example, they might require dividing $336 by 16, then $3.36 by 16, then $.336 (possibly a tax rate) by 16. As the children divided dimes, pennies, and mills, they could relate those values to tenths, hundredths, and thousandths. The use of a two-digit divisor would be new in this situation, but would require no new concepts.[9]

When the divisor is a whole number, there will always be as many decimal-fraction places in the quotient as there are in the dividend.

DIVISION BY A DECIMAL FRACTION

For the introduction of division *by* a decimal fraction, measurement-type situations are preferable (in contrast to the suggested partition-type situations for division of decimal fractions by whole numbers). The use of measurement situations is as important for division by a *decimal* fraction as it is in the intro-

---

[9] Of the suggested examples, only the last ($.336 ÷ 16) has a dividend that is a pure decimal fraction. The mixed decimal fractions are suggested for the first problems because the presence of the whole-number part of the mixed numbers helps orient the learner in relation to familiar whole-number place values. His continued orientation to ones place is very important.

duction of the common-denominator method for division by a *common* fraction.

Dividend a whole number. Various types of dividend will occur. A problem with a whole-number dividend is a good "starter."

Problem: The Girl Scouts are putting Christmas candy in bags. If the candy comes in boxes that hold 3 pounds and if they put .6 pound in each bag, how many bags can they fill from each box?

Given such a problem, children should be encouraged to work out their own solutions. Some might use a diagram. Some might use a common-fraction solution. Some might use successive subtractions. Some might even attempt a long-division algorism with decimal fractions. Other types of solutions might emerge and should be considered if they do. Supposing that the three listed types of solutions do occur, each can be used to further the understanding of the decimal-fraction form.

The diagram shows clearly the changing of the whole number 3 to 30 tenths, which are then divided by 6 tenths for a quotient of 5. The successive subtractions clearly show the emphasis on subtraction of successive groups of 6 tenths each. Of the common-fraction solutions, the common-denominator method is closest to the decimal-fraction algorism, though the inversion method without cancellation does also reach the division of 30 by 6; the inversion method with cancellation does not. Since the common-denominator method bears such a close relationship to the form to be developed, it is probably the most helpful final stepping-stone toward the new method to be taught. The teacher might suggest that the children see if they can use the common-denominator, common-fraction method to help them figure out how to write the computation using this form:

$$.6 \text{ pound} \overline{\smash{\big)}\ 3 \text{ pounds}}$$

Successive Subtractions:

3.0 pounds
− .6 pound (1st bag)
2.4 pounds
− .6 pound (2nd bag)
1.8 pounds
− .6 pound (3rd bag)
1.2 pounds
− .6 pound (4th bag)
.6 pound
− .6 pound (5th bag)
.0 pound

Diagram:

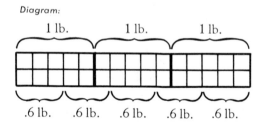

3 pounds ÷ .6 pounds = 5

Common-Fraction Solutions:

Common-denominator method:
$$3 \div \frac{6}{10} = \frac{30}{10} \div \frac{6}{10} = \frac{30}{6} = 5$$

Inversion method:
$$3 \div \frac{6}{10} = \frac{3}{1} \div \frac{10}{6} = \frac{30}{6} = 5$$

Inversion method with cancellation:
$$3 \div \frac{6}{10} = \frac{3}{1} \times \frac{\overset{5}{\cancel{10}}}{\underset{1}{\cancel{6}}} = \frac{5}{1} = 5$$

Or she might guide them by specific questions, such as:

Question: What did you do to the 3 in the common fraction example?
Answer: Changed it to 30 tenths.
Question: How can you write 3 pounds so it says 30 tenths of a pound?
Answer: As 3.0 pounds.

$$.6 \text{ pound} \overline{)3.0 \text{ pounds}}$$

Question: What is 30 (tenths) divided by 6 (tenths)?
Answer: It is 5.
Question: Where do you suppose you will write the "5"?

$$\overset{5}{.6 \text{ pound} \overline{)3.0 \text{ pounds}}}$$

This last question may be difficult to answer. If it is, the teacher might ask where it would be written if there were no decimal points in sight.

Reference to the diagram, to the common-denominator, common-fraction algorism, or to the successive subtractions will verify the accuracy of the whole number 5 as the quotient. Discussion of this solution (and others) should establish the fact that the dividend was changed to tenths so it would have the same denominator (same name) as the divisor, after which division could proceed as if both terms were whole numbers. The whole-number quotients should also be evaluated as to whether they seem reasonable; i.e., do they seem sensible?

Further verification of the quotient should be based on checking by the inverse process, multiplication:

$$5 \times .6 = 3.0.$$

This is always a reliable way of checking on the division of the numerators and on the "pointing off" and should be encouraged with all of the variants of division of decimal fractions.

The last problem dealt with division of a whole number by a decimal fraction. The order of introduction is not inflexible; in fact, the first variant to be developed below might well be presented before or along with the whole-number dividend.

Dividend a decimal fraction similar to the divisor. The same problem as that used above could be repeated with only a slight change in the dividend (4.2 pounds in the large box of candy instead of 3 pounds), making the computation the one shown in Form J.[10] Here the dividend and divisor already have the same place-value designation (the same name), tenths. The pupil needs only to recognize that "42 tenths" is another way to think of "4 and 2-tenths": 42 tenths ÷ 6 tenths = 7.

Form J
$$\overset{7}{.6 \overline{)4.2}}$$
$$\underline{4.2}$$

Other problems should also use similar decimal fractions as dividend and divisor. For example, $3.75 \div .75 = 5$, and $1.060 \div .265 = 4$. Notice that all examples given have whole-number quotients. This is desirable for some time until the idea is well established that when the dividend and denominator have the *same* number of decimal-fraction places, the division can proceed exactly as with whole numbers.

Dividend with fewer decimal-fraction places than in divisor. When the number of places in the decimal-fraction dividend is less than the number of places in the decimal-fraction divisor, the two unlike or *dissimilar* fractions must be made alike or *similar* in place value.

a. $.15 \overline{)3.6}$ b. $.025 \overline{).55}$ c. $.175 \overline{)3.5}$

These examples differ from the immediately preceding one only in the need to annex place-holder zeros in

---

[10] In the algorism, some teachers may consider the inclusion of the decimal point in the subtracted 4.2 as strange. It may help children remember the place value of the amount being subtracted. Otherwise, its inclusion or omission is not a crucial matter.

each dividend in order to make the place values of dividend and divisor similar. They are handled in the same fashion as for whole-number dividends; e.g., "3 ÷ .6" was changed to "3.0 ÷ .6" before the division was performed.

Changing a, b, and c to make the dividends agree with the divisors in place value of the last-recorded place, they become:

a. $.15\overline{)3.60}$ b. $.025\overline{).550}$ c. $.175\overline{)3.500}$

In a, "36 tenths" is changed to "360 *hundredths*," so that it can be divided by "15 *hundredths*." In b, "55 hundredths" is changed to "550 *thousandths*," so that it can be divided by "25 *thousandths*." In c, 35 tenths is changed to "3500 *thousandths*," so that it can be divided by "175 *thousandths*."

The analogous situation in the common-denominator method of division of common fractions is most useful as a stepping-stone to the long-division form for decimal fractions.

a. $3\dfrac{6}{10} \div \dfrac{15}{100} = \dfrac{36}{10} \div \dfrac{15}{100} = \dfrac{360}{100} \div \dfrac{15}{100} = \dfrac{360}{15} = 24$

b. $\dfrac{55}{100} \div \dfrac{25}{1000} = \dfrac{550}{1000} \div \dfrac{25}{1000} = \dfrac{550}{25} = 22$

c. $3\dfrac{5}{10} \div \dfrac{175}{1000} = \dfrac{35}{10} \div \dfrac{175}{1000} = \dfrac{3500}{1000} \div \dfrac{175}{1000} = \dfrac{3500}{175} = 20$

For those learners who do not see the common-denominator idea immediately in such algorisms, they may even be written out with words for denominators (names):

a. 3 and 6-tenths ÷ 15 hundredths =
    36 tenths ÷ 15 hundredths =
  360 hundredths ÷ 15 hundredths = 360 ÷ 15 = 24

b. 55 hundredths ÷ 25 thousandths =
  550 thousandths ÷ 25 thousandths = 550 ÷ 25 = 22

c. 3 and 5-tenths ÷ 175 thousandths =
    35 tenths ÷ 175 thousandths =
3500 thousandths ÷ 175 thousandths = 3500 ÷ 175 = 20

The importance of establishing the "same name" or the same place value *before* doing the dividing must be emphasized.

The changing of denominators, of course, necessitates the changing of numerators so that the resulting fraction still has the same value. The procedure recommended here rests on the assumption that children have already been taught the meanings of equivalent fractions and how to change to lower or higher terms. The common-denominator emphasis in division of decimal fractions cannot be taught meaningfully without that basis. It is essential that the children know that only *forms* are being changed, that *values* of the numbers remain the same, e.g., that 3.5 and 3.500 are different forms for the same number.

Another point that is particularly important before proceeding to the next type of division example is the idea that in using the common-denominator method (for either common fractions or decimal fractions), once the denominators are the same, the division proceeds *as with whole numbers*. Essentially, the approach has been to give dividend and divisor the same final place values and then operate *as if* the numerals referred to whole numbers.

Before reaching this point in the development, many experts on the teaching of arithmetic recommend that children be taught that they *are changing the divisor to a whole number*. This is an acceptable procedure. It is, however, postponed to this particular point in the present development for these reasons: (1) the common-denominator rationale is perhaps more readily followed by children as a first step toward the whole-number idea of the divisor, and (2) there is no conflict between the two ideas; so the whole-number-divisor idea can still be developed and, perhaps, with greater chance of its being understood.

When changing the dividend and divisor by the moving of decimal points, children should be helped to see that they are multiplying *both terms* by ten or some power of ten. That is, there is actually a multiplication by 1, though the form may be $\frac{10}{10}$, or $\frac{100}{100}$. For example, with 1 expressed as ten-tenths:

$$\frac{\text{Original dividend}}{\text{Original divisor}} \times \frac{10}{10} = \frac{\text{new dividend}}{\text{new divisor}}$$

Take the division "22.4 ÷ 1.6" (which occupies the central position among the three division examples below) as the starting point.

$$\text{a. } .16\overline{)2.24} \qquad \text{b. } 1.6\overline{)22.4} \qquad \text{c. } 16\overline{)224}$$

with the work below each showing 14, 16, 64, 64.

In the algorism to the left, both dividend and divisor have been *divided* by 10. In the algorism to the right, both dividend and divisor have been *multiplied* by 10. Obviously, all the quotients are the same, the whole number 14.

Expressing these same three divisions as common fractions, they become:

$$\text{a. } \frac{2.24}{.16} \qquad \text{b. } \frac{22.4}{1.6} \qquad \text{c. } \frac{224}{16}$$

It is a simple matter to change fractions a and b so they have whole numbers as numerators and as denominators. For a, both numerator and denominator must be multiplied by 100. For b, both numerator and denominator must be multiplied by 10. Thus:

$$\text{a. } \frac{2.24}{.16} = \frac{2.24 \times 100}{.16 \times 100} = \frac{224.00}{16.00} = \frac{224}{16} = 14$$

$$\text{b. } \frac{22.4}{1.6} = \frac{22.4 \times 10}{1.6 \times 10} = \frac{224.0}{16.0} = \frac{224}{16} = 14$$

In each of these examples, both the numerator (dividend) and the denominator (divisor) have been converted to whole numbers. The same would hold true for some of our earlier examples, such as 3.6 ÷ .15.

$$\frac{3.6}{.15} = \frac{3.6 \times 100}{.15 \times 100} = \frac{360.0}{15.00} = \frac{360}{15} = 24$$

In the next variant of division by a decimal fraction, this will not hold true. It is also with this next variant that the concept of changing the divisor to a whole number becomes particularly helpful.

Dividend with more decimal-fraction places than in divisor. In the next problem, the dividend has more decimal-fraction places than the divisor. Changing the divisor to a whole number is a logical procedure to follow.[11]

Problem: A new weather station in a certain city reported 81.25 inches of rain in the first 2.5 years of its operation. What was the average rainfall per year at that station?

The typical manner of handling the computation for solving this problem is to change algorism a to algorism b.

$$\text{a. } 2.5\overline{)81.25 \text{ in.}} \qquad \text{b. } 25.\overline{)812.5 \text{ in.}}$$

This change amounts to multiplying both dividend and divisor by 10. When children first meet this type of division problem, their attention can be focused more clearly on just what is being done

---

[11] Some people recommend changing *both* dividend and divisor to whole numbers. If that were done, the new algorism would be obtained by multiplying both divisor and dividend by 100 instead of by 10 to get:

$$250\overline{)8125}$$

This is really not a simplification because when the division is performed, it would probably be "carried out" to tenths anyway, introducing a difficulty that in the present discussion is postponed to the next chapter — the handling of divisions with remainders.

if they actually write the division form a second time to make the change. The computation then proceeds according to the pattern already established for the division of a decimal fraction by a whole number (pp. 407-09). The computation is really done as a partition division problem: If 812.5 inches of rain fell in 25 years, what would be the average rainfall per year?

The quotient is 32.5 inches. The "pointing off" is simple since in division of a decimal fraction by a whole number, the place values in the quotient are written directly above the corresponding place values in the dividend. See Form K.

Form K[12]

$$\begin{array}{r} 3\ \mathbf{2.5}\text{ in.} \\ 25.\overline{\smash{)}8\ 1\ 2.5\text{ in.}} \\ 7\ 5 \\ \hline 6\ 2 \\ 5\ 0 \\ \hline 1\ 2\ 5 \\ 1\ 2\ 5 \\ \hline \end{array}$$

NOTATIONAL QUESTIONS

In the notational forms used thus far no new notations have been used. They have not been necessary. When the divisor is a whole number, the number of fractional places in the quotient corresponds exactly with the number in the dividend. (That is, the decimal point in the quotient is directly above the decimal point in the dividend.) When the decimal fraction divisor is changed to a whole number and the algorism is written again to show the change in both divisor and dividend, the same treatment prevails for that situation. When the number of decimal-fraction places in the dividend is less than the number in the divisor, they are simply increased by annexation of place-holding zeros so that there are as many

[12] The omission of decimal points in the partial dividends is typical in the long-division algorism. Perhaps they should be included in children's early experiences. When they are not included, the numerals for the partial products indicate numerators only, not the place-value denominators (denominations).

places as in the divisor; then the division is treated *as if* a whole number were being divided by a whole number.

Some teachers are not willing to take the time to have children rewrite those examples which need rewriting because of the change in form. They are in a hurry to get to the short-cut way of doing it (which was very probably what they themselves were taught as *the* only way). Rewriting the division example until the background ideas are well established is certainly highly recommended.

Eventually, however, some sort of shortcut is desirable. An examination of various short-cut notations should be helpful. Some of these are shown below for three examples, which in their original forms appeared as:

Name of Notation	Effects of Applying Notation
Two decimal points	2.5.$\overline{\smash{)}4.7.5}$ .6.$\overline{\smash{)}3.0.}$ .15.$\overline{\smash{)}4.50.}$
Decimal points and arrow	2.5.$\overline{\smash{)}4.7.5}$ .6.$\overline{\smash{)}3.0.}$ .15.$\overline{\smash{)}4.50.}$
Arrow	2.5$\overline{\smash{)}4.7.5}$ .6$\overline{\smash{)}3.0}$ .15$\overline{\smash{)}4.50}$
Caret below numerals	2.5$\overline{\smash{)}4.7.5}$ .6$\overline{\smash{)}3.0}$ .15$\overline{\smash{)}4.50}$
Caret above numerals	2.5$\overline{\smash{)}4.7.5}$ .6$\overline{\smash{)}3.0}$ .15$\overline{\smash{)}4.50}$

Other variations are possible, but not necessary for an evaluation of procedures. The use of two decimal points is hardly conducive to clarity. How can the same number have two decimal points? If the decimal point's function is to mark ones place, how can there be two ones places in the same number? Further, when a child is to check his work at a later time, how does he know which decimal points were the originals? (The arrow with points takes care of this, but the two decimal points without the arrow do not.)

The caret meets the objections to the double-decimal-point procedures. The child can at least recognize that the caret indicates the position of the *new* ones place. If the caret is to be used, writing it above the numerals is preferable since in that position it points directly at the position of the decimal point in the quotient.

The decimal points that mark the location of ones place in the quotient have been entered in all the examples. When the learners have reached the stage of readiness for shortcuts, they should also be ready for the shortcut of marking the ones place of the quotient before doing the division. This has been done in all the examples.

Would it not be a better shortcut than any of those shown simply to mark the decimal point in the quotient? It is the next obvious step in the progression shown as one reads down the sets of examples. From marking the location of the decimal point with a caret above the numerals and pointing to the quotient location of the decimal point, why not just put the decimal point in the place it will occupy in the quotient? This is the most efficient method of all.[13]

If children need crutches like arrows and carets for a time, teachers should lead them eventually to discard these in favor of merely entering the decimal point in its appropriate location in the quotient (preferably *before* the division, not after it).

[13] The subtractive algorism for long division requires a somewhat different formal development of placement of the decimal point in the quotient, but the basic reasons underlying the "pointing off" are the same.

Since division is the inverse of multiplication, an inverse rule for locating ones place (placing the decimal point) should be available, and such is the case. The product in multiplication has as many decimal-fraction places as there are decimal-fraction places in both factors, multiplier and multiplicand. The number of decimal-fraction places in either factor, accordingly, is equal to the difference between the number of fraction places in the product and in the other factor. Since the quotient in division corresponds to one of the factors in multiplication, and since the dividend in division corresponds to the product in multiplication, the number of decimal-fraction places in the quotient is equal to the difference in number of such places in the dividend and in the divisor. Of course, this assumes that there are at least as many decimal-fraction places in the dividend as in the divisor, either originally or by changing the form of the number.

This is usually called the subtractive method of locating the decimal point in the quotient. It can be easily memorized and applied as a mechanical guide. It is hardly needed by learners who understand what really happens to place values in the division of decimal fractions.

All the division examples discussed in this chapter "come out even"; that is, they do not have remainders. Certain special problems of handling situations involving remainders are likely to occur. They will be discussed in the next chapter.

STUDY QUESTIONS

1. What is the numerator of each of these decimal fractions? (a) .25; (b) .05; (c) .178; (d) 1.3.
2. What is the denominator of each of the decimal fractions in question 1?
3. Make a list of the uses you have made of decimal fractions in the past week.

4. Practice using one or more of the classroom aids suggested on pages 394-95. Make some other aid of your own design that would be useful in helping children to see the meanings of decimal fractions.

5. After reading this chapter, how would you say that the meaning of "pointing off" in a product or quotient is presented differently from the way you first learned to point off in decimal answers?

6. Compare the use of zeros in the denominators in the left-hand column below with the use of place-value denominators in the right-hand column.

a. $\frac{24}{100}$ .24
b. $\frac{215}{1000}$ .215
c. $3\frac{4}{10}$ 3.4
d. $\frac{3434}{10000}$ .3434

7. What is the relation of the common-denominator method for dividing common fractions and the "pointing off" in division of decimal fractions?

CHAPTER 18

Common Fractions,
Decimal Fractions, and Per Cent

COMMON FRACTIONS ARE more useful than decimal fractions in certain situations, such as dealing with pieces of pie or parts of a candy bar. Decimal fractions are more useful in certain other situations, such as comparing the relative values of two fractions. (It is so much easier to tell which is larger, .875 or .85, than to compare $\frac{7}{8}$ and $\frac{17}{20}$.) Because each form of fraction is more appropriate in certain situations, skill in changing quickly from one form to the other is most useful.

Converting Common and Decimal Fractions

The easier conversion is from decimal-to common-fraction form. It will be considered first.

CHANGING DECIMAL FRACTIONS
TO COMMON-FRACTION FORM

Since only powers of ten may serve as denominators of decimal fractions and since they may easily be written as common-fraction denominators, converting a decimal fraction to a common fraction is very simple.

$$.85 \text{ becomes } \frac{85}{100}$$

$$.6 \text{ becomes } \frac{6}{10}$$
$$.025 \text{ becomes } \frac{25}{1000}$$
$$.9 \text{ becomes } \frac{9}{10}$$

In each of these cases except the last, another step is possible and sometimes desirable, that is, changing the common fraction to its lowest terms. Then:

$$\frac{85}{100} \text{ becomes } \frac{17}{20}$$
$$\frac{6}{10} \text{ becomes } \frac{3}{5}$$
$$\frac{25}{1000} \text{ becomes } \frac{1}{40}$$

If the decimal fraction is a complex one like $.12\frac{1}{2}$ or $.16\frac{2}{3}$, it must be remembered that the numerals (including the common-fraction numerals) are the numerator of the common fraction and that the place value of the last whole-number numeral is the denominator. Then:

$$.12\frac{1}{2} = \frac{12\frac{1}{2}}{100} = \frac{25}{2} \div 100 = \frac{\overset{1}{\cancel{25}}}{2} \times \frac{1}{\underset{4}{\cancel{100}}} = \frac{1}{8}$$

OR

$$.12\frac{1}{2} = \frac{12\frac{1}{2}}{100} = \frac{\frac{\overset{1}{\cancel{25}}}{\cancel{2}} \times \cancel{2}}{100 \times 2} = \frac{25}{200} = \frac{1}{8}$$

Children who have occasion to make such changes have probably also reached

417

the stage of building and learning tables of equivalent common and decimal fractions; so they should learn to recognize common equivalents such as $.12\frac{1}{2}=\frac{1}{8}$ and $.16\frac{2}{3}=\frac{1}{6}$.

CHANGING COMMON FRACTIONS
TO DECIMAL FRACTIONS

Changing common fractions to decimal fractions requires that the common fraction, which may have any denominator, must be changed to one that is ten or a power of ten. Beginning with easy conversions, children who have learned how to change common fractions to other common fractions will have little or no difficulty. Take the fraction $\frac{2}{5}$. The denominator is 5; it is to be changed to 10. In order to change it to 10, 5 must be multiplied by 2. If the denominator is multiplied by 2, the numerator must also be multiplied by 2. This gives $\frac{4}{10}$, which is then written as $.4$.

$$\frac{2}{5}=\frac{2\times2}{2\times5}=\frac{4}{10}=.4$$

Or take some fractions that cannot be changed to simple fractions with denominators of 10, in which case a denominator of 100 or 1000 or some higher power of 10 may be required.

$$\frac{4}{25}=\frac{4\times4}{4\times25}=\frac{16}{100}=.16$$

$$\frac{9}{200}=\frac{5\times9}{5\times200}=\frac{45}{1000}=.045$$

This method works fairly well if it is easy to recognize the needed multiplier to yield the required power of 10. For some denominators, no such multiplier exists. A method that always works may be taught as soon as children have learned to divide using decimal-fraction notation.

Since one of the meanings of a common fraction is an indicated division, an obvious way to change a common fraction to a decimal fraction is to divide the numerator by the denominator and record the quotient in decimal-fraction notation.

$$\frac{\text{Numerator}}{\text{Denominator}}=\frac{\text{Dividend}}{\text{Divisor}}$$

This division has a new feature not considered in any of the examples of division of decimal numbers in the preceding chapter. This is the fact that the whole-number dividend (numerator of the fraction) may be smaller than the divisor (denominator of the fraction). In order to divide, the whole-number dividend must be changed to a form that will "contain" the divisor. Thus, in Forms A and B, the numerator "1" of the fraction "$\frac{1}{4}$" must be changed to its equivalent, "1.00," or "100 hundredths"; and the numerator "3" of the fraction "$\frac{3}{8}$" must be changed to "3.000," or "3000 thousandths" in order to make it possible to complete the division.

Form A	Form B
.2 5	.3 7 5
4/1.0 0	8/3.0 0 0
8	2 4
2 0	6 0
2 0	5 6
	4 0
	4 0

Early instruction in changing common fractions to decimal-fraction form by division should be with this type of fraction called *terminating* decimal fractions. No matter how much further the division might be carried, there would never be any other numeral in the quotient except zero, and the annexation of more zeros would not change the value. The quotients as given are exact quotients.

Some common fractions, however, cannot be expressed in such exact decimal-fraction form; they do not "come out even." No matter how many zeros were added to the dividend and no matter how long the division process were to continue, there would always be a remainder. The fractions $\frac{1}{3}$ and $\frac{2}{7}$ are of this type. (See Forms C and D.)

Form C

```
      . 3 3 3
3/1.0 0 0
    9
    ─────
    1 0
      9
    ─────
      1 0
        9
      ─────
        1
```

Form D

```
      .2 8 5 7 1 4
7/2.0 0 0 0 0 0
    1 4
    ─────
      6 0
      5 6
    ─────
        4 0
        3 5
      ─────
          5 0
          4 9
        ─────
            1 0
              7
          ─────
            3 0
            2 8
          ─────
              2
```

Notice that the last remainder is the same numeral as the original dividend; so the whole pattern starts over again. There is no way to complete such a quotient except to change the remainder to a common fraction in the quotient. Then $\frac{1}{3}=.333\frac{1}{3}$, or $.33\frac{1}{3}$, and $\frac{2}{7}=.285714\frac{2}{7}$. Other ways to express these decimal fractions are:

.3 . . . or .33 . . . or .333 . . .   .285714 . . .

$.\dot{3}$ $.\overline{285714}$ or $.\dot{2}8571\dot{4}$

$.\overline{3}$ $.\overline{285714}$

The purpose of the dots or the bars is to indicate that these digits will repeat endlessly. Although these divisions never come out even, for all practical purposes of elementary school children, a greater degree of precision is not needed. For obvious reasons, these decimal fractions are called *repeating decimal fractions.*

All common fractions, when their indicated division is performed, will result in either terminating or repeating decimal fractions. Factoring the denominator of *any common fraction that has been changed to lowest terms* will indi-

cate whether it can be converted to a terminating decimal fraction. If the prime factors of the denominator are all 2's, or all 5's, or all 2's and 5's, it will terminate. If there are any prime factors other than 2's and 5's, it will not terminate. This, of course, follows from the fact that 2 and 5 are factors of 10 and that denominators of decimal fractions are all powers of 10.

$$\frac{1}{4}=\frac{1}{2\times 2} \qquad \frac{3}{8}=\frac{3}{2\times 2\times 2}$$

$$\frac{4}{25}=\frac{4}{5\times 5} \qquad \frac{9}{200}=\frac{9}{2\times 2\times 2\times 5\times 5}$$

$$\frac{1}{30}=\frac{1}{2\times 3\times 5} \qquad \frac{2}{7} \qquad \frac{1}{3}$$

The fractions $\frac{1}{4}$, $\frac{3}{8}$, $\frac{4}{25}$, and $\frac{9}{200}$ all have denominators that, when factored, give only 2's and 5's as the prime factors. These have all been demonstrated to "come out even" if the division is carried far enough. The fractions $\frac{1}{3}$ and $\frac{2}{7}$ have prime-number denominators other than 2 and 5 and will never "come out even" as decimal fractions. The fraction $\frac{1}{30}$ has a denominator that can be factored, but the factors include 3 along with 2 and 5; so this common fraction cannot be changed to a terminating decimal fraction.

Remainders and Rounding Off

REMAINDERS IN DECIMAL DIVISION

The same procedures used in changing a common fraction to a decimal fraction are frequently applied in other division computations with decimal fractions. Form E is like those discussed in chapter 17. When the digits in the original dividend have been used, there is no remainder. The quotient is a terminating decimal fraction.

In Form F, however, when the original dividend has been used, there is a remainder, 3. This remainder may be placed in the quotient as the numerator of the fraction $\frac{3}{12}$, giving a complete quotient of $.57\frac{3}{12}$, or $.57\frac{1}{4}$. Or the human computer may add a place-holding zero in the dividend and carry the division out for another place, as in G, or still another place, as in H. Finally, when the division has been carried out to 4 decimal-fraction places, there is no remainder.

Form E	Form F
57	$.5\ 7\frac{3}{12} = .57\frac{1}{4}$
12$\overline{)6.84}$	12$\overline{)6.8\ 7}$
6 0	6 0
84	8 7
84	8 4
	3

Form G	Form H
$.5\ 7\ 2\frac{6}{12} = .572\frac{1}{2}$	$.5\ 7\ 2\ 5$
12$\overline{)6.8\ 7\ 0}$	12$\overline{)6.8\ 7\ 0\ 0}$
6 0	6 0
8 7	8 7
8 4	8 4
3 0	3 0
2 4	2 4
6	6 0
	6 0

Notice the use of the concept of a common fraction as an indicated but unperformed division. In F, the fraction $\frac{3}{12}$ in the quotient uses the remainder but only as "3 still *to be divided* by 12." In G, the fraction $\frac{6}{12}$ declares a "6 still *to be divided* by 12." In this case, these divisions can be completed by changing the "3 hundredths" to "30 thousandths" and finally by changing the "6 thousandths" to "60 ten thousandths."

Though it was possible in this case to complete the division without having a complex decimal fraction for a quotient, the question still remains as to whether or not this continuation of the division was necessary. Recognizing that the "undivided part" is getting progressively smaller, one needs to appraise the situation for which the

computation is needed. If the problem requires taking $\frac{1}{12}$ of $6.84, obviously the practical answer is $.57, no matter how far the division is carried. In problems faced by children in the elementary school, the chances are very high that no greater degree of precision is going to be necessary.

Then there is also the decimal-fraction-division example in which the quotient turns out to be a repeating decimal fraction. In this case, the division must stop short of the limits to which it can be carried. To handle either of these situations, then, children need to know when and how to "round off" the quotient.

ROUNDING OFF THE QUOTIENT

The desired precision of the quotient determines the point at which it is rounded off. (Precision will be discussed in chap. 19 on measurement.) In elementary school problems, the quotient, if it does not "come out even," is usually rounded off to the nearest tenth or the nearest hundredth, with only rare instances of rounding off to the nearest thousandth.

In order to know what is the *nearest* tenth, hundredth, or thousandth, various procedures are acceptable. One way is to carry the division one place beyond that in which the quotient is to be stated. In Form G above, if the rounding off were to be to the nearest hundredth, the "2" in thousandths place would indicate that the answer should be stated as .57. If the digit in thousandths place had been "5" or higher, the answer would have been stated as .58. In Form H, if the answer were to be rounded to the nearest thousandth, it would be written .572, since the next digit is "5." (See p. 459.)

Another basis for rounding off the quotient at the chosen place value is to complete the division by entering the remainder as the numerator and the divisor as the denominator of a common fraction in the quotient. If this fraction is equal to $\frac{1}{2}$ or more, the preceding digit is increased by 1; otherwise it is left as it is. In either case, the common fraction is dropped.

A third method, used by those who are good at estimating relative number values, is perhaps the most efficient for general use. Instead of actually writing the common fraction as part of the quotient, one may simply note whether or not the remainder is half or more than half of the divisor and round off the last quotient figure accordingly.

Per Cent

Common fractions can have any number as the denominator. Decimal fractions are restricted to denominators that are powers of ten. In spite of this restriction, decimal fractions are growing in frequency of use as compared with common fractions. A still further restriction of denominators is represented in the special case of per cents, which have only one possible denominator, that is, 100. Also in spite of this sharp restriction, per cents are very much favored for everyday use in both public and private affairs.

MEANING OF PER CENT

Per cent means "per hundred" or "by the hundred" or "out of one hundred." If one hears on the radio that one candidate in an election campaign received 25 per cent of the votes, he knows that for every 100 votes cast, that candidate received 25.

The term "per cent" comes from the Latin "per centum," or "per hundred."

The common symbol for per cent is "%." The two zeros in the symbol may be related to the two zeros in the denominator $\frac{1}{100}$. Per cents are special fractions, easily introduced as a form of decimal fractions.

The % sign may be thought of as meaning "by the hundred" or "out of one hundred" or simply as "hundredths." The % sign indicates that the denominator of the fraction is 100. The numerator of the fraction is whatever number precedes the % sign. Thus 5% equals: 5 out of 100; 5 per hundred; 5 hundredths; $\frac{5}{100}$; .05; $5 \times .01$; $5 \times \frac{1}{100}$; or $5 \div 100$.

The frequency with which common denominators enter into the solutions of arithmetic problems indicates their usefulness and their importance. Per cent approaches the ultimate in common denominators. With hundredths as the *only* denominator in per cent situations, one does not even have to choose *which* common denominator to use. All common and decimal fractions are simply changed to that one common denominator. It is no wonder that per cent is so much a part of our conversation and our business practice.[1]

Per cent is the expression of a relationship, of a ratio, between two quantities or numbers. Any per cent, e.g., 15%, is not a complete idea except when it is used to express a relationship between *something* and *something*. For example, 15% of the children in a certain school are within walking distance of the school. Here the 15% tells the relationship between (a) the children who live within walking distance and (b) all the children in the school. The number of walking-distance children bears the

---

[1] An interesting historical note is the fact that per cent was used earlier than decimal fractions. Italian merchants were using the idea in the fifteenth century.

same relation to all the children in the school as 15 does to 100. For every 100 children in the school, 15 live within walking distance. The user of per cent *must* be clear as to *what* is being compared with *what*.

Per cents are widely used; they are also widely misused. Much of the misuse comes about because the user is not clear as to what 100% means in the particular situation; 100% simply means *all* of a certain number that is being used as a *basis* or *standard* of *comparison*. If two numbers are being compared, one must be the standard against which the other is judged. In figure 128, 4 miles is being compared with 5 miles. Five miles is the *basis* of the comparison. The distance five miles equals *all* of the standard of comparison; it represents 100%. Then the 4 miles that is being compared to that standard must represent 80% of the standard or basis.

which of the two shall represent the basis for comparison. Then that one is taken to represent 100% and the other distance corresponds to whatever per cent will tell its relationship to the standard.

COMMON FRACTION,

DECIMAL FRACTION,

AND PER CENT EQUIVALENTS

The changing of common and decimal fractions to per cents and the changing of per cents to common and decimal fractions can contribute to children's understanding of all these forms and the relations among them. Whether or not greater understanding is achieved depends on how the relations are developed.

Parts of 100: Some of the same learning aids that were used in earlier grades for teaching the meanings of

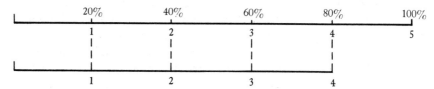

Figure 128. Ratio of Four to Five.

Figure 129, on the other hand, sets up the 4-mile distance as the basis or standard of comparison, as 100%. Then the 5-mile distance is 125% of the standard. In the two situations, the same two distances are being compared: 4 miles and 5 miles. But the correct per cent to associate with each must be determined only after someone has decided

hundred in relation to tens and ones are also useful at this point. The ten-by-ten square, the hundred-tag chart, and a string of 100 beads or spools are examples.

The teacher may wish to have a large ten-by-ten square for class discussion and manipulation while pupils have their own smaller ten-by-ten squares

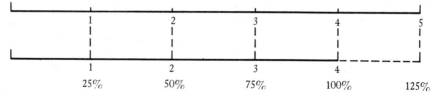

Figure 129. Ratio of Five to Four.

to use individually. Figure 130 shows such a square with its hundred equal parts. The teacher's first responsibility is to establish the meaning of the big square and of each small square. Children must understand that, in this case, the large square represents the whole number 1. It may help to call it "1 square mile," "1 square yard," "1 square foot," or "1 city block." Then each of the smaller squares must be established as *1 of the 100 equal parts of the whole.* Children should participate in thinking of all the different correct oral and written designations: $\frac{1}{100}$; .01; one-hundredth; 1%; 1 per cent.

5. What other common fraction is equal to the part you marked?

6. What per cent of the big square is $\frac{10}{100}$?

7. Mark off 4 small squares, each worth 1% of the big square.

8. How many such parts are in the whole big square?

9. $4\% = \dfrac{?}{?}$.

Figure 130 is marked to indicate possible approaches to answering these questions. Individual work should be followed by general discussion and a chance to clarify any misconceptions or inadequate conceptions.

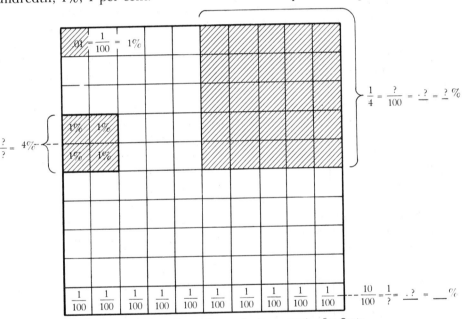

Figure 130. Ten-by-ten Square for Demonstrating Per Cents.

Once the teacher is sure that the children understand what represents 1 whole, or 100%, she may ask them to do exercises such as these:

1. Fold the whole big square to make fourths.

2. How many small squares are there in $\frac{1}{4}$ of the big square?

3. $\frac{1}{4} = $ _____ hundredths $= \cdot$ _____ $= $ _____%.

4. Mark off $\frac{10}{100}$ of the big square.

Miss Carr used 100 wooden spools on a wire in dealing with the parts of 100. She gave a small group of pupils these common fractions and told them to work out with the spools the meaning of each in terms of per cent. (The group understood that each spool was 1% of the whole chain.)

$$\frac{1}{4} \quad \frac{1}{2} \quad \frac{2}{5} \quad \frac{3}{4} \quad \frac{3}{5} \quad \frac{4}{5}$$

The children were able to work out these parts of a hundred without any trouble. Then the teacher assigned this harder group of common fractions, not so readily converted to per cents:

$$\frac{1}{8} \quad \frac{1}{3} \quad \frac{5}{8} \quad \frac{1}{6} \quad \frac{3}{8} \quad \frac{2}{3} \quad \frac{5}{6} \quad \frac{7}{8}$$

One boy soon approached the teacher to ask: "Is it all right to cut the spools?" She asked him why he wanted to do that. He said, "Because these don't come out as whole per cents."

After further discussion the children agreed that it might be better to mark the "cuts" with pencil lines first. They could do this without taking the spools off the wire. These children did later actually saw the spools in parts as needed to show such equalities as: $\frac{1}{8} = 12\frac{1}{2}\%$ (shown by the 12 whole spools and half of another one). By the time they had finished, they had a much better grasp of the relationships involved than if the teacher had given them the equivalent fractions and per cents "ready-made."

Similar activities might center around 100 tags on a hundred chart. The children might remove the tags and "partition" them into equal groups and then decide what per cent and what common or decimal fraction fits each of these equal subgroups of 100 tags. Again it is important that the children recognize that the *whole* group is the group of 100 tags.

Changing per cents to decimal fractions: After activities such as those described have helped the boys and girls establish adequate meanings, they should learn how to change common and decimal fractions to per cents and per cents to common and decimal fractions by computational procedures. The changing of per cents to decimal fractions is relatively easy for per cents between 1% and 99%. By definition

$1\% = .01$; so it is not hard to teach that the numerals preceding the % sign represent the numerator of the decimal fraction, and that the % sign takes the place of a notation for "hundredths." The numerals for any per cent from 1% to 99% must end in hundredths place. This is not too hard to learn.

Most of the difficulty children experience with the changing of per cents to decimal fractions occurs with per cents less than 1% and greater than 100%. Again, activities such as those suggested earlier help children with parts of 1%. On the 10 x 10 square, for example, $\frac{1}{2}\%$ can be shown as one-half of one of the 100 small squares. Guiding questions help to keep children oriented properly: Is this 1 whole per cent? (No.) Is it 1 whole hundredth? (No.) If you do not have any whole hundredths, how many zeros will you have after the ones place? (Two.) Then what will you write to show what part of 1 per cent you had? $(\frac{1}{2}.)$[2]

Many children and some of their elders have trouble with the meaning of more than 100%. They have been told that 100% means "all" of something; so they cannot see how it is possible to have "more than all." The fallacy is in not recognizing that 100% represents all of *whatever the basis or standard of reference is.* Here again the 10 x 10 squares are useful. The 100-squares used by the individual pupils may be particularly helpful here since one of these may be taken as 100%. Then 2 such squares can represent 200%; three squares, 300%; and so on. Then the teacher might present 1 whole 10 x 10 square and half of another one, with the question, "What per cent is this of one

[2] Children in the elementary school have very little occasion to deal with per cents less than 1%. They may come across them in their reading in science and social studies reports, in which case the teacher should make sure they recognize that they are dealing with less than $\frac{1}{100}$ of the whole.

whole square?" If the children do not know, they can even count the small squares if necessary to determine 150%, though it is doubtful they will need to do so after instruction such as that already outlined with per cents less than 100%.

So far as the written forms are concerned, here too it is necessary to remember the equivalence of "%" and "hundredths." If the per cent numerator is to end in hundredths place, 200% must be written as 2.00; 150% must be written as 1.50; 100%, as 1.00. The question is, "How many *hundredths*?" If you had $\frac{200}{100}$, what would you have? Reduce that common fraction. What does it equal in lowest terms? 200% = $\frac{200}{100}$ = 2.00, or 2.

Eventually, children can formulate their own rule for changing per cents to decimal fractions, such as: Instead of the per cent sign, mark off two (more) decimal-fraction places.

Changing decimal fractions to per cents: Children in the sixth- or some earlier grade level do not have much occasion for changing unusual decimal fractions to per cents. By procedures similar to those already suggested, they can be led to see that if hundredths are the equivalent of per cents, they must focus on the number of hundredths in the decimal fraction before translating the decimal fraction to a per cent. Thus, .05 is 5 hundredths; so it must be equal to 5%; .12 is 12 hundredths; so it must be equal to 12%; 1.25 is 125 hundredths; so it must be 125%; .375 is 37.5 hundredths; so it must be equal to 37.5%, or $37\frac{1}{2}$%.

The rule, developed through experiences with whatever aids are necessary, may finally be stated in the children's own words incorporating this idea: Instead of two fraction decimal places to show hundredths, use a per cent sign. (Or; multiply the decimal fraction by

TABLE 13

Equivalent Common Fractions, Decimal Fractions, and Per Cents

Common fractions	Decimal fractions	Per cents	Common fractions	Decimal fractions	Per cents
$\frac{1}{2}$	.50	50%	$\frac{3}{8}$	.375	$37\frac{1}{2}$%
$\frac{1}{3}$	$.33\frac{1}{3}$	$33\frac{1}{3}$%	$\frac{5}{8}$	.625	$62\frac{1}{2}$%
$\frac{2}{3}$	$.66\frac{2}{3}$	$66\frac{2}{3}$%	$\frac{7}{8}$	.875	$87\frac{1}{2}$%
$\frac{1}{4}$	.25	25%	$\frac{1}{10}$	.10	10%
$\frac{3}{4}$	.75	75%	$\frac{3}{10}$	.30	30%
$\frac{1}{5}$	.20	20%	$\frac{7}{10}$	.70	70%
$\frac{2}{5}$	.40	40%	$\frac{9}{10}$	.90	90%
$\frac{3}{5}$	.60	60%	$\frac{1}{12}$	$.08\frac{1}{3}$	$8\frac{1}{3}$%
$\frac{4}{5}$	.80	80%	$\frac{1}{20}$	.05	5%
$\frac{1}{6}$	$.16\frac{2}{3}$	$16\frac{2}{3}$%	$\frac{1}{25}$	.04	4%
$\frac{5}{6}$	$.83\frac{1}{3}$	$83\frac{1}{3}$%	$\frac{1}{50}$	.02	2%
$\frac{1}{8}$	.125	$12\frac{1}{2}$%			

100 to get rid of the hundredths; then write the % sign instead.)

Changing common fractions and per cents: Typically, the changing of common fractions to per cents proceeds from common- to decimal-fraction form, then to per cent. For example, $\frac{1}{4} = .25 = 25\%$. Similarly, when per cents are changed to common fractions, they are first changed to decimal-fraction equivalents, which in turn are translated into common-fraction form. Thus: $25\% = .25 = \frac{25}{100} = \frac{1}{4}$. Or: $12\frac{1}{2}\% = .125 = \frac{125}{1000} = \frac{1}{8}$.

Tables of equivalent fractions: Some fractions are so commonly used in business transactions that they are called "business fractions." These include those listed in table 13. Mr. Average Citizen and even young Average Child have use for these in reading the ads in the daily newspaper or listening to television and radio. Once the equivalence of these common fractions to decimal fractions and per cents has been established, much time will be saved by memorizing these equivalents.

Memorization will mean little, however, if the children do not understand the relationships in figure 131. Their ability to build such a diagram is a good test of their understanding. Figure 131 does not include some of the fractions and per cent equivalents listed in Table 13. The children may make another diagram that includes thirds, sixths, twelfths, or other common fractions with their per cent equivalents.

These equivalents may be practiced and used in work with circle or "pie" graphs. This is particularly true of the larger fractional parts. In this case, the whole circle area represents 1, or 1.00, or 100%. Improper fractions or mixed numbers or equivalent per cents greater than 100% could then be shown by having more than one full circle. Figure 132 shows 25% as the shaded part of

the first circle, 75% as the white part of the same circle, 50% as the half-circle at the right, and 150% as the combination of $1\frac{1}{2}$ circles. (In each case, reference is to the areas within the circles.)

Ratio and Proportion

Since per cent is the last of the ratio ideas to be presented, this is a good time to review various applications of the ratio concept. Ratio is a relational idea. Two numbers may be compared in terms of their difference, which is an absolute comparison: $\$5 - \$3 = \$2$. Two numbers may also be compared in terms of their relative size: $\frac{\$3}{\$5} = \frac{3}{5}$; $\$3$ is $\frac{3}{5}$ of $\$5$. Ratio is *relative comparison* of two numbers.

RATIO AS EXPRESSED
IN DIFFERENT FORMS

Ratio is expressed in arithmetic in various forms. Some of these forms may not be typically recognized as ratios, but the teacher who does recognize them will do a better job of teaching the ratio concept in a natural and developmental way.[3]

Whole numbers as ratios. Any whole number is a ratio to one. When dealt with as rational numbers, whole numbers may be written as: $\frac{4}{1}, \frac{7}{1}, \frac{12}{1}$. On the elementary level, this idea occurs simply as recognition that $4 = 4$ ones, $7 = 7$ ones, $12 = 12$ ones.

Multiplication as a ratio-to-one idea. While multiplication is introduced to children first as an additive idea, the

[3] No such concentration of ratio applications as the following should be expected of average elementary school children. The teacher's understanding will, however, affect her instruction in these situations. Her own recognition of the ratio concept will help her direct the children's attention to the relations among the numbers with which they deal even though she does not force the ratio terminology on them.

more general definition of the multiplication process recognizes that it depends on the ratio-to-one concept. (See chap. 9.) If one book costs $2 and another costs 3 times as much, we multiply 3 × $2 to find the cost of the other

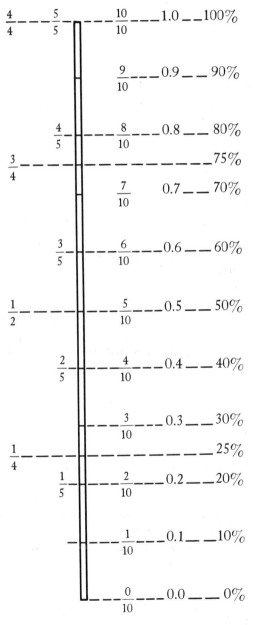

Figure 131. Common Fraction, Decimal Fraction, and Per Cent Equivalents.

book, which is $6. We find the number that is "3 times as large" as $2. We find the number that has the same ratio to 2 that 3 has to 1; 6 is "3 times as much" as 2, just as 3 is "3 times as much" as 1.

Division as a ratio-to-one idea. Since division is the inverse of multiplication, it uses the ratio-to-one idea in the inverse. The ratio idea in division was discussed in chapter 11. In measurement division situations, the known ratio is the ratio of the dividend to the divisor. The division is performed to find what number has that same relation to 1.

If $24 will be spent for books at $4 per book, the question becomes: How many books can be purchased at that price? $24 ÷ $4 = 6; $24 has the same ratio to $4 that 6 books have to 1 book; $\frac{\$24}{\$4} = \frac{6}{1}$.

Common fractions as ratios. Sometimes fractions express numbers and sometimes they express relations between numbers, that is, ratios. This idea was developed in chapter 14 and has been used continuously since that point. The direction of the expressed relation is always numerator to denominator. This manner of expressing relative size of two numbers may be used for any two numbers, except that zero may not be the denominator of the expression.

Three-fifths shows the ratio of 3-to-5. Five-thirds shows the ratio of 5-to-3. Obviously, these two meanings are quite different; $\frac{3}{5}$ and $\frac{5}{3}$ are two different relationships. Actually, they are reciprocals; multiplied together, they give a product of 1.

Ratios and multiplication of common fractions. The ratio-to-one concept of multiplication holds for multiplication of fractions as well as for multiplication of whole numbers. In fact, this idea of multiplication is very important in use of a fraction as a mul-

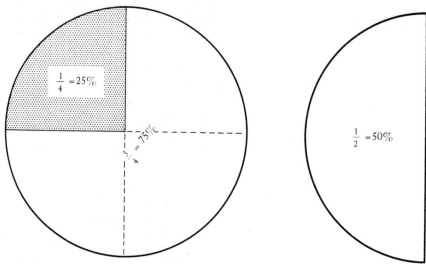

$$\frac{1}{4} = 25\%$$

$$\frac{3}{4} = 75\%$$

$$\frac{1}{2} = 50\%$$

Figure 132. Circle Graphs for Per Cents.

tiplier, in which case the additive idea of multiplication is not much help. Multiplication is a process of finding a number that has the same ratio to the multiplicand that the multiplier has to 1.

We find the cost of 4 yards of cloth at $6 a yard by multiplying *4 times* $6. The multiplier 4 has the same ratio to 1 that the product $24 has to $6.

Similarly, we find the cost of $\frac{1}{2}$ yard of the same cloth by multiplying $\frac{1}{2}$ *times* $6. The multiplier $\frac{1}{2}$ has the same ratio to 1 that the product $3 has to $6.

When the multiplier is a whole number, we typically use the terminology "4 *times* $6." When the multiplier is a fraction, we typically use the terminology "$\frac{1}{2}$ *of* $6"; the equivalence of the two forms was developed in chapter 16.

Ratios and division of common fractions. The ratio idea also applies to division of fractions. Perhaps it shows best as a parallel to a whole-number division.

If cloth sells for $3 a yard and Jane buys $12 worth, how many yards does she buy? $12 has the same ratio to $3 as the unknown quotient (4) has to 1. We have to find the number that has the same ratio to 1 that 12 has to 3: $12 ÷ $3 = 4.

If cloth sells for $\$\frac{1}{2}$ per yard and Jane spends $12 for cloth, how many yards does she buy? $12 has the same ratio to $\$\frac{1}{2}$ as the unknown quotient (24) has to 1: $12 ÷ $\$\frac{1}{2}$ = 24.

Decimal fractions as ratios. Because the numerator-denominator relation is less obvious with decimal fractions, the ratio concept is likely to go unnoticed. The relative comparison of two numbers can be highlighted by converting the decimal fraction to a common fraction with a power of ten as the denominator. Then, 2.5 can readily be seen as an expression of the ratio of 25 to 10, that is, $\frac{25}{10}$. Similarly, .025 is seen as $\frac{25}{1000}$, or the ratio of 25 to 1000.

Decimal-fraction ratios that appeal particularly to boys are batting averages and team standings. The former are ratios of number of hits to times at bat. The latter are ratios of number of games won to games played.

Per cents as ratios. The ratio concept is particularly important as applied to the meaning of per cents. This idea is prominent in the name "*per* cent." So 25% means 25 *per* 100, or a ratio of 25-to-100.

Part of the popularity of per cent in our society stems from the neat manner in which it may be applied to problems dealing with our monetary system, which also relates cents to dollars as a ratio-to-100. Discounts, interest, and tax rates are easily translated from per cents to money terms and from money terms to per cents. Per cents are also an extremely useful statistical expression of ratios.

The treatment of per cents in computations will be developed in a later section. The important consideration here is that the ratio uses of per cent should not enter the curriculum as something entirely new; they should be merely an extension of ratio concepts already developed for whole numbers, common fractions, and decimal fractions.

BASE, RATE, AND PERCENTAGE

Every problem dealing with per cent has three fundamental terms: *base, rate,* and *percentage.* Unfortunately, there is a good deal of confusion concerning the use of the word "percentage." Actually, it is used in a very general sense to refer to the whole broad area of the uses of per cents; for example, we speak of a "percentage problem," meaning one that deals with per cent. Or we might say that this chapter deals with "percentage" as a broad topic. This is acceptable usage of the term.

The incorrect uses of the term stem from a widespread notion that "percentage" refers to the term that is accompanied by the per cent symbol (%). Consider the statement: The interest will amount to 5% of $450. In that sentence "5%" is *not* the percentage. It is the rate. The percentage is the result of multiplying $.05 \times \$450$, or $22.50.

In every ratio, one number is compared with another. The number that is the standard or basis of comparison, the one *to which* the other is compared, is the *base.* The number being compared to the base is the *percentage.* The term that expresses the relation of the percentage to the base is called the *rate;* this is the term that is accompanied by the per cent symbol (%).

The same idea is stated below in different ways. Compare the statements; then notice the various names by which the terms in the statements may be designated.

	12 is the:	16 is the:	Relation of 12 to 16
a. 12 is $\frac{3}{4}$ of 16	part	whole	fraction (ratio)
b. 12 is 75% of 16	percentage	base	rate (per cent)
c. 12 ÷ 16 = .75, or 75%	dividend	divisor	quotient
d. $\frac{12}{16} = \frac{3}{4}$	numerator	denominator	ratio

Perhaps the most obvious description of 12 in this case is to call it the "part" contrasted with 16 as the "whole"; this works very well as long as the ratio is a proper fraction (or a per cent less than 100%). When, however, the ratio or rate is an improper fraction (or more than 100%), the term "part" does not seem appropriate. Notice the parallel terms in each column above; while they are interchangeable, some are more apt for certain statements. The "rate" or "ratio" is also a "quotient" or a common or decimal fraction (if the term "fraction" is being used in the ratio connotation).

PROPORTION

When two ratios are equal, their equality may be expressed as a proportion. Item d above is a proportion. A generation ago proportions were consistently stated in arithmetic books as:

$$12:16::3:4 \quad \text{OR} \quad 12:16::75:100$$

The common fraction form is growing in popularity and general use:

$$\frac{12}{16}=\frac{3}{4} \quad \text{OR} \quad \frac{12}{16}=\frac{75}{100}$$

If each ratio is expressed in lowest terms, the two fractions are not only equal; they are identical. In the examples above, $\frac{12}{16}$ changed to lowest terms is $\frac{3}{4}$. Any common fraction being changed to lower or higher terms uses the idea of proportion; so actually all the work children do with changing of fractions to equivalent fractions is work with proportion.

This may come as a surprise to some teachers who have learned (through their own sad experiences with the unnecessary "mysteries" of proportion in upper-grade arithmetic) to think of proportion as an advanced topic in arithmetic.

We may read either form—"12:16::3:4" or "$\frac{12}{16}=\frac{3}{4}$"—as "12 is to 16 as 3 is to 4" or "12 has the same relation to 16 that 3 has to 4" or "12 has the same ratio to 16 that 3 has to 4" or "12 sixteenths = 3 fourths."

According to earlier work with equivalent fractions, we know that $\frac{a}{b}=\frac{c}{d}$ if, and only if, $a \times d = b \times c$.

Another relation (ratio) and one that is basic to the changing of fractions to lower and higher terms is this: The first numerator has the same ratio to the second numerator that the first denominator has to the second denominator. In the two fractions we have been using above, 12 has the same relation to 3 that 16 has to 4, that relation being "4 times as much." Likewise, 12 has the same ratio to 16 that 75 has to 100.

Parallel Problems with Fractions and Per Cent

Three typical problems using common fractions, decimal fractions. and per cent recur so frequently that they merit special attention. In the typical arithmetic curriculum, they will usually occur first with common fractions, next with decimal fractions, and finally with per cents. They are presented together here to emphasize for the teacher their close relationship and the manner in which they can be introduced and reintroduced in a developmental sequence.

Stated in terms of what is to be found in each of the three problems, they may be listed as: (1) finding a part of a number; (2) finding what part one number is of another; and (3) finding the whole number when a certain part of that number is known.

FINDING A PART OF A NUMBER[4]

Problem 1-F: Joe lives 10 blocks from the park. If he walks $\frac{2}{5}$ of the way to the park, how far does he walk?

Problem 1-D: The hometown baseball team has played 10 games this year. Their record of games won is .400. How many games have they won?

Problem 1-P: The regular price of a pair of skates is $10. They have been marked down 40%. How much can Bud save by buying the skates while they are marked down?

In each of these problems the "whole" number is given. We might say the "base" number is given—the number to which another (unknown) number is being compared. The whole distance, the whole number of games played, and the whole price of the skates are known. The other known item is the fractional or per cent expression, which tells the relation (ratio) of the unknown part to the known whole. The question to be answered in each case is, respectively:

---

[4] In the following problems, these symbols are used: F (common fractions); D (decimal fractions); P (per cent).

1-F: What is $\frac{2}{5}$ of 10 blocks?
1-D: What is .400 of 10 games?
1-P: What is 40% of $10?

The solutions all involve multiplication of a common or decimal fraction $\times$ the whole or base number, so:

$$\frac{2}{5} \text{ of 10 blocks} = \frac{2}{5} \times \overset{2}{\cancel{10}}\text{ blocks} = 4 \text{ blocks}$$

$$.400 \times 10 \text{ games} = 4.000 \text{ games} = 4 \text{ games}$$
$$40\% \text{ of } \$10 = .40 \times \$10 = \$4.00^5$$

The solutions may be shown diagrammatically, as with number lines. The only difference in the lines is a difference in marking off and labeling of the parts of the whole for each problem. See figure 133.

In each of the lines in figure 133, the scale above the line locates the miles or games or dollars being considered in the problems. The scale below the line indicates the fractions or per cents of the whole distance or games played or full price.

When children approach this kind of problem, they may find it easier at first to think of the solution as being done in two steps, thus:

Problem 1-F: $\frac{1}{5}$ of 10 blocks = 2 blocks. If $\frac{1}{5} = 2$ blocks, then $\frac{2}{5}$ will be 2×2 blocks, or 4 blocks.

Notice that the same computations are performed as in the cancellation solution: $10 \div 5 = 2$; $2 \times 2 = 4$.

Problem 1-D: .100 of 10 games = .1 of 10 games = 1 game. If .1 = 1 game, then .4 will be 4×1 game = 4 games.
Problem 1-P: 100% of the price = $10. 10% of the price = $\frac{1}{10}$ of $10 = $1. 40% of the price = $4 \times \$1 = \$4$.

Many children find this *unitary-analysis* approach to be easier to follow. After they feel secure with such solutions, the

teacher can help them see that the same solutions can be found by more concise procedures.

Finally, the teacher should take note that the number line solutions actually use proportions. The scale entered above the line in each case is marked off in the units that fit the numbers in the problem. The whole or base number tells how long to make the line. The whole line is taken as 1 whole ($\frac{5}{5}$, or 1.000, or 100%) on the scale below the line. Then the known ratio ($\frac{2}{5}$, or .4000, or 40%) is found on the lower scale, and the unknown "part" or "percentage" can be read off the upper scale.

1-F: $\quad \frac{2}{5} = \frac{?}{10} \qquad \frac{2}{5} = \frac{4}{10}$

1-D: $\quad \frac{.400}{1.000} = \frac{? \text{ games}}{10 \text{ games}} \qquad \frac{.400}{1.000} = \frac{4 \text{ games}}{10 \text{ games}}$

1-P: $\quad \frac{40\%}{100\%} = \frac{\$?}{\$10} \qquad \frac{.40}{1.00} = \frac{\$4}{\$10}$

FINDING WHAT PART ONE NUMBER IS OF ANOTHER

Common fractions, decimal fractions, and per cents also appear in parallel problems in which the purpose is to find what part one number is of another. The question to be answered may be stated in various ways:

How does the first number compare with the second number?
What is the ratio of the first number to the second number?
The first number is what part of the second number?

In the case of common fractions the solution of such a problem is "so simple it is hard" for many people to see. What is the ratio of one whole number to another whole number? Simply the common fraction that has the first number as the numerator and the second number as the denominator!

$$\text{Ratio} = \frac{\text{first number}}{\text{second number}}$$

---

[5] Note that 40% is changed to .40 *before* computation.

Problem 2-F: Jim lived 10 blocks from the park. If he got a ride for 4 blocks, what part of the whole distance did he ride?

Problem 2-D: The home team has played 10 games. They have won 4 games. What is the team standing?

Problem 2-P: The regular price of a pair of skates is $10. Bud bought a pair on sale and saved $4. What per cent of the full price did he save?

If one recognizes that common fractions, decimal fractions, and per cents *are ratios,* the key to the solution of these problems is to state the two numbers in the appropriate ratio form and then do only that computation which will change the ratio to its simplest or most appropriate form for the particular case.

2-F: $\dfrac{4 \text{ blocks}}{10 \text{ blocks}} = \dfrac{2}{5}$ (Simply changing a fraction to lower terms!)

2-D: $\dfrac{4 \text{ games}}{10 \text{ games}} = 4 \div 10 = .400$ (This answer is carried out to three decimal-fraction places only because this is conventional in baseball statistics.)

2-P: $\dfrac{\$4}{\$10} = \$4 \div \$10 = .40 = 40\%$ (This answer is carried out to two decimal-fraction places because the question asked for per cent, or hundredths.)

The relationships between the numbers 4 and 10 can be read off the same number lines shown for another set of problems in figure 133. Again, there is a proportion for each problem. The only difference is that a different term in the proportion is missing.

2-F: $\dfrac{4}{10} = \dfrac{?}{?}$ Changing to lower terms: $\dfrac{4}{10} = \dfrac{2}{5}$

2-D: $\dfrac{4}{10} = \dfrac{?}{1.000}$ $\dfrac{4}{10} = \dfrac{.400}{1.000}$

2-P: $\dfrac{\$4}{\$10} = \dfrac{?\%}{100\%}$ $\dfrac{4}{10} = \dfrac{.40}{1.00} = \dfrac{40\%}{100\%}$

FINDING THE WHOLE NUMBER WHEN A CERTAIN PART OF IT IS KNOWN

This is usually the most difficult of the three types of problems. Perhaps it is a good thing that it is really not used very much. The part (percentage) is known and the ratio (per cent) is known; the whole (base) is to be found. Perhaps the reason this does not occur very often is that the "unknown" base would have to be known along with the part in order to establish the ratio. Therefore, a person who knows ratio and part is very likely to know the base and not have to seek it (unless he has known it and forgotten it). Another person — probably an inquisitive soul — might pick up two pieces of information (ratio and part) and want to figure out the base rather than ask the person who knows.

Problem 3-F: Ned said he walked $\frac{2}{5}$ of the way from his home to the park. He also said he had walked 4 blocks. How far did he live from the park?

Problem 3-D: The home team has a team standing of .400. They have won 4 games. How many games have they played?

Problem 3-P: Bud said he saved $4 by buying his skates when they were marked down 40%. What was the regular price of the skates?

Since the unitary-analysis method seems to be most readily understood, let us begin with that type of solutions. The first step is to establish an equality. The known items are equal to each other.

3-F: $\frac{2}{5}$ of the distance = 4 blocks

Then $\frac{1}{5}$ of the distance = 4 blocks ÷ 2 = 2 blocks

Then $\frac{5}{5}$ (all) of the distance = 5 × 2 blocks = 10 blocks

F

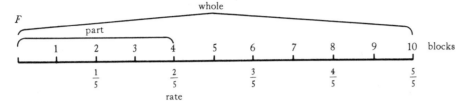

D

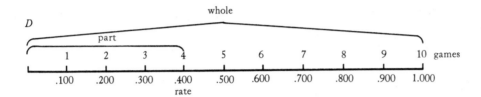

P

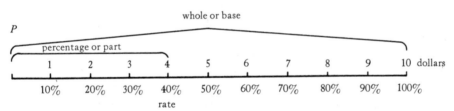

Figure 133. Number Line Representations of Three Types of Problems.

3-D: .400 (or .4) of the games played = 4 games
   Then .1 of the games played = 4 games ÷ 4 = 1 game
   Then 1.0 (all) of the games played = 10 × 1 game = 10 games

3-P: 40% of the price = $4
   10% of the price = $4 ÷ 4 = $1
   100% of the price = 10 × $1 = $10
           OR
   1% of the price = $4 ÷ 40 = $.10
   100% of the price = 100 × $.10 = $10.00

These problems also may be solved by using number lines like those shown in figure 133 or by using a proportion (in the form of finding the missing term in a pair of equivalent fractions). Of special interest in this case, however, is a further study of the analysis used above for each problem.

In problem 3-F, the operations were: dividing by 2 and multiplying by 5. This is exactly the same as multiplying the 4 blocks by the reciprocal of $\frac{2}{5}$; or it is the same as dividing by $\frac{2}{5}$, inverting and multiplying.

In problem 3-D, the operations are dividing by 4 and multiplying by 10. Notice the long-division algorism for $.4\overline{\smash{\big)}4.}$. The multiplication by 10 is done first in changing the division to $4\overline{)40}$, followed by the division by 4.

In problem 3-P, the operations are dividing by 40 and multiplying by 100: 40% is changed to .40, followed by this division: $.40\overline{)\$4.}$. Changing the form to $40\overline{)\$400}$ multiplies both terms by 100, after which one divides by the new divisor, 40.

Sometimes the "whole number" to be found is a smaller number than the "part" that is given. In such problems, the teacher needs to emphasize the idea of "the whole quantity that is being *used as a basis* of comparison."

Problem 4: This year's enrollment in Roosevelt School is 150% of last year's enrollment. This year there are 450 children enrolled in the school. How many were enrolled last year?

Last year's enrollment is considered as the basis of comparison or as the standard. This year's enrollment is being compared with it. Then 150% of the standard = 450 children. By various procedures, we may derive 100% of the standard.

a. $150\% = 450$

  $1\% = 450 \div 150 = 3$

  $100\% = 100 \times 3 = 300$

b. $150\% = \dfrac{3}{2}$

  $\dfrac{3}{2} = 450$

  $\dfrac{1}{2} = \dfrac{1}{3}$ of $450 = 150$

  $\dfrac{2}{2} = 2 \times 150 = 300$

c. $1.5 \times$ the base $= 450$

  $450 \div 1.5 = 300$

d. $450 \div \dfrac{3}{2} = \overset{150}{\cancel{450}} \times \dfrac{2}{\underset{1}{\cancel{3}}} = 300$

e. (See fig. 134.)

With such a problem, as with all the others, an absolute essential to correct problem solving is clear determination of what is the base or standard of comparison (100%).

Emphasis on Understanding Relationships

Junior high school tests may emphasize one or another of various "methods" of solving the problems discussed above. Some favor an equation method, some a formula method, some a case method (designating which case is involved and then applying the designated formula or equation). The approach through cases and formulas[6] has not been developed here since any elementary school problems of the three types that may occur can very well be solved by less formalized approaches. Even at the junior high school level, the teacher should certainly see that those procedures grow out of basic understanding of relationships. If they do not, the results will not be satisfactory either as to present understanding or as to future recall of the procedures themselves.

An adult may prefer setting up a proportion in the form $a:b::c:d$ with an "x" or other symbol for the unknown. Then by multiplying means and extremes, he can establish an equality and then solve for the unknown. For children, the setting up of a proportion simply as the statement of the equality of two common fractions is much better. Children can solve for the unknown number by the same procedures used for changing to higher and lower terms.

[6] Formulas used are of this type:

Case I (finding the percentage): percentage = base × rate

Case II (finding the rate): rate = percentage ÷ base

Case III (finding the base): base = percentage ÷ rate

Another form by which the three cases are identified is this:

Case I: $\underline{\ ?\ }$ is $\underline{15\%}$ of $\underline{60}$ (first term missing)

Case II: $\underline{\ 9\ }$ is $\underline{\ ?\ }$% of $\underline{60}$ (second term missing)

Case III: $\underline{\ 9\ }$ is $\underline{15\%}$ of $\underline{\ ?\ }$ (third term missing)

The word "proportion" may not even be mentioned; it is not necessary.

The meaningful use of formulas for these solutions depends heavily on understanding the inverse relation between multiplication and division. The teacher who teaches use of formulas should certainly build on that relationship.

share of elementary school instruction in per cent should be devoted to understanding of the basic concept of what per cent means rather than to extensive problem solving of the computational type. A sound basis of understanding of what per cent means in its everyday applications will be a better foundation for junior high school learning than a

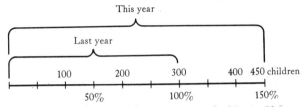

Figure 134. Number Line Solution of Problem Involving 150%.

All in all, the understanding of the meanings of common fractions, decimal fractions, and per cents as the expression of ratios rests at the foundation of whatever structure is built for solutions of problems in which ratio is involved.

If meanings and understandings have been stressed in the learner's previous learning, he *can* understand any of these problems he may encounter.

Practical Applications of Per Cent

Although per cents have very wide practical applications, these applications are not so widely applicable to the needs and interests of elementary school children. Perhaps the greatest use children will make of them is in the interpretation of the meanings of per cents that they encounter in their reading. They will read (or hear) about per cents of discount, per cents of population increase, or per cents of production. Most of their in-school uses of these ideas will relate to their understanding of references made to per cent in social studies and science. Therefore, a lion's

contused jumble of formulas and computational procedures with the decimal-fraction equivalents of per cents.

TABLE 14
Some Practical Applications of Per Cent

Applications	Base	Rate (%)	Percentage
Interest	Principal	Rate (of interest)	Amount (of interest)
Discount	List price	Rate (of discount)	Amount (of discount)
Commission	Gross proceeds (on sales) Prime cost (on purchases)	Rate (of commission)	Amount (of commission)
Profit and loss	Cost	Rate	Margin
	Sale price	Rate	Profit or loss (sale price —cost and expenses)
Insurance	Face of policy	Rate	Premium
Taxes: Income Real estate Sales	Net income Assessed value Sale price }	Tax rate	Amount (of tax)
Dividends	Value (par or market)	Rate	Dividend

Some children, of course, can benefit from and will be interested in adult-type applications. To meet their needs and interests, the teacher should consider such topics as those listed in table 14.

All the practical applications listed in the table happen to deal with bases and percentages that are expressed in dollars and cents. How convenient it is to have percents and monetary values so readily convertible one to the other!

Per cents of increase and decrease have not been discussed, nor has any mention been made of compound interest or installment buying—all very much tied to the concept of per cent. Junior high school texts in "general mathematics" or "business arithmetic" deal with these topics and those in the table in comprehensive fashion. The table merely serves to indicate the very close relationship of the listed topics to the meaning of per cent.

STUDY QUESTIONS

1. Change these decimal fractions to common-fraction form and express in lowest terms: (a) .64; (b) .375; (c) .202; (d) 1.5.

2. Change these common fractions to decimal fractions: (a) $\frac{3}{8}$; (b) $\frac{6}{25}$; (c) $\frac{2}{5}$; (d) $\frac{1}{500}$.

3. Change each of the fractions in questions 1 and 2 to per cent.

4. On page 419 you are told that if a common fraction can be converted to a terminating decimal fraction, its denominator must have only 2's and/or 5's as its prime factors. Try out this further statement and see if it "works." The highest power of 2 or 5 for the denominator will indicate the number of fraction decimal places in the terminating decimal fraction.

5. Summarize the per cents that appear in the advertisements of a current magazine. Which per cents occur most frequently?

6. If a teacher gives his pupils one spelling test of 20 words and another test of 15 words and grades each test in terms of per cent correct, is it all right for him to average the two grades? Why or why not?

7. Make a thorough study of one or more of the practical applications of per cent mentioned in Table 14. Give an oral report to the class, including some typical computations that are required.

CHAPTER 19

Measurement and Measures

MEASURES ARE an indispensable, everpresent feature of our everyday world. They are so much an integral part of personal, business, scientific, and industrial affairs that people tend to take them more or less for granted, seldom pausing to consider their contribution to modern life. Without them, modern civilization would collapse. The research workers seek continuously to learn more about our universe; as they do, they reach toward the infinitely great and the infinitesimally small. The layman usually does not even try to grasp the measures at these extremes; he is merely impressed that it is indeed possible to measure such small and such large quantities—quantities that are beyond human perception unaided by the instrumentation of modern science.

The prevalence of measures in routine affairs of living is easily demonstrated. Elementary school children may be started toward an appreciation of the extent of the use of measures by being asked to make a list of all the measures they come across by studying such readily available sources as labels and wrappers on cans, boxes, and bottles in the kitchen cupboard at home; the owner's manual for the family automobile; or the tools, nails, nuts, and bolts in a home workshop. (Incidentally, this is a much better homework assignment than working 24 examples from p. 134 of the text book.) As children do such an assignment, parents may also become involved and may enjoy very much the discussion that accompanies the children's explorations.

One box of cake flour yielded the following examples of measures:

Net weight 2 pounds (907 grams)
An offer of a booklet on cake making at high altitudes (3000, 5000, and 7000 feet)
Ingredients, of which this list from one frosting recipe called for:
$\frac{1}{2}$ cup butter or margarine
$\frac{1}{8}$ teaspoon salt
1 pound (about 4 cups) sifted confectioners' sugar
4 squares (ounces) unsweetened chocolate
1 egg, unbeaten
1 teaspoon vanilla
$\frac{1}{4}$ cup milk (about)
(One other frosting recipe called for a *dash* of salt)
The diameter of round layer cake pans, e.g., 8- or 9-inch pans
All the dimensions of a loaf cake pan, e.g., $13 \times 9 \times 2$-inch pan
Oven temperatures, e.g., moderate oven, or 350 degrees Fahrenheit
Time of baking (or beating or cooling after baking), e.g., 25 minutes

437

One expects the *cups* and *teaspoons* in recipes; but perhaps one may not expect to find the *inches, feet, pounds, grams, degrees,* and *minutes* tied in with cake flour and its use. Here are capacity measures of liquid and dry ingredients, weight, linear distance (vertical and horizontal), altitude (a special case of vertical distance), temperature, and time. The people who planned the wrapper did not start out to see how many measures they could use. They were required to give the contents, which they supplied both as pounds and as grams; but all the other measures they used simply to tell what they wanted to say to the users of their product.

Any resourceful teacher could use that one cake flour box as a ready-made instructional springboard to a lively venture into the world of measures.

The Meaning of Measurement

Unfortunately, understanding of the basic meaning of measurement is not as prevalent as are the uses of the results of measurement in daily affairs.

MEASUREMENT AS COMPARISON

The process of measurement is a process of comparison. The length of a piece of cloth is compared with the length of a yardstick; the weight of a chemical is compared on a balance scale with gram (or other) "weights" on the other pan of the balance; the capacity of a container is compared with the capacity of a container known to hold a quart.

The comparison does not have to be with a standardized amount or unit of measure. A mother says that her son is "up to my shoulder"; she is comparing his height with hers. A farmer says the corn is "knee-high"; he is comparing the height of the corn to the length of his leg to the knee. In each case, there must be comparison with something else if a thing is to be measured.

Strictly speaking, the boy is not measured, nor the chemicals, nor the container, nor the cloth. When we speak loosely of measuring a thing, we really mean we are measuring some property of the thing. We are measuring the boy's *height,* the chemical's *weight,* the container's *capacity,* the cloth's *length.* The comparison must be made with something that also has the property being measured.

Counting and measurement. In assembling the ingredients for a cake, the housewife *counts* the eggs that are needed; but she *measures* the milk, flour, and butter. She has to know *how many* eggs; so she counts them. She has to know *how much* milk, flour, and butter; so she measures them. In measuring she must manipulate the things being measured; she must compare them with some standard, in this case "cups." She does not *need* to manipulate the eggs; she merely counts them. The eggs may vary as to size, but she still counts each as 1 egg.

If counting is to be considered as measuring, it is a measuring of "numerosity." (How numerous? How many?) It is the matching of the eggs, for example, with the counting numbers to derive the cardinal number of the set or group of discrete or separate items (eggs). In the present chapter, stress will be placed on the measurement of *continuous* magnitudes or amounts, rather than the counting of discrete items.

Since the concept of a ratio is a comparison idea, measurement may be thought of as the determining of a number that expresses a ratio of what is being measured to the measuring unit. If a length of cloth is compared with a yardstick and found to have 3 times the length of the yardstick, the number

3 is a rational number expressing the 3:1 ratio of the cloth's length to the yardstick's length.

Typical measurement expressions are a combination of a unit of measure and a number (counter) of the units.

Exact and approximate quantities. In determining how many books he has, a man can count them exactly since each book is a clearly separate entity. He has no trouble telling where one book ends and the other begins. The number of books derived by counting tells *exactly* how many books he has.

If a man is moving and has his books packed for shipment, the carrier does not charge according to how many books there are but rather how much weight they represent. Therefore, the books must be weighed (measured) in terms of some standard such as pounds. The weight of the books is a continuous magnitude. No one can say where one pound ends and the other begins. The man or the freight agent cannot count the pounds; they must measure to get the number of pounds. The weight of the books is a *continuous* magnitude.

Further, the measurement of the weight of the books cannot be determined exactly. The number of pounds given as the weight is an approximation of the actual weight, perhaps to the nearest whole pound. (This will be discussed more fully later in this chapter.)

Of course, all numbers are exact. The term "approximate numbers" is sometimes used for numbers that are used to express continuous magnitudes, but it would be more correct to speak of "numbers applied to approximate quantities." Another term used a great deal in measurement situations is "denominate numbers," that is, numbers associated with the *names* of the units of measurement.

Just as denominators of fractions tell the names of the fractions, so denominate numbers are accompanied by names of the measuring units with which the numbers are associated. Thus "3 inches" becomes a denominate number; the number 3 is associated with the name of the measuring unit "inch." Really, it is the expression "3 inches" that is referred to as a "denominate number."

In counting, the units are not necessarily "exactly the same," but there need be no question as to how many there are; the number assigned to the group is not open to question. In measurement, the designated units are theoretically "exactly the same," but the procedure for determining the number of units is inexact; hence the term "approximate number" and the term "denominate number" are sometimes used interchangeably.

UNITS OF MEASUREMENT

Much of the history of measurement is a history of the development, refinement, and expansion of the "measuring sticks" or units of measurement against which that to be measured could be compared and thus quantified.

Informal or nonstandardized units of measure. In man's early history he did not have the need for precise measurement that we often have today. This need has grown steadily through the ages, though the less precise, informal measures are still good enough for some purposes.

As men turned from a nomadic to a more settled life, they needed to measure their land, their buildings, their building materials, the metals they used in manufacturing and trade, and all else concerning which they needed the answer "how much" but could not get that answer by simple counting. Measurement units were an essential. Just comparing two quantities and determining that one was larger than the other was not enough. How large was each?

How much larger was one than the other? In order to answer such questions, there had to be a unit of comparison, something with which all items to be measured could be compared.

Just as men used their fingers as a readily available "concrete aid" for counting, so they used parts of their bodies as readily available units of measure. Among such units were the digit (width of a finger), palm (width of the hand), span (distance from the outstretched tip of the thumb to the tip of the little finger), cubit (length from the elbow to the tip of the fingers), fathom (distance between the tips of fingers when both arms are outstretched), yard (half of a fathom), and foot (length of the foot).

Children will enjoy, and learn something from, marking these "units" on paper or at the chalkboard and then comparing to see what variation and similarity exist among the "same" measuring units for different children. The approximate nature of such units and the lack of accuracy will be abundantly evident. The boys and girls will readily see that in trade it would be to the advantage of the seller and the disadvantage of the buyer to have the cloth or rope measured by a man with short arms.

While recognizing the unreliability of using such measuring units, the children will be able to see that such readily available units have some use for situations not requiring high levels of accuracy. If a woman wants to know only "about how much" cloth she has, she can use the outstretched arm measure to tell her "about how many yards." If she has checked her own measure against a standard yard, she can make appropriate allowances and better approximate the correct measure.

Modern cookbooks have come a long way in improving the measurement units for ingredients in recipes; but skilled cooks still enjoy (and manage fairly well) to use a "dash of this" and a "pinch of that," knowing full well that one person's "pinch" of salt may be twice that of another person. (Besides, it is such a good way to keep secrets while seeming to be generous in sharing favorite recipes.) The outstretched arms of the fisherman as he shows the length of the "big one that got away" will stay with us indefinitely. First, how could he compare that leaping, fighting, uncaught creature with a standard unit, however accurate the unit? Second, why spoil a good story? Third, who cares?

That is just the point. Sometimes it does matter whether or not the measuring unit is stable and available to anyone who may have need of it.

Formal or standardized units of measure. The history of measures and their gradual and continuing standardization is a fascinating bypath. Capable pupils will enjoy doing some research on this subject, and other pupils will enjoy the results of their labors.[1] It has been reported that the first step in standardizing the yard was the decree of King Henry I of England that it should be settled as the length of *his* outstretched arm (nose to tip of fingers or thumb).

The further standardization of measures such as the yard has gone from there to the creation of a standard iron bar, to a bronze bar, to platinum-and-iridium bars. In the United States, the yard is officially defined as $\frac{3600}{3937}$ of the United States Prototype Meter 27, which is a bar made of 90 per cent platinum and 10 per cent iridium, carefully guarded and kept at a constant temperature at the Bureau of Standards in Washington, D. C. Changes continue to

[1] The list of good references on the subject is expanding rapidly. One excellent source of current material is the National Bureau of Standards, Washington, D.C.

be made in our own country and internationally in the direction of more precise standards.[2]

In spite of extreme efforts to develop a system of measures based on a natural measurement, this has been very difficult to achieve. The French meter was supposed to be 1 ten-millionth of the distance from the equator to the pole, making the earth itself the basic standard of length. This was a difficult undertaking and did not come out as planned. Even if it had turned out exactly as planned, the choice of the meter as a measure of length would still have been an arbitrary choice. It is important that children understand that all our standard units of measure are arbitrarily chosen. The legal standards of measure merely represent the establishment by law of arbitrary standards.

To say that the units of measurement are arbitrarily chosen does not mean that they are carelessly chosen. They are defined and described with the highest accuracy possible at the time, and they are subject to improvement and redefinition from time to time. Because of wide variations from country to country, much work is still needed before standard units are made the same throughout the world. Study of the pros and cons of worldwide adoption of the metric system is an excellent enrichment topic. The use of the metric system of measurement is growing, but the suitability of English measures for practical affairs has given them a strong hold. Combinations of ideas from metric

and English measures, such as thousandths of an inch, are widely used.

Characteristics of a good unit of measure. Buckingham has listed what he calls four essentials of a good unit of measure.[3] They are convenience, acceptance, uniformity, and system.

The use of parts of the body as measuring units is an illustration of the characteristic of convenience. Convenience of any unit must always be judged in terms of the purpose for which it is being used. The English system of measures ranks high on the convenience test.

Acceptance is important because the more widely any measure is used, the more useful it becomes. Although the metric system (initiated in France) is widely accepted in Europe and South America, it is not so well accepted in the English-speaking countries.

The advantages of having a unit that is the same whenever and wherever used are obvious. Uniformity is furthered by state and federal laws and by such agencies as the National Bureau of Standards.

Our English system of measures is not very systematic; it does not relate very well in terms of cross references. The metric system was worked out so as to relate the different subsystems into an over-all system. The measures of distance, weight, volume, and capacity are related, and all multiples and subdivisions are in ratios of 1-to-10 or 10-to-1. The meter, the basic unit of distance, is also basic to measures of capacity and weight, since the liter (basic unit of capacity) was originally defined as a cube whose edge measured $\frac{1}{10}$ of a meter and the gram (basic unit of mass or, practically, weight) was originally defined as the weight of 1 cubic centimeter of distilled water at the temperature of melting ice. These in-

[2] In 1959, the English-speaking nations of the world agreed on an "international inch" so that in all these countries the inch will be set at 2.540000 centimeters and the yard will be set at $\frac{3,600,000}{3,937,008}$ meters. Also scientists have discovered that a more reliable standard of length is derived from the wavelengths of light from certain isotopes such as mercury 198. Such a standard would be an improvement over the prototype bars since the measurement can be more precise and since it can be duplicated with confidence in case of destruction of the prototype bars.

[3] Buckingham, *op. cit.*, pp. 467-69.

terrelations are all contributory to more systematic handling of weights and measures, even though the original specifications have had to be revised in detail as measures have become more precise.

These characteristics of a *good* unit of measure are certainly highly desirable, though each must be judged in relation to the uses of measures in given situations. Another characteristic of units of measure is not merely desirable; it is truly essential for any unit that is to serve in any correct sense as a standard of measure. This is the relatedness of the unit of measure to the property being measured. Without this characteristic, a unit of measure cannot serve its function. Even informal, nonstandardized units of measure must meet this criterion.

If an iron bar is to be measured, the first question to be answered is: What property of the iron bar is to be measured? If its length is to be measured, it must be measured against a unit of length. If its weight is to be measured, it must be measured in terms of a unit of weight. If its temperature is to be measured, it must be measured in terms of a unit of temperature. This is more obvious with direct measurement than with indirect measurement (to be defined shortly), but it is essential in either case.

The neglect of this essential occurs frequently enough to be a matter of some concern to teachers of arithmetic. Take, for example, the measurement of areas and volumes. The unit of length, 1 foot, is appropriate for measuring the edge of a tabletop (length or width); it is not appropriate for measuring the area of the tabletop. The "surface-covered" concept of area requires that the unit of measure for areas must also have the property of covering surface.

A one-dimensional unit like the *foot* cannot do this; it takes a two-dimensional unit like 1 *square foot*. Lines cannot (by definition) cover a surface. Square feet *can* cover a surface. Similarly, the dimensions (length, depth, height) of a cardboard box can be stated in linear units such as inches or feet, but the capacity of the box cannot be measured with linear inches or feet. The capacity (volume) of the box must be measured in terms of some unit of measure that has the property of capacity or volume, such as *cubic inches* or *cubic feet*. If we are interested in the three-dimensional capacity of the box, we must measure it with a three-dimensional unit.

The misunderstandings attendant upon use of linear measures for the determination of areas and volumes stems partly from the all-too-common practice of teaching children formulas for finding areas and volumes *before* the children have learned enough about what is really being measured and how it is being measured.

In figure 135, a box top is shown as a surface that can be covered with square tiles. Let us say the tiles are 1-inch squares. It takes 3 rows of 4 tiles each to cover the whole top surface of the box. For each unit of length there is a tile. For each unit of width there is a row of tiles. By multiplying the *number* of rows times the *number* of tiles in each row, we get a product that is the *number* of tiles it takes to cover the whole surface. This *does not* mean that we can multiply 3 *inches* × 4 *inches* and get 12 *square inches* as the area! The surface is being measured in units of *area*, in this case *square inches*. There are 4 *square inches* in each row. Since the whole area needs 3 such rows to cover it, we multiply "3 × 4 square inches" and get a correct area of "12 square inches." The formula "area = length × width" is an oversimplification. Actually it is *"number* of area units corresponding to the length" that is to be multiplied by the *"number* of rows associated with the width." The abstract numbers 3 × 4 = 12 give a correct statement of the arithmetic involved. It is the erroneous insertion of linear unit names to describe the area situation that is wrong.

Right Usages	*Wrong Usage*
3 × 4 square inches = 12 sq. in.	3 inches × 4 inches =
OR	12 square inches
4 × 3 square inches = 12 sq. in.	
OR	
3 × 4 = 12	

If instruction began with use and meaningful development of pertinent units of measure in each situation, children would see what the units really were. Then they themselves could arrive at the formulas and would understand what they truly represent.

The confusion between linear and area measures is also partly due to a confusion between direct and indirect measures.

plication of a tape measure to encircle a lampshade to determine its circumference; the pouring of the contents of a container into a measuring cup (as many times as necessary) to determine the capacity of the container; and the actual covering of a surface with tiles or paper squares.

Indirect measures are those which are derived by measuring some other magnitude that varies proportionately with the magnitude being measured. Examples are: measuring temperature by noting the expansion or contraction of mercury in a thin tube (a distance) as temperature rises or falls, but expressing the temperature in degree-units; measuring time by mechanical contrivances that move the hands of a clock around a circumference at a rate to correspond to the passage of time, but expressing the time in seconds, minutes, and hours; and using mathematical formulas as in the determinations of areas. When the surface to be measured is covered with tiles or squares of paper to measure it, the measure-

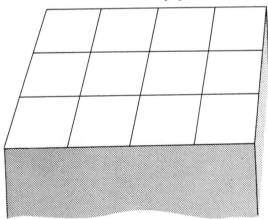

Figure 135. Area as Surface Covered.

DIRECT AND INDIRECT MEASURES

Direct measures are those which are made by actual comparison with the measuring unit. Examples are: the ap-

ment is direct. When the linear dimensions are found by use of a ruler and then inserted in a formula to find area, the measurement of area is indirect. In every case of indirect measurement there is a conversion of some sort from the direct measure to the indirect measure.

Similarly, the measurement of a volume by pouring the contents of the container into a cup or quart measure is direct, whereas the measurement of the volume of a box by measuring its linear dimensions and using them in a formula is indirect. Actually, a very large proportion of measures used in modern business and science are of the indirect type. The measures used in so-called "everyday" affairs are more likely to be direct. Certainly early instruction of children should emphasize direct measures.[4]

TYPES OF MEASURES

The types of measures and the units of measure for each that are commonly stressed in the elementary school are:

Linear measure: inch, foot, yard, mile
Square measure (area): square inch, square foot, square yard, acre, square mile
Cubic measure: cubic inch, cubic foot, cubic yard
Liquid measure: cup, pint, quart, gallon
Dry measure: pint, quart, bushel
Time measure: second, minute, hour, day, week, month, year, decade, century
Weight measure: ounce, pound, ton
Money measure: cent, dime, dollar
Counting measure: unit, dozen, gross

This is by no means a complete list of measures that may occur in the course of a child's elementary school experience, but it is fairly representative

of common experience. Among those listed, the cubic and dry measures are least likely to occur. If children really understand and learn to use correctly even this short list of measures, they will have a much sounder foundation for later work with other measures than if they touch superficially on many more than these.

ESSENTIAL IDEAS AND COMPETENCIES TO BE TAUGHT

Since teaching measurement to children should be much more than memorization of tables of measure and routine skills for converting one kind of unit to another, teachers need to consider very seriously how well they are teaching fundamental ideas of what measurement really means, such as these:

1. Measurement is a process of comparison of a magnitude with some unit or standard.
2. The unit of measurement must be appropriate for the property being measured.
3. The comparison may be direct or indirect.
4. Measures as expressed in "denominate numbers" are descriptive substitutes for that which has been measured.
5. Measurement (except for counting of discrete items) is inexact or approximate.
6. Measures vary as to precision and accuracy.
7. Modern standard measures have a long and fascinating history of development, which is continuing.

The abilities or competencies that elementary school children should develop include: (1) ability to recognize common standard measures and their interrelations one with the other; (2)

---

[4] This statement should not be interpreted as a recommendation to postpone unduly the teaching of telling time. Though the measurement of time by clocks is indirect, some phases of telling time are so much needed that they should be taught fairly early in a child's experience.

competence in measuring, which should include choice of appropriate units of measure and instruments for measuring; (3) skill in changing denominate measures from one unit to other units of a similar kind (such as feet to yards and yards to feet); (4) ability to perform the necessary computations for deriving simple indirect measures through use of formulas; and (5) ability to deal effectively with problem situations that include measures.

Helping Children Develop Adequate Measurement Concepts

Children will better understand standard measures if they have prior experience with informal or nonstandardized measures. They will be able to use tables of measures more intelligently if they know where the equivalences in those tables come from—historically and in simple experiences of derivation. They will compute more efficiently in measurement situations if someone will take the time to help them build a sound basis of experience in dealing with measuring problems as they occur in their everyday activities. The key to understanding of measurement lies in providing ample and constructive experience at a rate that allows optimum development of ideas and processes.

NONSTANDARD TO

STANDARD MEASURES

Sound instruction in the meaning of measurement does not begin with the memorization of tables of standard measures, but with simple situations in which pupils need to know how big or how long or how heavy or how much or how early. Perhaps the situations may include needing to find such facts as

which box is bigger and how much bigger, which box is heavier and how much heavier, which box holds more and how much more.

Skillful teachers of young children use such experiences as they use any worthwhile experience to expand and deepen children's vocabularies and skills and understandings. They may not think of these experiences specifically as laying a foundation for later instruction in arithmetic as much as they think of them as helping a child learn to know the everyday world in which he lives. To such teachers these questions are not insignificant, nor are they consistently answered *by* the teacher *for* the children. Rather, they are viewed as opportunities for children to experiment and to learn.

The child is learning about measurement when he tries a block to fill a given space and finds it is too long. He is comparing the block and the space and learning that the block is too long for the space. He is learning something more about measurement when he works an inlay-type puzzle. He may discard a piece too quickly; when his teacher cautions him to "try it first," that is, compare it with the opening, he may find that it does indeed fit into the space—that it was "just right." He is learning about measurement when he tries to reach for a book on a high shelf (high for him); he really measures the height of the shelf against his own reaching height. How much he learns from these experiences depends to a large degree on how well his teacher (or parent, perhaps) guides him to compare carefully and to use correct terms in telling what he did.

As the child develops his judgments about relative size, he needs to be encouraged to be more exact in his comparisons. One teacher thought of this need for more exactness when her pupils decided they needed a *long* wire on which to hang their Halloween drawings. John said he could bring the wire from home.

Teacher: How long a wire are you going to get, John?
John: Oh, a great, long wire. (He extended his arms at full length.)
Teacher: Is that long enough?
John: I'll bring a lot of wire so I'm sure to have enough.
Teacher: Don't you think it would be a good idea to know more exactly how much you need? Let's help John figure out how much wire to bring.

Various suggestions were made. After some discussion, it was decided to get a wire "long enough to reach all the way along the wall under the windows."

Teacher: That's a good idea. Now how is John going to know when he is at home that the wire is that long? He won't have the windows at home.

Further discussion — some fruitful and some not — led to the idea of measuring the length of the distance "with something John can carry home with him." Suggestions included: John's outstretched arms (his own private "fathom"), his leather belt, and a yardstick.

As soon as the yardstick was mentioned, some teachers would have just settled the matter by dropping the other suggestions. This teacher did not. She suggested that other children help John and that they try all the ways that had been suggested. The distance between his outstretched fingertips was discarded because the boy who helped John with that measurement complained that "he doesn't hold still while I mark the place." The belt, all agreed, was a better measuring aid; but it had an elastic insert and John noticed that how hard it was pulled made a dif-

ference. The yardstick "stayed the same"; so it was used for a final measurement, which showed that John needed to bring "about 6 yardsticks" of wire. At this point, the teacher reminded the children that this was not *exactly* the right length; but it was "good enough for now."

A neat little "crowning touch" was someone's suggestion that John would not need to carry the yardstick home with him to do the measuring because "I think he must have a yardstick at home." John said he knew his father had one in his tool shed. This gave the opportunity to discuss the fact that the yardstick at home and the yardstick at school were the same length. At this level, the variation among yardsticks is not a point of concern. What the teacher wanted to "put across" was the idea that standard measuring units (though she did not use that expression) are more useful than just any unit of measure since they are known to be the same (at least, approximately) and dispense with the need to carry the measuring unit about from place to place.

The progression from nonstandard to standard units of measure in this account is extremely important. One such experience is not enough, but it illustrates the sort of development that is helpful to children as they deal with situations requiring the use of measures. The wider the experience they have, the better the children can evaluate the appropriateness of both informal and standard units of measure. Adults as well as children have use for informal measures and can even handle them with a good deal of accuracy in situations where standard measures are not available. The performers on one popular television program have generated much merriment while using to good effect the question: Is it bigger than a bread box? Variable though bread boxes are as to size, there is still a broad boundary if not a narrow line between the objects which are clearly "bigger than a bread box" and those which are clearly smaller than that rough measure. The appropriateness of any such measure becomes important in terms of the demands of the situation; this is what children need to learn.

REFERENCE MEASURES

Anyone's concepts of distance, weight, or other measures relate to his own experiences. He judges them with reference to distance, weight, capacity, or time with which he has had "something to do." Miles are judged with reference to specific miles he has walked or ridden or looked at—the mile from home to a certain corner, the 5 miles between his place of work and his home, the 60 miles to the nearest large city. Pounds are judged with reference to lifting specific weights—1 pound of butter, a suitcase packed to the 40-pound limit for air luggage, or a 100-pound sack of dog food. Liquid measures are referred to his morning cup of coffee or a glass of milk, the contents of a quart milk bottle or the 5-gallon can in which he buys gasoline for his garden tractor.

Spitzer has developed the idea of reference measures very well.[5] The fundamental meaning of any standard measure is not derived from a memorized definition or a table of equivalents. It is derived from experiences with equivalents of the measure that are familiar to the person. How long is a foot? It is a little longer than a sheet of typing paper or standard loose-leaf notebook paper. How long is an inch? It is about as long as the distance between finger joints, with the choice of which finger and which joints depending on the individual child or adult. (Children have to revise this reference measure from time to time.) Not only unit reference measures but also non-unit reference measures should be set up, e.g., the height of the classroom door as 7 feet.

Spitzer lists some reference measures set up at each grade level in one school. Any teacher may use such a list to get an idea of appropriate reference measures; then she may proceed to develop similar—or different—reference measures that seem to be needed by her own pupils. Development of such a list is a continuing activity and should be resumed whenever the pupils or teacher recognize the need or opportunity.[6]

The identification of reference measures provides an excellent opportunity for meaningful use of measuring instruments. In the preceding account of John's search for a measurement of the distance under the windows, it was apparent that he needed an instrument for measuring. Under proper guidance, he moved from no instrument to crude instruments to a more efficient measuring instrument, the yardstick. By standards of scientific experimentation his instrument was a crude one; at his level of need and understanding and in relation to the others he had used, it was a relatively exact one.

Not only does identification of reference measures focus attention on the measuring instruments themselves, but it also emphasizes the need for careful use of the instruments. A ruler marked to sixteenths of an inch is no more useful in getting a reliable measurement

[5] Herbert F. Spitzer, *The Teaching of Arithmetic* 3rd ed., Boston: Houghton, 1961, pp. 235-37.

[6] See also: Marks, Purdy, and Kinney, *op. cit.*, pp. 284-86.

than is a ruler marked only in whole inches if the former is carelessly related to the thing to be measured or if the user does not read the ruler correctly. The teacher will want to check carefully to see that the instruments used are appropriate to the user's level of ability and that he is impressed with the need for care in "reading" the measurement.

A list of reference measures should include linear, weight, capacity, time, and other types of measures. Since time concepts are among the most difficult to build, perhaps it would be helpful to discuss them in some detail.

Reference measures for time. One cannot see or hear or touch time. One cannot pick it up and place it against a measuring stick. One cannot lift it even when it "weighs heavily" upon us. Adults have all these disadvantages in building their concepts of time. Children have those disadvantages and another very serious one, the shortness of the time they have lived, because the reference measures for time are particularly personal and particularly tied to individual experience.

Children have lived only a few years, which seem long to them but short to adults. A child's total 8 years of living are to him the total of existence; to his 80-year-old relative, those 8 years are a mere tenth of a lifetime. This is the reason that children have such a hard time waiting for time to pass, while their elders wish it would stand still so they could catch up with unmet duties and responsibilities. The time between birthdays is so long for a child, all too short for his parents. Comparison with the total time lived makes this contrast understandable. This comparison must also be in the mind of the elementary school teacher as she seeks to help children build time concepts.

While this lack of reference time is particularly acute with respect to longer periods of time, children also need much help with shorter time concepts, such as minute or half-hour, often because the names for those time units are so carelessly used by adults. Parents, teachers, and other adults tell Bobby to wait a "minute" and nothing happens for 10 or 15 or 30 minutes thereafter. Bobby does not know that it is 10 or 15 or 30 minutes since his mother said she would make a sandwich for him; he knows only that it is a long, long time. No wonder that he is confused when she later gives him a "minute" in which to pick up his toys and is irritated when it takes him "just a little while," which the clock could tell her is only 5 minutes. The fact is that the "minute" of everyday speech is a very different thing from the "minute" measured by the clock.

The basis for learning the meaning of 1 minute or 30 minutes or 1 hour or 3 hours or 5 days or 2 months is what can be experienced in the given length of time. Children may be asked to close their eyes on a given signal and to raise hands after they think a minute has passed. The teacher may keep time and note the raising of hands and later tell the children the results. Adults may be surprised at their own inability to make a good estimate of a minute under such circumstances. A better procedure is to have the children doing some familiar action while being timed. They may see how many words they can copy in a minute, how far they can walk at a steady rate in a minute, how far they can count in 2 minutes, or how much they can read in 5 minutes.

They may learn to count with a metronome set for 1 second per stroke, counting "one hundred one, one hundred two," etc., in time to the metronome. After they think they have the right rate pretty well mastered, they may be asked to count silently and tell when 60 seconds have passed. Checking on their accuracy, the teacher may find that they become rather good at judging a minute. The point is that they have something to which they can make reference for their judgment of the passage of time. Incidentally, as they practice counting from "one hundred" to "one hundred sixty," they may learn the number of seconds in a minute so well that they never need further study of that equivalence.

In helping young children to understand long amounts of time, the teacher should not expect too much. Learning that the Pilgrims landed at Plymouth Rock in 1620 and computing to find how long ago that was may not really help children to come to any real understanding of elapsed time. Taking 30 years as the measure of one generation, a group of children in the year 1950 could go back 11 generations (330 years) to find that a 10-year-old Pilgrim boy present at that famous landing would be the great-great-great-great-great-great-great-great-great-grandfather of his 10-year-old descendant of 1950. Even those children who have known their great-grandfathers cannot encompass the meaning of 11 generations, but they at least realize that 1620 was "way, way back there."

Time lines are very useful in the upper grades for helping children to gain some concept of relative historical time. This is an excellent example of the use of arithmetic in the study of history. Boys and girls are usually very much impressed after constructing a time line running back for centuries to find that their own lifetimes are hardly discernable on the line.

Difficult though it is, children need to develop (to the extent that is possible and feasible) relative notions of historical time. Dates of historic events mean nothing as mere numbers to be parroted; they mean much in terms of what happened before what and how much earlier one event was than another. Who else was living at the time Eli Whitney invented the cotton gin? Was he a contemporary of Thomas Edison? When a child asks some adult if he remembers George Washington or Abraham Lincoln, the child is not trying to be funny. He needs help in becoming oriented in time.

Reference measures in reading. The case for teaching measures in relation to arithmetic is pretty well proven, but this teaching should not be limited to the arithmetic class. In our reading-oriented schools and our reading-oriented civilization more attention should be paid to reference measures. Consider this sampling of mentions of measures from one newspaper:

"launched a great 1,300,000-pound thrust rocket"

"sold a 218-year-old violin for 9,000 British pounds"

"5-lb. fruitcake"

"Carat-weight . . . is the unit of measure in weighing diamonds. One carat equals exactly 100 points, just like cents in a dollar bill."

"large living room, 14 × 25"

"Canadian wild mink coat, size 14"

"less than 5 feet, 11 inches tall"

"130-degree temperature"

The first three items are particularly interesting in relation to each other because of the use of "pounds" in each of them. Pounds of thrust, British money, and pounds of fruitcake are certainly varied. The 5-lb. fruitcake is closest to children's experience. Even so, they need help in discovering just how much fruitcake that is, just how much weight that is. What else do they know that weighs 5 pounds?

The newspaper article about the sale of the old violin for £ 9,000 went on to tell that this was the equivalent of $25,200. But how much money is that? What would it buy? How many automobiles of a standard make and model would it buy? What kind of house would it buy? Can a good house be built for that amount? A school building? This is reference in terms of purchase value.

The 1,300,000 pounds of thrust are difficult to understand not only because of the size of the number but also because of the need to develop the meaning of "thrust." Perhaps some of the boys in an elementary school class can tell something about the power represented in terms of applications to other uses than rocket launching. They should be encouraged to share their knowledge with others.

The definition of a carat as a unit of measure is interesting. Notice that, if a person knew nothing more about carats than is told in the definition, he could memorize the definition and still have no notion of how large a 1-carat diamond is. How can a person best find out how large a 1-carat diamond is? The best way is to see a 1-carat diamond, or a smaller one if the relation to a full carat is known. A farm child might be helped by the knowledge that a carat is about the same measure of mass (weight) as 3 plump grains of wheat. If scales that weigh in ounces are available, something may be found that weighs 1 ounce. Then the equivalence of 1 ounce to 437.5 grains would at least establish the very small weight of the 1-carat diamond as compared with the weight of a book or even a pencil.

The "large living room, 14 ft. x 25 ft.," may be compared to a part of the schoolroom measured off to that size. The designation "*less* than 5 feet, 11 inches tall" may apply to everyone in the classroom. Who *is* that tall? Maybe the teacher is that tall; maybe the principal is that tall. The task is to find out. How hot is 130 degrees? Does the summer temperature reading here ever go that high? Is it as hot as the oven when Mother bakes a cake?

Any teacher wishing to pursue the matter of reference measures (and, along with it, uses of measures) can get plenty of clues from reading a mail-order catalog and noting the wide range of measuring units in use. An interesting example of reference measures is table 15, based on the user's manual for a "12-lb. automatic washer." Tables of capacity measures do not include pounds of capacity, but the modern homemaker knows that this form of measurement indicates the number of pounds of clothes that may be washed in the machine at full capacity.

Parents will usually be happy to help children assemble such helps on reference measures. The parents may also be happy to get the information that children assemble for them.

In addition to the measures used most in reading outside the classroom walls, children should be helped to find reference measures to help them understand what they read in school. Even a casual check on elementary school texts in social studies and science will yield hundreds of uses of weights and measures. If children are to understand what they are reading, they must have some basis for referring these measures to their own experience. While textbooks are not in such general use in curriculum areas like art and music, certainly reading in those areas involves measures, e.g., sizes and amounts of art materials and the measures that are essential in reading music.

TABLE 15
Excerpts from a Table of Washing Machine Capacity

Items weighing 1 lb. dry weight	No. of items
Blouses, women's	2-3
Dresses, children's	6
Jeans, children's	1
Napkins	8
Pajamas, men's	1
Pillowcases	3
Items weighing 2 lb. dry weight	
Coveralls, men's	1
Sheet, double	1
Tablecloth, large	1

BUILDING TABLES OF MEASURE

Smith and Henderson have called attention to children as "firm adherents to the old adage that *seeing is believing*. 'Well, I saw it with my own eyes, I ought to know' is a favorite justification of children for the validity of evidence."[7]

"Measurement provides another avenue for children to arrive at *truth*. This procedure also involves the element of *seeing is believing* . . . ."[8] Certainly, it does.

As children have opportunities to measure the linear dimensions of furniture, bulletin boards, window ledges, or sheets of drawing paper, they will use rulers, tape measures, and yardsticks. As they seek reference measures for larger distances out of doors, they will use yardsticks and 50-ft. or 100-ft. tapes. The need for noting the relations among the shorter linear units of measure is readily established. Children who really want to know how many inches equal 1 foot will probably have already observed from the ruler that 1 foot = 12 inches. Comparison of yardstick and

ruler is all that is necessary to show that 1 yard = 3 feet, or 36 inches. All that needs to be done is to put these statements of equivalence into an organized table.

Beyond the yard measure, there are no manageable standard units of linear measure that children are likely to use enough to discover relations among measures, e.g., rods or miles. The facts that 1 rod = $5\frac{1}{2}$ yards, or $16\frac{1}{2}$ feet, and that 1 mile = 1760 rods, or 5280 feet, should be given to children. This does not mean, however, that experience with these measures should be avoided. The $16\frac{1}{2}$ feet may be measured out to show the length of a rod. A mile may be measured with the odometer on a bicycle or in an automobile.

The commonly used liquid measures can all be handled by children in the classroom. Glass containers (or transparent plastic ones) should be used if possible, since they permit the children to see — so they may believe — the equivalence of measures as they gather the facts with which they build their own table of liquid measure. Aside from minor accidents (spilling and tipping and breaking) the children should have little difficulty in discovering for themselves that the contents of 2 standard measuring cups will fill 1 pint jar, that 2 pints will fill a quart jar, and that 4 quarts will fill a gallon container.

Sometimes teachers add a little food coloring to the water to enhance the children's interest and to make the liquid more "visible" to children who are watching but not participating in the demonstration. Some teachers highly recommend the use of fine sand or a cereal such as oatmeal, even though these are dry substances not strictly eligible for liquid measure. Let each teacher take her choice of the hazards — wet accidents or dry ones.

---

[7] Eugene P. Smith and Kenneth B. Henderson, "Some Common Uses of the Term *Proof*," 24th Yearbook of the National Council of Teachers of Mathematics, *The Growth of Mathematical Ideas, Grades K–12.* Washington, D.C.: 1959, p. 119.

[8] Smith and Henderson, *ibid.*, p. 118.

A supplementary benefit may be realized by having more than one shape of container for each standard measure: a wide, low cup and a tall, tapered cup measure; standard glass or plastic-coated milk bottles and other bottles of varying shapes that contain the standard quantities. Children need to know that it is not the shape but the capacity of the container that establishes the unit of measure for liquids. Collection of a large number of different-looking quart, pint, and cup containers can be an interesting project for the children. Eight-ounce containers with ounce markings are readily available (e.g., in baby's nursing bottles) and should be included.

In building a table of square measure, again the work should be restricted to the smaller manageable measures. Instead of telling the children the larger items, such as the number of square rods in an acre, the teacher will do well to suggest that they find this fact in a dictionary or encyclopedia. Many adults are not aware of the presence of detailed tables of weights and measures in these sources; they still think of them as being found only in "the back of the arithmetic book."

For the derivation of tables of cubic measures, it is highly desirable to have some ready-made aids available. Children can make drawings of square inches and square feet from which they can build a square yard, but their cubic inches and cubic feet will probably vary too much from correct standards. Because of the space they take, cubic-foot aids are often made of cardboard, which can be folded flat and assembled in cubic form for the occasion. Of course, standard plastic forms may be purchased.

For building tables of weight, balance scales should be used if possible. There is something about watching the balanc-ing of the weights on the scale that stresses in a special way the idea that what is on one pan *equals* in weight what is on the other pan. Often balance scales can be borrowed from the high school science laboratory.

Clocks and calendars are the principal aids in building a table of time equivalents. Unfortunately, the children will not be able to measure time units directly. If they could, they would not have the time. Indirectly, they can use an old alarm clock and calendars of various types to establish the facts for a table of time measure. For all these tables, with the exceptions mentioned, children do *not* need to have the tables dictated to them; they *can* derive them and will benefit a great deal from doing so. When they have finished their tables, they can then check them against an authoritative source. Some additional practice will be needed *after* the tables have been built.[9]

Approximation, Precision, and Accuracy

If children are really to understand measurement and denominate numbers, they must understand that all measurement (except in counting of discrete items) is approximate. Careless use of words by adults may lead to confusion rather than clarification of this point.

Consider a situation in which a group of fourth-grade children are engaged in the cooking of cranberry jelly. The teacher says to Carol, "Be sure to measure exactly now. You *must have exactly* $\frac{3}{4}$ *cup* of sugar for every cup of juice."

Correctly speaking, Carol *must not be expected* to measure *exactly* $\frac{3}{4}$ cup. She

[9] Building tables of measures will not be concentrated at a single grade level. Certain tables will be built earlier, some later. Parts of some tables will be built at earlier levels and extended later.

should be encouraged to measure *as exactly as she can* with the materials at hand. Adults should know and should help children realize that even the best of such measurements are not "exactly exact." What is needed is an approximation close enough to satisfy the conditions in each particular situation. Carol should know that neither she nor the teacher can guarantee the measurement of exactly $\frac{3}{4}$ cup of sugar.

ROOM FOR ERROR

Intermediate-grade children are not too young to begin the development of another meaning for the word "error" than as a synonym for "mistake." Actually, the concept can be developed without calling it "error," but children may as well know the name for the idea.

Since measurement necessarily yields an approximation rather than a certainty, young and older users of measurement need to recognize that the sources of inexactness of measurement reside partly in the instruments used for making the measurement and partly in the persons using the instruments.

Children sometimes observe this by themselves; if they do not, the teacher has a responsibility to lead them to see it. It is not at all difficult to set up a situation in which the facts of the case are readily apparent. Choose an object of which several are available, such as the half-pint cartons in which milk is delivered to the cafeteria or several copies of the same textbook. Ask each child in the group to measure the dimensions of the object in question, using his own ruler.

Differences will appear for any typical group. Some of the differences will arise from the fact that the rulers will not be exactly the same. Some children may have rulers marked off in quarter-inches; others will have rulers showing eighth-inches and sixteenth-inches. Consequently, the children will come up with different dimensions—perhaps only slightly different but nevertheless different. Some of the rulers having the same fractional parts of an inch marked on them will be different because some "cut off" a little from the first inch or others "start" a small distance from the actual end of the stick. (It is not hard to demonstrate that many rulers of the type used by elementary school children have first and last "inches" that are less exact than those between.) Other differences will arise because of actions of the children, such as not holding the ruler still while measuring, not measuring directly along the edge of the book but slightly in a diagonal direction, or not reading the measurement correctly.

After a listing of all the findings from such a simple experiment, the children will benefit from a discussion of the causes of the differences. As they are led to see the many sources of error, they will begin to understand the approximate nature of the measurement process. They will also be ready to consider a new kind of "error"—the possibility that there may be errors that are not due to mistakes, such as Joe's report of the length of the book cover as $9\frac{1}{4}$ inches (found with a ruler that showed no smaller unit than $\frac{1}{4}$ inch) while Jack used a ruler with smaller units and reported the length as $9\frac{3}{8}$ inches.

Insofar as possible, the teacher should try to help children see that it is not the numbers that are lacking in exactness, but the process by which the numbers are found. The children will know of other measuring instruments that are not perfect in their measurements. A good way to start their thought search for such instances is to mention one or two, e.g., the gas pump at the filling station and the odometer on the family automobile. Does the gas pump measure gasoline *exactly*? Does the odometer measure *exactly*? How close do these instruments come to being exact in their measurements? Have the children noticed signs along the highway by which the motorist can test the accuracy of his car's measurement of miles driven? Why are such devices helpful?

Of course, children will have experienced approximation in other situations in arithmetic. For example, when decimal numbers are divided and the quotient does not come out even, they learn to stop with a quotient which is not absolutely exact but which is "good enough" for the situation.

Lest the impression be left that only older elementary school children should receive instruction concerning the approximate nature of measurement, one illustration involving a younger child may be pertinent.

Sally's aunt came to visit in her home the day before Sally's seventh birthday. The aunt, seeking to break the conversational ice after a long absence, said, "Just think! You're seven years old!"

Sally quickly and very emphatically responded, "No! *Tomorrow* I'm seven. *Today* I'm *six!*"

In terms of measurement, Sally was certainly much closer to being seven years old than six years old. The expression "going on seven" would have been more accurate, though she had already "gone" so far toward seven that six was far, far from being a true statement of the number of years she had lived. Sally, as a typical seven-year-old, could benefit from a little discussion of this matter, not in language like "error of measurement" but in terms of how much closer she was to her seventh birthday than to her sixth birthday, which to her was "long, long ago." Such occasions give the alert adult a good opportunity to begin building the idea that measurement of time or distance or weight is not exact in the way that counting dolls and pencils and children is exact.

The subject of errors of measurement leads into the distinction between two important kinds of error, those which relate to *precision* of a measurement and those which relate to its *accuracy*.

MEANING OF PRECISION

Precision of measurement relates to the *size* of the *unit* of measurement. The smaller the unit of measurement being used, the more precise is the measurement.

In the case of Sally's age, she was using a year as the unit of measure. Months would yield a more precise measure of age; weeks would be more precise than months; days than weeks; and so on. Sally's aunt stated the child's age to the nearest year. If Sally had a new baby brother, his age might have been stated much more precisely — perhaps to the nearest day or even the nearest hour.

Two measurements cannot be compared as to precision unless they are both measures of the same property. Thus 14 inches is more precise than 14 feet, and 27 ounces is more precise than 15 pounds, but one cannot compare 14 inches and 15 ounces as to precision. Inches and pounds do not measure the same property.

Possible error. The greatest possible error of a measurement (not including mistakes in measurement) is one-half of the unit of measure being used.[10] Children who are ready for consideration of possible errors of measurement can figure this out for

---

[10] Other terms for "possible error" are "greatest possible error," "absolute error," "tolerance," and "apparent error."

themselves with proper guidance. The leading questions (with likely answers) relate to the measurement of the heavy line in figure 136.

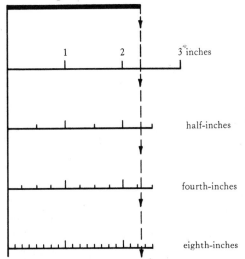

1   2   3″ inches

half-inches

fourth-inches

eighth-inches

Figure 136. Greatest Possible Error of Linear Measurement. (Reduced from original.)

Question: How long is the heavy black line, to the nearest inch?
Answer: 2 inches.
Question: Is it closer to being 2 inches or 3 inches?
Answer: 2 inches.
Question: How long could a line be and still be called 2 inches long?
Answer: $2\frac{1}{2}$ inches. (Some children would say this could be called either 2 inches or 3 inches.)
Question: If a line is over $2\frac{1}{2}$ inches long, how long would it be to the nearest inch?
Answer: 3 inches.
Question: How far away from the nearest inch can the measurement be?
Answer: Half an inch.

Similar questioning would relate to measurement to the nearest half-inch, the nearest fourth-inch, and so on. All the findings could be summarized thus:

When we measure to this unit:	The largest error is:
To the nearest whole inch	One-half inch
To the nearest half-inch	One-fourth inch
To the nearest fourth-inch	One-eighth inch

The same thing can be done with measuring time from the clock—to the nearest hour, the nearest half-hour, the nearest quarter-hour, the nearest five minutes, the nearest minute. In each case, the greatest possible error will be found to be half of the unit of measure being used. The children can draw their own generalizations if they have enough of the right kind of experiences of this type. Insurance companies use this idea when they compute "age as of nearest birthday"; the greatest possible error is one-half year.

Ways of showing precision. The degree of precision of a measurement can be shown in various ways. For most children, it is enough that they state the unit of measure, e.g., $12\frac{1}{2}$ inches to the nearest $\frac{1}{2}$ *inch*, 15 ounces to the nearest *ounce*, or 4.5 miles to the nearest *tenth of a mile*.

If the teacher is sure that they know the meaning, more advanced learners may merely assume that the last significant digit of the number indicates the degree of precision; e.g., 4.5 miles would be assumed to indicate precision to tenths and 4.50 would be assumed to indicate precision to hundredths of a mile.

An adult manner of indicating precision, seldom used by children, is to write the measurement "plus or minus" the possible error; e.g., "4.5 ± .05" would mean that the measurement is somewhere between 4.45 and 4.55, that is, between "4.5 − .05" and "4.5 + .05." Elementary teachers may not think of this as "elementary school content," but they should be able to help a child who is interested in this notation.

MEANING OF ACCURACY

Accuracy of measurement, like precision of measurement, does not refer to mistakes made in the measuring process. Nor is it the same as precision. Accuracy of measurement is defined in terms of relative rather than absolute error.

Relative error. Suppose that the contents of two jars of instant coffee are weighed to the nearest ounce, one weighing 2 ounces and the other weighing 6 ounces. Since both are weighed to the nearest whole ounce, the possible error (maximum error or absolute error) in each case is $\frac{1}{2}$ ounce. So far as precision of measurement is concerned, both quantities of coffee are weighed with the *same* precision. To indicate the degree of precision, we might say that the smaller jar contains somewhere between $1\frac{1}{2}$ and $2\frac{1}{2}$ ounces, and the larger jar contains somewhere between $5\frac{1}{2}$ and $6\frac{1}{2}$ ounces.

The precision of measurement is the same; but, quite obviously, the ratio of the possible error to the total measurement is very different.

$$\frac{\frac{1}{2} \text{ ounce}}{2 \text{ ounces}} = \frac{1}{2} \div 2 = \frac{1}{2} \times \frac{1}{2} = \frac{1}{4}$$

$$\frac{\frac{1}{2} \text{ ounce}}{6 \text{ ounces}} = \frac{1}{2} \div 6 = \frac{1}{2} \times \frac{1}{6} = \frac{1}{12}$$

The *relative* error for the 2-ounce jar is $\frac{1}{4}$; for the 6-ounce jar, it is $\frac{1}{12}$. Thus, though the measurement of the two amounts of coffee is *equally precise* (to the nearest ounce), they are *not equally accurate*. The measurement of the 6-ounce jar is much more accurate (absolute error only $\frac{1}{12}$ of the total measurement) than the measurement of the 2-ounce jar (absolute error $\frac{1}{4}$ of the total measurement).

Sometimes relative error is expressed as "per cent of error." In the two examples above, the per cents of error would be 25% and $8\frac{1}{3}$%.

A group of children who are "counting the time until vacation" may do so with attention to the precision and the accuracy of their measurement of the remaining time. Take four examples of error as summarized in the table below. Comparison of these examples will emphasize some similarities and contrasts among the various error terms.

Time until Vacation	Maximum Error	Relative Error	Per Cent of Error
A. 5 days	$\frac{1}{2}$ day	$\frac{1}{2} \div 5 = \frac{1}{10}$	10%
B. 10 days	$\frac{1}{2}$ day	$\frac{1}{2} \div 10 = \frac{1}{20}$	5%
C. 5 hours	$\frac{1}{2}$ hour	$\frac{1}{2} \div 5 = \frac{1}{10}$	10%
D. 10 hours	$\frac{1}{2}$ hour	$\frac{1}{2} \div 10 = \frac{1}{20}$	5%

Measurements A and B are equally precise; both are given to the nearest whole day, with a maximum error of measurement of $\frac{1}{2}$ day. Measurements C and D are also equally precise; both are given to the nearest whole hour, with a maximum error of measurement of $\frac{1}{2}$ hour. C and D are much more precise than A and B, since their unit of measurement is 1 hour rather than 1 day.

Measurements A and C are not equally precise, but they are equally accurate. Their per cent of error is identically the same. So also measurements B and D are not equally precise, but they are equally accurate.

The accuracy of the measurement, however, is independent of the unit of measurement. It depends on the ratio of the possible (or maximum) error to the total measurement. If the error is small in relation to the length of time being measured, the relative error is small; if the error is large in relation to the length of time being measured, the relative error is large.

Increasing precision and accuracy. Though the more precise measurement is not necessarily the more accurate measurement (as in B and C above), a person who feels that a measurement is not accurate enough can increase accuracy by increasing precision. If, for example, the measurement of 5 days until vacation is thought to have too large an error term (10% error), the measurement may be made more precise by counting the hours instead of the days until vacation. With the maximum error of measurement thus changed from $\frac{1}{2}$ day to $\frac{1}{2}$ hour, the relative error must be found by comparing $\frac{1}{2}$ hour with the new measurement (120 hours). The relative error will be $\frac{1}{240}$; the per cent of error will be slightly more than 4 tenths of 1%. Thus greater precision in making the same measurement also increased the accuracy of the measurement.

How precise and how accurate the measurements should be depends on the circumstances and the purpose for which the measurement is being made. Reference has already been made to the statements of age. For a very young baby, hours or days are appropriate; for the old man, years are precise and accurate enough. So also for considering the length of marriage by newlyweds and by a couple who have reached their golden-wedding date. For the newlyweds, measurement in hours or even minutes "makes sense" because the total measurement is so small. For the couple married for 50 years, the measurement by years is "good enough."[11]

A good question to ask is: What difference will it make if a smaller unit of measure is used? Is the difference important? Increased precision and increased accuracy make "more difference" when that which is measured is assessed as having greater value. To use ounces in measuring coal would be silly; coal is not that valuable. To use ounces in weighing cut diamonds is also out of line, but in the opposite direction. A more precise measure is needed for anything so valuable, hence, the use of carats and grains.

SIGNIFICANT DIGITS

Sometimes the precision and accuracy of a measurement are expressed in terms of *significant digits*. This is true whether we are dealing with denominate numbers or other so-called "approximate" numbers.

What are *significant digits*? Mueller says they are the digits that "occupy orders or places we are 'sure of.' "[12] Banks says, "The digits of an approximate number are significant if they serve a purpose other than merely helping to place the decimal point."[13]

Elementary school children do not need to learn a definition for "significant digits," but their teachers should recognize significant and nonsignificant digits in order to guide children properly in rounding off approximate numbers. The identification of significant digits is done best through examples.

Always Significant	*Examples (Significant Digits in Bold Face)*		
1. All nonzero digits	**12345**	**1.247**	**.5678**
2. Final zeros of decimal fractions	.**30**	1.2**50**	.**400**
3. Zeros between significant digits	**3006**	**3.05**	**30.0**
Never Significant			
Initial zeros of a decimal fraction	.0**5**	.00**6**	.00**25**

These cases are clear. The most difficult determination of significance or nonsignificance of digits concerns final zeros in a whole number. In the number 3400, one does not know whether the

---

[11] The definition of a second as one-sixtieth of a minute may be exact enough for most people, but the National Bureau of Standards uses an atomic clock according to which a second is 9,192,631,770 vibrations of an atom of the rare metal cesium.

[12] Mueller, *op. cit.*, p. 249.

[13] Banks, *op. cit.*, pp. 305-6.

number is exact to hundreds or tens or ones without some additional information. The "3" and the "4" are significant, but one cannot tell whether the zeros are the result of rounding off to the nearest hundred or the nearest ten or whether the number is exact to ones. When supplementary information is lacking, the terminal zeros of a whole number may be assumed as not being significant.

Precision and significant digits. The precision of a decimal number is shown by the *place value of the final significant digit*. In each example below, the bold-face digit is the final significant digit, and it indicates the precision of the number.

124   12.4   1.24   4509   123.45**0**   3600

The number 124 is precise to ones, 12.4 to tenths, 1.24 to hundredths, 4509 to ones, 123.450 to thousandths, and 3600 to hundreds. Suppose that 12.4 is used in the expression "12.4 feet"; then this is a measurement that is precise to tenths of a foot. The maximum error of measurement is $\frac{1}{2}$, or .5, of a tenth of a foot; the exact measurement is somewhere between 12.35 and 12.45 feet.

Suppose that 12.4 is the quotient of a division. Perhaps the "4" represents exactly 4 tenths (if the quotient came out even) or perhaps it means that the quotient was carried out to hundredths and rounded off to the nearest tenth. We are sure of the "4" as indicating the nearest tenth, either by measurement or by rounding; and we make no claims for precision beyond tenths place.

Accuracy and significant digits. The accuracy of a number is indicated by the *number* of significant digits. In fact, significant digits are sometimes defined as those which influence the accuracy of a measurement.

Some examples are organized below to indicate precision and accuracy of measurement in terms of significant digits. Study of these and other examples will provide more help than lengthy discussions.

Numbers	Precise to:	Significant Digits	Number of Significant Digits
375	Ones	375	3
.375	Thousandths	375	3
37500	Hundreds	375	3

Notice that all these numbers are of the same accuracy. They vary in precision of measurement, but not in accuracy. The smallest unit of measure indicated varies from hundreds to thousandths, but in each case there are 3 significant digits. Computing the relative error, one would get the same result for each of them, e.g., $\frac{.5}{375} = .0013$; or $\frac{.0005}{.375} = .0013$; or $\frac{50}{37500} = .0013$.

The numbers below vary both as to precision and as to accuracy. The number occupying more places than any other has the fewest significant digits. It is also the least accurate.

Numbers	Precise to:	Significant Digits	Number of Significant Digits
250,000	Ten thousands	25	2
152.64	Hundredths	15264	5
5.000	Thousandths	5000	4

Its relative error is: $5,000 \div 250,000$, or $\frac{1}{50}$. Notice that the number 5.000 has 4 significant digits and is therefore more accurate than the larger number 250,000. The relative error is: $.0005 \div 5.000 = \frac{1}{10,000}$. The smallest relative error belongs to the number with the most significant digits, 152.64. Its relative error is: $.005 \div 152.64 = \frac{5}{152640} = \frac{1}{30,528}$.

This makes it much easier to get a quick estimate of the comparative accuracy of two numbers; note the number of significant digits in each. The one with more significant digits will be more accurate.

ROUNDING OFF

One of the major applications that a teacher can make of the immediately preceding material is in guiding pupils in rounding off numbers. Often both children and adults are guilty of computing with numbers so they suggest more precision than they should.[14] Some acceptable rules to follow in rounding off a number are these:

1. When whole numbers are rounded off, zeros are used to replace the discarded digits (34,567 rounded to the nearest hundred becomes 34,600).

2. When fractions are rounded off, the discarded digits must *not* be replaced by zeros (34.567 rounded to the nearest tenth becomes 34.6, *not* 34.600). To replace the discarded terminal digits in the fraction with zeros would indicate just as much precision as before the rounding, since terminal zeros in the fraction are significant.

3. If more than one digit is dropped, consider the value of the dropped digit with the greatest place value. If it is less than "5," leave the digit in the last (right-hand) retained place as it was.

4. If the dropped digit with highest place value is more than "5," increase the last retained digit by 1.

[14] Defensible degrees of precision and accuracy in computation with approximate numbers must be based on the idea that computation does not increase precision or accuracy. Therefore: (1) in addition or subtraction, the sum or difference should not be expressed with greater precision than the terms from which it was derived; (2) in multiplication, the product should be expressed with the same number of significant digits as there are in the least accurate factor; and (3) in division, the quotient should be expressed with the same number of significant digits as there are in the dividend or divisor, depending on which of these two terms has the fewer significant digits.

5. If the highest place-value digit to be dropped is "5," treat the last retained digit (no change or increasing by 1) so that it will be an even number. (This serves to balance out the effects.)

Computations with Denominate Numbers

Computations with the numbers associated with units of measure is no different from computation with numbers not so associated. In fact, computations for numbers associated with dollars and cents, feet, inches, pounds, and other denominate numbers have been used generously in earlier chapters of this text in problems in which the various computational procedures have been applied. The special consideration given in the subsequent discussion is centered on ways to keep the units of measure straight rather than on any difference in computation with the numbers themselves.

COEFFICIENTS AND UNITS OF MEASURE

A denominate number expression like "12 feet" or "$31" or "5 hours" includes a numerical coefficient and a word or other symbol designating the unit of measure. The "12" and the "31" and the "5" are symbols for numbers, while "feet" and "$" and "hours" are symbols for the units of measure. Mathematicians typically omit the units of measure when they write their calculations. Elementary school arithmetic instruction usually includes the units for written calculations with denominate numbers, at least so long as children need them in order to keep their thinking straight. Unfortunately, sometimes they are used in such a manner as to promote confusion rather than clarification.[15] This is the reason for special consideration of computation with denominate numbers.

Relation to numerators and denominators. Many of the ideas concerning numerators and denominators of fractions are directly related to the proper use of coefficients and unit names for measurements.

3 books + 4 books = 7 books

3 eighths + 4 eighths = 7 eighths OR $\dfrac{3}{8} + \dfrac{4}{8} = \dfrac{7}{8}$

3 inches + 4 inches = 7 inches

Whether the numbers 3, 4, and 7 are associated with discrete, countable things like books, with fractional parts like eighths, or with units of measure like inches, the process of addition concerns the numerical coefficients in each of the expressions. In fraction terminology, it is the numerators that are added. In measurement terminology, it is the coefficients that are added.[16] The names or denominators (books, eighths, inches) are not added. Nor are they to be ignored.

7 books + 5 books = 12 books = 1 dozen

7 eighths + 5 eighths = 12 eighths = 1 whole and 4

eighths = 1 whole and 1 half OR $\dfrac{7}{8} + \dfrac{5}{8} = 1\dfrac{4}{8} = 1\dfrac{1}{2}$

7 inches + 5 inches = 12 inches = 1 foot

The numbers (numerators or numberers) 7 and 5 are added to give a sum of 12. The denominators or names (of discrete things, fractional parts, or units of measure) are the same for the addends and for the sum. Once the sum is obtained and expressed in terms of coefficient and name, the sum may be changed to a different expression in which both coefficient and name are changed. This change is *not* the addition; it is something done, in this case,

after the addition. It is a change in *form* of the complete expression to another form with the *same* value.

12 books = 1 dozen

$$\frac{12}{8} = 1\frac{4}{8} = 1\frac{1}{2}$$

12 inches = 1 foot

When $\frac{12}{8}$ is changed to $1\frac{4}{8}$, then to $1\frac{1}{2}$, the change is possible because we know that $\frac{8}{8}$ equal 1 and because we know that $\frac{4}{8} = \frac{1}{2}$. When "12 books" is changed to "1 dozen books", the change is possible because 12 things equal a dozen things. When "12 inches" is changed to "1 foot", the change is possible because 12 inches measure the same distance as that measured by 1 foot.

In each case, we substitute an equal value. If the value substituted is not equal, we cannot correctly make the change in form of expression. All this relates to the rule of likeness, which may be and often is misused but which has much utility in elementary school arithmetic when correctly applied.

Rule of likeness for denominate numbers. In each of the addition statements above, the numerical coefficients were added. They could rightly be added because we had established the fact that they were *like* quantities; that is, they were associated with the same kinds of units (books, eighths, inches). When unlike quantities are added, the addends must be changed to like quantities before the coefficients may be added.

Similarly, when like quantities are subtracted, it is the coefficients that are subtracted, one from the other. If the denominate expressions are unlike, the unlike terms must be changed to like terms before the coefficients are subtracted.

In multiplication of whole numbers a "named" product must be like the "named" multiplicand. In measurement division problems, the "named"

[15] Swain, *op. cit.*, pp. 192-93, 202-3.
[16] Of course, the term "coefficient" has wider application than this, particularly in algebraic expressions. It will serve the present situation in a more limited sense.

dividend indicates that the divisor must be similarly named before the computation is performed with the numerical coefficients. In partition division, the "named" dividend indicates the name to be associated with the quotient.

The common or same denominations or names of terms must be established in each case before the computations are done with the coefficients. This is true whether or not the names are written as part of the algorism.

CHANGING DENOMINATE NUMBERS

TO DIFFERENT TERMS

Situations requiring changing to different terms. Changing denominate number expressions to different terms is necessary or desirable in widely varied situations. It may be merely a matter of convenience. A measurement of 24 inches may seem more manageable or easier to remember as 2 feet.

The rule of likeness, already discussed, sometime requires that one or more denominate numbers be changed to other terms before the computational process can proceed, or perhaps before the next step in a total series of computations may proceed.

Sometimes two or more measures are to be compared as to size. This may be thought of as a special case of the preceding situation or merely as an informal comparison. For example, if a woman knows that a tablecloth is 72 inches long and that her dining room table is 6 feet 2 inches long, she changes the 72 inches to 6 feet or the 6 feet 2 inches to 74 inches and knows at once that the tablecloth will not be a good fit.

Sometimes an answer is obtained as the result of computation and must be changed to different terms to satisfy the needs of a given situation. For instance, if a girl is going to sew 4 aprons that use 27 inches of material each, her product

will be 108 inches. When she goes to the store to buy the material, she will not ask for 108 inches of cloth, but rather 3 yards.

Changing units of measure as a logical process.[17]   Assuming that children have been given a broad base of experience with the measurement process and with units of measure (pp. 438-52), changing of denominate numbers to other terms can proceed as a logical process of deduction. "If . . . then . . ." reasoning should be much in evidence.

If there are 4 cups in 1 quart (discovered through experience and used in setting up a table of liquid measure), *then* there should be 3×4 cups in 3 quarts: 3×4 cups $= 12$ cups. *If* 60 minutes $= 1$ hour (noted through study of clocks and the manner in which they record passage of time), *then* there must be 2×60 minutes, or 120 minutes, in 2 hours. There are 2 times as many hours; so there must be 2 times as many minutes.

The reasoning might also be expressed as: "This is known to be true; *so* this other ought also to be true." The younger generation might call this "so what?" thinking.

$$12 \text{ inches} = 1 \text{ foot; } \textbf{so: } 1 \text{ inch} = \frac{1}{12} \text{ foot}$$

$$1 \text{ inch} = \frac{1}{12} \text{ foot; } \textbf{so:}$$

$$16 \text{ inches} = \frac{16}{12} \text{ feet} = 1\frac{4}{12} \text{ feet} = 1\frac{1}{3} \text{ feet}$$

$$1 \text{ pound} = 16 \text{ ounces; } \textbf{so: } 1 \text{ ounce} = \frac{1}{16} \text{ pound}$$

$$1 \text{ ounce} = \frac{1}{16} \text{ pound; } \textbf{so: } 6 \text{ ounces} = \frac{6}{16} \text{ pound} = \frac{3}{8} \text{ pound}$$

[17] Here, as elsewhere in the book, the term "reduction" is avoided because of its connotations of decrease in quantity. The emphasis must be on *changing form* while *keeping* the same *value*. Children will learn to use the term "reduction" later, after they clearly understand the process.

If children cannot do this kind of reasoning from prior experience to the applications of that experience in new situations, they are probably not ready to be transforming denominate-number expressions from one form to another. The hub of understanding of later operations that revolve around such interpretations is ability to think from one denominate form to another of equal value.

Often children's texts and their teachers are too quick about providing a set of rules for such changes to other terms. If the experiential background with measuring and units of measure is adequate, children can develop their own rules. In doing so, they will know much more than does the memorizer of statements such as:

To change from smaller units of measure to larger units of measure, divide.
To change from larger units of measure to smaller units of measure, multiply.

Not only will they understand those statements better for having reasoned their way to them, but they will not even need to remember the specific statements. They will just reason out the relationship among units of measure and proceed according to the demands of the situation.

If children have learned the ratio idea well in their work with fractions, it will be used extensively in the reasoning process for changing denominate numbers to different terms.

Similarity to changing or regrouping of whole numbers.

Addition and subtraction of denominate numbers: The algorisms below use similar numerals to emphasize the similarities as well as the differences in adding and subtracting decimal whole numbers and adding and subtracting denominate numbers.

Decimal Whole Numbers		Denominate Numbers
Form A		Form B
1 ten	1	1 ft.
2 tens 8 ones	2 8	2 ft. 8 in.
+3 tens 7 ones	+3 7	+3 ft. 7 in.
6 tens 5 ones	6 5	6 ft. 3 in.

Form C		Form D
5 15	5 1 5	5 15
~~6~~ tens ~~5~~ ones	~~6~~ ~~5~~	~~6~~ ft. ~~5~~ in.
−3 tens 7 ones	−3 7	−3 ft. 7 in.
2 tens 8 ones	2 8	2 ft. 8 in.

The difference between A and B is not in the changing or regrouping procedure itself. The difference is that in A the regrouping is by *tens,* whereas in B the regrouping is by *twelves.* Ones were changed to tens in A to follow the dictates of our decimal-place-value system. In B ones were changed to twelves (of inches) to follow the dictates of our linear measuring system. If we had been changing cups to quarts, we would have regrouped by fours; if we had been changing seconds to minutes, we would have regrouped by sixties.

In the subtraction forms also (C and D), the likenesses between the two examples are more striking than the differences. The regrouping in C was based on changing 1 ten to 10 ones to fit our decimal-place-value system. In D the regrouping was based on changing "1 foot" to "12 inches" to fit our linear measurement system. If the change had been from yards to feet, the regrouping would have been three-for-one; if from pounds to ounces, the regrouping would have been sixteen-for-one.

The teacher will do well in introducing children to addition and subtraction of denominate numbers to emphasize the similarities of procedure. If the boys and girls see that this is just a new application of the regrouping idea with which they are already familiar, they will go into it with an attitude of security and confidence, freeing them to focus their attention on the one point of difference — the need to do the regrouping in terms of the *particular measure equivalents* that are involved.[18]

Multiplication of denominate numbers: The multiplicand can be a denominate number; the multiplier cannot. The product will have the same "denomination" or name as the multiplicand, since the product is made up of the subgroups represented by the multiplicand. The

Decimal Whole Numbers
3 × (1 ten + 4 ones) =
(3 × 1 ten) + (3 × 4 ones) =
3 tens +~~12 ones~~ =
3 tens + (1 ten + 2 ones) =
(3 tens + 1 ten) + 2 ones =
4 tens + 2 ones

multiplier tells how many such equal subgroups are being combined.

Forms E and F are different forms for indicating the procedure with decimal whole numbers; G and H are comparable forms for multiplication of denominate numbers.

Decimal Whole Numbers	Denominate Numbers
Form E	Form G
1 ten 4 ones	1 week 4 days
×3	×3
3 tens 12 ones	3 weeks 12 days
1 ten 2 ones	1 week 5 days
4 tens 2 ones	4 weeks 5 days
Form F	Form H
1	1
1 4	1 week 4 days
× 3	×3
4 2	4 weeks 5 days

The only difference between the processes for multiplying decimal whole

[18] The different bases for the regrouping are an excellent opportunity for recognition of bases other than ten. (This is, of course, a limited interpretation of bases.)

numbers and denominate numbers is in the number of smaller units that comprise each larger unit. With decimal whole numbers, the change is always 1 (ten) for 10 (ones). With weeks and days, it is 1 (week) for 7 (days). If it had been pounds and ounces, it would have been 1 (pound) for 16 (ounces).

The operation of the distributive law for multiplication and the associative law for addition are also apparent in the above algorisms. This may show a little more clearly in another form:

Denominate Numbers
3 × (1 week + 4 days) =
(3 × 1 week) + (3 × 4 days) =
3 weeks + ~~12 days~~ =
3 weeks + (1 week + 5 days) =
(3 weeks + 1 week) + 5 days =
4 weeks + 5 days

One would not ordinarily go into such a detailed step-by-step writing of the process, but such a form does emphasize what is really being done. The multiplication is distributed over the weeks and days parts of the multiplicand. The days part is changed to weeks and days. Then the various partial products are associated so that all terms with the same "denominations" are combined to give the final form of the product.

The units of measure are not multiplied; it is the numerical coefficients of the measures that are multiplied. The names of the measures serve three purposes: (1) their presence is a help in keeping clearly in mind just what is being multiplied at each step in the process; (2) one must know the units of measure in order to know how many units of one kind to exchange for how many units of another kind; and (3) the names are needed in order to assemble like terms for the more concise final statement of the product.

Division of denominate numbers: The division of denominate numbers poses some special problems and is over-all the most difficult of the fundamental processes with measurement numbers. Some situations are fairly easy to solve by applying principles and procedures used with decimal whole numbers. Such a situation is shown in Form K below in relation to two forms of a similar example with decimal whole numbers (shown in I and J).

Form I	Form J	Form K
2 tens 4 ones	2 4	2 ft. 4 in.
2) 4 tens 8 ones	2) 4 8	2) 4 ft. 8 in.
4 tens	4	4 ft.
8 ones	8	8 in.
8 ones	8	8 in.

The procedure becomes more difficult when a remainder occurs in the first step of the long-division procedure, as in Form L. The quotient thus far is clearly 2 ft., but there is a remainder of 1 ft. to be considered now along with 6 in. At this point it becomes necessary to change "1 ft. 6 in." to "18 in.," as in M, after which the division proceeds smoothly.

A neat evasion of the difficulty of having to stop midway to change (regroup) "1 ft. 6 in." into the form "18 in." is to do the changing before dividing. Thus: 5 ft. + 6 in. = 60 in. + 6 in. = 66 in. Then the division as shown in Form N is a regular division in one unit of measure. If a quotient in feet and inches is required or preferred, the inches in the quotient may be changed back to feet and inches: 33 in. = 2 ft. 9 in.

All the examples given were partition division examples. In measurement division examples, denominate num-

Form L

2 ft.
2) 5 ft. 6 in.
4 ft.
1 ft. 6 in.

Form M

2 ft. 9 in.
2) 5 ft. 6 in.
4 ft.
1 ft. 6 in.
18 in.
18 in.

Form N

33 in.
2) 66 in.
6
6
6

bers would occur in both dividend and divisor, making the change to a single unit almost necessary if the children are not to become confused. Forms O and P are examples of such divisions. It does not matter whether the changes are to larger or smaller units so long as both dividend and divisor are in the *same* terms. Usually it is more convenient to regroup into the smaller unit of measure to avoid fractional parts of the larger units of measure, but sometimes it is possible to move in either direction, as shown in P.

Form O

9
2 qt.) 4 gal. 2 qt. becomes: 2 qt.) 18 qt.
18 qt.

Form P

8 qt.) 4 gal. may be changed as shown in P1 or P2.

Form P1	Form P2
2	2
2 gal.) 4 gal.	8 qt.) 16 qt.
4 gal.	16 qt.

Similarity to changing or regrouping of common fractions. In changing denominate numbers to other terms, the procedure is very much like changing common fractions to other terms — higher or lower. The concept of "simpler terms" or "terms to fit the situation" are common to both fractions and denominate numbers.

A further analogy might be drawn between the numerators of fractions and the coefficients of the denominate numbers, as also between the denominators of the fractions and the units of measure of the denominate numbers. This analogy holds up very well in relation to situations requiring the addition, subtraction, or measurement-type division of denominate numbers and in some cases of multiplication of denominate numbers. Whether or not it applies depends, of course, on the particular interpretation of a fraction that is involved.[19]

The relation between units of measure and fraction meanings may be learn much about the meanings of the measuring units and about common equivalents among denominate numbers from their construction of such a chart for any common table of measure.

TABLE 16

Table of Equivalents for Liquid Measure

$16 \text{ cups} = \frac{16}{2} \text{ or } 8 \text{ pints} = \frac{16}{4} \text{ or } 4 \text{ quarts} = \frac{16}{16} \text{ or } 1 \text{ gallon}$

$15 \text{ cups} = \frac{15}{2} \text{ or } 7\frac{1}{2} \text{ pints} = \frac{15}{4} \text{ or } 3\frac{3}{4} \text{ quarts} = \frac{15}{16} \text{ gallon}$

$14 \text{ cups} = \frac{14}{2} \text{ or } 7 \text{ pints} = \frac{14}{4} \text{ or } 3\frac{1}{2} \text{ quarts} = \frac{14}{16} \text{ or } \frac{7}{8} \text{ gallon}$

$13 \text{ cups} = \frac{13}{2} \text{ or } 6\frac{1}{2} \text{ pints} = \frac{13}{4} \text{ or } 3\frac{1}{4} \text{ quarts} = \frac{13}{16} \text{ gallon}$

$12 \text{ cups} = \frac{12}{2} \text{ or } 6 \text{ pints} \doteq \frac{12}{4} \text{ or } 3 \text{ quarts} = \frac{12}{16} \text{ or } \frac{3}{4} \text{ gallon}$

$11 \text{ cups} = \frac{11}{2} \text{ or } 5\frac{1}{2} \text{ pints} = \frac{11}{4} \text{ or } 2\frac{3}{4} \text{ quarts} = \frac{11}{16} \text{ gallon}$

$10 \text{ cups} = \frac{10}{2} \text{ or } 5 \text{ pints} = \frac{10}{4} \text{ or } 2\frac{1}{2} \text{ quarts} = \frac{10}{16} \text{ or } \frac{5}{8} \text{ gallon}$

$9 \text{ cups} = \frac{9}{2} \text{ or } 4\frac{1}{2} \text{ pints} = \frac{9}{4} \text{ or } 2\frac{1}{4} \text{ quarts} = \frac{9}{16} \text{ gallon}$

$8 \text{ cups} = \frac{8}{2} \text{ or } 4 \text{ pints} = \frac{8}{4} \text{ or } 2 \text{ quarts} = \frac{8}{16} \text{ or } \frac{1}{2} \text{ gallon}$

$7 \text{ cups} = \frac{7}{2} \text{ or } 3\frac{1}{2} \text{ pints} = \frac{7}{4} \text{ or } 1\frac{3}{4} \text{ quarts} = \frac{7}{16} \text{ gallon}$

$6 \text{ cups} = \frac{6}{2} \text{ or } 3 \text{ pints} = \frac{6}{4} \text{ or } 1\frac{1}{2} \text{ quarts} = \frac{6}{16} \text{ or } \frac{3}{8} \text{ gallon}$

$5 \text{ cups} = \frac{5}{2} \text{ or } 2\frac{1}{2} \text{ pints} = \frac{5}{4} \text{ or } 1\frac{1}{4} \text{ quarts} = \frac{5}{16} \text{ gallon}$

$4 \text{ cups} = \frac{4}{2} \text{ or } 2 \text{ pints} = \frac{4}{4} \text{ or } 1 \text{ quart} = \frac{4}{16} \text{ or } \frac{1}{4} \text{ gallon}$

$3 \text{ cups} = \frac{3}{2} \text{ or } 1\frac{1}{2} \text{ pints} = \frac{3}{4} \text{ quart} = \frac{3}{16} \text{ gallon}$

$2 \text{ cups} = \frac{2}{2} \text{ or } 1 \text{ pint} = \frac{2}{4} \text{ or } \frac{1}{2} \text{ quart} = \frac{2}{16} \text{ or } \frac{1}{8} \text{ gallon}$

$1 \text{ cup} = \frac{1}{2} \text{ pint} = \frac{1}{4} \text{ quart} = \frac{1}{16} \text{ gallon}$

shown in a table of equivalents or, more strikingly perhaps, on a chart of equivalents such as Table 16. Children would

[19] If the denominator of the fraction is used as an operator, the analogy does not apply. See pp. 363ff. of chap. 16.

Table 16 deals with the more commonly used units of liquid measure. A skillful teacher can use it for various purposes, such as these: (1) In filling the blanks in such a table, the children will have to do much work with measures, actually measuring quantities to find the equivalents or computing to find equivalents. (2) After the table is completed, generalizations may be drawn from it (under guidance, but in the children's own words). It is obvious, for example, that the denominators in any one column are all the same. Why? Why that particular denominator? (3) Changing each fraction to its lowest terms as a whole number or mixed number suggests a further step in converting one stated denominate number to another equivalent one. (4) Once the table is complete it becomes a useful reference for equivalents. Practice in its use may almost incidentally lead to the mastery of the most frequently used equivalents, which are, of course, those most needed. (5) The need for proper fractions, rationally stated whole numbers, improper fractions, or mixed numbers can be studied in relation to the relative values of the units of measure; e.g., when cups are changed to gallons, they become proper fractional parts of a gallon; but when a gallon is changed to cups, it becomes an improper fraction or whole number of cups.

AVERAGES

Averages are representative measures. Children should learn not only how to compute averages, but also what they mean. In fact, the latter is more important than the former. Luckily, the person who understands what they mean is not likely to have much difficulty learning how to compute them, but the one who merely knows how to "get" averages may not know what he has "got."

The adults of the next generation will be more knowledgeable concerning common measures of central tendency if today's children are given better experiences involving all three: mean, median, and mode. Some teachers will think of these three terms as something out of a course in statistics, not for elementary school consumption. Children not only can learn to understand these statistics; they have occasion to use them.

One teacher devised this situation as a basis for the development of representative measures. She gave each of seven children a strip of paper marked off in inches as follows: Mary, 3 inches; Susan, 6 inches; Paul, 7 inches; Jack, 9 inches; Willis, 3 inches; Ellis, 3 inches; and June, 4 inches. She asked these children and others in the class to tell her what was the *average* number of inches of "ribbon" for each child in the group of seven children.

The discussion that ensued was halting and hesitant at first, becoming very lively as the boys and girls got involved in their attempts to answer the question. The beginnings of a heated argument between two children were diverted by the teacher's suggestion, "Maybe we can have more than one kind of average." When mean, median, and mode had all been suggested in some manner by the children, the teacher helped them organize their thinking by using some of their own comments, these three in particular.

"More kids have strips that are 3 inches long." (Mode)
"The average length is 5 inches." (Arithmetic average or mean)
"The middle-size one is 4 inches long." (Median)

To emphasize the idea of the most frequent measure (mode) and the median (the middle), the teacher quickly seized upon one child's suggestion to arrange the "ribbons" in order of size. When they were arranged as shown in figure 137, all the children could see better that the 3-inch strips were indeed the most "common" or "popular," hence "in style" or "the *mode.*" They could also see that the "middle one" as to size was the 4-inch strip, for which the teacher introduced the name "median."

had already actually *added* all the lengths and had *divided* the total length into 7 equal parts.

This is a particularly good beginning experience with the three different representative measures for central tendency because it uses relatively small

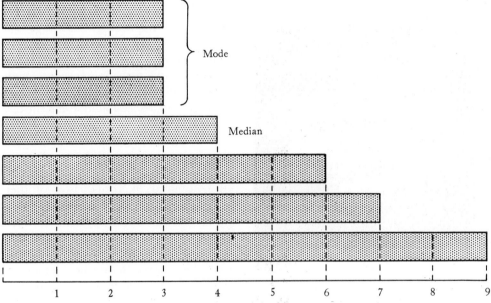

Figure 137. The Median and Mode for Seven Lengths of Ribbon.

One of the boys had figured out that 5 inches was the average length, but got confused in his own explanation. The teacher suggested that all the strips be laid end to end. See figure 138. They were fastened with transparent adhesive tape; so it was clear to all that the total amount of ribbon was 35 inches. "Now how could we give each of the children an equal amount of ribbon?" The suggestion to fold the full length into seven equal pieces was immediately forthcoming. This was finally accomplished and found to yield a 5-inch strip for each child. This measure was called by the teacher the "true average" or "arithmetic average." The easy transition from this action to the computation of the average is obvious. The children

whole numbers, because the mode, median, and arithmetic average are all different and can be more readily contrasted, and because the actions involved are relatively easy to perform without elaborate equipment.

The number of different experiences needed by different children before they truly understand the meaning of averages will vary widely, but all can probably benefit from development and use of these ideas in varying classroom situations such as those dealing with the children's own scores, heights, weights, ages, or distances traveled to get to school. (The children's ages within a class provide a particularly good setting for pointing out the usefulness of the mode, since such a large number of children in any class will be the "same age when ages are given in years (at last birthday or at nearest birthday).

As children proceed to the development of clearer ideas of each of these measures, the teacher will want to emphasize comparison of mean, median, or mode in terms of respective merits of the three measures: the mean in terms of representing most accurately the *size of each member* of the group being averaged; the median in terms of having the most representative *position* in the group; and the mode in terms of representing greatest *frequency.* Children will not learn this all at once, but they can well understand these ideas when developed in meaningful settings over a period of continued correct use.

In a very special way the concept of representative measures serves to highlight key ideas about measurement. The average is a representative measure; it "stands for" all the separate measures just as all measurements "stand for" that being measured. Just as all measurement is comparison, so groups may be compared by comparison of their averages. Averages, like all other measurements, must be expressed in terms of some unit of measure. The meaning and use of averages is worthy of considerable attention in the elementary school, particularly in the intermediate grades.

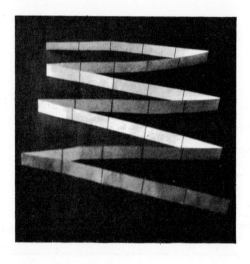

Figure 138. The Average or Mean of Seven Lengths of Ribbon.

STUDY QUESTIONS

1. Define in your own words and give an example of each: (a) unit of measure; (b) approximation; (c) standard units of measure; (d) indirect measures; (e) direct measures; (f) reference measures; (g) possible error; (h) precision; (i) accuracy; (j) denominate numbers.

2. Refer to a children's or an adult encyclopedia for information concerning various types of measures (e.g., linear, liquid, volume, weight). Pay particular attention to the historical development.

3. Make up problems that require addition, subtraction, multiplication, and division (each in a separate problem) in measurement situations. Draw a picture depicting each problem situation and its solution.

4. Find this book in the library: Asimov, Isaac. *Realm of Measure.* Boston: Houghton, 1960. Prepare an oral book report, perhaps emphasizing one section of the book that you like particularly.

5. Look up the tables of measures in a recent unabridged dictionary. How could you use these in teaching elementary school children?

6. Find the mean, mode, and median of these numbers: 15, 13, 9, 21, 18, 34, 15, 33, 29, 16, 17, 22, 35, 15, 17.

7. Estimate these measures; then measure and evaluate your ability to estimate accurately: (a) the height of the room in which you are reading this book; (b) the length of time it takes you to read one page; (c) the weight of this book.

CHAPTER **20**

Perspective on the Teaching
of Arithmetic

A GROUP OF ADULTS were looking at a set of maps that had been prepared to show each of the continents as it would appear to a person looking directly at that continent on a globe. Looking at such a map of Africa, one observer said: "Africa looks so big! The surrounding land and water masses seem to recede so sharply."

The person showing the maps answered: "That is what we wanted to do. We wanted to show each continent in the same prominence as one sees it when looking directly at that part of the globe. We thought that such a perspective would focus attention on that particular continent—in this case, Africa."

A second viewer observed: "I guess that is the way Africa does look to Africans. It does seem to them to be the center of the world. It's somewhat like the remark in *The Autocrat of the Breakfast Table* that to Bostonians 'Boston State-House is the hub of the solar system.'"

The appearance of the globe when Africa is turned toward the viewer is quite different from the appearance of the globe when Europe is the center of the view. In the first case, Europe is peripheral; in the second case, central.

So it is also with any one person's view of the teaching of elementary school

mathematics. What he sees as central and what he sees as peripheral depend on his point of view at any given time.

By way of conclusion, this chapter attempts to "spin the globe" of elementary school mathematics learning and teaching, recognizing the presence of many possible views but purposely turning special attention to certain ones.

FOCUS ON ARITHMETIC

Currently, there is a strong tendency toward the replacement of the term "arithmetic" by the broader term "elementary school mathematics." This is not merely a revision of names for this area of curriculum; it implies certain fundamental changes in the content so as to include more than arithmetic—particularly algebra and geometry.

This book centers on arithmetic, but no denial of the importance of algebraic and geometric ideas is intended. Such topics as equalities and inequalities, for example, are entirely appropriate in elementary school mathematics; in a treatment that focused on algebra, they would receive the attention not accorded in this text on arithmetic. In some instances the relation between arithmetic and other phases of mathematics is so natural that algebraic and geometric ideas have slipped in along

469

with arithmetic, e.g., algebraic statements and algorisms and geometric concepts such as area and the number line. They were a natural part of the total picture in which arithmetic occupied the central position.

Elementary school teachers should continue their study of elementary school mathematics in order to have adequate background for judging which ideas from algebra and geometry should be added to the elementary school curriculum. Inclusion in the curriculum must be based as well on serious weighing of the relative importance of content for the all-round development of the children in the area of mathematics.

Other phases of mathematics, once they have been adequately appraised, will no doubt become well-recognized parts of the established content for learning by most children. The probability is high that arithmetic ideas such as those presented in this book will continue to be the major part of elementary school mathematics.

FOCUS ON MATHEMATICAL STRUCTURE

Arithmetic as learned by many of today's adults was a routine study of facts and procedures to perform with numerals. Consequently, these same adults, looking at the "globe" of elementary school mathematics, tend to focus their attention on the mechanics of arithmetic rather than on basic structure and meanings that derive from structure. They tend to see a vast "continent" of forms and manipulations to be learned by memorization and drill.

The viewpoint of modern arithmetic promoted in the preceding chapters focuses instead on arithmetic as a plainly structured, logical framework of ideas. Therefore the features that loom large in such a view are concepts such as:

number system, including ideas like base and place value; principles such as commutation and association; relationships among numbers; meanings and interrelations of the processes of addition, subtraction, multiplication, and division; and operations as sensible actions growing out of the structure of the subject.

Again, the degree of structure that is desirable must be decided in the light of the pupil consumers and their present and future needs.

FOCUS ON PROBLEMS AND THEIR SOLUTIONS

Arithmetic problems usually cannot be solved without computation. On the other hand, computation has no function to serve without need for its use in solving problems. No matter which of the two occupies the center of attention, the other is present in the background of attention.

The present text has no separate chapter on problem solving. A serious attempt has been made, however, to magnify the importance of attention to understanding problem situations and to use of computation as the servant of problem-solving purposes. To place problem solving in the central role and computation in the peripheral position is really not a minimizing of accuracy and efficiency in computation. If computation is to contribute to the solution of problems, it must be accurate. Further, the efficient problem solver must also be efficient in computational procedures.

At times the development of computational procedures may have seemed to move slowly because of continuous reference to problem situations. This is a much less serious charge than may defensibly be made against hurried formal instructions for computation which ignore their meanings and their potential uses.

Computational manipulations have so long been overemphasized that perhaps a little overemphasis on problem settings and solutions is needed to get the situation back into proper balance.

FOCUS ON DISCOVERY AND UNDERSTANDING

Learning-teaching methods cannot be isolated from the content to be taught; but insofar as one can focus attention on a "method continent" for our figurative globe of arithmetic, certainly we should choose to focus on discovery and understanding rather than on routine drill procedures. To the degree that is feasible, the teacher's role should be that of stage manager in setting up learning situations within which pupils have a good chance of discovering for themselves the meanings and relations that make up arithmetic content.

Practice in computation, practice in problem solving, and practice in the use of arithmetic concepts in general certainly have their place along with and following the development of understanding, but it must always be a subsidiary place to concept development. If drill is magnified, meanings are less likely to be developed—hence, what is there to be practiced but forms and manipulations? Practice (or drill) should be practice of meanings and understood concepts and processes and relationships. The development of those meanings and concepts and relationships must not be subordinated to drill for drill's sake.

FOCUS ON THE LEARNER

Learners of arithmetic, as individuals and as groups, must be the center of attention. How to teach arithmetic can be decided only in relation to how children learn arithmetic. No one can teach arithmetic well without knowing *what* he teaches or without knowing *whom* he teaches. Effective teaching method for arithmetic consists entirely of effective development of the learner's concepts and skills and general competence in the area of arithmetic. This cannot be done without careful appraisal and use of the learners' abilities, past knowledge, and understanding. Helping them to "see point" in what they are doing is a large part of the task of the teacher.

That idea has been developed in this book chiefly by illustration of learning-teaching situations and procedures. That each child is different and that each learning situation is different are assumed. Adaptation to those differences is not only desirable but essential. Mass instruction of all children at a given grade level is no more defensible in arithmetic than in reading.

FOCUS ON THE BEST OF THE OLD AND THE BEST OF THE NEW

So much has been said about the "new mathematics" that some teachers and parents have accepted a false notion of the proportion of new and old. So far as elementary school mathematics is concerned, very little of modern content is really new. Most of it is old material that has been neglected or misunderstood or simply not understood. Much of the new is merely a return to basic meanings. Most of the really "new" mathematics is still to be learned at higher school levels.

Nor does the acceptance of modern emphasis on structure and meaning and relationships imply an abandonment of all that has been taught in elementary schools in recent years. Far from it! The ideas and processes developed in chapters 3 through 19 of this book are largely ideas and processes of long standing. What may seem new to a given person may not be really new at all. It may well be chiefly a revival of very old ideas that have been neglected and subordinated to mechanical and routine numeral juggling. The old forms need not necessarily be discarded; perhaps they need only to be understood. If that is "new," the newness arises from the inadequacies of past arithmetic instruction, not from the lack of prior discovery or use.

Much could be written about the numerous new mathematics materials that are being published for use in elementary schools. Experimental programs have resulted in a wealth of pub-lications that are more or less new as the case may be. Elementary school personnel have a responsibility to become acquainted with these materials. A sensible appraisal of their merits for school use must, however, rest not on claims of newness but on their merits for helping children understand fundamental mathematical ideas. Each teacher of children, pondering on what "new" content to adopt and what "new" methods of teaching to use, will do well to follow the path indicated by Abraham Lincoln in a letter to Horace Greeley: "I shall try to correct errors when shown to be errors, and I shall adopt new views so fast as they shall appear to be true views. . . ."[1]

[1] Letter of Abraham Lincoln to Horace Greeley, Aug. 22, 1862.

Bibliography

Adler, Irving and Adler, Ruth. *Numbers Old and New.* New York: Day, 1960.

Asimov, Isaac. *Realm of Measure.* Boston: Houghton, 1960.

Asimov, Isaac. *Realm of Numbers.* Boston: Houghton, 1959.

Banks, J. Houston. *Learning and Teaching Arithmetic.* Boston: Allyn, 1959.

Bell, Clifford; Hammond, Clela B.; and Herrera, Robert B. *Fundamentals of Arithmetic for Teachers.* New York: Wiley, 1962.

Brumfiel, C. F.; Eicholz, R. E.; and Shanks, M. E. *Fundamental Concepts of Elementary Mathematics.* Reading, Mass.: Addison-Wesley, 1962.

Buckingham, B. R. *Elementary Arithmetic: Its Meaning and Practice.* Boston: Ginn, 1953.

Clark, John R. and Eads, Laura K. *Guiding Arithmetic Learning.* Yonkers, N. Y.: World Book, 1954.

Dantzig, Tobias. *Number, the Language of Science,* 4th ed. Garden City, N. Y.: Doubleday, 1954.

DeVault, M. Vere (editor). *Improving Mathematics Programs.* Columbus, Ohio: Merrill, 1961.

Dutton, Wilbur H. and Adams, L. J. *Arithmetic for Teachers.* Englewood Cliffs, N. J.: Prentice-Hall, 1961.

Glennon, V. J. and Junnicutt, C. W. *What Does Research Say about Arithmetic?* Washington, D. C.: Association for Supervision and Curriculum Development, 1958.

Grossnickle, Foster E. and Brueckner, Leo J. *Discovering Meanings in Elementary Mathematics.* New York: Holt, 1963.

Gundlach, Bernard H. *Glossary of Arithmetical-Mathematical Terms.* River Forest, Ill.: Laidlaw, 1961.

Harding, Lowry W. *Arithmetic for Child Development.* Dubuque, Iowa: Brown, 1959.

Hollister, George E. and Gunderson, Agnes O. *Teaching Arithmetic in Grades I and II.* Boston: Heath, 1954.

Jones, Phillip S. *Numbers: Their History and Use.* Ann Arbor, Mich.: Ulrich's, 1954.

Kramer, Edna. *The Main Stream of Mathematics.* New York: Oxford U. P., 1951.

Lay, L. Clark. *Arithmetic: An Introduction to Mathematics.* New York: Macmillan, 1961.

Marks, John L.; Purdy, Richard; and Kinney, Lucien B. *Teaching Arithmetic for Understanding.* New York: McGraw, 1959.

Mueller, Francis J. *Arithmetic: Its Structure and Concepts.* Englewood Cliffs, N. J.: Prentice-Hall, 1956.

National Council of Teachers of Mathematics. *Arithmetic in General Education.* The Sixteenth Yearbook. Washington, D.C.: The Council, 1941.

_____. *The Growth of Mathematical Ideas.* The Twenty-fourth Yearbook. Washington, D.C.: The Council, 1959.

_____. *Insights into Modern Mathematics.* The Twenty-third Yearbook. Washington, D.C.: The Council, 1957.

_____. *Instruction in Arithmetic.* The Twenty-fifth Yearbook. Washington, D.C.: The Council, 1960.

_____. *The Teaching of Arithmetic.* The Tenth Yearbook. Washington, D.C.: The Council, 1935.

National Society for the Study of Education. *The Teaching of Arithmetic.* The Fiftieth Yearbook, Part II. Chicago: U. Chicago, 1951.

Osborn, Roger; DeVault, M. Vere; Boyd, Claude C.; and Houston, W. Robert. *Extending Mathematical Understanding.* Columbus, Ohio: Merrill, 1961.

Reiss, Anita. *So These Are Fractions!* Englewood Cliffs, N. J.: Prentice-Hall, 1962.

Risden, Gladys. *How Big? How Many?* Boston: Christopher, 1951.

Rosenquist, Lucy L. *Young Children Learn to Use Arithmetic.* Boston: Ginn, 1949.

Sanford, Vera. *A Short History of Mathematics.* Boston: Houghton, 1930.

Schaff, William L. *Basic Concepts of Elementary Mathematics.* New York: Wiley, 1960.

School Mathematics Study Group. *Studies in Mathematics. Vol. VI, Number Systems.* Stanford, Calif.: S.M.S.G., 1961, preliminary edition.

Smith, David Eugene. *History of Mathematics.* Boston: Ginn, 1925, Vol. I and II.

Smith, David Eugene and Ginsburg, Jekuthiel. *Numbers and Numerals.* Washington, D.C.: The National Council of Teachers of Mathematics, 1937.

Spencer, Peter L. and Brydegaard, Marguerite. *Building Mathematical Concepts in the Elementary School.* New York: Holt, 1952.

Spitzer, Herbert F. *The Teaching of Arithmetic,* 3rd ed. Boston: Houghton, 1962.

_____. *What Research Says about Teaching Arithmetic.* Washington, D.C.: National Education Association, 1962.

Stern, Catherine. *Children Discover Arithmetic: An Introduction to Arithmetic.* New York: Harper, 1949.

Stokes, C. Newton. *Teaching the Meanings of Arithmetic.* New York: Appleton, 1951.

Swain, Robert L. *Understanding Arithmetic.* New York: Rinehart, 1957.

Thorpe, Cleata B. *Teaching Elementary Arithmetic.* New York: Harper, 1962.

Wheat, Harry G. *How to Teach Arithmetic.* Evanston, Ill.: Row, 1951.

Index

Index

Abacus, 47-49, 70-71, 133-134
Accuracy, 455-459 (*see also* Estimating)
Adams, L. J., 291
Adams, Olga, 20
Addend, 89
  missing addend, 156
Addition:
  adding by endings, 126-129
  in bases other than ten, 96
  changing in, 115-23 (*see also* Changing)
  charts, 97, 106
  checking, 134-136
  column addition, 123-132
  combinations, 97-98
  as counting, 81-84, 98-104, 123-124
  basic facts, 96-112
  higher decade addition, 126-130, 217-218
  larger numbers, 115-143
  laws (*see* rules)
  meaning of process, 81-95
  regrouping by combining, 84-87, 104-105
    (*see also* Changing)
  relation to multiplication, 192-193, 195,
    196 (*see also* Relationships to multipli-
    cation and Relationships to subtrac-
    tion)
  rules, 91-96, 105-107, 116-117 (*see also*
    Association, Commutation, Likeness)
  terminology, 89-91
  union of sets, 87
Adler, Irving, 301
Adler, Ruth, 301
Algebraic expressions:
  for common fractions, 340-341, 373-374
  for decimal fractions, 392
  for proportions, 429-430
  for whole numbers, 92, 93, 95, 157-159,
    195-196, 198-201, 246, 251-252

al-Khowarizmi, 52, 54
Approximation, 452-459 (*see also* Estimating)
Area, 227-230, 442-443
Arithmetic:
  defined, 4-11
  as invented by man, 6-8
  logical order in, 8-9
  mathematical and social phases contrasted,
    13-14
  purposes for teaching, 12-18
  in use, 5, 13
Aryabhata, 50, 54
Association principle:
  addition, 92-94, 105-107, 117, 130-131
  multiplication, 199-200, 207-208, 230,
    238
Averages, 466-468
Axioms (see rules under Addition, Multiplication)

B

Banks, J. Houston, 194, 239, 291
Base, 40ff. (*see also* Numbers, Numerals, and
  Notation)
  in addition, 115-123
  decimal, 53ff, 69-73, 107-110, 166-169
    (*see also* Changing)
  in division, 260-261
  learning about, 69-75
  in multiplication, 204-206
  other than ten, 44, 45-46, 73-75, 96, 161,
    238
  in subtraction, 161, 174ff.
Bell, C., 55
Borrowing, 173 (*see also* Changing in subtraction)
Bridging, 126-127, 184-185